BRITISH COMMEMORATIVE MEDALS
and their values

No. 497

BRITISH COMMEMORATIVE MEDALS
and their values

CHRISTOPHER EIMER

Seaby

BY APPOINTMENT TO
HER MAJESTY THE QUEEN
B A SEABY LIMITED
NUMISMATISTS

LONDON

to Missi . . . a companion so dear

Typeset by Keyspools Ltd, Golborne, Lancashire
and printed and bound in Great Britain

for the publishers
B. A. Seaby Ltd, 8 Cavendish Square, London W1M 0AJ

Distributed by
B. T. Batsford Ltd, P.O. Box 4, Braintree, Essex CM7 7QY

ISBN 0–900652–94–2

Contents

Acknowledgements

In the course of compiling this catalogue I have been generously received by museums, institutions, and private collectors.

Material from the collections in the Ashmolean Museum, British Museum, Fitzwilliam Museum, Hunterian Museum, Imperial War Museum, Museum of London, National Army Museum, National Museum of Antiquities, National Museum of Wales, Royal Mint Museum, Royal Society, Science Museum, and the Victoria & Albert Museum has been used. The collection of medals in the British Museum has been particularly useful in the preparation of this catalogue. I am grateful to all the curators, keepers, and assistants for having put their collections at my disposal. In addition, I have been provided with information by the librarians and archivists of many museums, institutions and societies. I thank all of them and trust that the entries themselves bear witness to their efforts. Private collections have also provided significant pockets of material; my thanks to all who have allowed me into their homes to look at their medals, as well as to those who have offered me advice and suggestions. I should also like to express my gratitude for the co-operation I have received in the use of photographs from both public and private collections.

Auction sales have proved one of the most satisfactory sources for monitoring medals (and their prices) which come onto the market; particularly extensive use has been made of those of Messrs. Christie's, Glendining's, Sotheby's and Spink & Son.

The written contributions made by students of the series is something which should not go without mention; without such work not even the most general catalogue would evolve.

Laurence Brown made available his manuscript for volume two of *British Historical Medals 1760–1960*, thereby enabling me to continue with its concordance. Peter Clayton and James Spencer have both made a number of useful and welcome suggestions. Allan Hailstone kindly checked parts of the manuscript and has examined the page proofs. The practical help and encouragement which I have been given throughout the preparation of this work by my wife, Missi, has proved essential for its satisfactory conclusion and my sanity.

Preface

This catalogue is the first general summary of the British commemorative medal; a medium which has recorded the development and achievements of Britain and its people.

The first major survey of British medals was *Medallic Illustrations*, a two volume work by Edward Hawkins, which covered the series up to 1760. It was published in 1885, but still remains a model of accuracy and depth. By way of continuation, the first volume of Laurence Brown's *British Historical Medals* appeared in 1980, extending coverage of the series from 1760 to 1837. The second volume, continuing up to the death of Queen Victoria in 1901, will be published in 1987 and a final volume is planned, to complete the two hundred year span.

The steady growth of interest in the subject has made apparent the need for a summary treatment of the entire series; containing entries which are brief but informative, together with a guide to approximate and comparative values. Thus was born *British Commemorative Medals and their Values*.

Certain obstacles had to be overcome in order to present a catalogue which was accessible to the user, if not always apparently logical. The task of trying to create a balanced selection from a series containing well over twelve thousand medals was yet another dilemma. Consequently, in both these respects some degree of compromise has been unavoidable.

No doubt the exclusion of specific medals will invite criticism, as may the inclusion of others. With this in mind, I have tried to draw as few boundaries as possible, even if that meant representing certain subjects or types with just one example of a medal. Some sacrifices have been inevitable; non-metallic medals, such as those made of ivory, terracotta and wood, are sufficiently divorced from the two primary processes of medal making, those of casting and striking, and have not been included. Also excluded are entirely hand-engraved prize medals, used mostly by academies and volunteer regiments in the eighteenth and nineteenth centuries; trials or patterns; and touch-pieces (the 'King's Touch'), *c.*1650–1750 for relief of scrofulous ailments (the 'King's Evil'). Those medals forming part of a series but which contribute little more as a whole are represented by example alone; any relevant remarks being included in the annotations. Sporting, school attendance, and advertising medals are included if they introduce a topic which is considered of particular interest. Similar criteria have been used concerning tickets, passes and non-circulating eighteenth century tokens. This catalogue is not confined to those medals of purely British manufacture; whenever a foreign medal documents an event or person of relevance to Britain, and there are many, it has been considered for inclusion.

Catalogue entries have been presented in as clear and straightforward a manner as the subject allows, and the descriptions provided should be sufficient to identify particular medals. The prime references used, *MI* and *BHM*, have each been supplemented, when available and if necessary, with other specialist sources, and the index will enable location under various criteria. The weights and die-axes of medals have not been included here and the question of the quantities made of each medal is one which I have tried to avoid. Such figures can seldom be corroborated, and even when evidence does exist, the implied rarity becomes distorted when account is taken of examples lost, melted down for their intrinsic value, or otherwise destroyed.

While every effort has been made to ensure accuracy in the transcriptions and other information contained herein, it would be unrealistic to suppose that this has been achieved without human error. I apologise for any misleading statement which has been made.

I hope that this catalogue will provoke as many questions as it will provide answers, and stimulate the reader to explore further a unique source of fascination and historical information.

Introduction

When the subject of medals arises in polite conversation, the discussion tends to be about those given for bravery in battle; that other medals actually do exist often comes as a complete surprise. This is rather curious, considering the rôle which medals have played for more than five hundred years, in which time they have served many societies and touched upon so many aspects of our past. Most definitions of a medal are inadequate, except perhaps those which loosely suggest an object of handy proportions, conveying a passage of time or moment of expression. The word itself, according to the *Concise Oxford Dictionary*, derives from the Latin word for metal, *metallum*.

The two primary processes used in the making of medals are casting and striking. The essential difference is that in the former the design is produced by pouring molten metal into a mould, whilst in the latter an impression is created by striking a die (an engraved stamp often made of steel) upon a blank piece of metal. The creation of the medal took place in the Renaissance of fifteenth-century Italy, where it was an object with which to gratify and laud a private individual, expressing their identity and hopes in this new beginning. Expressions of art or records of achievement were nothing new; they existed on the official coinage of Greece in the fifth century BC, and on that of Imperial Rome, although the manufacture of an unofficial medal by one 'private' citizen for the gratification of another would then not have been tolerated. In this respect at least, the climate of Renaissance Italy was quite different and as the medal did not possess authority as a medium of exchange (the primary distinction separating it from coins), it was allowed to flourish free from government control or interference.

The Renaissance gradually spread through northern Europe during the latter part of the fifteenth century. In Germany and the Netherlands the first practitioners of this new art were native painters and sculptors such as Albrecht Dürer and Quintin Matsys. Craftsmen were quick to respond to the challenge of medal making, and formed, just as they had in Italy, various schools; each the exponent of a particular technique in this craft. The Renaissance was late in coming to England and its arrival did not signal the existence of a great native artist who could make medals and stimulate a local industry. Not until the 1540s is there any sign of a home-based medal activity, coming from engravers of coinage at the Mint. The characteristics of these first medals, of Henry VIII (No. 26) and Edward VI (No. 28), low in relief and with a somewhat coarse design, do not disguise the origins of their makers and are in contrast with the superior techniques used on the Continent. Not until the 1580s can we identify, with only slight reservations, the hand of a native master craftsman. Nicholas Hilliard, the celebrated miniaturist and goldsmith, extended his work to producing a handful of medals, which possibly include those of Elizabeth I made after the Spanish Armada (No. 62) and of James I for the peace with Spain in 1604

(No. 84). Some development of style slowly began to evolve, seen at its best on medals of James I (No. 80) and Henry, Prince of Wales (No. 90). The most prolific medallists during the reign of Charles I were Thomas Rawlins, who was responsible for many of the Stuart badges, and Nicholas Briot, a Frenchman who had brought with him some superior methods of production. Neither, however, came close to matching the portraiture on a small group of medals by Abraham and Thomas Simon (No. 148) which are unsurpassed in their sensitivity. That these two brothers were English makes their work particularly distinctive, for the majority of medals produced in England during the seventeenth century were made by foreign medallists.

After the Restoration, the series is dominated by medallists from Holland and in particular the Roettiers family. John Roettiers, Chief Engraver at the Mint, engraved the first large-size struck medals in England, principally of Charles II (No. 212) and James, Duke of York (No. 228). Other medallists of the Dutch school include Boskam, Luder and the Smeltzing brothers, who are largely responsible for medals recording events in the reign of William and Mary, although the series is largely derivative in style.

John Croker, a German, succeeded Roettiers as Chief Engraver in 1705. He produced definitive portraits of Anne, George I and George II, and was responsible for many of the medals recording the Continental military campaigns in which Britain was involved. The series of medals following the hopes of the exiled Stuart family form a continuous thread and can be seen as a means of keeping the Jacobite cause alive. Croker's imposing portrait medal of George II and Caroline (No. 528), with their children paraded on the reverse, might equally be seen as the counterblast to Jacobite claims of succession. The financial speculations of John Law in 1720 are plotted on an amusing and damning group of satirical medals (Nos. 489–91), mostly of German manufacture.

Admiral Vernon's victories in the 1740s were hailed by a large number of medals (Nos. 547–54) mostly struck in pinchbeck, a recently-made alloy of copper and zinc with characteristics of brass. It was cheaper and easier to use than bronze or copper, although the surface tended to deteriorate due to a temperamental composition. The expedience of this alloy allowed medal making to become a more egalitarian pursuit; one which more commonly embraced affairs at every level of society and not just those concerning the State. In the 1740s a series produced by James A. Dassier, a Swiss medallist, provides a glimpse of contemporary society (No. 556), although the opportunity to provide pictorial reverses was not taken. Actions at Carlisle and Culloden, and the further fortunes of the Jacobites, are recorded on many medals during this period, some with a satirical composition. In the 1750s, in response to an apparent debasement of medals, the [Royal] Society of Arts (Society Promoting Arts and Commerce) sponsored a group recording British overseas victories (No. 655), all of a uniformly pleasing standard.

The pioneer spirit and romance of the late eighteenth century are captured by medals marking the inventiveness of Merlin (No. 824), the experimentation of Priestley (No. 807), the expeditions of Cook (No. 744), and the balloon ascent of Lunardi (No. 784). Political and social events are extensively documented; three unsigned medals (Nos. 768–70), possibly by the same hand, are of Benjamin Franklin, the Scottish political economist David Hume and Chevalier D'Éon, a Frenchman living in London. D'Éon was a renowned transvestite about whose sex there was much uncertainty and financial speculation; the result of which was a legal action in 1777. Edward Burch's full-blooded medal of William Hunter (No. 754) is prominent amongst late eighteenth century portraiture, and a fitting tribute to the anatomist and collector.

The growth of the agricultural industry can be measured by the large number of prize medals which record the establishment of agricultural societies throughout Britain. In 1793 a collaboration between Conrad Heinrich Küchler, a continental medal engraver who came over to England, Matthew Boulton, medal manufacturer and founder of the Soho Manufactory in Birmingham, and James Watt, who had recently invented a steam-powered press, produced a number of well made medals recording events in the reign of King George III. Boulton's engineering capabilities in medal production are themselves the subject of an interesting medal (No. 901). Boulton, and later his former apprentice Edward Thomason, and George Collis who took over Thomason's Manufactory, did much to establish Birmingham as a centre of medal production in the nineteenth century, second only to the Royal Mint in London. The series published by James Mudie (No. 1136) and struck by Thomason in 1820 is the largest of several to record British victories during the previous fifty years. Whilst this period saw the emergence of Birmingham as a centre for the manufacture of private medals, it should be remembered that those medallists who worked for the Royal Mint had long enjoyed the perk of using Mint machinery after normal working hours in order to execute private commissions.

It was not until the early nineteenth century that the influence of neo-classicism was to make itself felt through the work of Benedetto Pistrucci and William Wyon, whose family dominated medal making for much of the century. Medals recording scientific achievement are extensive and those with documentary reverses are particularly pleasing. Monuments of engineering genius are illustrated on medals of the Brunels (Nos. 1372 & 1531), Rennie (No. 1166); the Stephensons (Nos. 1224 & 1441), Telford (No. 1206) and Watt (No. 1207). A medal of James Prescott Joule (No. 1751) reminds us of the unit of energy to which he gave his name. Political and social developments are marked by the large number of medals for the Reform Bill (No. 1244) and the abolition of slavery (No. 983), both of which are traced through their various parliamentary stages.

The introduction of the reducing machine, which produced an actual-sized die from the artist's original model, encouraged the wide-scale production of medals and, together with the huge industrial and social emancipation that was taking place, led to the height of medal making in Britain. The Great Exhibition in 1851 is recorded on numerous medals (No. 1455), and its influence is seen in the many local exhibitions subsequently held throughout Britain, for which medals were also struck.

In the second half of the nineteenth century the struck medal began to lose much of its character; the motivating force necessary to stimulate and inspire future medallists was missing. The Society of Medallists, established in 1885, sought the revival of the cast medal and the encouragement of all branches of medallic art. Their legacy is a portrait gallery providing an insight into contemporary society (*cf.* No. 1624), although the early momentum which they achieved was not sustained and the Great War compounded its decline.

The Jubilee celebrations of Queen Victoria in 1887 and 1897 are recorded on a vast number of medals of both national and local interest. The South African War gave rise to the tribute medal (No. 1860), issued by townships in honour of their local boys. This period of medal making is unremarkable, although the work of Emil

Fuchs and de Saulles are examples of excellence.

The Investiture of the Prince of Wales in 1911 is commemorated with a pleasing composition by William Goscombe John (No. 1925). It fully maintains the qualities of 'sculpture in miniature', an ideal which few medallists were able to achieve on the struck medal. The majority of those medals commemorating the Great War were produced on the Continent. The German issues, biting and prevalent, were roundly condemned by *The Times*, which stated that 'those which have any claim to consideration as works of art can be counted on the fingers of one hand'. Despite this partisan view, the deficiency of medal making in Britain was sufficient for the Royal Numismatic Society to offer prizes in a competition for a medal (Nos. 1948–50) celebrating the victory at Jutland Bank. Such initiatives were few and far between and did little to influence the numerous peace and tribute medals struck after the First World War. It was not until the 1920s that a concerted effort was made to revitalise medallic art in Britain, through Robert Johnson, newly-appointed Deputy Master of the Royal Mint, and the Royal Mint Advisory Committee of Taste.

The attack was launched against private medal manufacturers who, it was felt, had done much to denigrate the medal from an object of art to one purely of function. Several competitions were drawn up for medals commemorating the British Empire Exhibition in 1924 (No. 1987) and this brought forth a number of artists. Prominent amongst this group is Percy Metcalfe, whose work presents a refreshingly original and uncompromising approach to medal design. A medal by Gilbert Bayes for the commissioning of the *Queen Mary* in 1936 (No. 2036) also captures the mood of the moment, but the promise that this period of medal making was beginning to show became lost through the outbreak of war. Resources were directed to more urgent needs and one private manufacturer, Messrs John Pinches, was able to adapt a medal press for the construction of gun sights. In 1945 few victory or peace medals were made, and the tradition of the locally-issued tribute medal was almost dead. The marriage of Princess Elizabeth and Prince Philip in 1947 is commemorated by an unsatisfactory medal (No. 2073) which only serves to underline the austerity of this period.

No official commemorative was struck for the 1953 Coronation, and the inactivity of medal making in Britain during the following twelve years was equalled only by that of the previous period. With no initiative coming from any Government department or private body, the medal was allowed to founder. This indifference led to a climate in which the medal flourished as a medium of investment, fuelled by the low price of precious metals and the desire to perpetuate the memory of such as John Kennedy and Winston Churchill. Private medallists thrived on the demand for 'limited editions' but the sober realisation that such medals were not the way to riches soon quelled the public interest.

In 1982 the British Art Medal Society (No. 2141) was formed to revive the cast medal, and to foster medallic art and history, just as the Society of Medallists had done a century earlier, and indeed as had the Society of Arts in the 1750s. In its short life BAMS has reminded us that there is a public which appreciates the medal for reasons other than pure investment, and has been able to bring the medal to the attention of an ever-increasing audience.

What of tomorrow? The remark of Joseph Addison, the essayist and statesman, that 'we ought to look on [medals] as so many monuments consigned over to Eternity, that may possibly last when all other memorials of the same age are worn out or lost', is significant. In a relatively short life medals have attracted the attention of many, but are yet to prove of serious interest or value to the archaeologist. In this context at least, Addison's remarks invite speculation as to exactly what rôle medals will come to fulfil in the future.

Collecting and Understanding Medals

The history of the medal has been one of appreciation as much as it has been one of function. In its time it has embraced every social order, and today that ray of light which the medal sheds can be a vivid reminder of our past, providing information as valuable to the historian as a clue to a detective. In his preface to the Society of Medallists' Exhibition Catalogue of 1885, C. W. Freemantle, Deputy Master of the Royal Mint, echoed the sentiments of John Evelyn and Alexander Pope when he considered that 'medals form one unbroken chain of evidence; neither painting, sculpture nor any other area of art for that matter, can make this claim'.

Particular aspects of the medal which remain to be brought to light, and indeed those medals which have yet to be 'discovered', provide what are possibly the most rewarding features of the subject; factors which have kept my own interest on the boil. Despite the weight of scholarship already devoted to medals, they remain wide open for study and offer many areas about which we are still quite ignorant: initial marks on medals of the late sixteenth and seventeenth centuries; where and by whom were the medals for 'Peterloo' and of Vernon made?; what are the circumstances behind the medal of D'Éon, and that of Mansfield, the presiding judge in the affair? Studies of particular medallists and their work can be especially rewarding.

Familiarity leads to a greater understanding of the subject, and there are many opportunities to handle medals. Auction houses issue catalogues containing descriptions together with estimated prices, and hold appointed viewing times when medals can be examined prior to sale. They can also be seen by visiting dealers specialising in the subject, as well as those handling coins or antiques. Fine collections are housed in our national museums, particularly in the Ashmolean in Oxford, the Fitzwilliam in Cambridge, and the Hunterian in Glasgow. The British Museum has an unrivalled collection of British medals, in the care of an enthusiastic department. It is regrettable, however, that few permanent exhibitions of medals are maintained, and an appointment is normally necessary to look at pieces. The number of public exhibitions devoted to medals held in Britain since that of the Society of Medallists in 1885 may be counted on the fingers of both hands, but perhaps even more regrettable is the fact that there exists no one museum devoted entirely to the subject and all its aspects.

So far as literature is concerned, the bibliography in this catalogue contains references which may be useful in certain areas; those which play a prominent part in the series should be evident. The combined library of the Royal and British Numismatic Societies, which is situated in the Warburg Institute, London wc1, contains many books on the subject. Papers on medals are sometimes given at their meetings, although they are usually concerned with coins. Local numismatic societies throughout Britain also sometimes have speakers on the subject. The British Art Medal Society is concerned only with medals, and issues a regular journal

The Medal; in addition, guest speakers give papers on aspects of the subject during the winter. Membership details of all three societies are available from the British Museum, Department of Coins and Medals.

The question of investment has no place in this catalogue, although the collector who wishes to purchase a medal might equally wish to consider the question of resale, as the need could arise. Market forces dictate that the item in the best condition attainable is the most sought after and therefore normally the most saleable. In cases of extreme rarity, or where the illustration is sufficiently clear for a particular purpose, condition is less important, but if an object is to be enjoyed without the distractions of surface scratches, edge knocks or polish, then a greater emphasis should be placed on the medal's state of preservation than, for example, its rarity. Rarity alone plays little part in governing price; in fact the idea of arousing interest on the platform of a limited supply, as has been so often tried, is somehow alien to the genuine interest which the subject provides.

As has been said elsewhere, no attempt has been made here to quantify rarity, although some perspective may be gained by considering a few quoted (Royal Mint) figures of numbers struck: George II coronation (No. 510), 800 examples in silver; Victoria Diamond Jubilee (No. 1817), 41,000 in bronze; General Strike (No. 2003), 7000 in bronze; British Empire Union (No. 2010), 40,000 in bronze. In very general terms they may all be considered common and easy to acquire, although medals produced in these numbers (except perhaps the first) are the exception rather than the rule. Although figures in the hundreds may be a more realistic 'average' number, many medals could only have been made in quantities not exceeding double figures, and there are many instances where but one example has been noted. However common or otherwise a medal, each has a different tale to tell; sometimes correspondence or other material relating to their issue exists, telling a fascinating story which has lain hidden behind a seemingly innocent façade.

The question of cleaning is a thorny one. In my experience more medals have been spoiled than have been enhanced, often by a hand which, in a matter of seconds, has managed to replace centuries of patina with a brightly polished surface. If the urge is irresistible, the only cleaning which I could advocate is the removal of loose dirt or dust which sometimes collects on the medal's surface, and then only gently, with a dry and very light brush. However, as a general rule, my advice would be to leave well alone.

For almost twenty years I have found the subject of medals to be a generous source of stimulation, education and intrigue; it will no doubt continue to serve many who value this signpost of the art and social history of our past. The sentiments of Goethe place the medal in an elevated and, perhaps, a spiritual context, when he advised that 'every person should cultivate the fine habit daily to read in the Bible or in Homer, to listen to some good music, or to look at some beautiful medals'.

How to Use the Catalogue

Arrangement of the entries

Monarch and date of event: top of the page

Catalogue number: an asterisk against the number denotes that the medal is illustrated

Title of event and date

Obverse: description of scene followed by the inscription(s). Exergue, if present

Reverse: description of scene followed by the inscription(s). Exergue, if present

Edge: plain, unless otherwise indicated

Diameter: in millimetres, to the nearest whole number

Artist, designer or publisher

References: other works to which reference is made

Annotations: historical or biographical notes (usually given beneath the first entry for a person or event)

Valuations: provided on the right-hand side, given for very fine and extremely fine states of preservation, except for those post-1900.

General points

When two or more medals are listed for one event, they are given in descending order of diameter. Within each year, medals have been listed in chronological order, as closely as possible. Errors in the inscriptions, e.g. in the sitter's dates, are transcribed as on the medal. Where the stops and punctuation on a medal's inscription are of a decorative nature, e.g. a rose, star, or cinquefoil, they have generally not been transcribed (*see* Initial marks in the Glossary). Mottoes are most often found on armorial bearings, and have not usually been transcribed. The diameter of cast medals can vary by 5%, and sometimes as much as 10%, depending on various factors (*see* Cast). The diameter given of a cast medal is for an example which is believed to be an original, which often happens to be the broadest, although the two criteria are not always compatible. In the case of medals which are not circular, the width is always given before the height.

A format has been used to designate medallists (or designers, die-sinkers, editors, publishers, and sculptors).

(a) By J. Smith = signed and believed to be by J. Smith.

(b) [By J. Smith] = unsigned but believed to be by J. Smith.

(c) (By J. Smith?) = unsigned but possibly by J. Smith.

(d) By J. Smith/M. Brown = obverse by J. Smith; reverse by M. Brown, and signed respectively.

16

(e) By J. Smith, *obv.* after T. Bell = signed and believed to be by J. Smith; the obverse after T. Bell.

(f) Dutch (By?) = unsigned; the medal is thought to be Dutch.

(g) (By?) = unsigned; the medal is thought to be of British origin.

Some medals are signed by the die-sinker and/or publisher, as well as the engraver. In this case just the engraver's name is given in the entry; the appropriate index will reveal most other names which are present. When no other name is present on the medal except that of a die-sinker or publisher, then it is that which is stated. When the designer is known, details are provided after the engraver's name, although this has only been possible in a small number of cases. Some medallists signed their work discreetly; for example, in the exergual line, on or below the bow which ties the stem of a wreath, or on a leaf of the wreath. The signature on a medal struck from worn dies tends to be one of the first features to become indistinct.

Valuations are based primarily on auction prices, fixed price lists such as those of Messrs Seaby and Spink, and personal experience. Several factors govern value, not least of which is condition, stated here in two classes of grade (*see* Very fine and Extremely fine), except post-1900 medals which are stated only in the latter. The medal is assumed to be free from scratches, nicks, scuffs, and cleaning or other defects. A medal in its original case and condition can be expected to command a premium; similarly, one which retains an original gilding is also generally more desirable. Values given for cast medals are for those which are contemporary in their manufacture and are reasonably clean and tidy in their finish. (*See* Cast.)

Prize and award medals which commonly occur named are valued as such. The status of a medal which has been awarded is immediately altered, as it not only fulfils its intended function but becomes an object of greater social interest. The difference which this can make to its value is influenced by considerations of subject-matter, status of the recipient and the part which that person played in gaining the award; there are instances where it makes little or no difference, and others where the value is increased four- or five-fold. These reasons make anything more than a general statement impossible. *See* Prizes.

During the 1960s and 1970s many large-size gold medals were issued. In the present state of the market, and in relation to the current prices of precious metals, the intrinsic metal bullion value of these and some other gold medals far exceeds that of any collector interest; they are designated 'gold value' in the respective entries.

The values are quoted as an approximate guide, and to provide a point of comparison between one medal and another. The factor of demand, which cannot be quantified, can make a considerable difference if two people at an auction, for example, decide that they both want a particular medal. Medals which rarely appear on the market are left unpriced. Those which seldom appear in a high state of preservation are also unpriced.

The illustrations are actual size unless otherwise indicated. Many medals have just one side illustrated when, for example, the other side only has an inscription, or the use of space was considered better served by the illustration of a different medal.

Glossary of Terms

Calendar: in 1582 Pope Gregory XIII introduced a 'New Style' calendar (the Gregorian) in order to rectify the errors of that introduced by Julius Caesar (the

Julian) in 45 BC. The Gregorian calendar conformed more closely to the natural courses of the seasons and made the year correspond as nearly as possible to the true solar year. The Julian year, or 'Old Style', of $365\frac{1}{4}$ days, allowing for any leap years, resulted in an annual difference between the two calendars of 11 minutes 10 seconds. Most European countries made the change to the 'New Style' within twenty years of its introduction, but by the time that England wished to do so in 1752, its calendar had become eleven days out of sequence. In order to correct the discrepancy, 2 September was followed by 14 September in that year.

Correspondence of other calendars to AD 1900: Hegira 1317; Jewish 5660–1; Julian 6613; Masonic 5900 or 5904; Mohammedan 1318.

Cast: casting is one of the two primary methods of medal making (*see* Struck) and can take two forms. In the first procedure, a model of the proposed medal is made, from which a mould is taken (any extra definition required can always be added to the mould). When another mould has been made for the reverse (assuming a medal with two sides) the two are joined together and molten metal poured in through a recess. Sometimes the two sides of a medal are cast separately and then joined together by their edges.

In the second procedure, known as the *cire perdue*, or 'lost-wax' process, a completed model in wax (whether of a uniface medal or one with two sides) is tightly clad in moulding material so as to form an impression of the design. The outside casing is then heated, so that the wax inside runs out of an outlet provided, and is replaced by molten metal which fills the mould thus created.

In each case an engraving tool could be used to retouch the finished medal and remove air-bubbles or other defects which had occurred during the process. There are variations of both these procedures: in the materials used to make the models, which were often wax or wood; in the preparation of the moulds; in the methods of improving the medal after casting; in the drawing of the lettering on the mould or finished medal; and in the methods of patination. Medals which have not been cast from an original mould, but from one made by an already existing medal – an 'after-cast' – will, generally speaking, shrink in size to some degree. One method of determining the originality of a cast medal is to measure its diameter. However, some medallists 'finished' their cast by filing the edges to remove roughness; a more reliable method, therefore, is to compare measurements taken from two fixed points within the medal, and not from the edge.

This is only a brief sketch of the two processes; a more thorough discussion can be found in *Hill/Pollard* and *Dutton*, who describe, respectively, techniques used by craftsmen in the Renaissance and those employed by a living medallist.

Chronogrammatic date: the incorporation of a date in the inscription; Roman-numeral letters of a word or phrase are enlarged, and provide a date when added, as in: I LIke MeDaLs = $1 + 50 + 1 + 1000 + 500 + 50 = 1602$.

Colour: *see* Toning.

Copies: in the eighteenth century copies were made of some sixteenth and seventeenth century medals. One such copier was apparently James 'Athenian' Stuart, who was regarded by Forrer as a 'clever Medal-chaser and Die-engraver . . .'. Some of these copies, whoever did in fact make them, are quite creditable, and offer examples of some medals which are otherwise rarely available on the market. The quality in the tooling and retouching of the surface is variable, and although there is no one aspect which immediately separates them from the originals, they seem to share certain general characteristics: flans are heavier and sometimes broader; edges more sharply defined; lettering more squarely cut and sometimes unfaithful to the original. (The catalogue entry is annotated if such copies are known to have been made.) *See* Electrotype and Restrike.

Date: *see* Calendar; Chronogrammatic date *and* Roman numerals.

Diadem: type of open small crown.

Die: metal, often of steel, on which a design is engraved and then struck on a metal blank to create that design. (*See* Struck.) Two medals which are seemingly the same but which have been struck from more than one pair of dies, will usually show differences when compared closely. This applies to those made before the introduction of the reducing machine *c.*1820 (*q.v.*) which could duplicate a design.

Die flaws: defects usually found on a medal which has been struck from a flawed or cracked die.

Electrotypes: a process developed in the 1830s which was an electrical equivalent of metal casting. An artist's design in wax was put into a specially prepared wax mould, from which was taken a wax impression that was treated with powdered graphite, copper conductor pegs were inserted into the back of the wax impression and the whole was then immersed in a solution into which an electric current was introduced, connected from a battery via the wax to a copper sheet. The current would dissolve the copper, which would deposit on the surface of the wax, forming an exact impression. When the process was complete, the back of the plate could be filled with a packing material and joined to another similarly made shell to form a complete medal. *See* Burt (Bibliography).

The technique was developed successfully and one or two pieces were produced as contemporary medals (No. 1512). Convincing copies of old medals were also produced by this process. Sometimes, although not always, they display the tell-tale sign of a thin line running around the edge where the two halves have been joined. A more uncertain method of detection is the indistinct or muted sound which such medals give when they are 'rung' by another piece of metal, unlike medals that are cast or struck which usually emit a clear ring. A combination of factors will often be sufficient to detect an electrotype.

Exergue: an area of the medal often separated by a horizontal line and situated in the bottom portion of the design. It sometimes contains a date or inscription.

Extremely fine: a state of preservation in which the medal retains some of its original colour and shows little sign of wear. A medal which is in a particularly fine state of preservation might be described as *good extremely fine*. *See* Very fine.

Field: the plain background area of the medal.

Flaws: *see* Die flaws.

Frosted: struck with a fine, white matt or 'icing' finish, often applied to prize medals of the nineteenth century (which are often then set within a watch-style glass framed with a silver band). *See also* Glass cases.

Garter: a belt with a buckle. It is sometimes found enclosing an armorial shield, and inscribed HONI. SOIT. QVI. MAL. Y. PENSE.

Glass cases: some medals are occasionally found 'frosted' (*q.v.*) and set within a watch-style glass framed with a silver band; a practice beginning at the end of the eighteenth century and lasting about one hundred years. Prize medals and those of societies such as the Pitt Clubs are most frequently encountered glazed.

Incuse: [lettering or design] sunk into the surface of the medal. *See also* Relief.

Initial marks: these take various forms, such as a quatrefoil, rose, castle or star, and often occur between the lettering, or at the top or bottom of the medal. They may be symbols which certain medallists used, most usually on sixteenth and seventeenth century medals, or merely decorative devices employed by the medallist. No attempt has been made to transcribe these.

Integral suspension loop or clasp: that which forms part of the medal, 'built-in' during manufacture.

Laureate: wearing a laurel wreath.

Medallist: (in the context of this catalogue) a person involved in the making of a medal and not someone who has been awarded a medal.

Metals: although many medals are not listed in certain metals this does not mean to say that they do not exist in them. Experience has shown that there is a likelihood of medals appearing which have, hitherto, not been seen in that metal. The standard of gold medals varies, although those struck by the Royal Mint are often of at least 22 carat fineness. Generally speaking, silver medals struck during the last two hundred years are of sterling fineness (.925). Some gold and silver medals of this century bear hallmarks. For expedience some generalisations have been made in the designation of certain metals; Pinchbeck, a brass-coloured alloy of copper and zinc, and those medals of a similar appearance, have been placed under the general umbrella of brass. For much the same reason copper and bronze medals are included under the one heading of AE, and are referred to as bronze in the notes. Medals in pewter and tin have been placed under the heading of white metal; including those produced *c.*1887–1947, some of which have a high lead content.

New style: *see* Calendar.

Obverse: the premier side of the medal on which appears the principal design, such as a portrait; hence the expression 'heads' for the obverse of a tossed coin.

Old Style: *see* Calendar.

Prizes: (awards, premiums, presentations, military rewards, tributes): medals made expressly in order to be given as prizes, or serving these other functions, are so noted. Unless otherwise stated, the engraved inscription, if any, is to be found on the edge. Some prize medals were only awarded in certain metals; those which were otherwise made can be regarded as 'proof' or 'specimen' strikings. Institutions often had the manufacturer inscribe the recipient's name on the medals, but this was sometimes left to the recipient (e.g. Nos. 1987 and 2003) who may or may not have done anything about it. Civil War badges given as military rewards are rarely found inscribed. It should be noted that the inscribed date on a medal might be anterior to the date of its issue; this might occur on one commemorating the beginning of service, or membership of a society or institution, and suggests that the commencement of a recipient's period of service pre-dates the medal's issue. Prize medals used by a society or organisation for many years without renewing of the dies sometimes show indistinct lettering through their heavy use. The terms governing the award of a particular medal can change, such as its frequency and the metal in which it is presented (e.g. No. 1653). In some cases the recipient of a gold medal also received an inscribed replica in silver (e.g. No. 1186).

Reducing machine: three-dimensional pantograph which produces a master punch in relief from an electrotype copy of the artist's plaster model.

Registered designs: medals issued by some private manufacturers, *c.*1895–1920, can be found with the letters Reg. No. or RD followed by a series of numbers. These indicate the protection by copyright of the design.

Relief: lettering or design which is above the field, as is the case with the overwhelming majority of medals. *See also* Incuse.

Repoussé: hammered or worked into relief from the reverse side.

Restrikes: the Royal Mint does not have a tradition of restriking their medals. The Mints of France, the Netherlands and the United States have restruck medals from original or slightly altered dies. Since *c.*1830 many medals struck in France, and to a far lesser extent in the Netherlands, have a symbol such as an antique lamp, anchor or cornucopia on the edge, sometimes accompanied by the name of the metal. The presence of such marks can indicate whether a medal was made subsequent to the date which it bears. Restrikes can sometimes also be distinguished from the original by the lighter colour of the metal, in the case of bronze medals, and a more pronounced definition of the edge. Attention is drawn in the annotation to those medals which are known to have been restruck.

Reverse: the 'other' side of the *obverse*, which it normally complements and to which it is secondary; hence the expression 'tails' when tossing a coin.

Roman numerals: when given on a medal they are normally found in a conventional or chronogrammatic form (*q.v.*). A less usual arrangement takes the form of letters which need to be linked to form Roman numerals, e.g. CIƆIƆCCIIX

(No. 432). The first three letters are linked to form an M, whilst the following two are linked to form a D. The date which is then formed, when followed by the remaining letters, is MDCCIIX. *See also* Chronogrammatic date.

Rust marks: medals struck from dies which have deteriorated through age will exhibit pimples or speckling caused by rust marks.

Stops: *see* Initial marks.

Struck: the other primary process of medal making (*see* Cast) with which this catalogue is concerned, whereby the medal is formed by striking a die, usually in steel, creating an impression on a blank piece of metal. All medals in this catalogue are struck unless otherwise indicated.

Toning: in the 1920s the Royal Mint experimented with various techniques of toning; some medals occur with an almost black, matt finish (e.g. Nos. 1987,97, 2003).

Truncation: the line of the head or bust where it is cut off from the rest of the body. Here may be found a date or a medallist's name.

Varieties: some medals were struck from more than one pair of dies (sometimes a new die was made for one side only) and are almost identical, varying merely in small details.

Very fine: a state of preservation whereby a medal, although not still in the first flush of youth, has only a modest amount of wear on the high points. A medal which has rather more wear may be referred to as being in *fine* condition. *See* Extremely fine.

Abbreviations

AE	bronze or copper	*Ex.*	exergue	Pd.	palladium
Al.	aluminium	Fe.	iron	Pt.	platinum
AR	silver	l.	left	r.	right
AV	gold	Ni.	nickel	*Rev.*	reverse
Br.	brass	*Obv.*	obverse	VF	very fine
D.	diameter	Pb.	lead	WM	white metal
EF	extremely fine			★	medal is illustrated

Bibliography

ADELSON Adelson, Howard L. *The American Numismatic Society 1858–1958*, New York, 1958.

AFRIC. MUS. Africana Museum, *Commemorative Medals of the Z.A.R.* (compiled by Anna H. Smith), Johannesburg, 1958.

ALLEN Allen, D. G. C. 'The Early Medals of the Royal Society of Arts', *The Medal 3*, 1983, pp. 1–4.

ATTWOOD Attwood, Philip. 'Elinor Hallé', *The Medal 6*, 1985, pp. 16–22.

BAKER Baker, W. S. *Medallic Portraits of Washington*, Philadelphia, 1885.

BARTOLOTTI Bartolotti, Franco. *La Medaglia Annuale dei Romani Pontefici 1605–1967*, Rimini, 1967.

BEAULAH Beaulah, G. K. 'The Medals of the Art Union of London', *BNJ* 1967, pp. 179–85.

BÉNÉZIT Bénézit, Emanuel. *Dictionnaire des peintres, sculpteurs, dessinateurs et graveurs*, 8 vols., Paris, 1966.

BETTS Betts, C. Wyllys. *Colonial History Illustrated by Contemporary Medals*, 1894, reprinted Boston, 1972.

BHM Brown, Laurence. *British Historical Medals 1760–1837 (vol. I)*, London; 1980, *1837–1901 (vol. II)*, London, 1987.

BINGEN Bingen, Jean. *Les Roettiers Graveurs en Médaille des Pays Bays Méridionaux*, Brussels, 1952.

BNJ *British Numismatic Journal, Proceedings of the British Numismatic Society*, 1903–.

BOON Boon, George C. *Welsh Industrial Tokens and Medals*, Cardiff, 1973.

BRAMSEN Bramsen, L. *Médailleur Napoléon le Grand pendant le Consulat et l'Empire*, Paris, 1904.

BRETTAUER Brettauer, Josef. *Katalog Der Sammlung Medicina in Nummis* (compiled by E. Holzmair), Vienna, 1937.

BURT Burt, David J. 'Electrotype Medallions', *The Medal 5*, 1984, pp. 48–9.

CALDECOTT Caldecott, J. B. 'Brokers' Medals and Stockbrokers' Tokens', *The Stock Exchange Christmas Annual* (compiled by W. A. Morgan), Enfield, 1905–6, pp. 231–41.

CARLISLE Carlisle, Leslie J. *Australian Commemorative Medals and Medalets from 1788*, Sydney, 1983.

CARLISLE Carlisle, Nicholas. *A Memoir of the Life and Times of William Wyon*, London, 1837.

CHALLIS Challis, Christopher E. 'Mint Officials and Moneyers of the Tudor Period', *BNJ* 1975, pp. 55–75.

CP Cochran-Patrick, R. W. *Catalogue of the Medals of Scotland*, Edinburgh, 1884.

D & H Dalton, Richard, and Hamer, Samuel H. *The Provincial Token-Coinage of the 18th Century*, 1910, reprinted, Lawrence (Mass.), 1977.

D & W Davis, W. J. and Waters, A. W. *Tickets and Passes of Great Britain and Ireland*, London 1922, reprinted 1974.

DAVIS Davis, W. J. *The Token Coinage of Warwickshire*, Birmingham, 1895.

DORLING Dorling, H. Taprell (revised by A. A. Purves), *Ribbons and Medals*, London, 1983.

DUTTON Dutton, Ronald. 'How I Cast Medals', *The Medal 4*, 1984, p. 24.

DYER Dyer, Graham. 'Thomas Humphrey Paget (1893–1974)', *NC* 1980, pp. 165–77.

EIDLITZ Eidlitz, Robert J. *Medals and Medallions relating to Architects*, New York, 1927.

EIDLITZ —— *Portraits of Matthew Boulton & James Watt*, New York, 1928.

EIMER Eimer, Christopher. 'Sir Robert Johnson, The Mint and Medal Making in Inter-War Britain', *BNJ* 1985, pp. 169–91.

ENGSTROM Engstrom, J. Eric. *The Medallic Portraits of Sir Winston Churchill*, London, 1972.

EPM Grueber, Herbert A. 'English Personal Medals from 1760', *NC* 1887, pp. 245–73; 1888, pp. 60–94, 250–84; 1890, pp. 52–98; 1891, pp. 66–104, 377–412; 1892, pp. 228–46, 300–23.

ERLANGER Erlanger, Herbert J. *Origin and development of the European prize medal to the end of the XVIIIth century*, Haarlem, 1975.

FARQUHAR Farquhar, Helen. 'Portraiture of the Stuarts on Royalist Badges', *BNJ* 1905, pp. 243–90.

FARQUHAR —— 'Patterns and Medals bearing the legends Jacobus III or Jacobus VIII', *BNJ* 1906, pp. 229–70.

FARQUHAR —— 'Portraits of our Tudor Monarchs', *BNJ* 1907, pp. 79–143.

FARQUHAR —— 'Portraiture of our Stuart Monarchs on their Coins and Medals', *BNJ* 1908 (*part i*) pp. 145–262; 1909 (*ii*) pp. 213–85; 1910 (*iii*) pp. 199–267; 1911 (*iv*) pp. 207–73; 1912 (*v*) pp. 237–94; 1913 (*vi*) pp. 199–266; 1914/15 (*vii*) pp. 219–87, (refs. are to part and page no.).

FARQUHAR —— 'Some Portrait Medals struck between 1745 and 1752', *BNJ* 1923/24, pp. 171–233.

FEARON Fearon, Daniel. *Catalogue of British Commemorative Medals*, 1558 to the present day, with valuations, Exeter,1984.

FELDER Felder, Peter. *Medailleur Johann Carl Hedlinger*, Aarau, 1978.

FORRER Forrer, Leonard. *Biographical Dictionary of Medallists,* 8 vols. London, 1904–30, reprinted 1980.

FRAZER Frazer, William. 'Irish Medallists and their work', *Journal of the Royal Historical & Archaeological Association of Ireland*, Vol. 7, 4th series 1887 (*part I*, 1885, pp. 443–66, 608–19; *part II*, 1886, pp. 189–208, 313–26); *Journal of the Royal Society of Antiquaries of Ireland*, Vol. 3, 5th series 1893 (pp. 7–26).

FRIEDENBERG Friedenberg, Daniel. *Great Jewish Portraits in Metal, selected Plaques and Medals* from the Samuel Friedenberg Collection of the Jewish Museum, New York, 1963.

FRIEDENBERG —— *Jewish medals from the Renaissance to the fall of Napoleon (1501–1815)*, New York, 1970.

GARNETT Garnett, Alan. 'City Livery Badges', *BNJ* 1931/33, pp. 110–18.

GENT. MAG. *Gentleman's Magazine*, 1736–1870.

GORDON Gordon, L. L. *British Battles and Medals*, London, 1971.

GRANT Grant, M. H. 'British Medals since 1760', *BNJ* 1936/37, (*1760–1820*) pp. 269–93; 1938/39, (*1820–61*) pp. 119–52; 1939/40, (*1862–1909*) pp. 321–62; 1940/41, (*1910–37*) pp. 449–70, (addenda and index) pp. 470–80.

GRAVES Graves, Algernon. *The Royal Academy of Arts: Complete Dictionary of Contributors and their Work . . . 1769 to 1904*, London, 1905–6.

GRAVES —— *The Society of Artists of Great Britain, 1760–1791; The Free Society of Artists, 1761–1783: A Complete Dictionary . . .* London, 1907.

GRIMSHAW Grimshaw, M. E. *Silver Medals, Badges and Trophies from Schools in the British Isles 1550–1850*, Cambridge, 1961.

GUEST *Catalogue of the Montague Guest Collection of Badges, Tokens & Passes* (in the British Museum), London, 1930.

GUNNIS Gunnis, Rupert. *Dictionary of British Sculptors 1660–1851*, London, 1951.

HAWKINS Hawkins, Roy N. P. 'Dictionary of British Makers of Metallic Tickets and Counters', *Part I* 1960, *Part II* 1966–7, *Part III* 1968, *SCMB*.

HENNIN Hennin. *Histoire Numismatique de la Revolution Française*, Paris, 1826.

HENNING *John Henning 1771–1851 '. . . a very ingenious Modeller'*, by John Malden, Paisley Museum & Art Gallery, 1977.

HIBBARD Hibbard, M. G. *Boer War Tribute Medals*, Sandton, 1982.

HILL Hill, George Francis. 'The Medal of Henry VIII as Supreme Head of the Church', *NC* 1916, pp. 194–5.

HILL —— *A Corpus of Italian Medals of the Renaissance before Cellini*, London, 1930.

HILL/POLL. —— *Medals of the Renaissance*, 1920, (revised and enlarged by Graham Pollard), London, 1978.

HOCKING Hocking, W. J. *Catalogue of the coins, tokens, medals, dies and seals in the museum of the Royal Mint*, (vol. II), pp. 145–318, London, 1910.

HYCKERT Hyckert, Bror Edv. *Minnespenningar öfver enskilda Svenska Män och Kvinnor*, vols. I–II, Stockholm, 1905.

INGLIS Inglis, Allison. 'The Medals of Edward Poynter', *The Medal 7*, 1985, pp. 17–31.

JAMIESON Jamieson, Allan Melville. *Medals awarded to North American Indian Chiefs 1714–1922*, London, 1936.

JMC *Catalogue of the Jewish Museum, London*, edited by Richard D. Barnett, London, 1974.

JOHNSON Johnson, Velia. *Dieci Anni Di Studi Di Medaglistica 1968–78*, Milan, 1979.

JONES Jones, Mark. *The Art of the Medal*, London, 1979.

JONES —— 'Emil Fuchs in England', *The Medal 6*, 1985, pp. 23–9.

JULIAN Julian, R. W. *Medals of the United States Mint, The First Century, 1792–1892*, El Cajon, 1977.

KIENAST Kienast, Gunther W. *The Medals of Karl Goetz*, Cleveland (Ohio), 1967.

KORMIS 'Medals by Fred J. Kormis' (compiled by Mark Jones), *The Medal 5*, 1984, pp. 32–5.

KRESS *Renaissance Medals from the Samuel H. Kress Collection at the National Gallery of Art* (based on the 1931 catalogue of the Dreyfus collection by George Francis Hill, revised and enlarged by Graham Pollard), New York, London, 1967.

LAW Betts, Benjamin. *The Medals Relating to John Law and the Mississippi System*, New York, 1907.

LEROUX Leroux, Joseph. *Médaillier du Canada*, Montreal, 1892, reprinted, 1964.

LESSEN Lessen, Marvin. 'The Cromwell Lord Protector Medal by Simon', *BNJ* 1977, pp. 114–26.

LESSEN —— 'The Cromwell Lord General Medal by Simon', *BNJ* 1979, pp. 87–98.

LESSEN —— 'The Cromwell Lord Dunbar Medals by Simon', *BNJ* 1981, pp. 112–33.

LESSEN —— 'The Cromwell Funeral Medal by Simon', *BNJ* 1982, pp. 151–57.

LOUBAT Loubat, Joseph F. *The Medallic History of the United States of America, 1776–1876*, New York, 1878, reprinted 1967.

MACKAY Mackay, James. *The Dictionary of Western Sculptors in Bronze*, Woodbridge, 1977.

MACLEOD Macleod, Roy. 'Of Medals and Men: A Reward System in Victorian Science 1826–1914', *Notes and Records of the Royal Society of London*, vol. 26, no. 1, June 1971.

MAGOR Magor, R. B. 'The Royal Visits by T.R.H.s. The Princes of Wales to India in 1875/6, 1905/6 and 1921', *OMRS* 1980, 37–59.

MEDAL, THE Journal of the British Art Medal Society, 1982–   , (No. 1–).

MEDINA Medina, José T. *Medallas Europas Relativas a América*, Buenos Aires, 1924.

MH Milford Haven, Admiral the Marquess of *British Naval Medals*, London, 1919.

MH —— *Naval Medals of France, The Netherlands, Spain, and Portugal*, vol. I, London, 1921.

MH —— *Naval Medals of Europe (part II), North and South America, Japan and China*, vol. II, London, 1928.

MI Hawkins, Edward. *Medallic Illustrations of the History of Great Britain and Ireland to the death of George II*, (ed. A. W. Franks and H. A. Grueber) 2 vols. (*i* 1066–1690; *ii* 1690–1760) London 1885, reprinted 1969.

MI *Plates*, I–CLXXXIII, London 1911, reprinted 1979.

MOYAUX Moyaux, Auguste. *Les Chemins de Fer Autrefois et Aujourd'hui et Leurs Médailles Commémoratives*. Brussels, 1905; *supplement i*, 1910.

MUDIE Mudie, James. *An Historical and Critical Account of a Grand Series of National Medals*, London, 1820.

MÜSELER Müseler, Karl. *Bergbaugepräge, Dargestellt auf Grund der Sammlung der Preussag Aktiengesellschaft*. vols. I–II (all refs. are to vol. I), Hanover, 1983.

NAU Nau, Elisabeth. *Lorenze Natter 1705–1763. Gemmenschneider und Medailleur*, Biberach an der Riss, 1966.

NC *Numismatic Chronicle*, Journal of the proceedings of the Royal Numismatic Society, 1836–.

NIGGL Niggl, Paul. *Musiker Medaillen*, Darmstadt, 1965.

NPG *National Portrait Gallery, Complete Illustrated Catalogue 1856–1979* (compiled by K. K. Yung), London, 1979.

OGDEN Ogden, W. Sharp. 'Shakespeare's Portraiture: Painted, Graven and Medallic', *BNJ* 1911, pp. 42–54.

OMRS *The Journal of the Orders and Medals Research Society*, 1961–.

PARKES WEBER Parkes Weber, F. 'Medals and Medallions of the Nineteenth Century, Relating to England by Foreign Artists', *NC* 1894–1900, pp. 286–335, 101–78, 219–71.

PAYNE Payne, A. A. *British and Foreign Orders, War Medals and Decorations*, Sheffield, 1911.

PEARSON Pearson, Fiona. *Goscombe John at the National Museum of Wales*, Cardiff, 1979.

PECK Peck, C. Wilson. *English Copper, Tin and Bronze coins in the British Museum*

1558–1958, London, 1970.

PINCHES Pinches, John Harvey. *The Family of Pinches*, London, 1981.

POLLARD Pollard, Graham. 'Matthew Boulton and Conrad Heinrich Küchler', *NC* 1970, pp. 259–318.

POOLE *A Catalogue of Masonic Medals in the Museum of the Provincial Grand Lodge of Worcestershire* (edited by H. Poole), Worcester, 1939.

POULSOM Poulsom, Neville. *The White Ribbon*, St. Albans, 1968.

PYKE Pyke, E. J. *A Biographical Dictionary of Wax Modellers*, Oxford, 1973.

R. MINT *Royal Mint, Annual Report of the Deputy Master and Comptroller* (refs. are to year and plate no.), 1870–.

RWE *Royal Wedding Exhibition, A Princess for Wales*, The Guildhall, Windsor, 20 July–8 August 1981, Nottingham, 1981.

SCMB *Seaby (B.A.) Coin and Medal Bulletin*, 1936–.

SEABY Seaby, B. A. *Standard Catalogue of British Coins, Vol. I*, London, 1987.

SHACKLES Shackles, George. *The Medals of British Freemasonry*, Hamburg, 1901.

SNC Spink (and Son) Numismatic Circular, 1892–.

STAINTON Stainton, Thomas. 'John Milton, Medallist, 1759–1805', *BNJ* 1983, pp. 133–59.

STORER Storer, Horatio R. *Medicina in Nummis*, Boston, 1931.

SVARSTAD Svarstad, Carsten. *Medals of Actors, Singers & Dancers*, London, 1963 (and serialised in *SNC*).

SYMONDS Symonds, Henry. 'English Mint Engravers of the Tudor and Stuart periods, 1485–1688', *NC* 1913, pp. 349–77.

TANCRED Tancred, George. *Historical Records of Medals and Honorary Distinctions conferred on the British Navy, Army & Auxiliary Forces*, London, 1891.

TAYLOR Taylor, Jeremy. *The Architectural Medal*, England in the Nineteenth Century, London, 1978.

THOMASON Thomason, Edward. *Sir Edward Thomason's Memoirs*, London, 1845.

TOURNEUR Tourneur, Victor. 'Steven van Herwijck, médailleur anversois (1557–1565)', *NC* 1922, pp. 91–132.

V. LOON van Loon, Gerard. *Histoire Métallique des XVII Provinces des Pays-Bas, vols. I–V*, French edition (different pagination to the Dutch), The Hague, 1732–37. suppl. *Beschrijving van Nederlandsche Histoire-Penningen*, 1822–1869, The Hague, 1869.

W & Z Wielandt, Friedricy, and Zeitz, Joachim. *Die Medaillen Des Hauses Baden*, Karlsruhe, 1980.

WELCH Welch, Charles. Numismata Londinensia: *Medals struck by the Corporation of London to commemorate important municipal events, 1831 to 1893*, London, 1894.

WENT Went, Arthur E. J. 'The Medals of the Royal Dublin Society 1761–1973' (Reprinted from the *Scientific Proceedings of the Royal Dublin Society*, series B, vol. 3, No. 13), Dublin, pp. 165–90.

WENT —— 'Irish Coins and Medals', *The Irish Heritage Series 4,* Dublin, 1978.

WOLLASTON Wollaston, Henry. *British Official Medals for Coronations and Jubilees*, Nottingham, 1981.

WOODWARD Woodward, Horace B. *The History of the Geological Society of London*, London, 1907.

WURZBACH Wurzbach-Tannenberg, Wolfgang R. *Katalog Meiner Sammlung von Medaillen, Plaketten und Jetons*, 2 vols., Hamburg, 1978.

CATALOGUE

		VF	EF
		£	£

WILLIAM I, 1066–87 — HENRY III, 1216–72

1 William I, Memorial 1087
Obv. Bust three-quarters r., armoured. GULIELMUS. I. CONQUÆSTOR. D.G. ANG. REX. *Rev.* A
captive and a mourning figure of England upon a tomb. *Ex.* NAT. 1023. COR. 1066. MORT. 1087.
D. 41 mm. By J. Dassier. *MI i*, 2

| AR | 27 | 55 |
| AE | 4 | 9 |

Struck in 1731, from Dassier's series of English kings and queens. *See* No. 526.

2 William II, Memorial 1100
Obv. Bust three-quarters l., crowned and armoured. GULIELMUS. II. D.G. ANGLIÆ. REX. *Rev.*
A decorated tomb in the form of a casket. *Ex.* NAT. 1060. COR. 1087. MORT. 1100. *D.* 41 mm. By
J. Dassier. *MI i*, 2

| AR | 27 | 55 |
| AE | 4 | 9 |

Struck in 1731, from Dassier's series of English kings and queens. *See* No. 526.

3 Henry I, Memorial 1135
Obv. Bust three-quarters r., crowned and armoured. HENRICUS. I. D.G. ANGLIÆ. REX. *Rev.* A
decorated tomb. *Ex.* NAT. 1070. COR. 1100 MORT. 1135. *D.* 41 mm. By J. Dassier. *MI i*, 2

| AR | 27 | 55 |
| AE | 4 | 9 |

Struck in 1731, from Dassier's series of English kings and queens. *See* No. 526.

4 Stephen, Memorial 1154
Obv. Bust l., helmeted and armoured. STEPHANUS D.G. ANGLIÆ REX. *Rev.* A winged infant
upon a decorated tomb. *Ex.* NAT. 1105. COR. 1135. MORT. 1154. *D.* 41 mm. By J. Dassier. *MI i*,
3

| AR | 27 | 55 |
| AE | 4 | 9 |

Struck in 1731, from Dassier's series of English kings and queens. *See* No. 526.

5 Henry II, Memorial 1189
Obv. Bust r., crowned, helmeted and armoured. HENRICUS. II. D.G. ANG. ET. HIB. REX. *Rev.*
Mars seated, amidst arms, before a decorated monument, inscribed NATUS 1133 CORONAT.
1155 MORT. 1189. *D.* 41 mm. By J. Dassier. *MI i*, 3

| AR | 27 | 55 |
| AE | 4 | 9 |

Struck in 1731, from Dassier's series of English kings and queens. *See* No. 526.

6 Richard I, Memorial 1199
Obv. Bust three-quarters r., helmeted, laureate and armoured. RICHARDUS. I. D.G. ANG. HIB.
ET. CYPRI. REX. *Rev.* Fame seated upon clouds above a decorated monument. *Ex.* NAT. 1157.
COR. 1189. MORT. 1199. *D.* 41 mm. By J. Dassier. *MI i*, 3

| AR | 27 | 55 |
| AE | 4 | 9 |

Struck in 1731, from Dassier's series of English kings and queens. *See* No. 526.

7 John, Memorial 1216
Obv. Bust l., crowned and draped. IOANNES D.G. ANG. ET. HIB. REX. *Rev.* A decorated
monument. *Ex.* NAT. 1166. COR. 1199. MORT. 1216. *D.* 41 mm. By J. Dassier. *MI i*, 4

| AR | 27 | 55 |
| AE | 4 | 9 |

Struck in 1731, from Dassier's series of English kings and queens. *See* No. 526.

8 Henry III, Memorial 1272
Obv. Bust three-quarters r., crowned and armoured. HENRICUS. III. D.G. ANG. ET. HIB.
REX *Rev.* A monument flanked by two figures in a landscape. *Ex.* NAT. 1206. COR. 1216.
MORT. 1272. *D.* 41 mm. By J. Dassier. *MI i*, 4

| AR | 27 | 55 |
| AE | 4 | 9 |

Struck in 1731, from Dassier's series of English kings and queens. *See* No. 526.

EDWARD I, 1272–1307 — RICHARD III, 1483–85

				£	£
9	**Roger Bacon, Memorial 1294**				

Obv. Bust r., draped, ROGERIUS BACON *Rev.* NATUS ILCHESTER COM. SOMMERSET IN ANGLIA AN.   *AR*   15   28
M.CC.XIV. OBIIT AN. M.CC.XCIV   *Ex.* SERIES NUMISMATICA UNIVERSALIS VIRORUM ILLUSTRIUM.   *AE*   3   7
M.DCCC.XVIII. DURAND EDIDIT   *D.* 42 mm. By R. Gayrard. *MI i*, 4/1; *Storer* 135

Roger Bacon (1214?–94), philosopher and scientist. Struck in Paris in 1818, from a series commemorating famous people of all countries.

10   **Edward I, Memorial 1307**
Obv. Bust three-quarters l., crowned and armoured. EDOUARD. I. D.G. ANG. ET. HIB.   *AR*   27   55
REX   *Rev.* A decorated circular temple, flanked by History and two figures. *Ex.* NAT. 1230.   *AE*   4   9
COR. 1272. MORT. 1307. *D.* 41 mm. By J. Dassier. *MI i*, 5/2

Struck in 1731, from Dassier's series of English kings and queens. *See* No. 526.

11   **Edward II, Memorial 1327**
Obv. Bust r., crowned and draped. EDOUARD. II. D.G. ANG. ET. HIB. REX. *Rev.* A decorated   *AR*   27   55
monument. *Ex.* NAT. 1284. COR. 1307. MORT. 1327. *D.* 41 mm. By J. Dassier. *MI i*, 5   *AE*   4   9

Struck in 1731, from Dassier's series of English kings and queens. *See* No. 526.

12   **Edward III, Memorial 1377**
Obv. Bust three-quarters l., helmeted, laureate and armoured. EDOUARD. III. D.G. ANG. FR. ET.   *AR*   27   55
HIB. REX. *Rev.* A circular temple flanked by two cupids upon its base, inscribed NAT. 1312.   *AE*   4   9
COR. 1327. MORT. 1377. *D.* 41 mm. By J. Dassier. *MI i*, 9/8

Struck in 1731, from Dassier's series of English kings and queens. *See* No. 526.

13   **Richard II, Memorial 1399**
Obv. Bust r., crowned and draped. RICHARDVS. II. D.G. ANG. FR. ET. HIB. REX. *Rev.* Two   *AR*   27   55
cherubs, one displaying a skull and dagger, seated upon a decorated monument. *Ex.* NAT.   *AE*   4   9
1366 COR. 1377 MORT. 1399. *D.* 41 mm. By J. Dassier. *MI i*, 10/2

Struck in 1731, from Dassier's series of English kings and queens. *See* No. 526.

14   **Winchester College Medal 1404**
Obv. Bust l., mitred and draped. WILHELMUS DE WYKEHAM *Rev.* Prince of Wales' plumes and   *AV*   400   500
motto. HONOREM PRINCEPS PROPONIT   *D.* 50 mm. By J. Milton. *MI i*, 11/3; *BHM* 931;   *AR*   25   48
Stainton 16; *Grimshaw* 13

Struck *c.* 1795 and awarded from 1797 in gold and silver. From *c.* 1830 a succession of Royal medals were given; *see* No. 1240. William of Wykeham (1324–1404), bishop of Winchester; Chancellor of England.

15   **Henry IV, Memorial 1413**
Obv. Bust l., crowned, veiled and draped. HENRICUS. IV. D.G. ANG. FR. ET. HIB. REX. *Rev.*   *AR*   27   55
Death reclining upon a decorated monument, inscribed NATUS 1366 CORONAT. 1399 MORT.   *AE*   4   9
1413. *D.* 41 mm. By J. Dassier. *MI i*, 12/6

Struck in 1731, from Dassier's series of English kings and queens. *See* No. 526.

16   **Henry V, Memorial 1422**
Obv. Bust r., crowned, helmeted, laureate and armoured. HENRICUS. V. D.G. ANG. FR. ET. HIB.   *AR*   27   55
REX. *Rev.* Fame crowning a reclining figure of Henry V, upon a decorated monument,   *AE*   4   9
inscribed NATUS 1388 CORONAT. 1413 MORT. 1422. *D.* 41 mm. By J. Dassier. *MI i*, 12/6

Struck in 1731, from Dassier's series of English kings and queens. *See* No. 526.

17   **Henry VI, Memorial 1471**
Obv. Bust l., crowned and draped. HENRICUS. VI. D.G. ANG. FR. ET. HIB. REX. *Rev.* Statue of   *AR*   27   55
Time within a temple, the base inscribed NAT. 1421. COR. 1422. MORT. 1471. *D.* 41 mm. By J.   *AE*   4   9
Dassier. *MI i*, 16/6

Struck in 1731, from Dassier's series of English kings and queens. *See* No. 526.

18   **Federigo Duke of Urbino, Knight of the Garter 1474**
Obv. Bust l., of Federigo, armoured, within the Garter. HONY. SOYT. QY. MAL. Y.   *AE*   1200   —
PENSE   *Rev.* Five putti support a shield, on which stands an eagle between two cornucopiae.   *Pb.*   350   —
FE DVX across field. *D.* 118 mm. Cast. [By P. Torregiani] *MI i*, 16/1; *Hill* 1118

Made *c.* 1515; Federigo da Montefeltro (1422–82), created Duke of Urbino by Pope Sixtus IV. The Most Noble Order of the Garter (K.G.) was founded by Edward III in 1349, and has been awarded continuously since; it is the premier order of Great Britain. It has as its motto Honi Soit Qui Mal y Pense [Evil be who evil thinks].

19   **John Kendal, Turkish Siege of Rhodes 1480**
Obv. Bust r., armoured. IO. KENDAL. RHODI. TVRCVPELLERIVS. *Rev.* Armorial shield.   *AE*   550   —
TEMPORE. OBSIDIONIS. TVRCHORVM. MCCCCLXXX *D.* 58 mm. Cast. Italian (By?) *MI i*, 17/3;
Hill 934

John Kendal (d. 1501?), 'Turcopolier' or general of infantry to the Knights of St. John. The first medal to honour an Englishman.

20   Edward IV, Memorial 1483
Obv. Bust r., crowned, helmeted, armoured and draped. EDOUARD. IV. D.G. ANG. FR. ET. HIB.   *AR*   27   55
REX. *Rev.* Statue of Fortune within a monument. *Ex.* NAT. 1441. COR. 20. IUN. 1461. MORT. 9.   *AE*   4   9
APRIL. 1483. *D.* 41 mm. By J. Dassier. *MI i*, 18/4
Struck in 1731, from Dassier's series of English kings and queens. *See* No. 526.

21   Edward V, Memorial 1483
Obv. Bust l., draped. EDOUARD. V. D.G. ANG. FR. ET. HIB. REX. *Rev.* Two infants embracing   *AR*   27   55
upon a decorated monument, inscribed NAT. 8. OCTOB. 1470. MORT. 1483. *D.* 41 mm. By J.   *AE*   4   9
Dassier. *MI i*, 18
Struck in 1731, from Dassier's series of English kings and queens. *See* No. 526.

22   Richard III, Memorial 1485
Obv. Bust r., diademed and draped. RICHARDVS III. D.G. ANG. FR. ET. HIB. REX. *Rev.* Figure of   *AR*   27   55
fury holding a crown and dagger, lying beside the two murdered princes, upon a decorated   *AE*   4   9
sarcophagus. *Ex.* CORONAT. 6. IVL. 1483. MORT. 22. AVG. 1485. *D.* 41 mm. By J. Dassier. *MI i*,
19
Struck in 1731, from Dassier's series of English kings and queens. *See* No. 526.

HENRY VII, 1485–1509

23*   Archbishop Schevez 1491
Obv. Bust l., wearing a cap and draped. WILHELMVS. SCHEVEZ. SCI. ADREE. ARCHIEPS   *Rev.*   *AE*   1800   —
Armorial shield upon an archiepiscopal cross. LEGATVS. NATVS. &. TOTIVS. REGNI. SCOTIE.
PRIMAS. 1491. *D.* 79 mm. Cast. (By Q. Matsys?). *MI i*, 20/2; *Hill/Pollard* pl. 22/1. *See* **Plate 1**
William Schevez (*c.* 1435–97), Archbishop of St. Andrews; papal legate and Scottish Ambassador.

24   Princess Elizabeth of York, Memorial 1503
Obv. Bust three-quarters l., draped. ELIS. EBOR. UXOR HENRICI VII REG. ANG. *Rev.* Two rose   *AR*   18   30
sprigs, crossed. HINC NOSTRÆ CREVERE ROSÆ NUPT. 1486. MORT. 1503 *D.* 39 mm. By   *AE*   5   8
D. F. Loos. *MI i*, 22/5
Struck *c.* 1800. Princess Elizabeth (1465–1503), eldest daughter of Edward IV; married Henry VII in 1486.

25   Henry VII, Memorial 1509
Obv. Bust three-quarters l., wearing a cap and draped. HENRICUS. VII. D.G. ANG. FR. ET. HIB.   *AR*   27   55
REX. *Rev.* A decorated monument adorned, above, by two roses. *Ex.* NAT. 1457. COR. 30. OCT.   *AE*   4   9
1485. M. 22. APRIL. 1509. *D.* 41 mm. By J. Dassier. *MI i*, 23/6
Struck in 1731, from Dassier's series of English kings and queens. *See* No. 526.

HENRY VIII, 1509–47

26*   Henry VIII, Supreme Head of the Church, 1545
Obv. Bust r., wearing a cap and draped. HENRICVS. OCTA. ANGLIÆ. FRANCI. ET. HIB. REX. FIDEI.   *a AV*   2500   —
DEFENSOR. ET. IN. TERR. ECCLE. ANGLI. ET. HIBE. SVB. CHRIST. CAPVT. SVPREMVM   *Rev.*   *AR*   1400   —
Inscriptions in Hebrew and Greek [= Henry VIII, King of England, France and Ireland,
defender of the faith, under Christ the supreme head on earth of the Church of England and   *b AR*   70   130
Ireland]. H.R above; LONDINI below. 1545 *D.* 53 mm. Cast. (By H. Basse?). *Mi i*, 47/44;
Hill/Pollard pl. 28, 1. *See* **Plate 1**
Type *b* is an eighteenth century copy.

27   Henry VIII, Memorial 1547
Obv. Bust almost facing, wearing a bonnet and draped. HENRICUS. VIII. D.G. ANG. FR. ET HIB.   *AR*   35   65
REX. *Rev.* Hercules within a temple destroying religious objects. *Ex.* NAT. 1491. COR. 24 IUN.   *AE*   7   15
1509. MORT. 28 IAN. 1547. *D.* 41 mm. By J. Dassier. *MI i*, 52/54
Struck in 1731, from Dassier's series of English kings and queens. *See* No. 526.

EDWARD VI, 1547–53

28   Coronation of Edward VI 1547
Obv. Half-length figure r., crowned and armoured, holding a sword and orb. EDWARDVS. VI.   *a AV*   2800   —
D.G. ANG. FR. ET. HI. REX. FIDEI. DEFNS. ET. IN. TERRIS. ANG. ET. HIB. ECCLE. CAPVT. SVPREMVM.   *AR*   1500   —

                                                                  £   £

CORONATVS. EST. M.D.XLVI. XX. FEBRVA. ETATIS. DECIMO. *Rev.* Inscriptions in Hebrew and Greek [= Edward VI, by Grace of God, King of England, France and Ireland, defender of the faith, the supreme head on earth of the Church of England and Ireland, crowned 20 February, 1546, at age of ten years]. LAMBHITH (Lambeth), above. *D.* 62 mm. Cast. (By H. Basse?). *MI i*, 53/1; *Wollaston* 31   *b AR*   70   130

Type *b* is an eighteenth century copy. Dated in the old style.

29   **Christ's Hospital, Marker's Medal 1553**
Obv. Bust r., crowned and draped. EDWARD. VI. D.G. ANG. FR. ET HIB. REX   *Rev.* An open Bible. HEAR. READ. MARK. LEARN   *Ex.* CHRISTS HOSPITAL INST. MDLIII   *D.* 35 mm. By L. Pingo. *MI i*, 61/16; *D & W* 242/305–6; *Grimshaw* 90   *AR*   10   18   *AE*   4   9

Struck *c.* 1790 and awarded in silver up to *c.* 1890. The edge was inscribed with the date and the name of the marker, whose function was to supervise the behaviour of other boys. Previously, a cast medal of similar design had been used since its introduction *c.* 1755.

30   **Edward VI, Memorial 1553**
Obv. Bust three-quarters l., wearing a feathered hat and draped. EDOUARD. VI. D.G. ANG. FR. ET. HIB. REX. *Rev.* A decorated monument. *Ex.* NAT. 12. OCTOB. 1537. COR. 20. FEBR. 1547. M. 6. IUL. 1553. *D.* 41 mm. By J. Dassier. *MI i*, 62/20   *AR*   27   55   *AE*   4   9

Struck in 1731, from Dassier's series of English kings and queens. *See* No. 526.

MARY, 1553–58

31   **Return of England to the Papal Church 1554**
Obv. Bust r., draped, IVLIVS TERTIVS PONT. MAX. A.V. *Rev.* The Pope, standing beside two cardinals and Philip and Mary, raises the kneeling figure of England. ANGLIA RESVRGES   *Ex.* VT NVNC NOVISSIMO DIE   *D.* 47 mm. Cast. By G. Cavino. *MI i*, 70/15; *Forrer* I/371   *AE*   350   —

Struck copies were made during the eighteenth and nineteenth centuries. Pope Julius III (1487–1555), real name Giammaria Ciocchi del Monte.

32*   **Philip and Mary 1555**
Obv. Half-length figure l., wearing a veiled coif and draped. MARIA. I. REG. ANGL. FRANC. ET. HIB. FIDEI. DEFENSATRIX   *Rev.* Half-length figure r., armoured. PHILIPPVS. REX. PRINC. HISP. ÆT. S. AN. XXVIII   *D.* 69 mm. Cast. By J. da Trezzo. *MI i*, 71/17; *v. Loon* I, 5/2. *See* **Plate 1**   *a AE*   300   —   *b AR*   80   150

Type *b* is an eighteenth century copy. Mary I or Mary Tudor (1516–58), queen 1553–58. Philip II (1527–98), king of Spain; married Mary in 1554.

33*   **Mary, State of England 1555**
Obv. Sim. to No. 32. *Rev.* Seated figure of Mary r., as Peace, applies a torch to a pile of arms before a temple and holds aloft palm and olive-branches. CECIS VISVS TIMIDIS. QVIES   *D.* 69 mm. Cast. By J. da Trezzo. *MI i*, 72/20; *Hill/Pollard* pl. 18, 9; *v. Loon* I, 11/5. *See* **Plate 1**   *a AV*   —   —   *AR*   700   —   *AE*   350   —

Type *b* is an eighteenth century copy.

                                                                     b AR   80   150

34   **Bishop Hugo Latimer, Memorial 1555**
Obv. Bust r., of Latimer, wearing a cap and draped. *Rev.* HUGO LATIMERUS ANGLUS WIGORNIENSIS EPISCOPUS OCTUAGENARIO MAIOR CHRISTI CAUSA VIVUS EXUSTUS OXONII AN. 1555   *D.* 28 mm. By J. Dassier. *MI i*, 76/28   *AR*   8   15   *AE*   3   5

Hugo Latimer (1485–1555), bishop of Worcester. Struck *c.* 1725, from Dassier's series of twenty-four European Protestant reformers. Others of British interest are Thomas Cranmer, Patrick Hamilton, John Knox, Nicholas Ridley, John Tillotson (No. 361), and John Wicklif. *See* No. 500.

35*   **Siege and Capture of St. Quentin 1557**
Obv. Bust r., laureate and armoured. PHILIPPVS. D.G. HISP. ET. ANGLIÆ. REX   *Rev.* Full-face medallion of S. QVINTINVS. MARTIR in the centre. ANNO M.D.LVII. DEN X. TAG AVG. WARD DVRCH KVNIG PHILIP ZV HISPAN. VND ENGELLAND. DER FRANZOS GESCHLAGEN DER CONNESTABEL VND BEST ADEL GEFANG. VOLGEND DEN XXVII DES SELBEN DIE STAT SANCT QVINTIN MIT DEM STVRM BEROB. VND GEPLVNDERT   *D.* 34 mm. Cast. By J. Jonghelinck. *MI i*, 84/47; *v. Loon* I, 17; *Hill/Pollard* pl. 23, 2. *See* **Plate 1**   *AV*   —   —   *AR*   140   270

St. Quentin is in northern France.

36   **Philip II, Counter 1557**
Obv. Bust r., armoured. PHILIPPVS. D.G. HISPANIARVM. REX   *Rev.* 1557 divided by a crowned shield. GITONES. DEL. BVREAV. DE. SV. MAG.   *D.* 30 mm. Dutch (By?) *MI i*, 79/34; *v. Loon* I, 9 (sim.)   *AE*   12   25

Varieties occur dated 1556 and 1558.

37   **Philip and Mary, Counter 1557**
Obv. Busts of Philip, armoured, and Mary, draped, facing each other. PHS. D.G.
HISPANIARVM. REX. *Ex.* 1557   *Rev.* Arms in a lozenge-shaped shield. GECT. DE. LA. CHAMBR.
DES. COPT. A. LILLE. 1557   *D.* 29 mm. French (By?) *MI i*, 85/49

			£	£
		AE	12	25

There are several varieties of this piece.

38   **Mary, Memorial 1558**
Obv. Bust three-quarters r., with a veiled coif and draped. MARIA. I. D.G. ANG. FR. ET. HIB.
REGINA   *Rev.* Religion seated before a monument; to r., a column decorated with a
medallion of a pope. *Ex.* NATA. 18. FEBR. 1516. COR. 1. OCTOB. 1553. MORT. 17. NOV. 1558. *D.*
41 mm. By J. Dassier. *MI i*, 89/59

	AR	27	55
	AE	4	9

Struck in 1731, from Dassier's series of English kings and queens. *See* No. 526.

ELIZABETH I, 1558–1603

39   **Accession of Elizabeth I 1558**
Obv. Bust three-quarters l., of the Queen, crowned and draped. ET ANGLIÆ GLORIA   *Rev.* A
phoenix amid flames, crown above. SOLA PHOENIX   *D.* 29 mm. (By?) *MI i*, 91/3;
Hill/Pollard pl. 27, 5

	AE	70	—
	Pb.	40	—

Two similar pieces were also struck. Elizabeth I (1533–1603), only child of Henry VIII and Anne Boleyn.

40   **Marriage of Mary, Queen of Scots and the Dauphin Francis 1558**
Obv. Busts of Mary, draped, and Francis, armoured, face to face; a crown above. FRAN. ET.
MA. D.G. RR. SCOTOR DELPHIN. VIEN. *Rev.* Shields of the couple, crowned, between F. and M.
crowned. FECIT. VTRAQVE. VNVM. 1558. *D.* 52 mm. [By J. B. Salmson]. *MI i*, 92/5

	AV	500	600
	AR	18	30
	AE	7	10

First struck in 1832 at the Paris Mint, and subsequently restruck. Mary, Queen of Scots, or Mary Stuart (1542–87),
daughter of James V of Scotland. Francis II, the Dauphin (1544–60), king of France 1559–60.

41*   **Reform of the Coinage** *c.*1560
Obv. Bust sim. to No. 39; floral wreath border. *Rev.* Justice, seated, holding scales and
sword; floral wreath border. *D.* 29 mm. (By?) *MI i*, 100/23. *See* **Plate 1**

	AR	150	—
	AE	70	—

A quantity of base coin was in circulation when Elizabeth came to the throne; their nominal value was reduced and their
withdrawal completed by 1561.

42   **William Parr 1562**
Obv. Bust r., armoured; 1562 on truncation. GVILE. MARCHIO NORTHAMPTON   *Without
reverse*. *D.* 40 mm. Cast. By S. v. Herwijck. *MI i*, 103/28; *Tourneur* 22

	AR	400	—

William Parr (1513–71), Marquis of Northampton and Earl of Essex.

43*   **Elizabeth, Marchioness of Northampton 1562**
Obv. Bust l., wearing a cap and draped. ELZABET. MARQVI. NORTHAMPTON   *Rev.* Faith
standing r., supporting a cross. SOLA. TVTA FIDES. Aᵒ 1562   *D.* 40 mm. Cast. By S. v.
Herwijck. *MI i*, 104/29; *Tourneur* 23. *See* **Plate 1**

	AR	400	—

Elizabeth Brook (?–1565), Marchioness of Northampton; daughter of Lord Cobham.

44   **William Herbert 1562**
Obv. Bust r., armoured and draped. GVILI. COMES. PENNEBROCK. Aᵒ 1562   *Rev.* Female figure,
standing beside a dragon, indicating the temple of Virtue. DRACO. HIC. VER' VIRTVTV. CVSTOS.
D. 45 mm. Cast. By S. v. Herwijck. *MI i*, 104/30; *Tourneur* 24

	AR	400	—

William Herbert (1501?–70), 1st Earl of Pembroke.

45*   **Richard and Dorcas Martin 1562**
Obv. Bust r., wearing a bonnet and draped. RICHARD. MARTIN. ÆT. Z8, Aᵒ 1562   *Rev.* Bust l.,
wearing a Dutch-style cap and draped. DORCAS. EGLESTONE. VX. RICHARD. MARTIN. ÆT.
Z5   *D.* 58 mm. Cast. By S. v. Herwijck. *MI i*, 107/33; *Hill/Pollard pl.* 23, 6; *Tourneur* 20.
See **Plate 1**

	AR	500	—
	AE	300	—

Sir Richard Martin (1534–1617), goldsmith and Master of the Mint; Lord Mayor of London. Married Dorcas (1537–99)
in *c.* 1560.

46   **Thomas Stanley 1562**
Obv. Bust r., wearing a bonnet and draped. THOMAS. STANLEY. ÆT. 50   *Rev.* Armorial
shield. *D.* 44 mm. Cast. By S. v. Herwijck. *MI i*, 105/32; *Tourneur* 30

	AR	400	—

Thomas Stanley (*c.* 1512–76), Assay Master and Comptroller of the Mint.

47*   **Defence of the Kingdom** *c.*1572
Obv. Bust of Elizabeth I., crowned and draped, between portcullis and rose. QVID. NOS. SINE.
TE   *Rev.* Castle on a mount, between ER; below, a ribbon, inscribed O QVANTO, across a

	AV	500	800
	AR	100	170

sphere, QVID. HOC. SINE. ARMIS   *D.* 24 mm. (By?) *MI i*, 120/57. *See* **Plate 1**

This piece is not unlike the milled coinage of Elizabeth, *c.* 1561–72, produced on machinery introduced by the Frenchman Eloye Mestrell. See *Forrer* IV/48.

		VF	EF
		£	£

48*   **Phoenix Badge** *c.*1574

Obv. Bust l., draped. ELIZABETHA. D.G. ANG. FR. ET HIB. REGINA + HEI MIHI QVOD TANTO VIRTVS PERFVSA DECORE. NON HABET ETERNOS INVIOLATA DIES   *Rev.* Phoenix amid flames; above, ER monogram crowned. FELICES ARABES MVNDI QVIBVS VNICA PHŒNIX PH NICEM REPARAT DEPEREVNDO NOVAM. O MISEROS ANGLOS MVNDI QVIBVS VNICA PHŒNIX VLTIMA FIT NOSTRO TRISTIA FATA SOLO. *D.* 42 mm by 47 mm. Oval, cast. (By J. Rutlinger?) *MI i*, 124/70; *Hill/Pollard pl.* 28, 4; *v. Loon I*, 558. *See* **Plate 1**

a AR   1200   —
b AR   100   170

Type *b* is an eighteenth century copy.

49   **Sir Richard Shelley 1577**

Obv. Half-length bust r., armoured. RICARDVS. SCELLEIVS. PRIOR. ANGLIÆ. *Rev.* A griffin, ducal crown around neck, standing l., in a rugged landscape. PATRIARVM. EXCVBITOR. OPVM. *D.* 71 mm. Cast. By B. Rantwic. *MI i*, 127/75; *Kress 640*

AR   650   —
AE   300   —

Made *c.* 1620; a copy of an unsigned Italian version. Richard Shelley (1513–89?), Grand Prior of the Knights of St. John.

50   **Mary, Queen of Scots 1579**

Obv. Shield of Scotland, crowned. MARIA. D.G. SCOTOR. REGINA. FRAN. DOI. *Rev.* Vine with a withered branch receiving water from an urn in the clouds. MEA SIC MIHI PROSVNT *Ex.* 1579 *D.* 28 mm. French (By?) *MI i*, 129/80; *CP* 13/13

AR   50   90

A number of similar pieces were struck.

51   **Assistance given to the United Provinces 1585**

Obv. The Queen enthroned, r., presents roses to two kneeling figures. MACTE. ANIMI. ROSA. NECTARE. IMBVTA. *Rev.* Two Spaniards eat out of a trough together with a horse and an ass. SPRETA. AMBROSIA. VESCITOR. FENO. 1585. *D.* 30 mm. Dutch (By?) *MI i*, 133/86; *v. Loon I*, 355/2

AR   55   100
AE   15   32

52   **Assistance Given to the United Provinces 1586**

Obv. The Queen, enthroned, a courtier (Earl of Leicester?) beside her, presents a sword to two kneeling figures. E.R. EST. ALTRIX. ESVRIENTIVM. EVM. *Ex.* 1586. *Rev.* An upright sword, its tip through radiate celestial clouds. SERMO. DEI. QVO; ENSE. ANCIPI: ACVTIOR *D.* 30 mm. Dutch (By?) *MI i*, 133/87; *v. Loon I*, 359

AR   45   85
AE   15   32

53*   **Protestants Supported in the United Provinces 1587**

Obv. The Queen, enthroned, attended by a courtier (Earl of Leicester?), tramples on a hydra; around, five naked boys each kneeling with a shield of one of the Provinces. .DEO. OPT. MAX. LAVS. ET. HONOR. IN. OE. ÆVVM. QVOD. *Ex.* 1587 *Rev.* Popes, bishops and other religious figures and objects fall from celestial clouds. QVEM. DEVS. CONFICIET. SPIRITV. ORIS. SVI. *D.* 53 mm. [By G. v. Bijlaer] *MI i*, 139/99; *v. Loon I*, 369. *See* **Plate 2**

AR   300   550

Robert Dudley, 1st Earl of Leicester (1532?–88), courtier; favourite of Elizabeth I.

54*   **Departure of the Earl of Leicester from the Low Countries 1587**

Obv. Bust three-quarters l., wearing a feathered cap, armoured and draped. ROBE. CO. LEIC. ET. IN. BELG. GVBER. 1587 *Rev.* A dog in a landscape departs from a flock of sheep. INVITVS DESERO in field. NON. GREGEM. SED. INGRATOS *D.* 48 mm. Cast (By?) *MI i*, 140/100; *Hill/Pollard pl.* 28, 5; *v. Loon I*, 375/1. *See* **Plate 2**

a AR   400   —
Pb.   80   —
b AR   70   120
AE   40   70

Type *b* is an eighteenth century copy.

55   **Dissensions of the United Provinces 1588**

Obv. Two oxen l., over which are an English rose and Belgic lion, ploughing a field. TRAHITE. ÆQVO. IVGO. 1588 *Rev.* Two earthenware vessels floating on rough water; beyond, a town. FRANGIMVR. SI. COLLIDIMVR. *D.* 35 mm. Cast. Dutch (By?) *MI i*, 143/107–8; *v. Loon I*, 379/1

AR   50   90

There are a number of varieties, both struck and cast, one of which is dated 1587.

56*   **Defeat of the Spanish Armada 1588**

Obv. Fleet of ships, some of which are capsizing; .VENI. VIDE. VIVE. .1588., above. TV. DEVS. MAGNVS. ET. MAGNA. FACIS. TV. SOLVS. DEVS. *Rev.* Heads of the Church and State, blindfolded, seated in discussion, their feet on a spiked floor. O. COECAS. HOMINVM. MENTES. O. PECTORA. COECA above. DVRVM. EST. CONTRA. STIMVLOS. CALCITRARE. *D.* 52 mm. [By G. v. Bijlaer] *MI i*, 144/111; *MH* 1919, 4; *v. Loon I*, 384/1. *See* **Plate 2**

AV   —   —
AR   300   580

57   ——

Obv. Large fleet of ships dispersed; above, celestial clouds. FLAVIT. ET. DISSIPATI. SVNT. 1588. *Rev.* Church on an island rock buffeted by heavy waves; below, armorial shield of Prince

AR   300   580

PLATE 1

23 (× ⅔)

26

32

33

35

41

43

47

45

48

PLATE 2

53

54

56

64

72

75

77

Maurice. ALLIDOR. NON. LÆDOR. *D.* 52 mm. (By G. v. Bijlaer?) *MI i*, 145/112; *MH* 1919, 5;   £   £
v. Loon I, 386

<small>Maurice, Prince of Orange (1567–1625), Stadholder of the Dutch Republic; commanded allied armies against Spain.</small>

58 ——
Obv. Two ships in an engagement. VENIT. IVIT. FVIT. 1588. *Ex.* .CLASSIS. HISP. *Rev.* Shield of   AR   50   90
Zeeland, crowned. .SOLI. DEO. GLORIA. *D.* 32 mm. Dutch (By?) *MI i*, 146/113; *MH* 1919, 6;   AE   22   35
v. Loon I, 384/2

59 ——
Obv. Fleet sailing; above, clouds dispersed by the sun. POST. NVBILA. PHOEBVS. A°. 1588. *Rev.*   AR   55   100
Crowned shield of Zeeland in centre; around, shields of her eight principal towns. CALCVLI.   AE   15   32
ORDINVM. ZELANDIÆ. *D.* 30 mm. Dutch (By?) *MI i*, 147/115; *MH* 1919, 8; *v. Loon I*, 384/3

60 ——
Obv. Four people kneeling, l., in prayer. HOMO. PROPONIT. DEVS. DISPONIT. *Ex.* .1588. *Rev.* A   AR   65   120
ship breaking up. HISPANI. FVGIVT. ET. PEREVT. NEMINE. SEQVETE   *D.* 29 mm. Dutch (By?)   AE   22   35
MI i, 147/116; *MH* 1919, 9; *v. Loon I*, 386/2

61 ——
Obv. Bust l., elaborately draped and jewelled. ELIZABETH. D.G. ANGLIE. F. ET. HI. REG. *Rev.*   *a* AR   1800   —
Ark on waves, smoke emitting from chimney; above, clouds and a radiate sun. SEVAS:
TRANQVILLA: PER: VNDAS. Suspension loop on edge. *D.* 44 mm. by 62 mm. Oval, cast. (By?)   *b* AR   80   150
MI i, 148/119; *MH* 1919, 11; *Hill/Pollard pl.* 28, 8

<small>This medal may have served as a naval reward. Type *b* is an eighteenth century copy.</small>

62 ——
Obv. Bust almost facing of Elizabeth I, crowned, elaborately draped and jewelled. DITIOR.   *a* AV   —   —
IN. TOTO. NON. ALTER. CIRCVLVS. ORBE. *Rev.* A bay tree, untouched by lightning and winds,   AR   —   —
flourishing on an island inscribed NON. IPSA. PERICVLA. TANGVNT. Three ships in distance,
one hit by lightning; above, ER. Suspension loop on edge. *D.* 44 mm. by 55 mm. Oval, cast.   *b* AR   100   180
(By N. Hilliard?) *MI i*, 154/129; *MH* 1919, 18; *Hill/Pollard pl.* 28, 7

<small>This medal may have served as a naval reward. Type *b* is an eighteenth century copy.</small>

63   **Defeat of the Spanish Armada, Thanksgiving 1589**
Obv. Seated figure in a carriage, l., holds an open book inscribed with the Lord's Prayer in   AR   75   140
Dutch. TANDEM. BONA. CAVSA. TRIVMPHAT. 1589. *Rev.* Young birds in their nest defend   AE   25   45
themselves against a bird of prey; below, BELLV NECESS divided by tree trunk. .SI. NON.
VRIBVS. AT. CAVSA. POTIORES. *D.* 29 mm. Dutch (By?) *MI i*, 153/128; *MH* 1919, 16; *v. Loon I*,
388/2

64*   **Trinity College, Dublin 1591**
Obv. Half-length bust of Elizabeth I, three-quarters r., elaborately draped and jewelled.   AV   500   600
COLL. SS. ET. INDIVID. TRIN. REG. ELIZABETHÆ. JVXTA. DVBL. 1591. *Rev.* Large heraldic shield.   AR   25   40
POLITICA ET LITERIS ANGLICIS; space around (for recipient's name). *D.* 51 mm. By W.
Woodhouse. *MI i*, 158/138; *Frazer* 1887/191–2, and 614–5. *See* **Plate 2**

<small>Struck *c.*1850 and awarded for several subjects: politics & literature, ethics & logic, natural science, history, literature &
humanities, science & mathematics; in each case a separate die was used. 1591 was the year in which a grant for the erection
of a college was conferred by Elizabeth I.</small>

65   **Alliance of England, France and the United Provinces 1596**
Obv. Hand issuing from heaven holds a cord connecting shields of England and France and   AV   —   —
a heart containing arrows of the United Provinces; 1596 above. RVMPITVR. HAVD. FACILE.   AR   280   550
Rev. Bundle of arrows within six shields of the Provinces. NEXOS. FAVORE. NVMINIS. QVIS.
DISSOLVES. *D.* 51 mm. [By G. v. Bijlaer] *MI i*, 160/140; *v. Loon I*, 471

66 ——
Obv. An altar, inscribed LIBERT. PATR (incuse), upon which three armed soldiers unite   AR   45   80
hands. COMMVNIS. QVOS. CAVSA. MOVET. SOCIAT. *Rev.* A soldier indicates a tablet, inscribed   AE   15   28
ODIVM TYRANNIDIS (incuse), attached to a column. TITVLVS. FOEDERIS. CIƆ.IƆ.XCVI   *D.*
29 mm. Dutch (By ?) *MI i*, 161/144; *v. Loon I*, 471/4

67   **Defeat of Attempted Invasion by Spain 1596**
Obv. Similar to No. 65 but undated. *Rev.* Fleet of ships in distress; above, celestial clouds,   AR   280   550
radiate. QVID. ME. PERSEQVERIS. 1596. *D.* 52 mm. [By G. v. Bijlaer] *MI i*, 163/148; *MH* 1921,
481

68   **Battle of Turnhout 1597**
Obv. Belgic lion l., holding a sword and arrows. SOLI. DEO. HONOR. ET. GLORIA. *Rev.*   AR   280   550
ORDINVM. AVSPICIIS. PRINCIPIS. MAVRITII. DVCTV. HOSTE. AD TVRNHOVTVM. CÆSO DECEM.

OPIDIS. ET. TRIBVS. ARCIBVS. EXPVGNATIS. ET. TOTA CISRHENANA. DITIONE. PACATA. 1597. *D.*   £   £
51 mm. [By G. v. Bijlaer] *MI i*, 166/152; *v. Loon I*, 484
<small>Commemorates the victory of Prince Maurice over Spain. A number of smaller pieces based on this medal were also struck.</small>

69 ——
    Obv. Spanish troops in flight, pursued by those of Maurice. VICTORIA. TVRNOTANA. 24.   AR 55 100
IANVARII. 1597. *Rev.* Shields of England, France and the United Provinces connected by a   AE 15 32
cord. .A. DOMINO. FACTVM. EST. ISTVD. *D.* 30 mm. Dutch (By?) *MI i*, 165/151; *v. Loon I*, 479
<small>See No. 68.</small>

70 ——
    Obv. Spanish troops in flight, pursued by those of Maurice. .A. DNO. FACTVM. EST. ISTVD. ET.   AR 300 550
EST. MIRABILE. IN. OCVLIS. NOSTRIS. *Ex.* VICTORIA TVRNOTANA. IANV. 1597. *Rev.* VENIT VIDIT
DEVS VICIT/VICTORIA. PARTA. SPATIO. TRIMESTRI, within and around a central band. Around,
views of nine towns captured by the Allies; 1597 above. ALPEN BERC. MEVRS. GROL. BREVORT.
ENSCH. OLD. OTM. LINGEN   *D.* 51 mm. [By G. v. Bijlaer] *MI i*, 170/163; *v. Loon I*, 482
<small>See No. 68.</small>

71   **Carisbrooke Castle, Isle of Wight 1598**
    Obv. View of a castle in landscape. CARISBROOKE CASTLE. *Ex.* ISLE OF WIGHT. *Rev.*   AR 25 40
CARISBROOKE CASTLE ORIGINALLY BUILT BY THE ANCIENT BRITONS REBUILT BY HENRY Ist   WM 5 9
ANNO. 1125. ENLARGED BY Q^N ELIZABETH ANNO 1598   *D.* 37 mm. By T. R. Pinches. *BHM*
2668
<small>Struck c.1850.</small>

72*   **Battle of Nieuport 1600**
    Obv. Overhead plan of a fort under siege. COMPVLSO AD DEDIT: PRÆSID: ANDREÆ: CÆSO   AV —
FVGATOQ' A. NEOP: ALB: AVST   *Rev.* Armed equestrian figure, r.; beyond, a battle scene and   AR 300 550
fleet off the coast. 1600 in field; celestial clouds, above. CAPTIS CXXX MILIT: SIGNIS. ORD: AVSP:
PRINCEPS MAVR: VICTOR REDIIT. *D.* 55 mm. [By G. v. Bijlaer] *MI i*, 174/171; *v. Loon I*, 535.
See **Plate 2**
<small>Commemorating Prince Maurice's victory over the Spaniards.</small>

73 ——
    Obv. Crowned shield. CALCVLVS. ORDINVM. TRAIECTEN. 1600. *Rev.* An army in flight, pursued   AR 50 90
by soldiers; ships on the horizon. HOC. OPVS. DOMINI. EXERCITVVM. *D.* 31 mm. Dutch (By?)   AE 15 32
MI i, 176/173; *v. Loon I*, 535
<small>See No. 72.</small>

74   **Capture of Rheinberg: Defence of Ostend 1601**
    Obv. Celestial clouds, radiate; below, a town. HANC. CAPIMVS. VIRTVTE. DEI. *Rev.* Celestial   AV 300 550
clouds, radiate, above a harbour with two ships; S.C on water. DEFENDIMVS. ISTAM. CIƆIƆCI.   AR 45 85
D. 29 mm. Dutch (By?) *MI i*, 178/178; *v. Loon I*, 544   AE 15 28

75*   **Maurice, Prince of Orange 1602**
    Obv. Bust r., armoured and draped; ÆT. 34 (incuse) on truncation. MAVRITIVS. PR. AVR. CO.   AV 700 1200
NASS. CAT. MARC. VER. ET. VLIS   *Rev.* An orange tree growing from a stump. TANDEM. FIT.   AR 80 150
SVRCVLVS. ARBOR. ANNO 1602. *D.* 34 mm. Cast. By G. v. Bijlaer. *MI i*, 181/182; *v. Loon I*, 553
var. *See* **Plate 2**
<small>A similar medal, but of 41 mm., was made by Conrad v. Bloc.</small>

76   **Defeat of Spanish Squadrons 1602**
    Obv. Overhead view of Grave, landscape and rivers identified; celestial clouds, radiate,   AR 300 550
above. GRAVIA CAPTA. TVRMIS EQVIT. VII. CÆSIS. *Rev.* Two scenes: a cavalry engagement near
Maastricht, and a naval engagement off Goodwin Sands; the areas identified. Above each,
respectively, is an arm issuing from celestial clouds holding a sword, and a thunderbolt (?).
TRIREM VI DEPRESS. FRACT. FVGATISQ' A.° CIƆ.IƆ.CII. OR. F.P.F.F. *D.* 55 mm. [By G. v. Bijlaer]
MI i, 179/180; *MH* 1919, 23; *v. Loon I*, 555
<small>The action at Goodwin Sands was under the command of Admiral Sir Robert Mansell (1573–1656).</small>

77*   **Successes of Elizabeth I 1602**
    Obv. Half-length figure of the Queen, three-quarters l., in elaborate dress and holding an   AV — —
orb and sceptre. CADET. A. LATERE. TVO. M^C ET. X. M^A A DEXTRIS. TVIS. ELIZ. REGINA. *a.w. Rev.*   AR 1200 —
Minerva l., tramples upon a dragon and a snail; MINERVA. 1602 across field. CASTIS. DIADEMA.
PERENNE. *D.* 40 mm. (By C. Anthony?) *MI i*, 181/184; *Hill/Pollard pl.* 27, 6. *See* **Plate 2**

78   **Elizabeth I, Counter** *c.*1602
    Obv. Equestrian figure of the Queen, r., preceded by a warrior. ELISABETA REG. ANG. *Rev.*   AE 15 28
Shield of England and France, crowned. POSVI DEVM ADIVTOREM *D.* 28 mm. By H.

Krauwinckel. *MI i*, 184/190   £   £

One of a large number of counters struck at Nuremberg, *c.*1600–1730, depicting European monarchs, and mythological and biblical subjects; *see* Forrer III/220–22; J. M. Pullan (pp. 76–9), *The History of the Abacus*, London, 1968.

79   **Elizabeth I, Memorial 1602**
Obv. Bust three-quarters l., wearing a coronet and draped. ELISABETH D.G. ANG. FR. ET. HIB.   *AR*   35   65
REGINA. *Rev.* A decorated monument, flanked by figures of Religion and Minerva. *Ex.* NATA.   *AE*   6   14
7. SEPT. 1533. COR. 15. IAN. 1559. M. 24. MART. 1602. *D.* 41 mm. By J. Dassier. *MI i*, 185/193

Struck in 1731, from Dassier's series of English kings and queens. *See* No. 526.

JAMES I, 1603–25

80*   **Coronation of James I 1603**
Obv. Bust r., laureate, armoured and draped. IAC: I: BRIT: CÆ: AVG: HÆ CÆSARVM CÆ. D.D.   *AR*   350   600
Rev. Rampant lion crowned, l., holding beacon and wheatsheaf. ECCE. PHAOS. POPVLIQ´.
SALVS   *D.* 29 mm. (By C. Anthony?) *MI i*, 191/11; *Wollaston* 1. *See* **Plate 3**

James (1566–1625) I, (VI of Scotland, 1567–1625), son of Henry Stuart, Lord Darnley, and Mary Queen of Scots.

81*   **Queen Anne 1603**
Obv. Bust three-quarters l., draped and jewelled. ANNA. D´.G´. REGINA. MAG´. BRIT´. FR´. ET.   *AV*   —   —
HIB´. FILIA & SOROR REGV̄. DANIÆ: *Rev.* Armorial shield, crowned. ASTVTIA. FALLAX; TVTIOR.   *AR*   350   600
INNOCENTIA. *D.* 29 mm. (By C. Anthony?) *MI i*, 192/12; *Hill/Pollard pl.* 27, 8; *Wollaston* 33.
See **Plate 3**

Queen Anne of Denmark (1574–1619), married James I (VI of Scotland) in 1590. This piece occurs on flans of varying thickness, and with a portrait of low relief; it is probably of English manufacture and appears to be a companion to No. 80, although not as technically accomplished.

82   **Thomas Sackville 1603**
Obv. Heraldic shield within the Garter. T. SACKVIL. B. D. BVCH. ANG. THES. EQ´. AVRA´. *Rev.*   *AR*   80   150
Crest: rampant leopard, l.; 1602 across field. SEMPER FIDELIS   *D.* 29 mm. (By C. Anthony?)
MI i, 188/3

Dated in the old style; Thomas Sackville, Earl of Dorset and Baron Buckhurst (1536–1608), Lord High Treasurer. Similar heraldic pieces were struck at this time for Thomas Cecil, Sir Edward Coke, Sir John Fortescue and Sir John Hele. *See* No. 83.

83   **Sir Robert Cecil 1603**
Obv. Heraldic shield. R⁰. CECYLL. PRI. SECR. REG. MAᵀ. Mᴿ. CVR. WARD⁰. *Rev.* Crest: bundle of   *AR*   80   150
arrows below a helmet. SERO: SED: SERIO: 1602: *D.* 29 mm. (By C. Anthony?) *MI i*, 189/6

Dated in the old style; nineteenth century strikings were made in gold and bronze. Robert Cecil, Earl of Salisbury (1563?–1612), statesman. *See* No. 82.

84*   **Peace between England and Spain 1604**
Obv. Bust almost facing, wearing a crowned and plumed hat, and draped. IACOBVS. D´. G´.   *a AV*   —   —
ANG´. SCO´. FR´. ET. HIB´. REX   *Rev.* Standing figures of Peace and Religion, facing each   *AR*   400   —
other. HINC. PAX. COPIA. CLARAQ. RELIGIO   *Ex.* A⁰ 1604   *D.* 37 mm. (By N. Hilliard?) *a*
struck; *b* cast. *MI i*, 193/14–5; *Farquhar* 1908/160; *v. Loon II*, 19. *See* **Plate 3**   *b AV*   900   1600
   AR   140   260

Sometimes found with a suspension loop on edge, or set within an open-work frame.

85   **Blundell's School 1604**
Obv. Façade of school building. IN PATRIAM POPVLVMO FLVXIT   *Ex.* PETRVS BLVNDELLVS   *AR*   15   25
FVND. DON MDCIV   *Rev.* Minerva seated, l., holds wreath above head of a kneeling boy.
DETVR DIGNIORI   *D.* 40 mm. [By L. Pingo] *Grimshaw* 23; *D & W* 274/534

A prize medal struck *c.*1775 from two pairs of dies, unsigned and undated. Peter Blundell (1520–1601), merchant and benefactor. The school is situated near Tiverton in Devon.

86*   **Gunpowder Plot 1605**
Obv. Snake gliding amongst lilies and roses. DETECTVS. QVI. LATVIT. S.C. *Rev.* Name of   *AR*   60   110
Jehovah in Hebrew, radiate, within a border of thorns. NON DorMItastI antIstes IaCobI   *AE*   20   35
(chronogrammatic date). *D.* 30 mm. Dutch (By?) *MI i*, 196/19; *v. Loon II*, 22. *See* **Plate 3**

The conspiracy originated in 1604 after the edict banishing priests. The plot to blow up Parliament was revealed by an anonymous letter on 4 November, the day before its assembly.

87   **Alliance between England, France and the United Provinces 1609**
Obv. Hand issuing from heaven holds a cord uniting the three shields of the Allies. .A.   *a AR*   250   400
DOMINO. FACTVM. EST. ISTVD. *Rev.* ORD. FOED. BELG. A. REGE. HISP. ET. ARCHID. LIBERI. AGNITI
POST BEL. CONT. XLII. AN INDVCIAS PACISCVNTVR. INTERV. REGVM GAL. ET. MAG. BRIT. ET. CVM   *b AR*   45   80
IISDEM. FOEDVS RENOVANT A⁰ CIↃ. IↃ.CIX   *D. a* 52 mm.; *b* 30 mm. Dutch (By?) *MI i*,   *AE*   13   25
197/22–3; *v. Loon II*, 50

The inscription on the reverse of type *b* differs slightly.

		£	£

88 ——
Obv. Celestial clouds, radiate, above three conjoined hearts. .IVNCTA. CORDA. FIDELIVM. *Rev.*   AV   —
Belgic lion; above, crowned rose and fleur-de-lys. CONTRA. VIM. TIRANNORVM. 1609. *D.*   AR   250   400
52 mm. Dutch (By?) *MI i*, 198/25; *v. Loon II*, 50

89 Thomas Bodley, Memorial 1612
Obv. Bust r., draped. TH. BODLY. EQ. AVR. PVBL. BIBLIOTH. OXON. FVNDATOR   *Rev.* Female   AR   400   —
figure standing, l., holding busts of Diana and Apollo in outstretched hands. .RP.   Pb.   60   —
LITERARIAE. AETERNITAS. *D.* 50 mm. Cast. By C. Warin. *MI i*, 200/28; *Forrer VI*/356
Made c.1635. Sir Thomas Bodley (1545–1612), diplomatist and scholar; founder of the Bodleian Library in Oxford.

90* Henry, Prince of Wales 1612
Obv. Bust three-quarters l., armoured and draped. HENRICVS. .PRINCEPS. *Rev.* Armorial   AV   700   1200
shield, crowned. FAX. MENTIS. HONESTÆ. GLORIA. *D.* 29 mm. (By C. Anthony?) *MI i*, 200/29;   AR   130   250
Hill/Pollard pl. 27, 7; *Farquhar* 1908/214. *See* **Plate 3**
Struck from more than one pair of dies. Henry Frederick, Prince of Wales (1594–1612), eldest son of James I and Anne.

91 Marriage of Princess Elizabeth and Frederick of Bohemia 1613
Obv. Bust r., armoured and draped. FRID. COM. PAL. R.S. ROM. IMP. ELECTOR   *Rev.* Bust l.,   AV   —   —
draped and jewelled. ELISAB. D:G:C. PAL R.S.R. IMP. ELEC. FIL. R. MAGN. BRIT. *D.* 30 mm. by   AR   170   300
37 mm. Oval, cast. By I.D.B. (German?) *MI i*, 201/32; *v. Loon II*, 89
Princess Elizabeth (1596–1662), daughter of James I and Anne. Frederick, Count Palatine (1596–1632), Frederick V of Bohemia 1619–32.

92 Maurice, Prince of Orange, Knight of the Garter 1615
Obv. Bust three-quarters r., armoured and draped. MAVRITIVS. AVR. PRINC. COM. NASS. ET.   AR   250   450
MV. MAR. VE. FL. EQ. OR. PERISCELIDIS. 1615 *Rev.* Armorial shield within the Garter,   AE   100   170
crowned. *D.* 45 mm. by 55 mm. Oval, cast. (By A. Rottermont?) *MI i*, 205/39; *v. Loon II*, 87
Occurs with a suspension loop on edge, and sometimes gilt. One of several medals which record the bestowal of the Garter on European nobility and sovereigns.

93 Princess Elizabeth and Frederick, Count Palatine 1615
Obv. An equestrian figure, r.; beyond, a town and river. FRIDERICVS V. S.R.I. ELEC. COM. PAL.   AR   100   180
R.D.B. *Ex.* C: PRIVI: CÆ. *Rev.* Electoral crown upon conjoined shields of the couple, within   Pb.   30
the Garter. QVAM BENE CONVENIVNT. ANNO M.D.CXV. *D.* 33 mm. By C. Maler. *MI i*, 206/40

94 Royal Family c.1615
Obv. Busts almost facing, draped, of James I, Queen Anne and Prince Charles. *Rev.*   AR   1200   —
Armorial shields of the King and Queen with supporters, crest and motto; below, Prince of
Wales' plumes and motto. POTENTISS: IACOBVS D.G. MAG: BRITT: ET. HIB: REX. ET SERENISS:
ANNA D.G. MAG. BRITT REGINA VNA CVM ILL: P. CAROLI. M: BRIT. PRINCIPIS *D.* 50 mm. by
63 mm. Oval. By S. van de Passe. *MI i*, 217/68
A wholly engraved medal; de Passe executed a number of similar portraits of Elizabeth I, James I, Queen Anne, Prince Charles, Count Frederick, Princess Elizabeth. Prince Charles (I), (1600–49), king 1625–49; younger son of James I and Anne.

95 William Shakespeare, Memorial 1616
Obv. Bust three-quarters r., draped. GUILIELMUS SHAKESPEARE. *Rev.* Landscape scene. WILD   AR   45   80
ABOVE RVLE OR ART. *Ex.* NAT. 1564   *D.* 42 mm. By J. Dassier. *MI i*, 208/42; *Ogden* 45   AE   7   15
Struck c.1740; William Shakespeare (1564–1616), dramatist and poet.

96 Prince Charles, Matriculation at Oxford 1616
Obv. Prince of Wales' plumes and motto. *Rev.* A rose in the centre. SI. VIS. OMNIA. SVBIICERE.   AV   350   650
SVBIICE. TE. RATIONI. *D.* 19 mm. (By?) *MI i*, 219/71   AR   90   150

97 John Napier, Keith Medal 1617
Obv. Bust l., draped. IOANNES NEPERUS DE MERCHISTON *Rev.* INGENII FELICITER EXCULTI   AE   8   15
PRÆMIUM KEITHIANUM, within a wreath. SOC: REG: EDIN: ADJUDICAVIT *D.* 45 mm. By C. F.
Carter. *MI i*, 219/72; *BHM* 1470
Struck c.1847, a prize awarded by the Royal Society of Edinburgh from a bequest by Alexander Keith; John Napier, or Neper (1550–1617), inventor of logarithms.

98* Nicholas and Dorothy Wadham, Memorial c.1618
Obv. Bust of Nicholas, three-quarters r., draped, WHEN CHRIST WHO IS OVR LIFE SHAL   aAR   250   450
APPEARE *Rev.* Bust of Dorothy, three-quarters l., wearing a hat and draped. WE SHAL
APPEARE WITH HIM IN GLORY   A wreath border on each side decorated with four skulls. *D.*   bAR   40   70
46 mm. by 54 mm. Oval (By?) *MI i*, 220/73; *Hill/Pollard* pl. 28, 10. *See* **Plate 3**
A primitively made piece, consisting of two low-relief repoussé plates joined at the edge. Nicholas Wadham (1532–1609), founder of Wadham College, Oxford. Dorothy Wadham (1534–1618), married Nicholas in 1555. Cast copies, type b, were made in the eighteenth(?) century.

			£	£
99	**Synod of Dort 1619**			
	Obv. Panoramic view of the long chamber in which the Council assemble. ASSERTA. RELIGIONE. *Ex.* CVM PRIV. 1619 *Rev.* Pilgrims ascend a rock, assailed by the four winds, upon which is a temple; above, celestial clouds, radiate. ERVNT. VT. MONS. SION. CIϽ. IϽ.CXIX. D. 58 mm. [By W. v. Bijlaer]. *MI i*, 222/77; *v. Loon II*, 105	*AV* *AR*	— 250	— 400
	Struck from more than one pair of dies. Representatives from several European states met to consider local religious disputes.			
100	——			
	Obv. Belgic lion, crowned, l.; above, celestial clouds. RELIGIONE. ET. IVSTICIA. RESTITVTIS. *Rev.* Shield of Prince Maurice, crowned and dated 1619, within the Garter. IE. MAIN. TIENDRAY (his motto). RESPUBLICA. DEMVM. FLOREBIT. VNANIMITAS. D. 58 mm. By C. Wijntjes. *MI i*, 223/79; *v. Loon II*, 113	*AR*	250	400
	Struck from more than one pair of dies.			
101*	**Coronation of Elizabeth and Frederick V of Bohemia 1619**			
	Obv. Busts r., conjoined, armoured and draped. FRIDERICVS ET ELISABETHA D.G. R.R. BOHEMIÆ. *Rev.* Inscription DANTE DEO ET ORDINVM CONCORDIA, around a central vignette with a crown supported by five hands. FRIDERI: D:G: COM: PALAT: RHENI S.R.I. ELEC: DVX BAV CORON: ET CRE: IN REG: BOHE: MARCH: MORA: DVCEM SIL: ET MARCH. VTR: LVSAT: ANNO CIϽ IϽ CXIX. DIE IV NOVEM: D. 35 mm. by 42 mm. Oval. By C. Maler. *MI i*, 225/82; *Forrer* III/541. *See* **Plate 3**	*AR*	200	350
	Another obverse carries the single bust of Frederick.			
102	**William Camden, Memorial 1623**			
	Obv. Bust l., wearing a skull cap and draped. GUILIELMUS CAMDEN. *Rev.* NATUS LONDINO AN. M.D.L I. OBIIT AN. M.DC.XXIII. *Ex.* SERIES NUMISMATICA UNIVERSALIS VIRORUM ILLUSTRIUM. M.DCCC.XXIII. DURAND EDIDIT D. 41 mm. By A. Caqué. *MI i*, 230/90	*AR* *AE*	15 3	28 7
	Struck in Paris in 1823, from a series commemorating famous people of all countries. William Camden (1551–1623), antiquary and historian.			
103*	**Naval Victories over Spain 1624**			
	Obv. Bust three-quarters r., armoured and draped, within a central medallion. MAURITIUS D.G. PRINCEPS AURIACÆ, COM: NAFS: & C., PROV: CONFOE: GUB. Around, seven shields of the United Provinces divided by scrolls identifying each one. *Rev.* Garnished shield of Prince Maurice, crowned, within the Garter; motto below. D. 68 mm. [By J. v. Bijlaer] *MI i*, 231/91; *MH* 1921, 511; *Betts* 22. *See* **Plate 3**	*AR*	300	500
104	**James I, Memorial 1625**			
	Obv. Bust r., draped. IACOBUS. I. D.G. M. BR. FR. ET. HIB. REX. *Rev.* Monument decorated with an armorial shield, flanked by two genii, one of whom adds the Scottish lion to the arms. *Ex.* NAT. 19. IUN. 1556. CORON. 25. IUL. 1603. MORT. 27. MART. 1625. D. 41 mm. By J. Dassier. *MI i*, 237/104	*AR* *AE*	27 4	55 9
	Struck in 1731, from Dassier's series of English kings and queens. *See* No. 526.			

CHARLES I, 1625–49

105*	**Marriage of Charles I and Henrietta Maria 1625**			
	Obv. Busts draped, face to face; above, celestial rays. CH. MAG. ET. HEN. MA. BRIT. REX. ET. REG *Rev.* Cupid walking, r., scatters roses and lilies; above, celestial rays. FVNDIT. AMOR. LILIA. MIXTA. ROSIS. *Ex.* .1625. D. 23 mm. (By N. Briot?) *MI i*, 238/1. *See* **Plate 3**	*AV* *AR*	400 25	750 40
	There are several varieties of this piece and cast copies were also made. Henrietta Maria (1609–69), daughter of Henry IV of France.			
106	**Coronation of Charles I 1626**			
	Obv. Bust r., crowned and draped. CAROLVS. I. D.G. MAG. BRITAN. FRAN. ET. HIB. REX *Rev.* An arm issuing from clouds holds an upright sword. DONEC. PAX. REDDITA. TERRIS. *Ex.* CORON. 2. FEBRV. 1626. D. 30 mm. By N. Briot. *MI i*, 243/10; *Wollaston* 2	*AV* *AR*	900 160	1700 300
	Struck from more than one pair of dies.			
107	**Francis Bacon, Memorial 1626**			
	Obv. Bust three-quarters r., draped, FRANCISC. BACON. *Rev.* Aurora, floating on a cloud, approaches the earth; sun rising. NON PROCUL DIES. *Ex.* NAT. 1560. M. 1626 D. 42 mm. By J. Dassier. *MI i*, 245/14	*AR* *AE*	45 7	80 15
	Struck c.1740; Francis Bacon, Lord Verulam (1561–1626), Lord Chancellor; philosopher and author.			

		£	£

108 **Frederick Henry, Prince of Orange, Knight of the Garter 1627**
Obv. Bust r., armoured and draped, within a central medallion. FREDER. HENR. D.G.   AR 300 500
PRINCEPS. AVRIAC. COM. NASS. Around, seven linked shields of the United Provinces held by
two hands. *Rev.* Shield of the Prince, crowned, within the Garter. *D.* 57 mm. [By J. v.
Bijlaer] *MI i*, 246/17; *v. Loon II*, 166
Frederick Henry, Prince of Orange-Nassau (1584–1647), stadholder of the Dutch Republic; brother of Maurice.

109 **Isle of Rhé, British Attack and Retreat 1627**
Obv. Bust r., laureate, armoured and draped. LVDOVIC. XIII REX CHRISTIANISS. PIVS IVSTVS AR 350 600
FEL. AVG. CIƆIƆCXXVII. *Rev.* Statue of Louis XIII upon a column amidst arms and trophies; AE 160 280
beyond, a fleet at sea. VICTIS FVSIS FVGATIS TERRA MARIQ. ANGLIS 1627 *D.* 44 mm. Cast.
French (By P. Regnier?) *MI i*, 247/20; *MH 1921*, 9
Louis XIII (1601–43), king of France 1610–43; son of Henry IV.

110 **Henrietta Maria 1628**
Obv. Conjoined shields of England and France, crowned; below, HM monogram. HENR. AR 20 35
MAR. BORBON. D.G. MAG. BRIT. FRAN. ET. HIB. REG. *Rev.* A tree in the foreground of a grove
dwarfs the others; beyond, ships at sea. SVPEREMINET. OMNES. *Ex.* 1628 *D.* 29 mm. [By N.
Briot] *MI i*, 249/23
Struck from more than one pair of dies, one of which is signed but undated.

111* **Charles I and Henrietta Maria 1628**
Obv. Bust r., crowned and draped. CAROLVS. I. D:G. ANG. SCOT. FRAN. ET. HIB. REX. FIDEI. DEF. AR 60 100
Rev. As the obv. of No. 110. *D.* 29 mm. [By N. Briot] *MI i*, 250/25. *See* **Plate 3**

112 **Charles I 1628**
Obv. Royal shield within collar and badge of the Order of the Thistle, crowned; all within AR 50 80
the Garter. CAROLVS D:G. ANG. SCO. FRAN. ET. HIB. REX. FIDEI. DEF. *Rev.* Crossed sceptre and
trident, united by a cord. REGIT. VNVS. VITROQVE. *Ex.* .1628. *D.* 29 mm. [By N. Briot] *MI i*,
250/27
Struck from more than one pair of dies, one of which is dated 1629.

113 **Order of the Garter Augmented by the Star 1629**
Obv. As No. 111. *Rev.* Star of the Order of the Garter. PRISCI. DECVS. ORDINIS. AVCTVM. *Ex.* AR 60 100
.1629. *D.* 29 mm. [By N. Briot] *MI i*, 253/33   AE 25 45

114 **Birth of Prince Charles 1630**
Obv. Bust l., crowned, armoured and draped. CAROLVS. D'.G'. MAG'. BRIT'. FR'. ET. HIB'. REX. AV 550 900
Rev. Infant in a cradle over whom Mars and Mercury each hold a wreath. REDDAT. AVOS. *Ex.* AR 90 160
MAII. 29. 1630 *D.* 31 mm. [By N. Briot] *MI i*, 254/37; *Farquhar 1908*/184
Prince Charles (II) (1630–85), 1st son of Charles I and Henrietta Maria; king 1660–85.

115 ――――
Obv. Four heart-shaped shields of England and France, Scotland, France and Ireland, AV 180 350
united in the centre at their bases. HACTENVS. ANGLORVM. NVLLI. *Rev.* HONOR'. PRIN'. MAG'. AR 20 35
BRIT'. FRA'. ET. HIB'. NAT'. 29. MAI'. ANN'. 1630., within a decorative square tablet. *D.* 30 mm.
(By?) *MI i*, 253/34; *v. Loon II*, 188
Struck from several pairs of dies.

116 ――――
Obv. Similar to No. 115 but shields are oval and radiate. *Rev.* IN. HONOR'. CARO'. PRINC'. *a* AV 180 350
MAG'. BRI'. FR'. ET. HI'. NAT'. 29. MAII. 1630 *D. a* 30 mm.; *b* 24 mm. (By?) *MI i*, 254/35, 6 AR 20 35
Each struck from more than one pair of dies.

                           b AV 130 220
                           AR 15 28

117 **Birth and Baptism of Prince Charles 1630**
Obv. Shields of England, Scotland, France and Ireland, crowned and radiate, united in the *a* AV 180 350
centre by links at their bases. HACTENVS. ANGLORVM. NVLLI. *Rev.* .MEM. CAROLI. PRIN. MAGN. AR 20 35
BRITANN. FRANC. HIBERN. NATI. XXIX MAII. BAPTIZ. XXVII. IVN. MDCXXX. S. *D. a* 29 mm.; *b*
25 mm. By N. Briot. *MI i*, 255/38–9; *v. Loon II*, 188   *b* AR 15 28
Each struck from more than one pair of dies.

118* **Dominion of the Sea 1630**
Obv. Bust r., armoured and draped. CAROLVS. I. D.G. MAG. BRITANNIÆ. FRAN. ET. HIB. REX. *a* AV — —
Rev. A ship in full sail. NEC. META. MIHI. QVI. TERMINVS. ORBI. *D.* 58 mm. Cast. By N. Briot. AR 450 800
MI i, 256/40; *MH 1919*, 25; *v. Loon II*, 227. *See* **Plate 3**   AE 180 300
Type *b* is an eighteenth century copy.

                           b AR 70 120

PLATE 3

80

84

86

90

98

81

101

103 ($\times \frac{2}{3}$)

105

111

118

PLATE 4

123

137 ($\times \frac{2}{3}$)

142

125

143

144

146

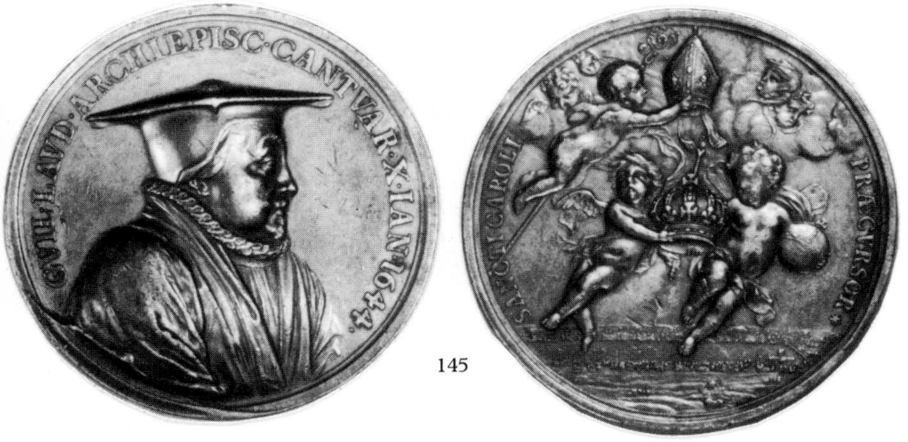

145

147

156

162

163

			£	£

119 ——
Obv. Bust r., armoured and draped. CAROLVS. D:G. ANG. SCO. FRAN. ET. HIB. REX. FIDEI.   *a AR*   60   110
DEFENSOR. *Rev.* A ship in full sail, l. NEC. META. MIHI. QVÆ. TERMINVS. ORBI. *Ex.* .1630. *D. a*
29 mm.; *b* 27 mm. By N. Briot. *MI i*, 257/42–3; *MH* 1919, 27–8; *Farquhar* 1905/255   *b AR*   40   70
<small>Type *b* differs in minor details; it is usually cast.</small>

120 Lord and Lady Baltimore 1632
Obv. Bust of Lord Baltimore three-quarters r., armoured and draped. DMS. CÆCEILIVS.   *a AR*   —   —
BARO. DE. BALTEMORE. ABSOLV. DMS. TERRÆMARIE. ET. AVALONIÆ. & C. *Rev.* Bust of Lady
Baltimore three-quarters r., draped. D : ANNA. ARVNDELIA. PVLCHERRIMA. ET. OPTIMA.   *b AR*   —   80
CONIVX. CÆCILII. PRÆDICTI. *D.* 48 mm. Cast. (By?) *MI i*, 261/52; *Betts* 34
<small>Type *b* is a nineteenth century electrotype. Cecil Calvert, 2nd Lord Baltimore (1605–75), received the charter of Maryland in 1632.</small>

121 ——
Obv. Bust l., armoured and draped. CÆCILIVS: BALTEMOREVS. Sun shining over map of   *a AR*   —   —
TERRAMARIÆ, crowned shield in the centre. VT: SOL: LVCEBIS: AMERICÆ. *D.* 33 mm. by 35 mm.
Oval, cast. (By?) *MI i*, 261/53; *Betts* 35   *b AR*   —   100
<small>Type *b* is a nineteenth century electrotype.</small>

122 Siege of Maastricht: Recapture of Limburg 1632
Obv. Bust three-quarters r., armoured and draped, within an oval frame. AVSPIC. POTENT.   *AR*   250   450
BELG. ORDD: ARMIS. ET INDVSTR. INVICT. PRINC. ARAVS. FR. HENR. E.S.I. LIB. MOSA LIMB.
RECEPT. A DEO ILL. VICT. *Rev.* Overhead plan of a city under siege; in lower section of field, an
army crossing a river. TRAIECT. AD. MOSA. RECEPT. 1632   *D.* 56 mm. (By J. v. Bijlaer?) *MI i*,
263/56; *v. Loon II*, 202
<small>*See* No. 108.</small>

123* Scottish Coronation of Charles I 1633
Obv. Bust l., crowned and draped. CAROLVS. D:G. SCOTIÆ. ANGLIÆ. FR. ET. HIB. REX. *Rev.* A   *AV*   700   1200
thistle flower. HINC. NOSTRÆ. CREVERE. ROSÆ. *Ex.* CORON. 18. IVNII. 1633. *D.* 29 mm. By N.   *AR*   100   220
Briot. *MI i*, 265/60; *Farquhar* 1908/198; *Wollaston* 3. *See* **Plate 4**
<small>Struck from more than one pair of dies; variations occur in both the lettering and thickness of flans. One type has a lettered edge: EX. AVRO. VT. IN. SCOTIA. REPERITVR. BRIOT. FECIT. EDINBVRGI. 1633</small>

124 Return of Charles I to London 1633
Obv. Equestrian figure of the King, l., holding an upright baton. CAROLVS AVGVSTISS'. ET   *a AV*   —   —
INVICTISS'. MAG'. BRIT'. FRAN'. ET HIB'. MONARCHA. *Ex.* .1633. *Rev.* View of London seen   *AR*   250   400
from the south bank of the Thames; above, radiate sun. ∴E∴ (Edinburgh) SOL ORBEM
REDIENS SIC REX ILLVMINAT VRBEM. *D. a* 44 mm. struck; *b* 43 mm. cast. [By N. Briot] *MI i*,   *b AV*   1200   2200
266/62; *CP* 20/4   *AR*   100   170
<small>Each type occurs with varying diameters.</small>

125* ——
Obv. Bust r., armoured and wearing a large lace collar. CAR. D:G. MAG. BRITAN. FRAN. ET. HIB.   *AR*   270   450
REX. *Rev.* As No. 124. *D.* 42 mm. Cast. [By N. Briot] *MI i*, 267/63; *CP* 20/5; *Farquhar*
1908/182. *See* **Plate 4**

126A Birth of James, Duke of York 1633
Obv. Prince's arms within garnished shield, with ducal coronet. NON. SIC. MILLE. COHORTES.   *AR*   25   45
Rev. Heraldic lion, crowned, displays a shield inscribed DVX. EBORA. NATVS OCT. 14. 1633   *D.*
30 mm. (By?) *MI i*, 267/64
<small>James II (1633–1701), king 1685–8; 2nd son of Charles I and Henrietta Maria.</small>

126B Baptism of Prince James 1633
Obv. As No. 126a. *Rev.* IACOBVS. DVX. EBOR: NAT'. 15: OCT: BAPTIZ: 24. NOVE: .1633., within a   *AR*   25   45
wreath of lilies and roses. *D.* 30 mm. (By?) *MI i*, 268/65
<small>Struck for more than one pair of dies.</small>

127 Royal Family 1635
Obv. Half-length draped figures of the King and Queen facing towards each other, their   *AV*   700   1200
hands joined. CARO'. D'.G'. MA'. BR'. REX. ET. HEN'. MARIA. REGINA. *Rev.* Half-length draped   *AR*   100   170
busts, facing, of Prince Charles, Prince James and Princess Mary. REGIS. REGNORVM.
POPVLIQVE. SALVS. 1635. *D.* 31 mm. [By N. Briot] *MI i*, 273/72; *Farquhar* 1908/194
<small>Struck from more than one pair of dies. Mary, Princess Royal (1631–60), daughter of Charles I and Henrietta Maria; married Prince William of Orange in 1641.</small>

128 Anglo-Dutch Fishing Treaty 1636
Obv. Conjoined busts of the King, armoured and draped, three-quarters r., and the Queen,   *a AR*   700   —
draped r., dividing the date 1636 in the field. CAR. ET MAR. D.G. ANGL. FRANC. ET HIBER. RR.

Rev. Seated figures of Justice and Peace, embracing, attended by two infant genii holding scales and olive-branch. IVSTITIA ET PAX OSCVLATÆ SVNT PSAL. 84. *D. a* 77 mm.; *b* 55 mm. Cast. Dutch, [By H.R.] (?) *MI i*, 278/81, 4   *b AR*   400   —

Type *a* also occurs without a date. The portraits are similar to those of No. 159.

129   **William Juxon 1637**
Obv. Heraldic shield, with mitre, dividing the date 1637 in field. GVIL'. LOND'. EPVS. ET.   *AR*   90   160
ANGLIÆ. THESAVR'. *Rev.* Hand issuing from clouds holds an upright crozier, upon which sits   *AE*   35   60
a stork; beyond, a view of London. NON. DORMIT. QVI. CVSTODIT   *D.* 27 mm. (By N. Briot?)
MI i, 279/85

William Juxon (1582–1663), Archbishop of Canterbury and Bishop of London; Lord High Treasurer.

130   **Henry, Duc de Rohan 1638**
Obv. Bust l., armoured and draped. HENR. ROH. D. FR. PAR. ARM. REG. MASC. SOB. NAV. &.   *AR*   200   350
SCOT. PR   *Rev.* A flourishing young tree emerging from a decayed stump. ET. ADHVC. SPES.   *AE*   90   160
DVRAT. AVORVM. *D.* 43 mm. Cast. French (By?) *MI i*, 280/86; *CP* p. 132

Henry, Duc de Rohan (1579–1638), Huguenot leader and court favourite; connected by marriage with the royal houses of France and Scotland.

131   **Prince Charles, Knight of the Garter 1638**
Obv. Sheep shelter beneath the tallest tree in a forest marked by the Prince's coronet; ship at   *AR*   60   90
sea on the horizon. SERIS. FACTVRA. NEPOTIBVS. VMBRAM. *Rev.* CAROL. M.B. REGIS. FILIVS.
CAROL. PRINC. INAVGVRATVR XXII. MAII. M.D.C.XXXIIX. within the Garter. *D.* 31 mm. [By N.
Briot] *MI i*, 281/88

132   ——
Obv. Half-length figure, almost facing, wearing hat and robes of the Garter. CAROLVS. PRIN: *AR*   80   150
MA: BR: NOB^MI. ORD: GART: MILES. 22. MAII. 1638. *Rev.* C P divided by the Prince's plumes and
motto, within the Garter. MAGNI. SPES. MAGNA. PARENTIS   *D.* 27 mm. (By N. Briot?) *MI i*,
281/87

133   **Charles, Prince of Wales 1638**
Obv. Bust l., crowned, armoured and draped. CAROLVS. I. D.G. ANGL. SCOT. FR. ET. HIBER. REX.   *AR*   120   220
Rev. Equestrian figure r., holding a staff; behind, Prince's plumes. ILLVST. CAROLVS.
PRINCEPS. WALLIÆ. *Ex.* Two interlinked C's. *D.* 32 mm. By N. Briot. *MI i*, 282/89

134   **Scottish Rebellion 1639**
Obv. Equestrian figure, l., holding a staff, tramples upon symbols of war. CAROLVS. D'.G'.   *a AV*   700 1200
MAG'. BRIT'. FRAN'. ET. HIB'. REX. *Ex.* .1639. *Rev.* Hand issuing from clouds holds a cord   *AR*   130   250
linking a rose and thistle, QVOS. DEVS. *D. a* 32 mm.; *b* 27 mm. By T. Simon. *MI i*, 282/90–4;
CP 20/6–10   *b AV*   500   800
                                                                             AR   100   180

Each struck from more than one pair of dies: type *a* occurs with and without date and signature; type *b* is undated.

135   **Spanish Fleet Destroyed by the Dutch off Dover 1639**
Obv. Two large fleets in battle; in foreground, a crew escapes from sinking ship. *Rev.*   *AR*   300   500
Fourteen line inscription ÆTERNATI S. OB HISP. CLASSE. NAVIB. 67 SPECTATIS BELLI DUCIB'.
NAUCL. MILIT. . . . REG. DECEDERE IUSSA 21 OCTB. MAGNA VIRT. DELETA ORDD. FOED. BELG. F.F.,
within a wreath. *D.* 63 mm. By J. Looff. *MI i*, 284/95–6; *MH* 1921, 534–5; *v. Loon II*,
245/1–2

Struck from more than one pair of dies.

136   **Dominion of the Sea 1639**
Obv. Bust of Charles r., wearing a large plain collar, armoured; 1639 (incuse), on truncation.   *a AV*   —   —
CAROLVS. I. D: G. MAG. BRITANN. FRAN. ET. HIB. REX. *Rev.* Similar to No. 118. *D.* 60 mm. Cast.   *AR*   450   800
By N. Briot. *MI i*, 285/97; *MH* 1919, 29; *Farquhar* 1908/203   *b AR*   70   120

The portrait is based on No. 118. Type *b* is an eighteenth century copy.

137*   **Marriage of Princess Mary and William of Orange 1641**
Obv. Standing figures of William and Mary facing each other, their hands clasped; a cherub   *AR*   220   400
over each, holding a wreath. Beyond, distant view of a palace. ALBIONUM GENUIT REX ME
SUMMUSQUE MONARCHA CAROLUS, ET SPONSAM ME JUBET ESSE TUAM, to l.; PRINCEPS ME
HENRICUS GENUIT FORTISSIMUS HEROS NASOUIÆ, ET SPONSUM ME JUBET ESSE TUUM, to r. *Ex.*
LONDINI DESPONSATI WILHELM' ET MARIA, ANO 1641. 12 MAJ. *Rev.* Pallas receiving an olive-
branch from Peace. BELLONAM PRINCEPS PALLAS PEDIBUS TERIT ET PAX FLORET, ET ALMA
CERES, CONFERT SACRO ALITE FRUGES   *Ex.* NOUI IMPERII AUSPICIO BONO. *D.* 72 mm. By J.
Blum. *MI i*, 287/100; *v. Loon II*, 251. *See* **Plate 4**

William II (1626–50), Stadholder of the United Provinces 1647–50; son of Frederick Henry of Orange.

			£	£

138   **Princess Mary, Arrival in Holland 1642**

Obv. Frederick Henry, Prince of Orange, seated l., on a throne decorated with trophies, his sword raised victoriously and his feet on prostrate foes. Shields of the seven United Provinces suspended from a cord held in his left hand. LIBERTAS PATRIÆ, ME DEFENSORE, TRIUMPHAT, INSIDIATA NIHIL VIS INIMICA NOCET. *Rev.* Palace and gardens enclosed by an elaborate fence; at the entrance William receives his bride. QUO TE MARS ET AMOR VOCAT INTRA DIVA VIRETUM FRUCTUM HIC LIBERTAS TE GENITRICE FERET. *D.* 72 mm. By S. Dadler. *MI i*, 290/105; *v. Loon II*, 257
    AR   250   450

139   **Declaration of Parliament 1642**

Obv. Bust of Charles I, r., crowned and draped. SHOULD HEAR BOTH HOUSES OF PARLIAMENT FOR TRUE RELIGION AND SUBIECTS FREDOM STAND (incuse, in running script). *Rev.* Two equal horizontal sections containing the two Parliaments in which the King and the Speaker are seated. Suspension loop on edge. *D. a* 36 mm. by 52 mm. with wreath borders; *b* 28 mm. by 42 mm. Oval, cast. [By T. Rawlins] *MI i*, 292/108–9
    a AR   280   500
    b AR   180   350

Type *b* has a different obverse legend: PRO. RELIGIONE. LEGE. REGE. ET. PARLIAMENTO.

140   **Earl of Essex, Military Reward 1642**

Obv. Half-length figure of Essex, almost facing, armoured and holding an upright sword; above, SX (incuse). SHOULD HEAR BOTH HOUSES OF PARLIAMENT FOR TRUE RELIGION AND SUBIECTS FREDOM STAND. PRO RELIGIONE. LEGE. REGE. ET. PARLIAMENTO (incuse, in running script). *Rev.* Similar to No. 139. Suspension loop on edge. *D. a* 38 mm. by 54 mm. with wreath borders; *b* 27 mm. by 38 mm. Oval, cast. [By T. Rawlins] *MI i*, 295/113; *Farquhar* 1905/248
    a AR   280   500
    b AV   500   900
    AR   180   350

Robert Devereux, 3rd Earl of Essex (1591–1646), parliamentary general.

141   **Battle of Edgehill 1642**

Obv. Half-length figure of Charles I, three-quarters l., his hand upon hat lying on a table. CAR. D.G. MAG. BRI. FRAN. ET HIB. REX (incuse). *Rev.* Equestrian figure of the King, r., holding a baton; Genius hovering above, with wreath and palm. HONNI. SOIT. QVI. MAL. LE. PANS. (incuse). *D.* 32 mm. by 41 mm. Oval, cast. [By T. Rawlins] *MI i*, 298/118
    a AR   800   —
    b AR   70   120

Type *b* is an eighteenth century copy.

142*   **Peace or War 1643**

Obv. Bust r., laureate, armoured and draped. CAROLVS. D:G. ANG. SCO. FR. ET. HIB. REX. *Rev.* Sword and olive-branch, crossed, between the letters CR, CROWNED. IN. VTRVMQVE. PARATVS. *Ex.* .1643. *D.* 29 mm. By T. Rawlins. *MI i*, 308/134. *See* **Plate 4**
    AR   60   110
    AE   18   32

A state of uncertainty followed the capture of Bristol by the Royalists, under Prince Rupert. This medal was struck from more than one pair of dies, one of which is unsigned. It also occurs with a similar obverse by N. Briot. *See* No. 154.

143*   **Earl of Manchester, Military Reward 1643**

Obv. Armoured bust of Manchester, three-quarters l. *Rev.* Arms of Montagu within an ornamental shield, coronet above. Suspension loop on edge. *D. a* 30 mm. by 40 mm. with wreath borders; *b* 21 mm. by 31 mm. Oval, cast. (By T. Rawlins?) *MI i*, 309/137; *Farquhar* 1905/249. *See* **Plate 4**
    a AR   170   320
    b AR   120   220

Edward Montagu, 2nd Earl of Manchester (1602–71), parliamentary general.

144*   **Sir Richard Brown, Military Reward 1644**

Obv. Bust of Brown three-quarters l., armoured and draped. NON. VIR. SED. VIRTVS. *Rev.* Armorial shield. FOR KING AND PARLIAMENT 1644. With wreath borders and suspension loop on edge. *D.* 28 mm. by 40 mm. Oval, cast. (By?) *MI i*, 312/142. *See* **Plate 4**
    AR   160   300

Sir Richard Browne (1610?–69), parliamentary general; Lord Mayor of London.

145*   **Execution of Archbishop Laud 1645**

Obv. Bust r., in robes and cap. GVIL. LAVD. ARCHIEPISC. CANTVAR. X. IAN. 1644. *Rev.* Infant angel ascending to heaven, carrying mitre and crozier, followed by two others bearing the King's crown, sceptre and orb; below, view of London. SANCTI. CAROLI. PRÆCVRSOR. *D.* 58 mm. By J. Roettiers. *MI i*, 315/147; *v. Loon II*, 273. *See* **Plate 4**
    AV   1000   1700
    AR   90   170

Struck *c.*1670. William Laud (1573–1645), Archbishop of Canterbury. Dated in the old style.

146*   **Sir Thomas Fairfax, Military Reward 1645**

Obv. Bust l., armoured and draped. THO: FAIRFAX. MILES. MILIT: PARL: DVX. GEN. *Rev.* MERVISTI, in the centre. POST. HAC. MELIORA. 1645. *D. a* 28 mm. by 34 mm.; *b* 20 mm. by 25 mm. Oval, cast. [By T. Simon] *MI i*, 317/150–1; *Farquhar* 1905/249. *See* **Plate 4**
    a AR   150   280
    b AV   300   550
    AR   90   160

This medal usually occurs with a suspension loop. Type *b* is without obverse legend. Thomas Fairfax, 3rd Baron Fairfax (1612–71), parliamentary general.

			£	£
147*	——	AR	140	260

Obv. Bust of Fairfax almost facing, armoured. *Rev.* Armorial shield. SR. THO: FAIRFAX KNT. FOR KING & PARLMT. (incuse). Suspension loop on edge and wreath borders. *D.* 24 mm. by 33 mm. Oval, cast. (By?) *MI i*, 317/149. *See* **Plate 4**

148   Earl of Loudoun 1645
Obv. Bust of Loudoun l., wearing a cap and draped. *Rev.* IOHAN: COM: LOVDOVN. SVMMVS.   *a* AR   350   ——
SCOTIÆ CANCELLARIVS. 1645. *D.* 37 mm. Cast. By A. and [T.] Simon. *MI i*, 321/157; *CP* 97/5
                                                                   b AR   35   60
Type *b* is an eighteenth century copy. John Campbell, 1st Earl of Loudoun (1598–1663), Lord Chancellor of Scotland. This is one from a group of personal portrait medals by Thomas and Abraham Simon; *see* Nos. 150–2, 227. Others include Baron de Reede, William Pope, Earl of Dunfermline, and the Earl of Lauderdale.

149   Prince Rupert, Count Palatine 1645
Obv. Half-length armoured bust of Rupert, three-quarters l., holding a staff. *Rev.* Elaborate   AR   1000   ——
armorial shields, the crest dividing letters .R. .P. *D.* 30 mm. by 37 mm. Oval, cast. (By?) *MI i*, 323/159
Prince Rupert (1619–82), son of Frederick V and Elizabeth of Bohemia; commander of the Royalist forces.

150   Lord Inchiquin 1646
Obv. Bust of Inchiquin l., armoured and draped. *Rev.* 1646. HON: D: MOR: BAR: D'INCHIQVIN   *a* AV   ——   ——
D: PRÆSES. PROV MOMONIÆ. ÆT. 30. *D.* 36 mm. Cast. By A. and [T.] Simon. *MI i*, 324/161   AR   400   ——
                                                                    b AR   35   60
Type *b* is an eighteenth-century copy; *see* No. 148. Murrough O'Brien, 1st Earl of Inchiquin (1614–74), fought for both the King and Parliament; governor of Munster, Ireland.

151   Albert Joachim 1646
Obv. Bust of Joachim l., draped. *Rev.* .1646. ALB: IOACHIMI. EQ: FÆDERAT: BELG: POST. VARIAS.   *a* AV   ——   ——
IN. EVROP. LEGAT: IAM. ORDINAR: IN. BRIT: AN: 22. ÆT: 86. *D.* 36 mm. Cast. By A. and [T.]   AR   350   ——
Simon. *MI i*, 324/162; *v. Loon II*, 287
                                                             b AR   35   60
Type *b* is an eighteenth-century copy; *see* No. 148. Albert Joachim (1560–?), ambassador of the United Provinces.

152   Sidenham Pointz 1646
Obv. Bust of Pointz l., armoured and draped. *Rev.* .1646. SIDEN: POINTZ. 10000. EQVIT: ET.   *a* AR   400   ——
PED: ASSOCIAT: SEPTENT: DVX. SVM: EBOR: GVBER: *D.* 36 mm. Cast. By A. and [T.] Simon.
MI i, 325/163; *Hill/Pollard* pl. 30, 1   *b* AR   35   60
Type *b* is an eighteenth-century copy; *see* No. 148. Sir Sidenham Pointz (Poyntz) (*c.*1607–?), Parliamentary commander; governor of York.

153   Release of Giles Strangways 1648
Obv. Bust r., armoured and draped. ÆGIDIVS. STRANGWAYS. DE. MELBVRY. IN. COM.   AV   1400   2400
DORCESTR. ARMIGER. *Rev.* The White Tower of London with the Royal Standard flying;   AR   120   220
above, sun piercing clouds. DECVSQVE. ADVERSA. DEDERVNT   *Ex.* INCARCERATVS. SEPT. 1645.
LIBERATVS. APR. 1648   *D.* 60 mm. By J. Roettiers. *MI i*, 333/177; *Forrer* V/168
Struck *c.*1670. Giles Strangways (1615–75), commander in the King's army; persecuted and imprisoned by Parliament. At the Restoration, he was Member of Parliament for the constituency of Dorset.

154   Call to Unanimity 1648
Obv. Bust r., laureate, armoured and draped. CAROLVS. I. D:G. ANGL. SCOT. FR. ET. HIB.   AR   70   120
REX   *Rev.* Three crowns united by a cord. VNITÆ. INVICTÆ. *D.* 29 mm. By N. Briot. *MI i*,   AE   20   35
336/180
An appeal to those wishing to see the King's release. Struck from two pairs of dies, one of which is dated. *See* No. 142.

155   Charles Louis, Elector: Restored to the Palatinate 1648
Obv. Bust r., armoured and draped. CAR. LVD: D.G. C. PAL. RHEN. ELECT. DVX. BAV: *Rev.*   AV   ——   ——
Heraldic crest: lion sejant, crowned, upon wreath. SEDENDO NON. CEDO   *Ex.* 1648   *D.*   AR   1200   ——
45 mm. Cast. (By T. Simon?) *MI i*, 337/182
Charles Louis, Elector Palatine (1617–80), son of Frederick V and Elizabeth, brother of Prince Rupert; came to England to speak on behalf of Charles I, his uncle, after sentence of death had been passed.

156*   Marriage of Charles Louis and Charlotte of Hesse Cassel 1649
Obv. Busts of Charles Louis and Charlotte, draped, face to face. VNIENDO. MVLTIPLICAMINI.   AV   270   500
Rev. Cupid standing, almost facing, holding laurel wreath and bow. PERFECI   *Ex.* 1648   *D.*   AR   70   120
21 mm. (By?) *MI i*, 339/184–5. *See* **Plate 4**
Dated in the old style; struck from more than one pair of dies.

157   Death of Charles I 1649
Obv. Bust of the King, l., armoured and draped. SVCCESSOR VERVS VTRIVSQVE. *Rev.*   AR   170   320
Salamander, l., amid flames. CONSTANTIA CÆSARIS IAN 30 1648   *D.* 42 mm. Cast. [By T. Rawlins] *MI i*, 341/188; *Farquhar* 1905/270
Dated in the old style. This piece sometimes occurs with a suspension loop.

158   ——
                                                                  £   £

Obv. Bust l., armoured and draped. CAROLVS. D:G: MAG: BRIT. FRAN: ET. HIB: REX. FIDEI.   *AR*   70   130

DEFEN^SOR. *Rev.* Island rock buffeted by a storm. IMMOTA. TRIVMPHANS   *Ex.* IAN. 30. 1648. *D.*
29 mm. By T. Rawlins. *MI i*, 341/190; *v. Loon II*, 321

Dated in the old style.

159   **Charles I, Memorial 1649**

Obv. Conjoined busts of the King, armoured and draped, three-quarters r., and the Queen,   *AR*   800   —

draped, r. (sim. to No. 128). CAROLVS ET MARIA D.G. MAG. BRITAN. FRANE ET HIBER. R^X. ET R^A.

Rev. A rampant seven-headed monster, r.; below, the King's head lying on the ground

beside his crown and sceptre. HEV. QVÆNAM HÆC INSANIA VULGI! *D.* 75 mm. Cast. Dutch. By

H.R.(?) *MI i*, 350/209; *Forrer* VIII/155–6

This medal occurs with a suspension loop.

160   ——

Obv. Bust r., armoured. CAROL. I. D.G. M.B. F. ET. H. REX. &. GLOR. MEM. *Rev.* REX PACIFICVS   *AR*   120   220

VICTVS VINCEBAT HOSTES VICTOR TRIVMPHAT IN COELIS   *D.* 59 mm. By N. Roettiers. *MI i*,   *AE*   50   90

346/199; *v. Loon II*, 320

Struck *c.*1680.

161   ——

Obv. Bust r., armoured. CAROLVS REX POPVLE MEVS QVID FECI TIBI. 1649   *Rev.* Head of   *AR*   150   280

Medusa, facing; below, an upright flaming sword. To either side: arms, l.; a thunderbolt, r.

CONCILIABVLVM ANGLIÆ BLASFEMANT DEVM NECANT REGEM SPERNVNT LEGEM   *D.* 57 mm.

Cast. Dutch (By?) *MI i*, 349/208; *v. Loon II*, 321

This medal has a stippled surface.

162*   ——

Obv. Bust r., armoured and draped. CAROL. D.G. M.B. F. ET. H. REX. &. GLOR. MEM   *Rev.*   *a AR*   80   150

Hand issuing from heaven holds a celestial crown; below, sheep in a landscape. VIRTVT. EX.   *AE*   22   38

ME. FORTVNAM. EX. ALIJS. *D. a* 50 mm.; *b* 34 mm. By J. Roettiers. *MI i*, 346/200–1; *Farquhar*

1908/199; *v. Loon II*, 320. See **Plate 4**   *b AV*   280   500

Struck *c.*1680; type *b* is unsigned.   *AR*   30   55
                                                                  AE   20   35

163*   ——

Obv. Bust three-quarters l., armoured and draped. CARL.I. V. G. G. KÖNIG VON ENGEL: *AR*   90   170

SCHOTT: UND IRRLAND. LEYDEN GOTT UND OBRIGKEIT. *Rev.* A rampant seven-headed

monster, r.; below, the King's head lying on the ground beside his crown and sceptre. BEY

DES PÖFELS MACHT UND STREIT   *D.* 46 mm. Dutch or German. By F (?) *MI i*, 352/210; *v.*

Loon II, 321. See **Plate 4**

The reverse is based on No. 159.

164   ——

Obv. Bust l., laureate, armoured and draped. CAROLUS. I. D.G. M. BR. FR. ET. HIB. REX. *Rev.*   *AR*   35   65

Britannia, seated mournfully upon a monument, raises a pall revealing the King's head. *Ex.*   *AE*   4   9

NAT. 13. NOV. 1600. COR. 2. FEBR. 1626. M. 30. IANV. 1649. *D.* 41 mm. By J. Dassier. *MI i*,

353/212

Struck in 1731, from Dassier's series of English kings and queens. *See* No. 526.

165   ——

Obv. An altar, inscribed P.M. ACAD. OXON., dividing the date 1648   *Rev.* DEO, ECCLEFIA,   *AR*   90   —

PRINCIPI VICTIMA   *D.* 29 mm. Cast. (By?) *MI i*, 348/205

A tribute from the University of Oxford who issued a similar oval medal. Dated in the old style.

166*   **Charles I and Henrietta Maria, Royalist Badge**

Obv. Bust r., crowned and draped. CAROLVS. D.G. MAG. BRITAN. FRAN. ET. HIB. REX. FI.   *a AR*   180   350

D   *Rev.* Bust l., wearing a coronet and draped. HENRETTA. MARIA. D.G. MAG. BRITAN. FRAN.

ET. HIB. REG   Suspension loop on edge. *D. a* 37 mm. by 53 mm. wreath borders; *b* 33 mm. by   *b AR*   150   250

44 mm. Oval, cast. By T. Rawlins. *MI i*, 355/216; *Farquhar* 1905/262. See **Plate 5**

More than forty royalist badges, produced *c.*1649–60, commemorate the Stuart family; they were worn by those loyalists
who had to pay tribute. Most occur with suspension loops, which can vary in size, and some were gilt. *See* Nos. 167–73.

167   **Charles I, Royalist Badge**

Obv. Bust r., draped and wearing a lace collar. CAROLVS. D.G. MAG. BRI. FR. ET. HIB. RX.   *a AR*   270   430

(incuse). *Rev.* (incuse) Royal arms, crowned, within the Garter. Suspension loop on edge.

D. a 41 mm. by 58 mm. with wreath borders; *b* 33 mm. by 44 mm. Oval, cast. [By T.   *b AR*   120   220

Rawlins] *MI i*, 360/231; *Farquhar* 1905/263

See No. 166.

			£	£

168* ——— *Obv.* Similar to No. 166. *Rev.* Royal arms within the Garter, crowned. Suspension loop on edge. *D. a* 37 mm. by 53 mm., with wreath borders; *b* 33 mm. by 44 mm. Oval, cast. [By T. Rawlins] *MI i*, 360/232; *Farquhar* 1905/261. *See* **Plate 5**
See No. 166.

     a AV   1100   —
     AR   200   380
     b AR   120   220

169   **Charles I and Henrietta Maria, Royalist Badge**
Obv. Bust of the King r., similar to No. 167. *Rev.* Bust of the Queen l., similar to No. 166. Suspension loop on edge. *D.* 34 mm. by 44 mm. Oval, cast. By T. Rawlins. *MI i*, 354/215; *Farquhar* 1905/251
See No. 166.

     AR   130   250

170* ——— *Obv.* Bust of the King l., laureate, armoured and draped. *Rev.* Bust of the Queen, as that on No. 166, but no inscription. Suspension loop on edge. *D. a* 28 mm. by 39 mm., with floral borders; *b* 22 mm. by 33 mm. Oval, cast. [By T. Rawlins] *MI i*, 355/218; *Farquhar* 1905/262. *See* **Plate 5**
See No. 166.

     a AR   90   150
     b AR   60   110

171*   **Charles I and Prince Charles, Royalist Badge**
Obv. Similar to No. 170*b. Rev.* Bust of Prince Charles three-quarters r., armoured and draped. Suspension loop on edge. *D.* 22 mm. by 33 mm. Oval, cast. By T. Rawlins. *MI i*, 371/261. *See* **Plate 5**
See No. 166.

     AR   90   150

172*   **Charles I and Henrietta Maria, Royalist Badge**
Obv. Bust of the King l., armoured and draped. *Rev.* Bust of the Queen l., crowned and draped. Suspension loop on edge. *D.* 22 mm. by 28 mm. Oval, cast. (By T. Rawlins?) *MI i*, 358/224; *Farquhar* 1905/254. *See* **Plate 5**
See No. 166. This obverse occurs with two other portraits of Henrietta Maria.

     AR   70   120

173   **Charles I, Royalist Badge**
Obv. Bust of the King l., as No. 172. *Rev.* (incuse) Shield with Royal arms, crowned, within the Garter. Suspension loop on edge. *D.* 22 mm. by 28 mm. Oval, cast. (By T. Rawlins?) *MI i*, 361/235; *Farquhar* 1905/254
See No. 166.

     AV   300   500
     AR   70   120

174   **James I and Prince Charles**
Obv. Bust of James I, almost facing, wearing a jewelled hat and draped. GIVE THY JUDGEMENTS O GOD UNTO THE KING   *Rev.* Bust of Prince Charles, almost facing, draped. AND THY RIGHTOUSNESSE UNTO THE KINGS SONN   *D.* 27 mm. Cast. (By?) *MI i*, 376/272; *Farquhar* 1908/155
In imitation of engraving (after S. v. de Passe), on a thin flan. One of a series of counters portraying British monarchs which sometimes occur collectively in contemporary silver boxes. *See also* Nos. 175–6.

     AR   15   25

175   **Charles I**
Obv. Bust almost facing, crowned and draped, with orb and sceptre. CAROLVS. DEI. GRATIA. ANGLIÆ. SCOTIÆ. ET HIBERNIÆ R. *Rev.* Shield of the Royal arms, crowned, within the Garter. *D.* 25 mm. Cast. (By?) *MI i*, 380/282
In imitation of engraving (after S. v. de Passe), on a thin flan. One of a second group of counters portraying British and European monarchs. *See* No. 174.

     AR   15   25

176   **Henrietta Maria**
Obv. Bust of Henrietta Maria, three-quarters r., draped. *Rev.* MARIA DEI. GRATIÆ MAGNÆ. BRITANNIÆ FRANCIÆ. ET HIBERNIÆ REGINA 1638   *D.* 26 mm. Cast. (By?) *MI i*, 381/284
In imitation of engraving (after S. v. de Passe), on a thin flan. One of a third group of counters portraying British and European monarchs. *See* No. 174.

     AR   15   25

177*   **John Lilburne, Trial and Acquittal 1649**
Obv. Bust l., draped. IOHN. LILBORNE. SAVED. BY. THE. POWER. OF. THE. LORD. AND. THE. INTEGRITY. OF. HIS. IVRY. WHO. ARE. IVGES. OF. LAW. AS. WEL. AS. FACT. OCT 26. 1649. *Rev.* A rose in the centre. MYLES. PETTY. STE. ILES. ABR. SMITH. ION. KING. NIC. MVRIN. THO. DAINTY. EDM. KEYSAR. EDW. PARKINS. RAL. PACKMAN. WIL. COMINS. SY. WEEDON. HEN. TOWLEY. (jurymen) OCTOBER. 26. 1649. *D.* 34 mm. (By T. Simon?) *MI i*, 385/3. *See* **Plate 5**
John Lilburne (1614?–57), political agitator.

     AR   120   220
     AE   70   110

178   *Obv.* Bust l., as No. 177. IOHN. LILBORNE   *Rev.* Armorial shield. OCTOBER. 26. 1649. *D.* 22 mm. by 26 mm. Oval. (By T. Simon?) *MI i*, 386/4
This medal sometimes occurs with a suspension loop.

     AR   80   140

COMMONWEALTH 1649–60

                                                         £   £

179*   **Naval Reward 1649**
Obv. Shields of England and Ireland, bearing the cross of St. George and a harp, suspended   AV   —   —
from the beam of an upright anchor. MERVISTI   *Rev.* Speaker seated facing in the long   AR   800   —
Parliament. *D.* 21 mm. by 24 mm. Oval. By T. Simon. *MI i*, 390/12; *MH* 1919, 33; *Lessen*
1981, pl. VII/1. *See* **Plate 5**

This medal sometimes occurs with a suspension loop. It was struck by order of Parliament.

180   **Oliver Cromwell, Lord General 1650**
Obv. Bust three-quarters r., armoured and draped. OLI: CROMWEL. MILIT: PARL: DVX. GEN: *a* AV   350   600
Rev. Plain. *D. a* 36 mm. *b* 27 mm. by 30 mm. Oval. [By T. Simon] *MI i*, 388/7   AR   70   130
                                                                     AE   30   50

Oliver Cromwell (1599–1658), Lord Protector of England. Type *a* struck *c.*1740, from an oval die on a round flan of
variable thickness. Examples usually exhibit rust marks, although they were sometimes removed by Mint personnel. A   *b* AV   150   280
horizontal die crack running above the oval frame containing the portrait is sometimes visible; *Lessen 1979/B.* Type *b* is a   AR   40   75
later striking, *c.*1800, on an oval flan and with more widespread rust marks and flaws; *Lessen 1979/E.*   AE   20   35

181A   **Battle of Dunbar, Military Reward 1650**
Obv. Bust of Cromwell l., armoured and draped; in the distance, a battle scene. THE LORD OF   *a* AR   750   —
HOSTS. WORD. AT DVNBAR. SEPTEM: Y. 3. 1650   *Rev.* Similar to No. 179. *D.* 28 mm. by 35 mm.   AE   —   —
Oval. By T. Simon. *MI i*, 392/14

Type *a* is an original example with full horizon and battle scene, and exhibiting no die flaws or rust marks; Lessen   *b* AR   40   75
1981/9–12. Type *b* is a cast copy of type *a*; Lessen 1981/13–15. Type *c* is a restrike *c.*1750–1850 with die flaws and rust marks
in varying stages of deterioration; *Lessen 1981/16–22.* Type *d* is from false dies made in the late nineteenth century,   *c* AV   200   350
differing in many respects to that of the original; *Lessen 1981/23–31.*   AR   80   150
                                                                            Pb.   15   25

                                                                             d AR   45   75

181B*   **——**
Obv. Bust of Cromwell l., similar to No. 181A. *Rev.* Similar to No. 179. *D.* 22 mm. by   *a* AV   —   —
28 mm. Oval. By T. Simon. *MI i*, 391/13; *Hill/Pollard* pl. 30, 7. *See* **Plate 5**   AR   —   —

Type *a*, an original example without die flaws or rust marks; *Lessen 1981/2–6.* Type *b* is a restrike *c.*1750–1800 of the   *b* AR   35   65
obverse only (reverse is plain), and exhibits rust and die flaws in varying stages of deterioration; *Lessen 1981/7–8.*   AE   15   25

182*   **William II of Orange (Memorial) and Princess Mary 1650**
Obv. Bust three-quarters r., armoured and draped. WILHELMVS II. D.G. PRINC. AVRICÆ COM.   AR   380   750
NASS. Eᶜᴼ   *Rev.* Bust l., draped. MARIA D.G. PRINCEPS M. BRIT. AVRANT. DOTARIA. ETC   *D.*
64 mm. By P. v. Abeele. *MI i*, 393/17; *v. Loon II*, 340. *See* **Plate 5**

This medal consists of two repoussé plates joined at the edge by a broad rim. William's armorial shield occurs on another
reverse.

183*   **Charles II, Scottish Coronation at Scone Palace 1651**
Obv. Bust r., crowned and draped. CAROLVS. 2. D.G. SCO. ANG. FRA & HI. REX. FI. DE. COR. 1. IA.   AV   1600   2800
SCON. 1651. *Rev.* Rampant lion l., holding thistle in paw. NEMO. ME. IMPVNE LACESSET   *D.*   AR   800   1300
32 mm. Cast. (By?, after J. Balfour) *MI i*, 394/18; *CP* 21/1; *Wollaston* 4. *See* **Plate 5**

184   **Inigo Jones, Memorial 1652**
Obv. Bust three-quarters l., wearing a cap and draped. INIGO. IONES. ARCHITECTUS. *Rev.*   AE   50   90
Plain. *D.* 30 mm. By J. Kirk. *MI i*, 398/25; *Eidlitz* 1927/609   Pb.   25   40

Struck *c.*1740. Inigo Jones (1573–1652), architect.

185*   **Naval Reward 1653**
Obv. Shields of England, Ireland and Scotland suspended from the beam of an upright   AV   4000   —
anchor. *Rev.* Large naval engagement; in foreground, a Dutch ship sinking. *D.* 36 mm. by
46 mm. Oval. By T. Simon. *MI i*, 400/28; *MH* 1919, 36. *See* **Plate 5**

This medal is sometimes referred to as the Captain's Medal. It occurs with a suspension loop on edge. Also found with two
different forms of decorated outer borders: laurel wreaths and Dutch naval trophies.

186   **Death of Martin Tromp 1653**
Obv. Bust of Tromp three-quarters r., armoured and draped, within an oval frame   AR   350   600
decorated with palm branches and naval trophies. Above, a naval crown supported by two
infant genii; below, a ribbon inscribed MYN HERT EN HANDT WAS VOOR HET LANDT (in running
script). *Rev.* Naval engagement; in foreground an English ship sinking. WAAROM DOET
MÜLLER TROMP DOOR KUNST VAN GOUT EN SILVER LEEVEN: OM DAT HY DYSER EEW DOOR
KRYGSDEUGD HEEFT VERDREVEN. OBŸT DEN. 10 AUG. 1653 (in running script). *D.* 75 mm. By O.

			£	£

Müller. *MI i*, 404/34–5; *MH* 1921, 542–3; *v. Loon II*, 364

This medal consists of two repoussé plates joined at the edge by a broad rim. There is some variance in the diameter of examples examined. A variety omits the word OBŸT on the reverse. Martin Harpetszoon Tromp (1597–1653), Dutch admiral; fought against England in 1652–3.

187 ——

Obv. Bust almost facing, armoured and draped. MARTEN. HARPERSTEN. TROMP. RIDDER. *Rev.*   *AR*   170   300
Naval engagement. LIEVTENANT. ADMIRAAL. VAN. HOLLAND. VOOR. HET. VAADERLAND.
GESNEVVELT. DEN. 10. AVGVSTI. ANNO. 1653. *D.* 69 mm. By J. Pool. *MI i*, 403/33; *MH* 1921,
541; *v. Loon II*, 364

Examples may have been struck some years later.

188* **Oliver Cromwell, Lord Protector 1653**
Obv. Bust l., armoured and draped. OLIVERVS. DEI. GRA'. REIPVB'. ANGLIÆ. SCO'.ET. HIB'. &.   *a AV*   —   —
PROTECTOR. *Rev.* Lion displays the arms of Cromwell and the Commonwealth. PAX.   *AR*   600   —
QVÆRITVR. BELLO   *D.* 39 mm. By T. Simon. *MI i*, 409/45; *v. Loon II*, 367. *See* **Plate 5**

Issued as a reward for political or military service. Type *a* is struck, *c.*1656; *Lessen* 1977/1–2. Type *b* is a cast, varying in   *b AR*   80   150
quality, produced during the 18th and 19th centuries; *Lessen* 1977/3–5.

189 ——

Obv. Bust three-quarters r., armoured and draped, similar to No. 180. OLIV. D.G. R. P. ANG.   *AR*   60   110
SCO. ET. HIB. PRO. *Rev.* Similar to No. 188. *D.* 33 mm. (By?), after T. Simon. *MI i*, 410/46;   *AE*   30   40
Lessen 1979, 95/ Copy 1

Struck *c.*1730; a continental copy based on Simon's Lord General (No. 180) and Lord Protector (No. 188) medals.

190 **Peace between England and Holland 1654**
Obv. Peace stands between England and Holland and decorates the shafts of their respective   *AR*   500   800
flags with an olive wreath. HIER BINT DE HEIL'GE VREE DEN BRIT, EN BATAVIER, DE WERELT EER'.
T VERBONT, EN VREEZ' ER KRYGSBANIER. *Rev.* Fully-rigged ship assisted by winds; above,
Fame proclaims the Peace. WAAROM ZEILT. T'VREDESCHIP OP T. SILVER. IN. DE. ZEE? OM. DAT.
DE. BROEDERKRIIG. VERANDERT. IS. IN. VREE. *Ex.* A° 1654   *D.* 80 mm. (By O. Müller?) *MI i*,
413/50; *MH* 1921, 550; *v. Loon II*, 371

This medal consists of two repoussé plates joined at the edge by a broad rim.

191 ——

Obv. Britannia and Holland, seated, jointly hold up the cap of liberty. MENTIBUS UNITIS   *AR*   200   380
PRISCUS PROCUL ABSIT AMAROR, PILEA NE SUBITO PARTA CRUORE RUANT. *Rev.* A British and a
Dutch frigate sailing together upon a tranquil sea. LUXURIAT GEMINO NEXU TRANQVILLA SALO
RES. EXCIPIT UNANIMES TOTIUS ORBIS AMOR. *D.* 61 mm. By S. Dadler. *MI i*, 415/52; *MH*
1921, 549; *v. Loon II*, 371

192* **Princess Mary and Prince William (III) of Orange 1654**
Obv. As the reverse of No. 182. *Rev.* Bust three-quarters r., wearing a feathered hat and   *AR*   400   700
draped; below, WILHELMVS III. D.G. PRINC. ARAVS. ETC. AN. 1654 on a ribbon. A broad wreath
border of oranges. *D.* 64 mm. By P. v. Abeele. *MI i*, 417/55; *v. Loon II*, 375. *See* **Plate 6**

This medal consists of two repoussé plates joined at the edge by a broad rim. Prince William (1650–1702), stadholder of
Holland; William III (1689–1702) of England.

193 **John Selden, Memorial 1654**
Obv. Bust three-quarters l., draped. IOANNES SELDEN   *Rev.* Seated figure of Science.   *AR*   45   80
holding a cornucopia, upon a cube within the serpent of Eternity. SEDES FRUCTUSQUE   *AE*   7   15
PERENNIS   *D.* 43 mm. By J. Dassier. *MI i*, 419/58

Struck *c.*1740. John Selden (1584–1654), statesman; jurist and antiquary.

194* **Subservience Paid to Britain by France and Spain c.1655**
Obv. Bust l., laureate and armoured. OLIVAR. D G RP. ANG. SCO. HIBERNIÆ. PROTECTOR   *Rev.*   *AV*   1000   1800
Kneeling figure (Cromwell) in state of undress, his head on the lap of Britannia, seated l.; the   *AR*   300   500
French and Spanish ambassadors await their turn to pay such respect. RETIRE. TOY.   Pb.   50   —
L'HONNEVR. APPARTIËT. AV. ROY. MON. MAISTER. *Ex.* LOVIS. LE. GRAND   *D.* 47 mm. Dutch
(By?) *MI i*, 420/60; *v. Loon II*, 395. *See* **Plate 6**

The portrait on this satirical medal appears to have been copied from No. 202; it may have been struck some years later. A
number of electrotypes have been noted.

195 **Oliver Cromwell c.1655**
Obv. Equestrian figure of Cromwell, l., holding a baton.; London and the Thames in   *AE*   80   —
distance. OLIVARIVS. DEI. GRA. REIP ANGLIÆ. SCOTIÆ. ET. HIBERNIÆ &. PROTECTOR   *Rev.*
Plain. *D.* 82 mm. Cast. (By?)

Based on Thomas Simon's Great Seal of the Lord Protector.

PLATE 5

166

168

170

171

172

177

179

181B

182

183

185

188

PLATE 6

192 (× 2⁄3)

194

197

199

201

202

205

207

209 (× 2⁄3)

211

			£	£

196   **William Harvey, Memorial 1657**

Obv. Bust r., draped. GULIELMUS HARVEY. *Rev.* NATUS FOLKSTONII IN CANTIO AN.   AR   16   35
M.D.LXXVIII. OBIIT LONDINI AN. M.DC.LVII. *Ex.* SERIES NUMISMATICA UNIVERSALIS VIRORUM   AE   3   7
ILLUSTRIUM. M.DCCC.XXIII. DURAND EDIDIT   *D.* 41 mm. By W. Binfield. *MI i*, 423/64; *Storer*
1476

Struck in Paris in 1823, from a series commemorating famous people of all countries. William Harvey (1578–1657), physician; discoverer of the circulation of the blood.

197*   **Elizabeth Claypole, Memorial 1658**

Obv. Bust of Claypole r., lightly draped. *Rev.* ANN CLEYPOLE DAUGHTER OF OLIVER   AR   30   55
CROMWELL within a wreath. *D.* 34 mm. By J. Kirk. *MI i*, 430/75. *See* **Plate 6**   AE   15   25

Struck *c.*1750. Elizabeth Claypole (1629–58), second daughter of Cromwell; incorrectly named on the medal.

198   **Oliver Cromwell and Tommaso Aniello 1658**

Obv. Bust three-quarters r., armoured and in large plain collar, between two soldiers   AR   300   550
supporting a wreath above his head. A cartouche below, inscribed OLIVAR CROMWEL
PROTECTOR V̄. ENGEL: SCHOTL: YRLAN. 1658 (incuse). *Rev.* Bust three-quarters r., draped,
between two sailors supporting a naval crown above his head. A cartouche below, inscribed
MAS'ANIELLO VISSCHER EN CONINCK V̄. NAPELS 1647 (incuse). *D.* 71 mm. (By O. Müller?) *MI i*,
432/78.

This medal consists of two repoussé plates joined at the edge by a broad rim. Tommaso Aniello, or Masaniello (1623?–47), Italian fisherman; leader of a revolt in Naples.

199*   ——

Obv. Bust l., laureate and draped. OLIVAR. D.G. R. P. ANG. SCO. ET. HIB. & C. PRO   *Rev.* Bust l.,   AR   150   250
in tall cap, draped. THOMAS. ANIELLO. DE. AMALPHI. *D.* 46 mm. By F. St. Urbain. *MI i*,   AE   60   110
432/79. *See* **Plate 6**   Pb.   20   38

Struck *c.*1700.

200   **Death of Oliver Cromwell 1658**

Obv. Bust l., laureate and armoured. OLIVAR. D.G. RP. ANG. SCO. HIBERNIÆ. PROTECTOR (as   AV   700   900
No. 194). *Rev.* Shepherd attending his flock near an olive tree. NON. DEFITIENT. OLIVA. SEP. 3.   AR   150   280
1658. *D.* 48 mm. Dutch (By?) *MI i*, 435/85; *v. Loon II*, 420

Nos. 200 and 201 are copies of No. 202. They were struck for several years after the event, and each from more than one pair of dies.

201*   ——

Obv. Bust l., laureate and draped. OLIVAR. D.G. RP. ANG. SCO. HIB. PRO. *Rev.* Similar to No.   AV   270   450
200. *D.* 28 mm. Dutch (By?) *MI i*, 434/84; *v. Loon II*, 420. *See* **Plate 6**   AR   90   160

Some examples have a grained edge. *See* No. 200.

202*   ——

Obv. Bust l., laureate, armoured and draped. OLIVAR. D.G. RP. ANG. SCO. HIB & C   *a* AV   800   —
PROTECTOR   *Rev.* Young olive-tree growing beside a dead stump; shepherd with flock   AE   —   —
nearby. NON. DEFITIENT. OLIVA. SEP. 3. 1658   *D.* 19 mm. by 21 mm. Oval. By T. Simon. *MI*   Pb.   —   —
i, 433/82; *v. Loon II*, 420; *Lessen 1982/1–5*. *See* **Plate 6**
    b AR   50   80

Occurs with a suspension loop. Type *b* is a cast copy, *c.*1750; *Lessen 1982/7–11.*

203   **Oliver Cromwell, Memorial 1658**

Obv. Bust l., laureate, armoured and draped. OLIVARIUS CROMWELL. *Rev.* Shield, helmet and   AR   25   55
palm upon a decorated monument, inscribed ANGLIÆ. SCO. ET HIB. PROTECTOR.; around,   AE   6   14
four infant genii. *Ex.* NAT. 3. APRIL. 1603. MORT. 3. SEPT. 1658. *D.* 38 mm. By J. Dassier. *MI i*,
435/87

Struck in 1731, from Dassier's series of English kings and queens. *See* No. 526.

CHARLES II, 1660–85

204   **Charles II, Royalist Badge**

Obv. Bust of Charles II, r., crowned, armoured and draped. *Rev.* (incuse) Shield of royal   AV   400   —
arms within the Garter; above, crown dividing C R. Suspension loop on edge. *D.* 29 mm. by   AR   100   180
36 mm. Oval, cast. (By T. Rawlins?) *MI i*, 444/19

One of a group of more than twenty-five badges made *c.*1649–60, during the King's exile, for display by loyalists; most have suspension loops which can vary in size, and some were gilt. *See* Nos. 205–8.

205*   ——

Obv. Bust l., crowned, armoured and draped; C R 2 in field. Floral border. *Rev.* As obverse.   AR   60   90
D. 25 mm. by 29 mm. Oval. (By T. Rawlins?) *MI i*, 446/23. *See* **Plate 6**

Consisting of two repoussé plates joined at the edge by a rim. A similar piece has the busts facing right. *See* No. 204.

			£	£

206 —— *Obv.* Bust three-quarters l., armoured and draped. CAROLVS SECVNDVS (incuse). *Rev.* (incuse) Shield of royal arms within the Garter; above, crown dividing C R. With suspension loop. *D.* 22 mm. by 33 mm. Oval, cast. [By T. Rawlins] *MI i*, 439/6; *Farquhar* 1905/276   *AR*   80   150
See No. 204.

207* —— *Obv.* Bust r., crowned and draped. CAROLVS SECVNDVS (incuse). *Rev.* (incuse) Similar to No. 206. With suspension loop. *D.* 22 mm. by 33 mm. Oval, cast. [By T. Rawlins] *MI i*, 440/9; *Farquhar* 1905/274. *See* **Plate 6**   *AR*   80   150
See No. 204.

208 —— *Obv.* Bust l., crowned and draped. CAROLVS SECVNDVS (incuse). *Rev.* (incuse) Two angels, standing, support a crown. With suspension loop. *D.* 17 mm. by 23 mm. Oval, cast. [By T. Rawlins] *MI i*, 439/7; *Farquhar* 1905/276   *AR*   70   120
See No. 204.

209* **Charles I (Memorial) and Charles II 1660**
Obv. Bust three-quarters r., draped. CAROLVS. D.I. *Rev.* Bust almost facing, armoured and draped. CAROLUS. II. D:G. MAGNÆ. BRIT. FRA. ET. HIB. REX. *D.* 71 mm. [By P. v. Abeele] *MI i*, 450/34; *v. Loon II*, 462. *See* **Plate 6**   *AR*   400   650
This medal consists of two repoussé plates joined at the edge by a broad rim.

210 **Charles II, Embarkation at Scheveningen 1660**
Obv. Bust of Charles II, as the reverse of No. 209. *Rev.* Fame with ribbon, inscribed SOLI DEI GLORIA (incuse), flying over a fleet under sail. IN NOMINE MEO EXALTABITUR CORNU EIUS. PSAL.89. Below, a shell inscribed S.M. IS ÚIT HOLLANT VAN SCHEVELING AFGEVAREN NAER FŸN CONINCRŸKEN Aᵒ. 1660 JÚNI 2 (incuse, in running script). *D.* 70 mm. By P. v. Abeele. *MI i*, 455/44; *MH* 1919, 42; *v. Loon II*, 462   *AR*   350   600
This medal consists of two repoussé plates joined at the edge by a broad rim. Variations occur with the inscription on the shell.

211* **Charles II, Landing at Dover 1660**
Obv. Bust r., draped, within branches of laurel. CAROLUS. II. D.G. MAGN: BRITANN: FRANC: ET. HIBERN: REX: DEUM. PROVIDENTIA. ATQ. MISERICORDIA. VIVO: ANNO. RESERATÆ. SALUTIS. 1660. DIE. 29. MAII. *Rev.* Standing figures of England, Ireland and Scotland await the arrival of an approaching ship, its flag inscribed IPSO FAVENTE COELO. To l., a castle with flag inscribed PRÆDESTINATO. Above in centre, Eye of Providence within radiate sun. SI DEUS EST CUSTOS QUIS MEUS HOSTIS ERIT   *D.* 57 mm. By J. Roettiers. *MI i*, 457/48; *MH* 1919, 46; *v. Loon II*, 464. *See* **Plate 6**   *AR*   350   700

212 **Charles II, Restoration 1660**
Obv. Bust r., armoured and draped. CAROLVS. SECVNDVS. D.G. MAG. BRIT. FRAN. ET. HIB. REX   *Rev.* Britannia seated beneath a cliff, r., receives an olive-branch from Justice, standing before her accompanied by Hercules and Pallas. FELICITAS BRITTANIÆ. 29. MAII. 1660. *D.* 83 mm. [By J. Roettiers] *MI i*, 460/53; *Farquhar* 1908/252; *v. Loon II*, 464; *Forrer V*/164

AV	— —
AR	600 1100
WM	40 75

Some examples exhibit flaws and may have been struck a little later.

213* —— *Obv.* Bust l., draped in robes of the Garter. CAROLVS. II. DEI. GRATIA. MAG. BR. FRA. ET. HIB. REX   *Rev.* Jupiter, seated on an eagle in clouds, hurls thunder down at prostrate giants on rocks. Rich ornamental border each side. *D.* 64 mm. By G. Bower. *MI i*, 458/50. **Plate 7**   *AR*   400   750

214 —— *Obv.* Bust r., armoured and draped, AVGVSTISS. CAROLO. SECVNDO. P.P. *Rev.* Hercules, Minerva, Peace and Mercury standing around an altar: Prudence, beyond; Plenty reclining in the foreground. NVLLVM. NVMEN ABEST   *Ex.* BRITANNIÆ   *D.* 63 mm. By J. Roettiers. *MI i*, 460/54; *Farquhar* 1909/243; *v. Loon II*, 464

AV	1500 2800
AR	250 450

215* —— *Obv.* Bust r., armoured and draped. CAROLVS. II. D:G. MAGNÆ. BRIT. FRA. ET. HIB. REX. *Rev.* Three crowns threaded onto branches of a leafless oak tree; above, sun piercing clouds. TANDEM REVIRESCET   *D.* 35 mm. [By T. Rawlins] *MI i*, 453/38; *Farquhar* 1905/273. **Plate 7**

a AR	80 150
b AR	35 65
AE	20 35

This medal sometimes occurs with a suspension loop on the edge. Type *a* consists of two repoussé plates joined together at the edge; type *b* is cast.

		£	£

216 ——

Obv. Bust r., laureate, armoured and draped. CAROLVS. II. D.G. MAG. BRI. FRAN. ET. HIB. REX.   AV   600   1100
Rev. Pallas seated, l., pierces the prostrate figure of Envy with spear and points to heaven.   AR   120   220
.INVIDIA . MAIOR. *D.* 35 mm. By G. Bower. *MI i*, 459/52; *v. Loon II*, 461

217 ——

Obv. Moses watches the Israelites making bricks under their Egyptian taskmasters. CVM.   AR   80   150
DVPLICATVR. ONVS. REDIT. MOYSES. *Rev.* .IN. ÆTER: MEMOR: CAROLI. II. MA: BR: FRANC: ET:
HIBERN: CLEMENTISSIMI REGIS: RED^S. 29. MAII: 1660. within a wreath. *D.* 31 mm. [By T.
Rawlins] *MI i*, 462/56; *v. Loon II*, 464

A similar type of 37 mm. occurs without a wreath and with differently arranged lettering.

218* General Monk *c.*1660

Obv. Bust l., armoured and draped. GEORGE DVKE OF ALBEMARLE (incuse). *Rev.* Armorial   AR   400   700
shield within the Garter, ducally crowned. With wreath borders and a suspension loop. *D.*
32 mm. by 41 mm. Oval, cast. (By T. Rawlins?) *MI i*, 466/65; *MH* 1919, 49. See **Plate 7**

George Monk, 1st Duke of Albemarle (1608–70), commander of the British forces.

219* Coronation of Charles II 1661

Obv. Bust l., laureate and draped. CAROLVS. II. D.G. MAG. BRIT. FRA. ET. HIB. REX. FI. DE. *Rev.*   AV   —   —
A flourishing oak-tree, three crowns among the branches; radiate sun above. IAM.   AR   400   750
FLORESCIT. *Ex.* 23. APR. 1661   *D.* 44 mm. Cast. [By T. Simon] *MI i*, 475/83; *Farquhar*
1908/251. See **Plate 7**

220 ——

Obv. Bust l., crowned and draped. CAROLVS. II. D:G: MAG: BRI: FRA: ET. HI: REX.   AR   120   220
CORONATVS   *Rev.* The King as a shepherd standing among three flocks of sheep. DIXI
CVSTODIAM. XXIII. APRIL. 1661. *Edge:* CORONATO. PASTORE. OVAT. OVILE   *D.* 33 mm. By T.
Rawlins. *MI i*, 473/78

Struck from more than one pair of dies.

221* ——

Obv. Bust r., crowned and draped. CAROLVS. II. D.G. ANG. SCO. FR. ET. HI. REX. *Rev.* The King   AV   600   1100
enthroned, l., crowned by Peace hovering above. EVERSO. MISSVS. SVCCVRRERE. SECLO. XXIII.   AR   70   150
APR. 1661   *D.* 29 mm. By T. Simon. *MI i*, 472/76; *v. Loon II*, 470; *Wollaston* 5. See **Plate 7**

The official coronation issue.

222* Marriage of Charles II and Catherine of Braganza 1662

Obv. Bust r., laureate, armoured and draped. CAROLVS. II. D.G. MAG. BR. FRA. ET. HIB. REX.   AR   400   750
Rev. Bust r., hair tied with a bandeau, draped. .CATHARINA. D.G. MAG. BR. FRA. ET. HIB. REG.   AE   150   280
D. 62 mm. By G. Bower. *MI i*, 491/115. See **Plate 7**

Catherine of Braganza (1638–1705), daughter of John IV, king of Portugal. More than fourteen medals and badges
commemorate the marriage.

223* ——

Obv. Busts face to face, draped. CAROLVS. II. ET. CATHARINA. D.G. MAG. BRIT. FRAN. ET. HIB.   *a* AR   160   290
REX. ET. REGINA. *Rev.* Fame stands blowing her trumpet and holding an olive-branch.
QVANTVM. SAT. ERIT. HIS. DICERE. DIGNVM. ANNO. 1662. *D.* 53 mm. By G. Bower. *MI i*,   *b* AR   60   110
480/90. See **Plate 7**

Type *a* is struck, the reverse from more than one die. Type *b* is cast.

224 ——

Obv. Bust r., laureate, armoured and draped. CAROLVS. II. DEI. G. MAG. BRI. FRAN. ET. HIB.   AV   700   1400
REX   *Rev.* Bust r., hair decorated with pearls, and draped. CATHARINA. D.G. MAG. BRI. FRAN.   AR   120   280
ET. HIBER. REGINA. *D.* 43 mm. [By J. Roettiers] *MI i.* 489/111; *Farquhar* 1908/255; *v. Loon
II*, 471

Another reverse occurs with a standing figure of St. Catherine.

225 ——

Obv. Bust of the King, l., crowned and draped, dividing the letters C R crowned. PACE.   AR   45   80
TRIVMPHANS. *Rev.* Bust of the Queen, l., crowned and draped; before her a crown. FVTVRI.
SPES. *D.* 28 mm. by 36 mm. Oval. (By?) *Mi i*, 483/96; *Farquhar* 1905/278

This medal consists of two repoussé plates joined at the edge; it sometimes occurs with a suspension loop. A number of
similar badges commemorate the marriage.

226 ——

Obv. Busts r., conjoined, Catherine draped. CAROLVS. II. ET. CATHARINA. D.G. MAG. BRIT. FR.   AR   40   70
ET. HIB. REX. ET. REGINA   *Rev.* Venus, cupid behind her, seated beside Jupiter upon clouds.
MAIESTAS ET AMOR. *D.* 27 mm. By G. Bower. *MI i*, 481/91–2

The reverse was struck from more than one die.

			£	£

227   **Earl of Southampton 1664**
Obv. Bust l., of Southampton, wearing a cap and draped. *Rev.* THOMAS. COMES   *a AV*   —   —
SOVTHAMPTONIÆ SVMMVS. ANGLIÆ THESAVRARIVS &. MDCLXIIII   *D.* 43 mm. Cast. By T. [and   *AR*   400   —
A.] Simon. *MI i*, 502/137; *Hill/Pollard pl.* 30, 4

Type *b* is an eighteenth century copy; *see* No. 148. Thomas Wriothesley, 4th Earl of Southampton (1607–67), adviser to   *b AR*   30   50
Charles I during the Civil War; Lord High Treasurer.

228   **Naval Victory against Holland 1665**
Obv. Bust r., armoured and draped. IACOBVS. DVX. EBOR. ET. ALBAN. DOM. MAGN.   *AR*   400   850
ADMIRALLVS. ANGLIÆ. & C. *Rev.* View of a naval engagement. NEC MINOR IN TERRIS   *Ex.* 3.
IVNII. 1665   *D.* 77 mm. By J. Roettiers, *MI i*, 504/142; *MH* 1919, 55; *v. Loon II*, 505

James, Duke of York, was commander-in-chief at this battle. Twenty-four Dutch ships were captured or destroyed off the
Lowestoft coast and 3,000 prisoners taken.

229   ———
Obv. Bust r., armoured and draped. IACOBVS. DVX. EBOR. ET. ALBAN. FRATER. AVGVSTISS.   *AR*   300   550
CAROLI. II. REGIS. *Rev.* Classical trophy of arms; naval engagement beyond. GENVS.
ANTIQVVM. *D.* 63 mm. By J. Roettiers. *MI i*, 505/143; *MH* 1919, 56; *v. Loon II*, 505

This medal and Nos. 230–1 may have served as naval rewards for officers and captains.

230*   ———
Obv. Bust r., laureate and draped. * CAROLVS. SECVNDVS. D.G. MAG. BRI. FRAN. ET. HIB.   *AV*   2200   4000
REX   *Rev.* The King, as a Roman general, stands viewing a naval engagement from the sea-   *AR*   300   500
shore. .PRO. TALIVBS. AVSIS. *D.* 62 mm. [By J. Roettiers]. *MI i*, 503/139; *MH* 1919. 52;   *WM*   25   45
v. Loon II, 504. *See* **Plate 8**

See No. 229.

231   ———
Obv. Bust r., laureate. * CAROLVS. SECVNDVS. DEI. GRATIA. MAG. BRI. FRAN. ET. HIB. REX. *Rev.*   *AR*   250   450
Similar to No. 230. *D.* 56 mm. [By J. Roettiers] *MI i*, 504/141; *MH* 1919, 54

See No. 229. This medal was also struck from another obverse die, with the bust laureate and draped.

232*   **Dominion of the Sea 1665**
Obv. Bust r., laureate and draped. CAROLVS. II. D.G. M. BR. FR. ET. HIB. REX   *Rev.* The King,   *AV*   —   —
crowned and royally robed, is drawn across the sea in a marine car. ET. PONTVS. SERVIET   *AR*   300   550
1665   *D.* 27 mm. By T. Simon. *MI i*, 506/145; *MH* 1919, 59; *v. Loon II*, 507. *See* **Plate 8**
Some examples exhibit die flaws on the reverse.

233*   **Naval Action against Holland 1665**
Obv. Naval engagement within a harbour. *Rev.* OP DE ROOF ZUGT VAN CAREL DE TWEEDE   *AR*   250   400
VOORGEVALLEN DEN 10 AUGUSTI 1665 VOOR BERGEN IN NOORWEEGEN DUS WORT BRITTANJES
TROTZ GESTUŸT, DIE ZELFS BŸ VRIENDT VAERT OP VRŸBUŸT; EN TERGT DE NOORTSCHE WALLEN.
HŸ SCHAEKT VORST FREDRICKS HAVEN RECHT DOG KRŸGT SŸN LOON, DOOR BOEG EN PLECHT VAN
NEERLANDTS DONDERBALLEN. Branches of laurel, below. *D.* 54 mm. By J. Pool. *MI i*,
508/149; *MH* 1921, 557; *v. Loon II*, 509. *See* **Plate 8**

The English squadrons attacked the Dutch East India fleet which sought refuge in the harbour at Bergen. The reverse was
struck from another two similar dies.

234   **The Royall Oake** *c.*1665
Obv. Bust of the King, r., upon an oak tree, its three branches each threaded with a crown;   *AE*   15   25
above, sun piercing clouds. THE ROYALL OAKE   *Rev.* Royal arms within the Garter; above,
crest dividing letters C R crowned. *D.* 28 mm. By L. G. Lauffer. *MI i*, 493/119
See No. 78.

235   **George, Lord Berkeley 1666**
Obv. Bust r., armoured and draped. GEORGE. DE. BERKELEY. PAIR. D'ANGLETERRE. 1666   *Rev.*   *AR*   400   —
Armorial shield, crowned, with supporters upon a tree; below, a crown, inscribed CIMBRIA,   *AE*   150   —
round its trunk. VIRTVTE. NON. VI. REGIBVS. ATAVIS   *D.* 51 mm. By J. B. Dufour. *MI i*,
513/156

George Berkeley, 1st Earl of Berkeley (1628–98), royal emissary.

236   **Proposed Commercial Treaty with Spain 1666**
Obv. As No. 231. *Rev.* Statue of Charles II, as a Roman general; beyond, sea crowded with   *AV*   1400   2600
shipping. REDEANT. COMMERCIA. FLANDRIS   *Ex.* 1666   *D.* 56 mm. [By J. Roettiers] *MI i*,   *AR*   300   500
517/162   *AE*   55   90

Also struck from another obverse die, bust laureate and draped.

237   **Naval Action against Holland 1666**
Obv. Bust three-quarters r., draped; ribbon across his breast, inscribed M.A.D. RUYTER LUYT   *AR*   400   700
ADMIRAAL. GEÑ. (incuse); a naval crown above his head, supported by a Triton and Nereid.

PLATE 7

213 ($\times \frac{2}{3}$)

215

218

219

221

222 ($\times \frac{2}{3}$)

223

PLATE 8

				£	£

DE RUYTER DIE DEN BRIT SYN MOET GETEUGELT HEEFT, ALDUS DOOR MULLERS HANT, INT GOUT EN SILVER LEEFT. A°. MDCLXVI DEN XIIII IUNY. (incuse). *Rev.* Naval engagement, ship sinking in foreground. HIER STRYCKT HET BRITSCH GEWELT VOOR NEDERLANT DE VLAGH. DE ZEE HEEFT NOIT GEWAEGHT VAN ZULK EEN ZWAEREN SLAGH. (incuse). *D.* 79 mm. [By O. Müller] *MI i*, 522/168; *MH* 1921, 567; *v. Loon II*, 527

This medal consists of two repoussé plates joined at the edge by a broad rim. Michael Adriaanszoon de Ruyter (1607–76), Dutch admiral and naval hero. Both sides had claimed victory at this action in the North Sea Downs. A similar medal by Müller, with the same reverse, commemorates the death of Admiral Cornelius Evertsen at this battle.

238 ——

Obv. Bust three-quarters r., draped; ribbon across his breast, inscribed CORNELIS TROMP LUYT. ADMIRAAL. V. HOLL. (incuse); a wreath above his head supported by two Tritons. SOO BEELDT MEN TROMP HIER AF. DES AMSTELS ADMIRAAL. HY STEECKT DE ZEE IN BRANDT, GELYCK EEN BLIXEMSTRAAL. A°. 1666. *Rev.* Similar to No. 237. *D.* 79 mm. [By O. Müller] *MI i*, 524/172; *MH* 1921, 577; *v. Loon II*, 529   AR   300   550

This medal consists of two repoussé plates joined at the edge by a broad rim. Cornelis Tromp (1629–91), Dutch admiral; son of Martin.

239 ——

Obv. Bust of de Ruyter almost facing, armoured and draped. MICHAEL DE RVITER PROVINCIARVM CONFOEDERAT: BELGIC: ARCHITHALASSVS DVX ET EQVES. *Rev.* Naval engagement; burning ship in foreground. *Ex.* PVGNANDO   *D.* 68 mm. By C. Adolfszoon. *MI i*, 522/169; *MH* 1921, 568; *v. Loon III*, 176   AV / AR / WM   1000 1800 / 200 350 / 30 55

From c.1830 a medal was struck from dies based almost exactly on this medal, but with a diameter of 72 mm.

240 Peace with Holland 1667

Obv. Holland, facing, tramples upon Discord; at her feet repose lion and lamb. Beyond, burning ships in a harbour. MITIS ET FORTIS   *Ex.* PROCVL. HINC. MALA. BESTIA. REGNIS! IVN: 22. 1667. *Rev.* Peace, holding sheathed sword and cornucopia, tramples upon arms; beyond, fleet of ships. Above, a celestial hand displays shields of Britain and Holland over a ribbon inscribed IRATO BELLUM PLACATO NUMINE PAX EST   *Ex.* REDIIT. CONCORDIA. MATER. BREDÆ. IUL. 31. A°. 1667. *Edge.* NUMISMA. POSTERITATI. SACRUM. BELGA. BRITANNOQUE. RECONCILIATIS. CUM. PRIVIL: ORDIN: HOLLAND: ET. WEST: *D.* 71 mm. By C. Adolfszoon. *MI i*, 528/176; *MH* 1921, 585; *v. Loon II*, 534   AV / AR   1500 2800 / 300 550

More than ten medals record the peace concluded at Breda.

241 ——

Obv. As No. 231. *Rev.* Britannia seated on the sea-shore, l., reviews her fleet; above, sun piercing clouds. FAVENTE DEO   *Ex.* BRITANNIA   *Edge.* CAROLVS * SECVNDVS * PACIS * ET * IMPERII * RESTITUTOR * AVGVSTVS. *D.* 56 mm. [By J. Roettiers] *MI i*, 535/186; *MH* 1919, 65; *v. Loon II*, 522   AV / AR   1400 2500 / 120 280

Also struck from another obverse die, bust laureate and draped.

242 ——

Obv. An English and a Dutch ship sail peacefully side by side. *Rev.* Shields of Britain and Holland upon a festoon of fruit, crowned by an olive wreath. Below, BRITAN: BATAV: PAX (on ribbon) 1667 *D.* 45 mm. By C. Adolfszoon. *MI i*, 534/184; *MH* 1919, 63; *v. Loon II*, 538   AV / AR   800 1500 / 140 250

243 Charles II and Catherine *c.*1667

Obv. Bust r., draped. CAROLVS. II. REX   *Rev.* Bust r., wearing a tiara and draped. CATHERINA REGINA   *D.* 28 mm. By P. Roettiers. *MI i*, 540/192   AR   70 120

Possibly struck to celebrate the stability after Breda. *See also* No. 244.

244 Charles II *c.*1667

Obv. Bust r. CAROLO SECVNDO. *Rev.* Sleeping lion, l. QVIESCIT. *Ex.* BRITAN. *D.* 28 mm. By P. Roettiers. *MI i*, 541/193   AR   70 120

Another reverse has a rose-bush. *See* No. 243.

245* British Colonization 1670

Obv. Busts r., conjoined, he armoured and draped. CAROLVS. ET. CATHARINA. REX. ET. REGINA   *Rev.* A terrestrial globe. DIFFVSVS. IN. ORBE. BRITANNVS. 1670. *D.* 42 mm. [By J. Roettiers] *MI i*, 546/203; *Betts* 44. *See* **Plate 8**   AV / AR   1200 2000 / 170 320

246* John George II, Knight of the Garter 1671

Obv. St. George and the Dragon. EN HONNEUR DU SOUVERAIN DU TRES NOBLE ORDRE DE LA IARTIERE   *Rev.* DU TRÉ HAUT TRÉ PUISSANT ET TRES EXCELLENT PRINCE CHARLES. II. PAR LA GRACE DE DIEU ROY DE LA GRANDE BRETAG: FRAN: ET IRLANDE DEFENSEUR DE LA FOY. M.D.C.LXXI., within a wreath. *D.* 48 mm. German (By?) *MI i*, 548/205. *See* **Plate 8**   AV / AR   800 1300 / 100 180

John George II (1613–80), Elector of Saxony. A similar piece, dated 1678, commemorates a festival held in Dresden in honour of the Order.

                                                                   £   £

247   **Charles XI, Knight of the Garter 1671**
Obv. St. George and the Dragon. CAROLVS. XI. REX. SVE. EQ. NOB. ORD. PERISC. INAVG   *Ex.* 29.   *AV*   800   1300
MAII. 1671. *Rev.* Star of the Order in centre; around is the Garter, decorated with two crowns   *AR*   100   180
and two pairs of interlinked c's, and the Collar of the Order. CONCORDIA. REGVM. SALVS.
POPVLORVM. *D.* 45 mm. [By J. Roettiers] *MI i*, 549/206.
<small>Charles XI (1655–97), King of Sweden 1660–97; installed with the Order in 1671. The investment took place in 1669 and is commemorated on three uniform Swedish medals by Arfvid Karlsteen.</small>

248   **Duke of Lauderdale 1672**
Obv. Bust of Maitland, r., armoured and draped. *Rev.* Minerva seated, r., beside a Scottish   *AR*   270   500
armorial shield within the Garter, supports a ducal crest in her left hand. CONSILIO. ET.
ANIMIS. *Ex.* 1672   *D.* 62 mm. By J. Roettiers. *MI i*, 550/208; *CP* 100/10
<small>John Maitland, 1st Duke of Lauderdale (1616–82), Scottish statesman; English Cabal minister (*see* No. 260). Raised to the Dukedom and made Knight of the Garter in 1672.</small>

249   **Charles II: Liberty of Conscience 1672**
Obv. Bust r., armoured and draped. OPTIMO. PRINCIPI. CAROLO. II. D.G. M. BRIT. FRAN. ET.   *AR*   250   450
HIB. REGI   *Rev.* Female figure of LIBERTAS seated, facing, holding a book inscribed FIDES,
and sword and cornucopia. FIDEI. DEFENSORI. RELIGIONIS. REFORMATÆ. PROTECTORI   *D.*
59 mm. By P. Roettiers. *MI i*, 553/214; *Forrer* V/188
<small>Some examples have a lettered edge: ARCHITECTVRÆ NAVALIS ET MONETÆ INSTAVTORI.</small>

250*   **Duchess of Portsmouth 1673**
Obv. Bust r., draped. LVCIA. DVCISSA. PORTSMOVTHENSIS. *Rev.* Cupid seated upon a globe.   *AR*   140   220
OMNIA VINCIT   *D.* 28 mm. [By G. Bower] *MI i*, 554/215; *Forrer* I/258. See **Plate 8**   *AE*   50   90
<small>Louise Renée de Querouaille (1649–1734), the King's mistress; created Duchess in 1673.</small>

251   **Christ's Hospital 1673**
Obv. Bust r., armoured and draped. CAROLVS. SECVNDVS. D.G. MAG. BRI. FRAN. ET. HIB.   *AR*   350   680
REX   *Rev.* Standing figure of Arithmetic, together with those of Geometry and Astronomy,   *WM*   28   60
encourages a Bluecoat boy to whom she displays an inscribed tablet; beyond, fleet under sail
assisted by Zephyrs. INSTITVTOR AVGVSTVS. 1673   *D.* 72 mm. [By J. Roettiers] *MI i*,
556/217; *Farquhar* 1908/257
<small>Commemorating the foundation of a Mathematical and Nautical School; two medals by J. Roettiers (obverses as No. 231) illustrate, diagrammatically, recent ideas in military engineering and may have served as prizes at the school.</small>

252*   **Christ's Hospital, School Badge 1673**
Obv. A scene similar to the reverse of No. 251. AVSPICIO CAROL SECVNDI. REGIS. 1673. Without   *AR*   65   100
reverse. *D.* 81 mm. [After J. Roettiers] *MI i*, 557/218; *Grimshaw* 1. See **Plate 8**
<small>Consisting of a thin plate with a broad border, sometimes pierced to facilitate sewing onto a pupil's dress.</small>

253   **Peace with Holland Concluded in London 1674**
Obv. Equestrian figure, l., of William III of Orange; beyond, troops storming a town.   *AV*   1200   2200
Above, an orange branch interlaced with a ribbon, inscribed VIRES ULTRA SORTEMQUE   *AR*   270   500
IUVENTÆ   *Rev.* Dove, an olive-branch in its beak, flying over a tranquil sea. A DoMIno
VeNIt paX et VICtorIa LÆta. (chronogrammatic date). *D.* 61 mm. Dutch (by C.
Adolfszoon?) *MI i*, 561/225; *v. Loon III*, 131

254   **John Milton, Memorial 1674**
Obv. Bust three-quarters r., draped. IOANNES MILTON   *Rev.* Adam and Eve beneath a tree   *AR*   45   80
with serpents; demons entering Paradise and wolves devouring sheep. DIRA DULCE CANIT   *AE*   7   15
ALTER HOMERUS   *D.* 42 mm. By J. Dassier. *MI i*, 564/229; *Brettauer* 4665
<small>Struck c.1740; John Milton (1608–74), poet.</small>

255   **Countess of Dorset, Memorial 1676**
Obv. Bust three-quarters l., veiled and draped. ANN: COVNT: OF: DORSETT: PEMB: & MOVNTG   *a AR*   150   250
& C. *Rev.* Figure of Faith, standing, r. SOLE. DAVGHTER. & HEIRE. TO GEORGE. EARLE. OF.
CVMBERLAND. *D.* 42 mm. Cast. (By?) *MI i*, 567/233   *b AR*   35   60
<small>Type *b* is an eighteenth century copy. Anne Clifford, Countess of Dorset, Pembroke and Montgomery (1590–1676), benefactress; erected almshouses.</small>

256*   **Marriage of Mary and William III of Orange 1677**
Obv. Bust r., armoured and draped. GVILH. III. D.G. PRIN. AVR. HOL. ET. WES. GV. *Rev.* Bust l.,   *AR*   90   160
hair braided with pearls, and draped. MARIA. D.G. AVR. PRIN. NAT. DE. IORC. *D.* 41 mm. [By N.
Chevalier] *MI i*, 568/235; *Farquhar* 1910/208; *v. Loon III*, 222. See **Plate 8**
<small>Struck from at least two pairs of dies. Mary II (1662–94), elder daughter of James (II), Duke of York and Anne Hyde.</small>

257*   **Murder of Sir Edmundbury Godfrey 1678**
Obv. Bust r., draped, being strangled with his own cravat by two hands. MORIENDO.   *a AR*   65   110
RESTITVIT. REM. E. GODFREY   *Rev.* A prostrate figure being strangled by a man leaning over

		VF	EF

him; the scene blessed by a papal figure holding a BVLLO (decree). TANTVM. RELLIGIO. POTVIT. *Edge.* CERVICE. FRACTA. FIDEM. SVSTVLIT. ATLAS. XNS. 1678. *D.* 39 mm. [By G. Bower] *MI i*, 577/247. *See* **Plate 9** — *b AR* — 35 — 65

Struck from two obverse dies. Type *b* is a copy signed by J. Milton, struck *c.*1790. Sir Edmundbury [or Edmund Berry] Godfrey (1621–78), Justice of the Peace for Westminster; heard the deposition of Titus Oates (*see* No. 260) and was considered active in counteracting the schemes of the papal Party. He was found dead under mysterious circumstances; the Catholics were credited with his murder.

258* ——
Obv. As No. 257. *Rev.* A man advancing on foot, l., precedes a man riding a horse who supports a body, seated before him, around the waist; a moonlit landscape and a hill, beyond. EQVO. CREDITE. TVCRI. *Edge.* As No. 257. *D.* 39 mm. [By G. Bower] *MI i*, 577/248; *Storer* 1243. *See* **Plate 9** — *AR* — 80 — 150

See No. 257. Struck from more than one pair of dies.

259 ——
Obv. Similar to No. 257. *Rev.* Heads of the Pope and Devil joined to form one face. ECCLESIA. PERVERSA. TENET. FACIEM. DIABOLI. *Edge.* As No. 257. *D.* 38 mm. [By G. Bower] *MI i*, 578/250 — *AR* — 60 — 100

See No. 257.

260 The Popish Plot 1678
Obv. A janiformed head, composed of a Jesuit wearing a beretta, r., and a monk, l., wearing a cowl. O. WHY. SO. FICKLE. *Rev.* Cluster of seven faces. BIRDS. OF. A. FEATHER. FLOCK. TOGETHER *D.* 36 mm. [By G. Bower] *MI i*, 579/252 — *a AR* / *WM* — 80 / 20 — 130 / 35

Type *b* is cast. Titus Oates (1649–1705), fabricator of the Popish plot against the Roman Catholics. He alleged that they had conspired to massacre Protestants, burn London and assassinate the King. In consequence of these allegations, to which he swore before Sir Edmund Berry Godfrey, a number of Catholics were tried and executed; *see* No. 257. The faces on the reverse may be those of Lord Clifford, Lord Ashley, Duke of Buckingham, Lord Arlington, and the Duke of Lauderdale; all members of the King's cabinet, sometimes referred to as the Cabal, an acronym of their names. — *b AR* / *AE* — 40 / 18 — 70 / 35

261 Earl of Shaftesbury, Acquittal of High Treason 1681
Obv. Bust r., draped. .ANTONIO COMITI DE SHAFTESBVRY. *Rev.* View of London and the Tower seen from the south bank of the Thames; above, sun piercing clouds. .LÆTAMVR. *Ex.* 24 NOV 1681. *D.* 40 mm. By G. Bower. *MI i*, 583/259 — *AR* — 70 — 130

Anthony Ashley Cooper, 1st Earl of Shaftesbury (1621–83), Lord Chancellor. Supported claims of Monmouth; committed for treason but released on the date specified.

262* Moroccan and Bantamese Ambassadors in England 1682
Obv. Bust of the Moroccan ambassador, r., wearing a turban, and draped. HAMET BEN HAMET BEN HADDV OTTOR. 1682 *Rev.* Bust of the Bantamese ambassador, three-quarters r., in oriental head-dress, and draped. KEAY NABEE NAIA-WI-PRAIA. 1682 *D.* 40 mm. By G. Bower. *MI i*, 584/260. *See* **Plate 9** — *a AR* / *b AR* / *AE* — 220 / 45 / 20 — 380 / 75 / 35

Type *b* is cast.

263* Duke of Ormonde 1682
Obv. Bust r., armoured and draped. .IACOBVS. DVX. ORMONIÆ. *Rev.* Sword and olive-branch, crossed, within a ducal coronet. PRÆSIDIVM ET DVLCE DECVS. 1682 *D.* 50 mm. By G. Bower. *MI i*, 585/262. *See* **Plate 9** — *AR* — 300 — 500

James Butler, 1st Duke of Ormonde (1610–88), soldier and statesman; Lord Lieutenant of Ireland.

264 Duke of York, Shipwrecked off the Yorkshire Coast 1682
Obv. Bust r., draped. IACOBUS. DUX. EBORACENSIS. ET. ALBANENSIS. *Rev.* Ship, off a rocky coast, from which departs a rowing boat. .IMPAVIDVM. FERIUNT. *D.* 42 mm. By G. Bower. *MI i*, 586/263; *MH* 1919, 68; *Farquhar* 1909/268 — *AR* — 200 — 350

James was on his way to Scotland to fetch the Duchess of York when his frigate, the *Gloucester*, ran onto a sandbank.

265 The Rye House Plot 1683
Obv. The King in a landscape, reposing as Hercules on lion's skin, wards off a hydra (with heads of the Duke of Monmouth, Lord William Russell, John Hampden, Algernon Sidney, Lord Howard, Earl of Essex and the Devil). Hand issuing from heaven brandishes thunder. PERIBVNT FVLMINIS ICTV. 1683 *Rev.* Shepherd, seated upon a mound, watches over his flock in a vale where two wolves are hanging on a gibbet; above, dove with olive-branch. DEVS NOBIS HÆC OTIA FECIT *D.* 46 mm. By G. Bower. *MI i*, 593/274 — *a AR* / *b AE* — 300 / 30 — 500 / 55

Supposedly a conspiracy to secure the succession of the Duke of Monmouth in place of James II through the assassination of the King and his brother. Lord William Russell and Algernon Sidney, said to be the chief conspirators, were illegally convicted and executed. Rye House was situated near Hoddesdon in Hertfordshire. Type *b* is cast.

266 Marriage of Princess Anne and George of Denmark 1683
Obv. Busts of George, armoured, and Anne, draped, face to face. GEORGIVS CIMBRORVM PRINCEPS ET ANNA IACOBI DVCIS EBORACENSIS FILIA *Rev.* Acorns lying beneath a flourishing — *AR* — 130 — 220

oak tree. FACTVRA NEPOTIBVS VMBRAM   *D.* 37 mm. By G. Bower. *MI i*, 593/275; *Farquhar*   £   £
1913/253
<small>Princess Anne (1665–1714), daughter of James II and Anne Hyde; Prince George of Denmark (1653–1708).</small>

267	**Charles II** *c.*1683	AV	1400	2600
	Obv. Bust r., armoured and draped. CAROL. II. D.G. ANGL. SCOT. FRAN. ET. HIB. REX. *Rev.*	AR	220	420
	Royal arms within the Garter, supporters and crest. *Ex.* Motto on ribbon DIEV. ET. MON.	AE	50	90
	DROIT. *D.* 53 mm. By J. Roettiers. *MI i*, 595/277; *Payne* 221			

<small>The portrait on this medal seems to date from the latter part of the reign. Although its precise purpose is unclear, the reverse does suggest the function of an award, possibly for loyalty or service to the Crown. Examples in silver are most common and a number of these have been noted with suspension loops.</small>

268	**Calendar Medal 1684**	AR	60	—
	Obv. Table of days and dates, with months of the year. A PERPETUAL ALMANACK OF	AE	30	—
	EXCELLENT & READY USE *Rev.* Two circular bands containing days and dates; 1684, above.			
	D. 27 mm. By W. Foster.			

<small>An example of an early struck English calendar or almanack medal. Most were made during the eighteenth and nineteenth centuries by Birmingham manufacturers, in brass, copper or white metal, and are generally between 37 and 45 mm. in diameter. Signed pieces have been noted of the following: J. Powell, 1750; J. Sheppard, 1775; J. Davies, 1793; C. Twigg, 1794; P. Kempson, 1798; Kempson & Kindon, 1804; T. W. Ingram, 1827; T. Halliday, 1828. *See* R. N. P. Hawkins, 'Dates of English Calendar Medals Bearing Makers' Signatures', *SCMB* 1986, 172–3.</small>

269	**Death of Charles II 1685**	AR	300	550
	Obv. Bust r., wearing a lion's scalp. CAROLUS II. D.G. MAG : BRI : FRAN : ET HIB : REX. *Rev.* Sun	WM	20	45
	setting over a calm sea. OMNIA ORTA OCCIDUNT. *Ex.* MDCLXXXV. *D.* 49 mm. (By J. Smeltzing?)			
	MI i, 601/288; *v. Loon III*, 301			
270	——	AR	90	150
	Obv. Seated figure of Time, r. ALL. HEADS. MVST. COME TO. THE. COLD. TOMB. *Rev.* KING:	AE	35	65
	CHARLES: THE: SECOND: ÆTAT 55: OBIJT: FEBRV: 6 ANNO: DOM. 1684 *D.* 39 mm. [By J. or N.			
	Roettiers?] *MI i*, 601/289–90; *v. Loon III*, 301			

<small>Dated in the old style. The obverse struck from two dies differing only in the arrangement of the inscription.</small>

271	**Charles II, Memorial 1685**	AR	27	55
	Obv. Bust r., laureate, armoured and draped. CAROLUS. II. D.G. M. BR. FR. ET. HIB. REX. *Rev.*	AE	4	9
	Mercury seated upon a tomb, which he inscribes NAT. 29. MAI 1630. C. 23 APR. 1661. M. 16.			
	FEBR. 1685. *D.* 41 mm. By J. Dassier. *MI i*, 602/291			

<small>Struck in 1731, from Dassier's series of English kings and queens. *See* No. 526.</small>

JAMES II, 1685–8

272	**Accession of James II 1685**	AR	25	35
	Obv. Bust almost facing, armoured and draped. IACOBVS. II. D.G. ANG: REX *Rev.* Burning			
	lamp upon an altar. TVEBITVR OMNES *D.* 17 mm. By [C. Wermuth] *MI i*, 604/4			
273	**Coronation of James II 1685**	AV	750	1400
	Obv. Bust r., laureate, armoured and draped. IACOBVS. II. D.G. ANG. SCO. FR. ET. HI. REX *Rev.*	AR	60	120
	Laurel wreath upon a cushion; above, a crown held by a hand issuing from heaven. A.	AE	35	65
	MILITARI. AD. REGIAM. *Ex.* INAVGVRAT. 23. AP. 1685 *D.* 34 mm. By J. Roettiers. *MI i*,			
	605/5–6; *v. Loon III*, 303; *Wollaston* 6–7			

<small>Struck from more than one pair of dies; the obverse is sometimes found coupled with that of No. 274.</small>

274	**Coronation of Mary 1685**	AV	850	1600
	Obv. Bust r., laureate and draped. MARIA. D.G. ANG. SCO. FR. ET. HI. REGINA. *Rev.* The Queen	AR	60	140
	seated, r., upon a mound. O. DEA. CERTE *D.* 34 mm. By J. Roettiers. *MI i*, 606/7; *Wollaston*			
	8			

<small>Struck from more than one pair of dies. *See* No. 273. Mary (of Modena) Beatrice (1658–1718), daughter of Alphonso IV, Duke of Modena; married James (II) in 1673.</small>

275*	**Scottish Parliament Opened 1685**	AR	270	500
	Obv. Bust r., laureate, IACOBUS II. D.G. MAG : BRI : FRAN : ET HIB : REX. *Rev.* Lion couchant,	AE	70	130
	crowned, his paws upon sceptre and globe. NEMO ME IMPUNE LACESSET. *Ex.* MDCLXXXV. *D.*	WM	20	45
	49 mm. By J. Smeltzing. *MI i*, 607/10; *CP* 22/1; *v. Loon III*, 303. See **Plate 9**			
276	**Duke of Monmouth Defeated 1685**	AR	250	450
	Obv. Bust of Monmouth r., armoured and draped. *Rev.* Monmouth fails to scale an island	WM	30	55
	rock and seize the three crowns on the summit. SVPERI RISERE. IVLY. 6°. 1685. *D.* 50 mm. By			
	G. Bower. *MI i*, 613/23; *CP* 46/5; *v. Loon III*, 306			

<small>James Edward Scott, Duke of Monmouth and Buccleuch (1649–85), natural son of Charles II and Lucy Walters; claimed legitimate right to the crown in place of James II and was defeated at the Battle of Sedgemoor.</small>

PLATE 9

257

258

262

263

275

280

285

PLATE 10

286

287

290 (× ⅔)

293

295

298

300

299

277 ——

  Obv. Bust r., armoured. IACOBUS DUX MONUMET: FID: ET LIBERT: DEFENSOR. *Rev.* A Roman *AR* 250 450
soldier attempts to prize open a lion's mouth. PARUM SUCCESSIT, FECI SEDULO. *Ex.* MDCLXXXV. *WM* 30 55
D. 49 mm. (By J. Smeltzing?) *MI i*, 613/22; *CP* 46/3; *v. Loon III*, 307
See No. 276.

278 ——

  Obv. Bust r., armoured and draped. IACOBVS. DVX. MONMOVTH. *Rev.* Monmouth fails to seize *AR* 220 400
three crowns upon a column amidst military trophies. .PROVIDENTIA. *Ex.* IMPROVIDENTIA. *AE* 45 —
D. 43 mm. [By B. Meier] *MI i*, 614/24; *CP* 47/6
Also struck from a die which is signed; *see* C. Eimer, 'James Duke of Monmouth, Battle of Sedgemoor', *SCMB*, May 1985.
Bronze examples are usually cast. *See* No. 276.

279 **Duke of Monmouth Beheaded 1685**

  Obv. Bust r., armoured and draped. IACOBVS. DVX. MONVMETHENSIS. *Rev.* Cypher of J E D M, *AR* 250 450
surrounded by clouds, over which two infant genii support a ducal coronet. .CAPVT. INTER
NVBILA. D. 49 mm. By G. Bower. *MI i*, 614/25; *CP* 46/4; *v. Loon III*, 307
See No. 276.

280* ——

  Obv. Bust r. IACOBUS INFELIX DUX MONUMETHENSIS. *Rev.* Monmouth's head on the ground *AR* 120 220
spouting blood. HUNC SANGUINEM LIBO DEO LIBERATORI. *Ex.* CÆSA CERVIS. LOÑ: IULŸ $\frac{15}{25}$ 1685. *WM* 20 40
D. 38 mm. [By J. Smeltzing] *MI i*, 615/26; *CP* 45/2; *v. Loon III*, 307. *See* **Plate 9**
See No. 276.

281 **Dukes of Monmouth and Argyle Beheaded 1685**

  Obv. Bust of James II, l., laureate and dressed as a Roman general, resting on four sceptres *AR* 220 420
upon a pedestal dated 1685 and displaying the Royal shield within the Garter, crowned; a
ribbon across the base, inscribed ARAS ET SCEPTRA TUEMUR. In the distance, Neptune driving
marine car across the sea. IACOBVS II D.G. MAG. BRI. FRAN. ET. HIB. REX. *Rev.* A pedestal
inscribed AMBITIO MALESUADA RUIT, upon which Justice stands; on either side is a block with
the severed heads of IACOBUS DE MONTMOUT, l., and ARGHIBALD D'ARGYL, r,. At the feet of
Justice lie their decapitated bodies. In the distance: troops fleeing, l.; two heads upon the
gates of the Tower, r. D. 61 mm. By R. Arondeaux. *MI i*, 615/27; *CP* 45/1; *v. Loon III*, 307
Archibald Campbell, 9th Earl of Argyll (?–1685), joined Monmouth's expedition and fought at the battle of Sedgemoor.
See No. 276.

282 **James II 1685**

  Obv. Bust r., draped. IACOBVS. II. DEI. GRA. ANG. SCOT. FRAN. ET. HIB. REX. *Rev.* As No. 229. *AV* 1800 3500
D. 63 mm. By J. Roettiers. *MI i*, 617/29; *MH* 1919, 70   *AR* 350 650
This medal may have served as a military or naval reward. Another obverse has a bust with short hair and lettering on a
raised border.

283 **James II c.1685**

  Obv. Bust r., laureate, armoured and draped. IACOBVS. II. D G. MAG. BRI. FRAN. ET. HIB. REX. *AR* 28 45
Rev. Britannia seated, l., holding spear and shield. ИVLLVM ИVMEИ ABEST D. 29 mm. By G. *AE* 15 30
Bower. *MI i*, 607/11; *Farquhar* 1909/250

284 **James II and Mary c.1685**

  Obv. As No. 283. *Rev.* Bust r., laureate and draped. .MARIA. D.G. MAG. BRI. FRИ. ET. HIB. *AR* 28 45
REGINA D. 29 mm. By G. Bower. *MI i*, 608/12   *AE* 15 30

285* **Spanish Wreck Recovered 1687**

  Obv. Busts r., conjoined, Mary draped, and James II laureate, armoured and draped. *AV* 1600 3000
IACOBVS. II. ET. MARIA. D.G. MAG. BRI. FRAN. ET. HIB. REX. ET. REGINA. *Rev.* Ship in an open sea *AR* 220 400
from which men in rowing boats search for treasure from a wreck. SEMPER TIBI PENDEAT
HAMUS. *Ex.* NAVFRAGA REPERTA 1687 D. 54 mm. By G. Bower. *MI i*, 619/33; *MH* 1919, 71;
Betts 67. *See* **Plate 9**
Struck from more than one pair of dies, and on flans of varying diameter. The expedition to recover treasure off the West
Indies was the second attempt by Captain William Phipps (1651–95), latterly Governor of Massachusetts (*see* No. 286). A
copy was made in 1971, signed DP below busts, hallmarked on the edge and 54. 25 mm. in diameter.

286* **Duke of Albemarle 1687**

  Obv. Bust r., armoured and draped. CHRISTOPHORVS. ALBEMARLIÆ. DVX. IAMAICÆ. LOC. TEN. *AR* 450 800
GEN. &. GVB. GEN *Rev.* Neptune reclining, l., upon the sea-shore. .EX. AQUA. OMNIA. D.
46 mm. By G. Bower. *MI i*, 620/34; *MH* 1919, 73; *Betts* 66. *See* **Plate 10**
Christopher Monk, 2nd Duke of Albemarle (1653–88), Governor of Jamaica; helped to finance Phipps' expedition to
recover Spanish treasure. *See* No. 285.

			VF	EF
			£	£

287*   **Seven Bishops Imprisoned 1688**

Obv. The White Tower of London, flying the Royal Standard: column approaching under guard, l.; surge of people, r. PROBIS HONORI INFAMIÆQUE MALIS. *Ex.* ARCHIEPISC: CANTAUAR: EPISCOPI. Sᵗ ASAPH, BATH ET WELS, ELY, PETERᴮ CHICHEST. BRIST. INCARCER: ⁸⁄₁₈ LIBERATI ¹⁵⁄₂₅ IUNII, 1688. *Rev.* Sun and moon equally balanced in scales suspended from clouds. SIC SOL LUNAQUE IN LIBRA   *D.* 59 mm. (By J. Smeltzing?) *MI i*, 621/36; *v. Loon III*, 340. *See* **Plate 10**

     AV   1400   2500
     AR   170   300
     WM   25   45

The Bishops were committed to the Tower for opposing the edicts of James II. *See* Nos. 288–9. The obverse composition is similar to the reverse of No. 153.

288   **Archbishop Sancroft and the Bishops 1688**

Obv. Bust r., wearing a cap and clerically robed. GVIL. SANCROFT. ARCHIEPISC. CANTAVR. 1688. *Rev.* Seven medallions containing busts, clerically robed, of (l. to r., from the top) William Lloyd, Francis Turner, John Lake, Henry Compton, Thomas Ken, Thomas White and Sir John Trelawney; a field of stars. *Edge.* SI FRACTUS ILLABATUR ORBIS IMPAUIDOS FERIENT RUINÆ   *D.* 51 mm. By G. Bower. *MI i*, 622/37; *v. Loon III*, 339

     a AV   1200   2000
     AR   80   150
     b AR   25   45

Type *b* is cast, with a plain edge and a thin flan. A close copy was made by Daniel Warou, a Swedish medallist; it is struck and signed D.W.F. on the bottom edge of the reverse. William Sancroft (1617–93), Archbishop of Canterbury; refused to read James II's 'Declaration of Indulgence' exempting Catholics and dissenters from penal statutes. *See* No. 287.

289   **Stability of the Anglican Church 1688**

Obv. Jesuit and monk, with spade and pickaxe, attempt to undermine a church supported by a hand issuing from heaven. THE GATES OF HELL SHALL NOT PREVAILE   *Rev.* Seven medallions containing portraits of the bishops, a mitre over each. WISDOM HATH BVILDED HER HOVS SHE HATH HEWEN OVT HER 7 PILLERS   *D.* 57 mm. Cast. Dutch? (By?) *MI i*, 625/42

     AR   60   110

See No. 288.

290*   **Birth of Prince James 1688**

Obv. Bust l., laureate and draped. IACOBUS II D.G. BRITANNIARUM IMPERATOR. *Rev.* Canopy over a bed in which a mother nurses her infant. FELICITAS PUBLICA. *Ex.* OB. FELICISS: M. BRIT: PRINC: NATIV: 20 IUN: 1688 IG: VITUS EQ: B. C. MARC: D'ALBYVILLE ET SA: ROM: IMP: APUD BAT: ABLEG: EXT: C.C. *D.* 60 mm. [By J. Smeltzing] *MI i*, 630/51; *CP* 49/4; *v. Loon III*, 343. *See* **Plate 10**

     AR   280   480
     WM   25   60

James Francis Edward Stuart, Prince of Wales (1688–1766), known as James III, 'Chevalier de St. George', or the Old Pretender; only son of James II and Mary of Modena.

291   ——

Obv. Truth stands leaning against an open cupboard door, inscribed IAC: FRANC EDUARD: SUPPOSIT: 20 IUNII 1688, revealing a Jesuit supporting a cushion upon which sits the Prince crowning himself. SIC NON HEREDES DEERUNT   *Rev.* Trojan horse, l., its saddle-cloth inscribed LIBERT. CONˢ SINE IURAM: ET LEG: P., and girth, ASTU; beyond, an open landscape. EQUO NUNQUAM TU CREDE BRITANNE   *D.* 58 mm. [By J. Smeltzing] *MI i*, 630/52; *CP* 50/6; *v. Loon III*, 345

     AR   220   420
     WM   20   45

292   ——

Obv. Armorial shield of the Prince supported by four infant genii. HONOR? PRIN? MAG. BRIT. FRA. ET. HIB. NAT: 10. IVN: 1688   *Rev.* Infant Prince, seated upon a cushion, looks up at two infant genii who display a crown and a ribbon, inscribed VENIAT. CENTESIMVS. HÆRES   *D.* 37 mm. (By G. Bower?) *MI i*, 627/46; *CP* 48/2

     AR   100   180
     AE   35   65

293*   ——

Obv. Busts r., conjoined, of James II, laureate and draped, and the Queen, draped. IACOBVS. II. M. BRIT. REX. MARIA. M. BRIT. REG   *Rev.* Map identifying ANGLIA HIBERNIA and SCOTIA; radiate sun, rising. ILLAS FVGAT. RECREAT ISTAS   *Ex.* OB NATVM WALLIÆ PRINCIPEM GAB. SILVIVS EQ. AVR. AD SER DANIÆ ET NORW. REG. ABL EXT C C MDCLXXXVIII   *D.* 35 mm. (By B. Meier?) *MI i*, 629/49; *CP* 48/3. *See* **Plate 10**

     AV   700   1300
     AR   180   320

294   ——

Obv. An infant seated in a cradle strangles two serpents. MONSTRIS. DANT. FVNERA. CVNÆ. *Rev.* Prince's plumes within a coronet. FVLTA. TRIBVS. METVENDA. CORONA. *Ex.* .1688. *D.* 30 mm. (By G. Bower?) *MI i*, 628/48; *CP* 48/1; *v. Loon III*, 342

     AR   80   140
     AE   35   55

295*   **AntiChristian Confederacy 1688**

Obv. Standing figures of Suleyman III of Turkey, Mezzo Morto of Algiers, Louis XIV, and James II, swear an oath of allegiance around an altar. SOLIMAN III. LVDOV: XIIII. MEZOMORTO. IACOBVS II. *Ex.* CONTRA CHRISTI ANIMUM   *Rev.* An imp. wearing a Jesuit's cap and brandishing a sword and thunder, hovers above three lilies supporting a crescent. IN FOEDERE QUINTUS   *Ex.* 1688. *D.* 37 mm. [By J. Smeltzing] *MI i*, 632/54; *v. Loon III*, 347. *See* **Plate 10**

     AR   130   250
     Wm   20   45

		£	£

296   **William and Mary Invited to Head the Protestant Party 1688**
Obv. Busts r., conjoined, of William, armoured and draped, and Mary, draped. ATAVUM PRO   AR   220   420
LIBERTATE FIDEQUE   *Ex.* M. WILH. HENR. ET MARIA D.G. AUR. PRINC. ETC. REFORMATIONIS
VINDICES   *Rev.* Religion, standing upon emblems of Popery, displays a scroll inscribed
LITTERÆ FAGELII; at her side is an altar, inscribed SS FIDES, on which is an open book; her
hand resting on the cap of liberty. IAM MIHI ROMA MINAX. FISTULA DULCE CANIT. *Ex.*
REFORMATIO ANGLIÆ MDCLXXXVIII   *D.* 62 mm. (By J. Smeltzing?) *MI i*, 634/58; *v. Loon III*,
348

297   **Landing of William at Torbay 1688**
Obv. Bust r., armoured and draped; 1688 on truncation. GVILIELMVS. III. D.G. PRIN. AVR. HOL.   *a* AR   90   170
ET. WES. GVB   *Rev.* Equestrian figure leads his army, assembled on a beach, below; beyond,
a large fleet at anchor. TERRAS. ASTRÆA. REUISIT. *Edge.* NON. RAPIT. IMPERIUM. UIS. TUA. SED.   *b* AR   25   45
RECIPIT   *D.* 50 mm. By G. Bower. *MI i*, 639/64; *MH* 1919, 76; *v. Loon III*, 353
Type *b* is cast, with a plain edge and thin flan.

298*   ——
Obv. William, as a Roman emperor, holds the arm of Britannia standing beside her shield   AV   1200   2200
affixed to an orange-tree entwined with roses and thistles. DEO VINDICE IUSTITIA COMITE.   AR   100   180
Rev. Troops disembark from boats near a fortified harbour; large fleet on the horizon.
CONTRA INFANTEM PERDITIONIS. *Ex.* EXPEDITIO NAUALIS PRO LIBERTATE ANGLIÆ.
MDCLXXXVIII   *D.* 49 mm. By R. Arondeaux. *MI i*, 639/65; *MH* 1919, 77; *v. Loon III*, 355.
See **Plate 10**

299*   **Arrival of William; Flight of Prince James 1688**
Obv. Standing figure of Belgium, armed, greeted by Britannia; fleet on the horizon. M. BRIT.   AR   220   420
EXP. NAV BAT. LIB. REST. ASSERTA   *Rev.* An eagle upon an island rock casts a young bird out
of a nest in which two eaglets remain; fleet on the horizon. INDIGNUM EIICIT. Wreath border
of roses and oranges. *D.* 59 mm. Dutch (By?) *MI i*, 644/73; *v. Loon III*, 367. *See* **Plate 10**

300*   **Flight of Prince James 1688**
Obv. A Jesuit, Father Petre, seated upon a lobster by the sea-shore, holds the infant prince; a   AR   80   150
French ship lying nearby. ALLONS MON PRINCE NOUS SOMMES EN BON CHEMIN. *Ex.* IAC. FRAN.   AE   35   65
EDUARD. SUPPOSEE. 20 JUIN 1688. *Rev.* Shield displaying a windmill within a rosary, inscribed
HONY. SOIT. QVI. BON. Y. PENSE   Above, a Jesuit's cap. LES ARMES ET L'ORDRE DU PRETENDU
PRINCE DE GALLES. *D.* 31 mm. [By C. Wermuth] *MI i*, 643/71; *v. Loon III*, 367; *CP* 52/10.
See **Plate 10**
Edward ('Father') Petre (1631–99), Privy Councillor and confidant of James II.

301   **Abdication of James II 1688**
Obv. Bust of William III, r., laureate. GVLIELMVS. III. DEI. GRATIA   *Rev.* James II,   WM   15   25
accompanied, in a rowing boat on the Thames, throws the Great Seal into the river. JAMES.
IIᴰˢ. ABDICATION. *Ex.* A.D. 1688   *D.* 38 mm. (By?) *MI i*, 646/75; *BHM* 287
Struck *c*.1788.

WILLIAM and MARY, 1688–94

302   **Flight of James II 1689**
Obv. Bust l., hair confined in a bag, draped. IACOBUS II BRITAN: REX FUGITIV. *Rev.* A column   AR   250   450
shattered by lightning; beyond, view of London from the south bank of the Thames. NON   AE   70   120
ICTV HVMANO, SED FLATV DIVINO. *Ex.* SPONTE FUGIT IACOB: II ANG: REX L. 20 DEC: CAPTUS 23 D.   WM   25   55
1688. ITERUM FUGIT 2 IAN: 1689. *D.* 49 mm. By J. Smeltzing. *MI i*, 649/3; *v. Loon III*, 370

303   **Arrival of James II in France 1689**
Obv. As No. 290. *Rev.* A vixen, torch in its mouth, sets fire to a tree in which an eagle has   AR   250   450
nested; beyond, another eagle carries off a fox's cub. MAGNIS INTERDUM PARVA NOCENT.   WM   25   60
REGNO ABDICATO IN GALLIAM APPULIT. *Ex.* 4. IAN: 1689. *D.* 60 mm. By J. Smeltzing. *MI i*,
652/7; *v. Loon III*, 371; *CP* 53/15

304   **James II Received by Louis XIV 1689**
Obv. Bust r. LUDOVICUS MAGNUS REX CHRISTIANISSIMUS. *Rev.* Gallia invites James II and   AR   75   140
Mary, holding the Prince, into her tent; shields of Britain and France either side.   AE   20   35
PERFUGIUM REGIBUS. *Ex.* IAC. II. M. BR. REX CUM REG. CONI. ET PR. WALLIAE IN GALL. RECEPTUS
M.DC.LXXXIX. *D.* 40 mm. By J. Mauger. *MI i*, 652/8; *v. Loon III*, 372; *CP* 54/16
This medal is from a large uniform French series recording events in the reign of Louis XIV, a small number of which
relate to Britain; restrikes have been made at various times.

			£	£

305 **Administration Offered to William 1689**
Obv. As No. 302. *Rev.* An orange tree flourishing beside an oak tree broken off at its trunk. `AR` 250 450
PRO GLANDIBVS AVREA POMA   *Ex.* POST FUGAM REGIS, DELATA REGNI ADMINISTRATIO PRINCIPI `WM` 25 55
AURIA: 3 IAN: 1689. *D.* 49 mm. By J. Smeltzing. *MI i*, 651/6; *v. Loon III*, 376

306 **British Crown Offered to William 1689**
Obv. Bust r., laureate, armoured and draped. GVLIELMVS. III. D.G. MAG. BRIT. FRAN. ET. HIB. `AR` 300 550
REX. *Rev.* Kneeling figures of England, Ireland and Scotland, holding the British shield,
receive cap of liberty from William, in Roman dress, standing before them. VENI. VICI.
LIBERTATEM. REDDIDI. *Ex.* 1688   *D.* 61 mm. By A. Meybusch. *MI i*, 657/17

307 **William and Mary, Restorers of the Anglican Church 1689**
Obv. Busts r., conjoined and draped, William laureate. GVLIELMVS. ET. MARIA. D.G. ANG. FRA. `a AR` 80 150
ET. HIB. REX. ET. REGINA. FIDEI. DEFENSORES & C. *Rev.* Statue of William in Roman dress, on a
pedestal inscribed .ÆRE. PERENNIVS, flanked by History and Time. .CÆLO. DELABITUR. ALTO. `b AR` 25 45
Edge. DUM. MICAT. HOC. GEMINUM. SYDUS. FUGIT. ATRA. TYRANNIS. *D.* 50 mm. By G. Bower.
MI i, 658/18; *v. Loon III*, 383
Type *b* is cast, with a plain edge and on a thin flan. Struck examples also occur with a plain edge.

308* **Roman Catholic Chapels Destroyed 1689**
Obv. As No. 307. *Rev.* People rejoicing around a bonfire in the centre of a square, along the `a AR` 130 250
perimeter of which a building stands in ruins. NEC. LEX. EST. IUSTIOR. ULLA. *D.* 53 mm. By G.
Bower. *MI i*, 660/21; *Farquhar* 1910/221. *See* **Plate 11** `b AR` 35 65
Type *b* is cast and on a thinner flan. Several Catholic chapels in London were destroyed, including one in Lincoln's Inn
Fields.

309* **Coronation of William and Mary 1689**
Obv. Busts of William and Mary facing each other, he laureate and armoured and she `AR` 280 480
draped. MAIUS. PAR. NOBILE. SCEPTRIS   *Ex.* G. HENR. ET MAR. PR. AUR. M. BRIT. R. 1689. *Rev.*
As obverse of No. 299. *D.* 59 mm. Dutch (By?) *MI i*, 672/44; *v. Loon III*, 379. *See* **Plate 11**
This coronation was the first to be commemorated with a large issue of medals. More than thirty different types were made,
mostly in Holland; a few record the festivities which took place in Amsterdam, Rotterdam and The Hague.

310 ——
Obv. Busts r., conjoined and draped, he laureate and armoured. GVLIELMVS. ET. MARIA. D G. `a AR` 100 180
MAG. BR. FR. ET. HIB. REX. ET. REGINA   *Rev.* The King and Queen, enthroned, beneath a
canopy of state; two bishops support a crown above their heads. IDOLOLATRIA. SERVITVTE. `b AR` 25 45
PROFLIGATIS. RELIGIONE. LEGIB. LIBERTAT. RESTITVTIS. *Ex.* .1689. *D.* 55 mm. By G. Bower.
MI i, 668/38; *v. Loon III*, 379
Type *b* is cast and on a thinner flan.

311 ——
Obv. Busts conjoined r., draped, he laureate. GVLIELMVS. ET. MARIA. D.G. ANG. FRA. ET. HIB. `a AV` 600 1000
REX. ET. REGINA. FID: DEF: & C. *Rev.* Perseus delivering Andromeda from a sea monster. `AR` 85 150
PRETIVMQ. ET. CAVSA. LABORIS. *Ex.* 1689   *D.* 38 mm. By G. Bower. *MI i*, 663/26; *Farquhar*
1910, 231; *v. Loon III*, 379 `b AR` 20 35
Type *b* is cast and on a thinner flan.

312* ——
Obv. Busts r., conjoined and draped, he laureate. GVLIELMVS. ET. MARIA. REX. ET. REGINA. `AV` 650 1200
Rev. Jove hurls thunder at Phaethon falling from his chariot. NE TOTVS ABSVMATVR   *Ex.* `AR` 75 150
INAVGVRAT. II. AP 1689   *D.* 35 mm. [By J. Roettiers] *MI i*, 662/25; *v. Loon III*, 379;
Wollaston 9. *See* **Plate 11**
The official coronation issue; struck from more than one pair of dies.

313 **Security of Britain 1689**
Obv. Busts r., conjoined and draped, he laureate and armoured. GVILIELMVS ET MARIA REX ET `AR` 120 220
REGINA BRITANNIÆ. *Rev.* Britannia, holding cross, scales, cornucopia and staff with the cap `AE` 45 75
of liberty, seated beneath an orange tree, decorated with a crown. AUREA FLORIGERIS `WM` 15 35
SUCCRESCUNT POMA ROSETIS. *Ex.* SECURITAS BRITANNIÆ RESTITUTA. 1689 *Edge.* (by F.
Kleinert) EXTERNO MALE PRESSA IUGO BRITANNIA PRIDEM, IN PRISCAS ITERUM RESPIRAT LIBERA
LEGES. *D.* 55 mm. By P. H. Müller. *Mi i*, 681/60; *v. Loon III*, 383

314 **Act of Toleration 1689**
Obv. Bust r., laureate, armoured and draped. GVLIELMVS REX ANGL. SCOT. FRANC. ET `AV` — —
HYBERN. PATRIÆ DECVS ANGLIÆ PRÆSIDIVM   *Rev.* Britannia, accompanied by Religion and `AR` 100 180
Liberty, grasps the hand of William. TE SERVATORE NON SERVIMUS. *Ex.* RESTITUTORI `AE` 35 60
BRITANNIÆ .1689. *Edge.* (by F. Kleinert) REGIA, CREDE MIHI, RES EST, SUCCURERE LAPSIS.

			VF	*EF*

D. 49 mm. By P. H. Müller. *MI i*, 683/64; *v. Loon III*, 392 — £ £

A variety occurs with a different edge reading. This Act enabled dissenters to practise their own religious beliefs without persecution.

315　Tribute to Mary 1689
Obv. Bust l., laureate. MARIA D.G. M. BRIT: FRAN: ET HIB: REGINA F.D.P.A. *Rev.* Mary standing, l., implores the protection of heaven upon the shield of Britain, attached to an orange branch. DIGNA QUÆ LONGE PLURES. *Ex.* MARIA II NOMINE, VIRTUTE I. 1689　D. 37 mm. By J. Smeltzing. *MI i*, 686/69; *v. Loon III*, 395 — AR 80 150 / WM 15 30

316　Relief of Londonderry 1689
Obv. Bust of William III, r., upon a pedestal, inscribed WILHELM: MAXIMUS IN. BELGICA LIBERATOR IN. BRITANNIA RESTAURATOR LIB: LONDONDERRY 1689, above whom Pallas and Plenty hold a wreath; fleet in the distance. *Rev.* Bust of Louis XIV, l., upon a pedestal, inscribed LUDOVIC: MAGNUS IN GERMANIA BARBARUS IN. GALLIA TYRANNUS OBS: MOGUNT: ET BONÆ., above whom Gallia and Germania hold a broken wreath; beyond, cities under siege. D. 45 mm. [By J. Smeltzing] *MI i*, 697/97; *v. Loon III*, 430 — AR 220 400

This medal also commemorates the siege and recapture of Mainz and Bonn from Louis XIV.

317　William and Mary *c*.1689
Obv. Busts r., conjoined, he laureate. GVLIELMVS. ET. MARIA. D.G. *Rev.* Two clasped hands hold a sceptre upon which is a crown. IVNGIT. AMOR. PATRIÆQ. SALVS. D. 26 mm. [By J. or N. Roettiers] *MI i*, 692/87 — AR 35 60 / AE 20 30

Struck from more than one pair of dies.

318　——
Obv. As No. 317. *Rev.* Three columns, inscribed RELIGIO/LEX. ET/LIBERTAS, support a crown. HISCE. SVFFVLTA. D. 25 mm. [By J. or N. Roettiers] *MI i*, 693/88 — AR 35 65 / AE 20 30

319　William and Mary *c*.1689
Obv. Bust r., laureate. GVLIELMVS. III. DEI. GRA. *Rev.* Bust r. MARIA. II. DEI. GRA. D. 22 mm. [By J. or N. Roettiers] *MI i*, 691/81 — AR 20 35 / AE 12 25

This medal also occurs with three other reverses: radiate sun; rose on branch; French ship in flames (sim. to No. 349).

320*　Mary as Regent 1690
Obv. Bust r., draped. MARIA. II. D.G. MAG. BR. FR. ET. HIB. REGINA. *Rev.* Full moon amid clouds and stars over a landscape. VELVT. INTER. IGNES. LVNA. MINORES. D. 49 mm. [By J. or N. Roettiers] *MI i*, 704/111–2; *Farquhar* 1910, 243. *See* **Plate 11** — AR 100 180 / AE 20 35

Examples in silver have a different reverse inscription: EX NOCTE DIEM.

321
Obv. As reverse of No. 319. *Rev.* Full moon, amid clouds, above a landscape. EX NOCTE DIEM　D. 22 mm. [By J. or N. Roettiers] *MI i*, 705/113 — AR 20 35

322　Arrival of William III in Ireland 1690
Obv. Bust r., laureate and draped. GULIELM: III D.G. BRIT: REX, ARAUS: PR: BELG: GUB. *Rev.* Large fleet approaches the coast; above, an eagle bearing a branch of orange and a sceptre. ALIS NON ARMIS　*Ex.* TRAIECTUS IN HIBERNI: LOND. $\frac{4}{14}$ IUN: 1690. D. 49 mm. By J. Smeltzing. *MI i*, 707/117; *v. Loon III*, 446 — AR 180 350 / AE 50 85 / WM 15 35

323　William III, Orange Association 1690
Obv. Equestrian figure of William III, l., baton drawn. THE GLORIOUS & IMMORTAL MEMORY 1690　*Rev.* Royal arms. KING AND CONSTITUTION　D. 43 mm. By W. Mossop. *BHM* 493; *Went* 1978, 154 — AR 15 25 / AE 8 15

Struck *c*.1800. More than twenty medals commemorate the Protestant Ascendancy and Orange Assocation, mostly made at the end of the eighteenth century. Some are found with a suspension loop on the edge. See *D & W* 172/544–69.

324　——
Obv. Bust of William III, l., laureate and draped. THE GLORIOUS & IMMORTAL MEMORY 1690　*Rev.* Royal arms. KING & CONSTITUTION　Integral suspension loop. D. 35 mm. By W. Mossop. *Went* 1978, 151; *D & W* 172/553 — AR 12 22 / AE 7 12 / WM 3 7

With an integral suspension loop. Struck *c*.1800. *See* No. 323.

325　Naval Engagement off Beachy Head 1690
Obv. Similar to No. 304. *Rev.* Victory upon a trophy of captured English and Dutch standards and ships. MERSA. ET. FVGATA. ANGLORVM. ET. BATAV. CLASSE　*Ex.* AD. ORAS. ANGLIAE. M.DC.XC. D. 41 mm. By J. Mauger. *MI i*, 709/121; *MH* 1921, 108; *v. Loon III*, 450 — AR 65 120 / AE 12 25

See No. 304.

326　Mary as Regent, Action off Beachy Head 1690
Obv. Busts r., conjoined and laureate. GULIELM: R. MARIA REGINA. F.D.P.A. *Rev.* Mary wields her trident and spills her cornucopia. Beyond, ships under repair, l.; a figure (Torrington) — AR 110 180

being led to the Tower, r. DISSIPAT ET REFICIT   *Ex.* REGINÆ REGENTI. MDCXC. D. 37 mm. By   £   £
J. Smeltzing. *MI i*, 713/129; *MH* 1919, 80; *v. Loon III*, 453

<small>The reverse occurs coupled with the obverse of No. 315, Arthur Herbert, Earl of Torrington (1647–1716), admiral of the fleet; he was accused of not fully engaging the enemy or assisting England's Dutch allies. His successful defence before a court-martial was that the French fleet was superior in numbers and that an engagement would have led to disaster.</small>

327   Battle of the Boyne 1690

Obv. Bust r., armoured and draped. GVILIELMVS. III. D.G. MAG. BRIT. FRAN. ET. HIB.   *AR*   280   550
REX   *Rev.* Equestrian figure of William III, l., before whom JACOB (James II) and LAUSUN
(A. N de Lauzun, French commander) flee into the distant landscape. The prostrate bodies
of SCHOMBERG (Friedrich) and WALKER (George) on the ground. APPARUIT ET
DISSIPAVIT   *Ex.* LIBERATA HIBERNIA MDCLXXXX   D. 57 mm. By J. Luder. *MI i*, 715/134; *v.*
Loon IV, 5

<small>At least eight medals commemorate this battle. George Walker (1618–90), Governor of Londonderry. Antonin Nompar, Duc de Lauzun (1633–1723). *See* No. 329</small>

328*   ——

Obv. Bust r., laureate, armoured and draped. GVILH. III. D.G. MAG. BRI. FRAN. ET HIB. REX.   *AV*   1200   2300
Rev. Equestrian figure of William III, r., leads his army across a river in pursuit of the   *AR*   150   280
fleeing enemy. ET VULNERA ET INVIA SPERNIT   *Ex.* EIICIT IACOBUM RES: TITUIT HIBERNIAM   *AE*   45   80
MDCXC   D. 48 mm. By R. Arondeaux. *MI i*, 716/136; *v. Loon IV*, 5. *See* **Plate 11**

<small>Examples in bronze are cast and have a modified obverse inscription.</small>

329*   **Death of Marshal Schomberg 1690**

Obv. Bust almost facing, armoured and draped. FRIDERICUS MARESCHALCUS SCHOMBERG. &c.   *AR*   130   270
Rev. Standing figure of Schomberg as Hercules, in Roman dress, holds a shield with   *AE*   45   80
christogram and an orange tree transformed from his club; behind, a laurel branch   *WM*   20   40
decorated with the shields of France, Germany, Spain, Scotland and Ireland, from his
military campaigns. PLANTAVIT UBIQUE FERACEM. *Ex.* CONTINVATIS TRIVMPHIS OBDVRATA IN
DEVM FIDE IN HIBER. MILITANTI 1690   *Edge.* (by F. Kleinert) PRO RELIGIONE ET LIBERTATE
MORI, VIVERE EST   D. 49 mm. By P. H. Müller. *MI i*, 717/139; *v. Loon IV*, 9. *See* **Plate 11**
<small>Friedrich Hermann Schomberg (1615–90), German soldier of fortune; cr. Duke in 1689. He was killed at the Boyne. *See* No. 327.</small>

330   Flight of James II from Ireland 1690

Obv. As No. 302. *Rev.* A stag with wings on its heels takes fright, l., and looks back over its   *AR*   230   450
shoulder; city in the distance. PEDIBUS TIMOR ADDIDIT ALAS   *Ex.* FUGIT EX HIBERNIA D. 12.   *WM*   25   45
IULII. 1690. D. 48 mm. By J. Smeltzing. *MI i*, 719/142; *v. Loon IV*, 10

331*   **Amnesty Declared in Ireland 1690**

Obv. Bust r., laureate, armoured and draped. WILH. III. D.G. ANG. SCO. FR. ET HIB. REX. DEF. FID. *Rev.*   *AR*   80   150
William in Roman dress standing, r., crowned with a wreath by Victory, presents an olive-   *AE*   30   55
branch to the supplicant figure of Hibernia. HIBERNIA RESTITVTA. *Ex.* MDCXC. *Edge.* ARMIS
IVNGIT AMOR NVNC TERTIA REGNA DVOBVS   D. 40 mm. By G. Hautsch. *MI i*, 721/146; *v.*
Loon IV, 12. *See* **Plate 11**

332   Return of William III to Holland 1691

Obv. Bust r., laureate, armoured and draped. GULIELM: III D.G. BRIT: R. AR: PR: BELG: GUB.   *AR*   300   550
Rev. Sun, rising, radiant over the Dutch coast and a large fleet. RECREO, DUM REDEO. *Ex.*   *AE*   55   90
MDCXCI. D. 59 mm. By J. Smeltzing. *MI ii*, 4/158; *v. Loon IV*, 25
<small>The King's return is commemorated by more than twenty medals, including some which record a grand firework display in The Hague.</small>

333   William's Triumphal Entry into The Hague 1691

Obv. Palace façade seen through a triumphal arch. HIC HEROUM HONOS   *Ex.* P.F.I.   *AR*   130   250
GULIELMO. III. TRIUMP. P.P. GUB. P.C.I.P. RESTAUR. BEL. FED. LIB. A. SERV. S. PAC. H. REDUCI. D.   *WM*   20   45
31. IAN. 1691. *Rev.* Passengers in an open boat approach the ORANIE POLD; fleet on the
horizon. Ribbon above, inscribed SERVANDUM SERVANTUS. *Ex.* DIE TOT: NOCTEQ: IN SCHAP:
FLUCT: APPUL: IN HOLL: D. 31 IAN: 1691. D. 50 mm. [By J. Smeltzing] *MI ii*, 12/174; *v. Loon*
IV, 33

334   Congress of the Allies, The Hague 1691

Obv. Jupiter, as William, presiding in the midst of gods seated in council. INGENTES ANIMO,   *AR*   110   200
DIGNAS IOVE CONCIPIT IRAS CONCILIUMQVE VOCAT. *Ex.* CONVENTUS FOEDERAT. PRINCIP.   *AE*   35   60
PRÆSIDE GUILIELMO III. R. BRIT. HAGÆ COMIT. CELEBR. 1691   *Rev.* Courage and Concord,   *WM*   15   30
standing before Prudence, clasp hands above an altar inscribed SAL. PVBL. S., and decorated
with a wreath. CONSILIO CONCORDIA ET FORTITVDINE. *Edge.* (by F. Kleinert) REX REGVM
CONSVLTA DEVS FORTVNET VBIQVE (chronogrammatic date). D. 50 mm. By P. H. Müller.
MI ii, 16/182; *v. Loon IV*, 41.

PLATE 11

308

309 (× ⅔)

312

320

328

331

329

337

340

342

PLATE 12

345

353

356

358

357

366

365

368

335   **Relief of Coni 1691**

Obv. Clouds behind rocks shroud the sun; city in the distance. NON PENETRANT RADII   *Ex.*   AR   150   280
STRAGE PRIMA AD ERIDANUM EDITA. *Rev.* French army in flight; beyond, a city and an
approaching army. ETIAM SUA FATA VOCANT. *Ex.* CONI OBSID: LIB: FUG: GALL. D. XXVIII IUN:
MDCXCI. *D.* 49 mm. (By J. Smeltzing?) *MI ii*, 27/199; *v. Loon IV*, 50

| | | £ | £ |

336   **Capture of Athlone, Galway and Sligo 1691**

Obv. Busts r., conjoined and laureate, he armoured and she draped. GULIELM: REX MARIA   AV   1200 2300
REGINA F.D.P.A. *Rev.* A sword and sceptre, decorated with an Irish shield, between three   AR   170   350
views of sieges: ATHLON. XXX IUN: X IUL./GALLOWAY D. XXVI IUL. V AUG./SLEGO D. XV XXV   AE   60   110
SEPT., each crowned. ARMIS, NOMINISQ: TERRORE   *Ex.* MDCXCI. *D.* 50 mm. By J. Smeltzing.   WM   25   55
MI ii, 35/212

<small>This medal also occurs with the single portrait of William III.</small>

337*   **Battle of Aughrim 1691**

Obv. Busts r., conjoined, laureate and draped, he armoured. GULI: ET MARIA D.G. M. BRIT: FR: AR   320   580
ET HIB: REX, ET REGINA. *Rev.* A fierce cavalry engagement; beyond, general view of battle.   AE   60   110
HIBERNIS, GALLISQ: DEVICTIS. *Ex.* PUGNA AD AGHRIM XXII IUL: MDCXCI. *D.* 55 mm. By J.   WM   25   55
Smeltzing. *MI ii*, 29/201; *v. Loon IV*, 50. *See* **Plate 11**

338   ——

Obv. Bust r., laureate. GULIELM: III D.G. M. BRIT: FR: ET HIB: REX F.D.P.A. *Rev.* Lion tramples   AR   100   170
upon a prostrate dog and claws an escaping cock. SIC UNO FERIT UNGUE DUOS   *Ex.* REBELL: ET
GALLI PROP: AGRI^M. HIB: FUSI. CAPT: AUT CÆS: DUC: EXC: CAST: REL: APPAR: BEL: UNIV:
1691 *D.* 37 mm. By J. Smeltzing. *MI ii*, 31/205; *v. Loon IV*, 52

<small>Another reverse depicts Hercules standing over a prostrate figure.</small>

339   **Pacification of Ireland 1691**

Obv. Busts r., conjoined, laureate and draped, he armoured. GULI: ET MARIA D.G. M. BRIT: FR: AV   1200 2200
ET HIB: REX. ET REGINA. *Rev.* Raging lion tramples upon a Hydra, watched by a dog cowering   AR   170   300
beside a lioness; beyond, distant view of city and ships in harbour. PARCERE SVBIECTIS, ET
DEBELLARE SVPERBOS. *Ex.* HIB: PACATA CIƆIƆCXCI. *D.* 54 mm. By D. Drappentier. *MI ii*,
39/220; *v. Loon IV*, 57

340*   ——

Obv. As No. 331. *Rev.* Victory flying, r., attended by infant genii displaying six shields, each   AR   120   220
with a plan: WATERFORT; ATHLONE; LIMRICH; KINSAL; LONDONDERY; GALOWAY   Below, an   AE   45   85
equestrian figure commanding a battle; in the distance are DROGHEDA and DVBLIN   *Ex.*   WM   20   45
RESTITVTORI HIBERNIÆ. MDCXCI. *Edge.* ANNORVM GESTA DVORVM CERNIS: QVID PLVRES
FACIENT? *D.* 41 mm. By G. Hautsch. *MI ii*, 41/224; *v. Loon IV*, 61. *See* **Plate 11**

341   ——

Obv. Bust of William r. as No. 331. *Rev.* William in Roman costume, as No. 331. *Ex.*   AR   90   170
MDCXCI. *D.* 41 mm. By G. Hautsch. *MI ii*, 38/219   AE   30   55
   WM   15   30

342*   **Peace Restored, the Throne Established 1691**

Obv. Bust r., laureate, armoured and draped; below, armorial shield upon wreath.   AR   130   230
WILHELMUS. III. D.G. BRITANNIARUM. IMPERAT   *Rev.* Four warriors, England, Scotland,
Ireland and Holland defend an orange tree from a coastal attack; fleet on the horizon. *Ex.*
CAUSA DEI EST. *Edge.* REGNA MARI TERRAQUE TEGIT. TEGITURQUE VICISSIM   *D.* 34 mm. by
38 mm. oval. By D. Koene. *MI ii*, 45/232. *See* **Plate 11**

343   ——

Obv. Bust r., draped. WILHELMVS. REX. ANGL   *Rev.* Radiate sun above sea. RESTITVIT LVCEM.   AR   25   40
D. 17 mm. [By C. Wermuth] *MI ii*, 47/236

<small>From a uniform series portraying European monarchs, sometimes found in a silver box.</small>

344   **Deventer Testimonial, Devotion to William III 1691**

Obv. Bust r., armoured and draped. GVLIELMVS MAGNVS   *Rev.* William, in Roman dress,   AV   1100 1900
raises a supplicant figure of Hibernia; behind, two figures place a wreath on a column.   AR   140   270
HIBERNIA SURGE   *Ex.* DAVEN. F.F. CVR. L.M. CIƆIƆCLXXXXI. *Edge.* SPONSOR. SECVRITATIS.
PVBLICAE   *D.* 47 mm. By J. Luder. *MI ii*, 48/237; *v. Loon IV*, 61

<small>Struck by the Master of the Mint at Deventer.</small>

345*   **Battle of La Hogue 1692**

Obv. As No. 337. *Rev.* Naval engagement; French ship sinking in foreground. ASSERTA   AR   280   650
MARIS IMPERII GLORIA. *Ex.* GALLORUM CLASSE DELETA D. XIX, XXIX MAJI. MDCXCII. *D.* 56 mm.
By J. Smeltzing. *MI ii*, 53/247; *MH 1919*, 83; *v. Loon IV*, 93. *See* **Plate 12**

<small>More than thirty medals commemorate this action in which the French fleet was defeated by that of Britain and Holland.</small>

			£	£

346 —— *Obv.* Busts r., conjoined and draped, he armoured. GVL: ET. MAR: D:G: M: B: F: ET. H: REX. ET. | AV | 1700 | 3300
REGINA. *Rev.* Naval engagement. NOX NVLLA. SECVTA. EST. *Ex.* PVGN: NAV: INT: ANG: ET. FR: | AR | 270 | 650
21. MAY. 1692. *D.* 50 mm. [By J. Roettiers] *MI ii*, 64/266; *MH* 1919, 102; *v. Loon IV*, 98;
Gordon 9

347 —— *Obv.* Neptune, with raised trident, drives Louis XIV from his marine car; beyond, a naval | AV | 1100 | 2000
engagement. NON ILLI IMPERIVM; SED MIHI SORTE DATVM. *Ex.* GUILIELMO. III. M. BRIT. R. OB | AR | 120 | 220
IMPERIVM MARIS ASSERT. *Rev.* Victory standing upon an antique galley; beyond, sun setting | AE | 35 | 70
over shipwrecks. SE CONDET IN UNDAS. *Ex.* DELETA AC INSENSA GALLORUM CLASSE. MDCXCII. | WM | 20 | 45
Edge. (by F. Kleinert) CONCASTIGATVS GALLORVM FASTVS ET ASTVS FLVCTIBVS, ET
PVGNA FRACTVS ATROCE FRAGOR (chronogrammatic date). *D.* 49 mm. By P. H. Müller. *MI*
ii, 55/251; *MH* 1919, 87; *v. Loon IV*, 98

348 —— *Obv.* As No. 331. *Rev.* Naval engagement; colours of a sinking French ship visible. NVNC | AR | 130 | 240
PLVRIBVS IMPAR *Ex.* OB CLASS. GALL. AB ANG. ET HOLL. VICT. ET DELET. D. 29. 31. MAI. A. 1692. | AE | 45 | 85
Edge. SIC PHAETHONTÆO TANDEM MARE SVFFICIT IGNI *D.* 40 mm. By G. Hautsch. *MI ii*, | WM | 20 | 45
59/258; *MH* 1919, 95; *v. Loon IV*, 104.

349 —— *Obv.* As No. 317. *Rev.* French ship in flames. IGNIBVS. IMPAR. *D.* 26 mm. [By J. or N. | AR | 35 | 65
Roettiers] *MI ii*, 64/267; *MH* 1919, 103 | AE | 20 | 35
See No. 319.

350 Namur Taken 1692
Obv. Similar to No. 304. *Rev.* Two river gods at the base of decorated pedestal surmounted | AR | 65 | 120
by Victory. NAMURCUM CAPTUM. *Ex.* SUB OCULIS GERM. HISP. ANGL. BAT. CENTUM MILLIUM. | AE | 12 | 25
M.DC.XCII. *D.* 40 mm. By J. Mauger. *MI ii*, 69/276; *v. Loon IV*, 88
More than five medals commemorate this action. *See* No. 304.

351 Battle of Steinkirk 1692
Obv. As No. 337. *Rev.* French cock attacks a retreating Belgic lion. 3 AUG: EX UNGUE LEONEM. | AR | 280 | 480
1692. PUGN: AD ANGIAM *D.* 56 mm. By J. Smeltzing. *MI ii*, 74/285; *v. Loon IV*, 110 | AE | 60 | 100
More than six medals commemorate this battle.

352 —— *Obv.* Similar to No. 304. *Rev.* Victory upon a trophy of captured standards. DE HISPANIS | AR | 65 | 120
ANGLIS GERMANIS ET BATAVIS *Ex.* AD STENKERCAM. M.DC.XCII. *D.* 40 mm. By J. Mauger. *MI* | AE | 12 | 25
ii, 72/281; *v. Loon IV*, 109
See No. 304.

353* **John George IV, Knight of the Garter 1693**
Obv. Bust r., armoured and draped. IOH. GEORG. IV. D.G. DVX. SAX. I. C. M. A. &. W. ELECT. *Rev.* | AR | 300 | 550
Armorial shield within the Garter. IUNGIMUR HOC SIGNO: QUO NON DISIUNGIMUR UNQUAM:
SIC NOSTRA ÆTERNUM PECTORA IUNCTA MANENT. *Edge.* CUSA EST ANGLORUM WILHELMO REGE
MONETA. 1693 *D.* 44 mm. By M. H. Omeis. *MI ii*, 79/292; *v. Loon IV*, 125. *See* **Plate 12**
John George IV (1668–94), Elector of Saxony.

354 **Naval Engagement in the Straits of Gibraltar 1693**
Obv. Similar to No. 304. *Rev.* Victory, armed with thunder, standing upon an antique galley | AR | 65 | 120
between the pillars of Hercules. COMMERCIA HOSTIBUS INTERCLUSA. *Ex.* NAVIBUS CAPT. AUT | AE | 12 | 25
INCENS. AD FRETUM GADITAN. M.DC.XCIII *D.* 40 mm. By J. Mauger. *MI ii*, 83/298; *v. Loon*
IV, 136
See No. 304.

355 **Battle of Landen 1693**
Obv. Bust l., armoured, his hair confined in a bag. GVLIELMVS. III. D.G. BRITANN: REX. *Rev.* | AR | 300 | 580
Hand from heaven beating a drum; beyond, cavalry in flight. MON SORT EST D'ESTRE BATTV.
D. 49 mm. [By J. Smeltzing] *MI ii*, 88/307; *v. Loon IV*, 138

356* **Prince Louis of Baden, Visit to London 1694**
Obv. Bust of William III almost facing, armoured and draped. WILLELMVS. III. D.G. REX. | AR | 450 | 850
F.D.P.A. *Rev.* William receives Prince Louis; in foreground, Silence seated beside shields | WM | 40 | 90
of the two royal houses. REC. P. BADENS. LOND. *Ex.* IUNXIT. LIBERTAS AUXIT. SECRETUM X. IAN.
MDCXCIV *D.* 50 mm. By J. Boskam. *MI ii*, 94/315; *v. Loon IV*, 156; *W & Z*, 45. *See* **Plate**
12
Prince Louis William, Margrave of Baden (1655–1707), German soldier and military engineer.

357*   **Bombardment of Havre 1694**
Obv. Bust r., laureate, armoured and draped. INVICTISSIMVS GVILLELMVS MAG   *Rev.* Bull standing, defiantly, upon a platform amid flames; in distance, boats before a burning city. SVIS PERIT IGNIBVS AVCTOR   *Ex.* PORTVS. GRATIÆ. EXVSTVS ET. EVERSVS. BOMBARD ANGLO. BATAV. MDCXCIIII   *D.* 60 mm. By J. Boskam. *MI ii*, 97/321; *MH* 1919, 111; *v. Loon IV*, 165. *See* **Plate 12**

     AR   £ 400   £ 750

358*   **French Coast Bombarded 1694**
Obv. William III, in Roman dress, stands holding a thunderbolt. IOVI TONANTI. *Ex.* GUILELMO III. D.G. M. BRITANN. REGI. *Rev.* Fleet of ships delivering a coastal bombardment. URBES ASPICIT ACCENSAS; NEC TANTOS SUSTINET ÆSTUS. *Ex.* VIBRATA IN MARITIMAS GALLIÆ URBES FULMINA. 1694. *Edge.* (by F. Kleinert) VANGIONVM NEMETVMQVE VRBES VLCISCITVR ANGLVS, DISCE TIMERE GRAVES NVNC LVDOVICE VICES   *D.* 44 mm. [By P. H. Müller] *MI ii*, 98/323; *MH* 1919, 113; *v. Loon IV*, 167. *See* **Plate 12**

   AV   1400   2700
   AR   280   480
   AE   70   120
   WM   28   60

359   **Siege and Capture of Huy 1694**
Obv. As No. 357. *Rev.* Equestrian figure of the Duke of Holstein commanding the siege. FVGITE. HINC. TESTES. A. LIMINE. BELLI   *Ex.* HVYA. CVM. ARCE. ET. FORT. PICARD. ET. RVBEO. EXP. A. D. HOLSAT. PLEVN. D. EXERC. FOED. XXVIII. SEPT. MDCXCIIII   *D.* 60 mm. By J. Boskam. *MI ii*, 100/325; *v. Loon IV*, 172

   AR   400   750

360   **Campaigns of 1694**
Obv. Seven genii, each holding a standard of the countries involved in military campaigns: Austria, England, Holland, Poland, Savoy, Spain and Venice. VIRTUTI ET CONCORDIÆ CHRISTIANORUM. *Rev.* Victory stands, facing, amongst three seated river gods. PETROVARADINO LIBERATO, HVYO RECEPTO, RHENO TRAIECTO. *Ex.* CONTRA TVRCAS EORVMQVE FOEDERATOS TRIPLEX XIANORVM VICTORIA. 1694. *Edge.* (by F. Kleinert) DOMINVS PROTECTIO TVA: PER DIEM SOL NON VRET TE, NEQVE LVNA PER NOCTEM. PS. 121   *D.* 49 mm. By P. H. Müller. *MI ii*, 101/327; *v. Loon IV*, 171

   AR   130   200
   AE   50   80
   WM   15   30

Commemorating the recapture of Huy, relief of Peterwardein, and passage of the Rhine.

361   **Archbishop Tillotson, Memorial 1694**
Obv. Bust r., draped. IOHANNES TILLOTSON   *Rev.* ARCHIEPISCOPUS CANTUARIENSIS NATUS SOWERBIÆ 3. OCTOBRIS 1630 MORT. LAMBETHÆ 22. NOVEMBRIS 1694   *D.* 28 mm. By J. Dassier. *MI ii*, 105/331

   AR   8   15
   AE   3   5

Struck *c*.1725, from Dassier's series of Protestant reformers. *See* No. 500.

362   **Death of Mary 1694**
Obv. Bust r., draped. MARIA. II. D.G. MAG. BR. FR. ET. HIB. REGINA. *Rev.* NAT. APR. 30. 1662. MOR. DEC. 28. 1694 in the centre. SVBLATAM EX OCVLIS QVÆRIMVS INVIDI   *D.* 49 mm. [By J. or N. Roettiers] *MI ii*, 111/343; *Farquhar* 1910, 255; *v. Loon IV*, 189

   AR   70   130
   AE   20   35

Struck from more than one pair of dies. More than thirty medals record the death of Mary.

363   ——
Obv. Mary seated, l., upon a globe, holding a palm branch. O: GRAVE: WHERE IS: THY: VICTORY. *Rev.* QVEEN: MARY. THE: SECOND: ÆTAT 32: OBIT: DEC: 28. ANNO: DOM. 1694   *D.* 40 mm. [By J. or N. Roettiers?] *MI ii*, 121/364

   AR   90   150
   AE   35   65

364   **Mary, Memorial 1694**
Obv. Bust r., draped, MARIA. II. D.G. MAG. BR. FR. ET. HIB. REGINA. *Rev.* Tomb beneath a canopy. *Ex.* NATA. 10. FEBR. 1662. COR. 11. APR. 1689. MORT. 29. DEC. 1694. *D.* 41 mm. By J. Dassier. *MI ii*, 123/368

   AR   17   35
   AE   4   9

Struck in 1731, from Dassier's series of English kings and queens. *See* No. 526.

365*   **Siege and Recapture of Namur 1695**
Obv. Bust r., laureate, armoured and draped. WILHELMVS. III. D.G. MAG. BRIT. FRANC. ET. HIB. REX   *Rev.* Equestrian figure of William commanding at the siege; beyond, city under bombardment. CORAM. C. M. HOST. REPRES. *Ex.* NAMURC. URBS. ARX. CAST. INVIA. VI EXPUGN 1. SEPT. MDCXCV   *D.* 59 mm. By J. Boskam. *MI ii*, 132/383; *v. Loon IV*, 197. *See* **Plate 12**

   AR   350   650
   AE   60   110

This action is recorded on more than thirty medals.

366*   ——
Obv. Hercules carries oval medallions of WILH. III. D.G. MAG. BRITAN. REX and MAX. EMA. D.G. BAV. EL.; a dragon and Cerebus at his feet. PROPVGNATORIBVS ORBIS. *Ex.* TESTANTVR FACTA TRIVMPHI. *Rev.* Town and fortifications upon a hill. NON AVRO, VIRTVTE DVCVM. *Ex.* NAMVRCVM RECEPTVM. MDCVC. *Edge* REX ANGLVS FVSO GAVDENT BAVARVSQVE NAMVRCO (chronogrammatic date). *D.* 45 mm. By G. Hautsch. *MI ii*, 139/395; *v. Loon IV*, 203. *See* **Plate 12**

   AV   1200   2000
   AR   170   320
   AE   50   90
   WM   20   35

Maximilian II Emanuel (1662–1726), Elector of Bavaria; governor of the Spanish Netherlands.

		£	£

367   Brussels Bombarded; Namur Recaptured 1695

Obv. Burning city under bombardment. MOMORDIT LAPIDEM. *Ex.* BRVXELLE A GALLO   *AR*   130   250
FRVSTRA IGNE TENTATAE. $\frac{IV}{XIV}$. AVG. M.DC.VC. *Rev.* Town and fortifications upon a hill. VICTA   *AE*   45   85
EST QVAE VINCI NON POTERAT. AMAT VICTORIA TESTES. *Ex.* NAMVRCVM RECEPTVM A BRITANNO   *WM*   20   45
ET BAVARO SPECTANTE GALLO CVM C.L.M. ARMAT. 1. SEPT. M.DC.VC. *D.* 42 mm. By C.
Wermuth. *MI ii*, 128/378; *v. Loon IV*, 205

The recapture of Namur is commemorated on more than twenty medals.

368*   Fortunes of James II 1696

Obv. Bust r., laureate and armoured. IACOB. II REX. M. BR   *Rev.* Crown in a boat upon a   *AV*   450   850
rough sea. FATO   *Ex.* 1696   *D.* 26 mm. (By?) *MI ii*, 149/411; *CP* 56/21. *See* **Plate 12**   *AR*   120   220

369*   Assassination Plot against William III 1696

Obv. Busts r., conjoined, of Louis XIV and James II. HERODES ATQVE PILATVS. *Ex.* ACTOR. IV.   *AV* 1300 2500
26. *Rev.* In foreground, within an enclosure, James II and Louis XIV jointly display a purse,   *AR*   180   350
inscribed CM PISTO (100,000 pistols): Father Petre, r.; Prince James astride a lobster, l. In a   *AE*   80   150
wood, beyond, are 40 armed conspirators; a fleet on the horizon. IRRITA CONSPIRATIO. *Ex.*   *WM*   25   50
GENESIS. XLIX. 5.6. ADVERS'. GVLIELMVM. III ANGLIAE REGEM. 3. MART. 1696. *D.* 43 mm.
German? (By C. G. Lauffer?) *MI ii*, 151/414; *CP* 56/22; *v. Loon IV*, 225. *See* **Plate 13**

Sir George Barclay (*c.*1636–?), Scottish soldier and ardent Jacobite; principal agent in the assassination plot.

370   Peace of Ryswick 1697

Obv. Bust r., armoured and draped; CAROLO REGNANTE SECUNDO on a pedestal, below.   *AR*   270   500
MAVORTE EXPVLSO PAX EXPECTATA REDIVIT   *Rev.* Equestrian figure of Max. Emanuel, l.,
trampling upon fallen Turks. HOSTES PERCVSSIT BAVARVS TVRCASQVE SVBEGIT   *Ex.* GANDA
MDCXCVII   *D.* 58 mm. By P. Roettiers. *MI ii*, 179/472; *v. Loon IV*, 253

Charles II of Spain (1661–1700), joined the Grand Alliance against Louis XIV. The peace formed the conclusion of wars
involving many European nations and is commemorated by more than sixty medals.

371

Obv. Peace locks the door of the Temple of Janus, inscribed ANNO MIƆCXCVII; on the steps   *AR*   130   250
are War and Discord, manacled. Beyond, Mercury stands beside a bountiful cornucopia
and displays a ribbon, inscribed EVROPÆ PAX REDDITA. *Rev.* Europe seated on sea-shore
displays an olive-branch to ships sailing peacefully. *Ex.* EVROPA   *D.* 48 mm. By D.
Drappentier. *MI ii*, 172/458; *v. Loon IV*, 273

372*   State of Britain 1697

Obv. Bust r., laureate, armoured and draped. GVLIELMVS. III. DEI. GRA: MAG: BR: FRA: ET: *AR*   350   700
HIB: REX. *Rev.* Britannia seated upon ground, l., holds her trident and shield; beside her, an   *AE*   80   180
olive-branch resting upon a book. RESTITVTORI. *Ex.* BRITANNIA: MDCXCVII. *D.* 69 mm. [By J.
Croker] *MI ii*, 192/499; *Farquhar* 1912/242–3; *v. Loon IV*, 250. *See* **Plate 13**

This refers to the stability of peace after Ryswick.

373*   Fortunes of Prince James 1697

Obv. Bust l., armoured and draped. IACOBVS. WALLIÆ. PRINCEPS   *Rev.* A ship in stormy   *AR*   170   320
seas; its stern decorated with a sun and flying the cross of St. George. 1697. IACTATVR. NON.   *AE*   80   130
MERGITVR. VNDIS: *D.* 45 mm. By N. Roettiers. *MI ii*, 192/500; *CP* 57/23; *v. Loon IV*, 247.
See **Plate 13**

The Peace of Ryswick endorsed William's sovereignty. This medal is one of many which record the fortunes of the Stuart
family and their claim of legitimacy of succession.

374

Obv. Bust l. IAC: WALLIÆ PRINCEPS   *Rev.* Radiate sun, partially eclipsed, above a calm sea.   *AR*   30   55
CLARIOR. E. TENEBRIS   *Ex.* 1697   *D.* 25 mm. By N. Roettiers. *MI ii*, 193/501; *CP* 57/24; *v.*   *AE*   15   30
Loon IV, 247

375

Obv. As No. 374. *Rev.* A mine exploding within a confined fortification. QVO. COMPRESSA.   *AV*   200   350
MAGIS   *Ex.* 1697   *D.* 25 mm. By N. Roettiers. *MI ii*, 194/502; *CP* 58/25; *v. Loon IV*, 247   *AR*   30   55
  AE   15   30

376

Obv. As No. 374. *Rev.* Radiate sun rising upon a calm sea. OMNIA. FACIT. IPSE. SERENA   *Ex.*   *AR*   30   55
1697   *D.* 25 mm. By N. Roettiers. *MI ii*, 194/503; *CP* 58/26; *v. Loon IV*, 247   *AE*   15   30

Struck from more than one pair of dies.

377

Obv. As No. 374. *Rev.* Dove with olive-branch above a calm sea. MANSVRÆ. NVNTIA.   *AV*   200   350
PACIS   *Ex.* 1697   *D.* 25 mm. By N. Roettiers. *MI ii*, 195/504; *CP* 58/27; *v. Loon IV*, 247   *AR*   30   55
  AE   15   30

Struck from more than one pair of dies.

378   Presentation of a New Collar to Dublin 1698

Obv. Bust r., armoured and draped. GVLIELMVS. TERTIVS. D.G. MAG. BRIT. FRAN. ET. HIB.   *AR*   700   1300
REX   *Rev.* GVLIELMVS III ANTIQVAM ET FIDELEM HIBERNIÆ METROPOLIN HOC INDVLGENTIÆ   *AE*   170   320
SVÆ MVNERE ORNAVIT. BARTH VAN HOMRIGH ARM. VRB. PRÆTORE. MDCXCVIII. *D.* 85 mm. By J.
Roettiers. *MI ii,* 197/509; *Farquhar* 1912/267–70

The King presented the New Collar to the city, of which Bartholomew van Homrigh had been elected Lord Mayor in
1697.

379   James II and Prince James, Legitimacy of Succession 1699

Obv. Bust r., laureate. IACOBVS. II. D.G. M. B. F. ET. H. REX 1699   *Rev.* Bust l., armoured and   *AR*   130   250
draped. IAC. WALLIÆ. PRINCEPS. *D.* 36 mm. By N. Roettiers. *MI ii,* 201/515; *CP* 59/28; *v.*
Loon IV, 290

380*   ——

Obv. Bust r., laureate, armoured and draped. IACOBVS: II: D:G: M: B: R.   *Rev.* Bust l.,   *AR*   35   65
armoured. IAC. WALLIÆ: PRINCEPS. *D.* 27 mm. By N. Roettiers. *MI ii,* 202/516; *CP* 59/29.
See **Plate 13**

Struck from two obverse dies, differing only in the legend.

381*   ——

Obv. As reverse of No. 380. *Rev.* Radiate sun rising over a calm sea dispels clouds and   *AV*   250   450
demons. SOLA. LVCE. FVGAT   *Ex.* 1699   *D.* 27 mm. By N. Roettiers. *MI ii,* 204/519; *CP*   *AR*   35   65
60/31. *See* **Plate 13**

382   ——

Obv. As reverse of No. 380. *Rev.* An upright bountiful cornucopia; beyond, open landscape   *AR*   35   65
and sea. PAX. VOBIS   *Ex.* 1699. *D.* 27 mm. By N. Roettiers. *MI ii,* 204/520; *CP* 60/32

383*   Toubucan stormed 1700

Obv. A Highland warrior on a parapet, sword raised, prepares to storm a fort surrounded by   *AR*   750   1300
soldiers, beyond. Inscription on a ribbon divided by compass QUID NON PRO PATRIA   *Ex.*
TOUBOCANTI UBI 1600 HISPAN FUDIT DUX ALEXANDER CAMPBELL. MDCC. 8. FEBR. *Rev.* Armorial
shield of the African and Indian Company of Scotland: ribbon above, inscribed QUA
PANDITUR ORBIS, and below, VIS UNITA FORTIOR   *D.* 56 mm. By M. Smeltzing. *MI ii,*
209/529; *CP* 100/11; *Gordon* 10; *Betts* 88. *See* **Plate 13**

William III had established a colony in the Isthmus of Darien, Central America. The colonists were continually attacked
by Spaniards; the African and Indian Company sent out a force under Captain Alexander Campbell who routed them at
Toubucan. Further attacks from Spanish reinforcements eventually drove the colonists into submission. Campbell
refused to surrender and returned to Scotland with his followers, who were given examples of this medal by the Company.
Some examples are gilt.

384   James II, Memorial 1701

Obv. Bust l., laureate, armoured and draped. IACOBUS II. D.G. MAG. BR. FR. ET. HIB. REX   *Rev.*   *AR*   35   65
Religion seated mournfully upon a tomb, inscribed NAT. 13. OCT. 1633. CORONAT. 23. APR.   *AE*   4   9
1685. MORT. 5. SEPT. 1701. *D.* 41 mm. By J. Dassier. *MI ii,* 215/537

Struck in 1731, from Dassier's series of English kings and queens. *See* No. 526.

385   Princesses Matilda and Sophia, Hanoverian Succession 1701

Obv. Bust r., veiled and draped. MATILDA. FILIA. H. II. R. ANGL. VX. H. LEON: D. BAV: ET. SAX: *AV*   1600   2800
MATER. OTT: IV. IMP: PRIVS. DVCIS. AQVIT H. PAL: RHEN: D.S. WILH: SATORIS. DOMVS. BRVNS: *AR*   180   320
Rev. Bust r., veiled and draped. SOPHIA. EX. STIRPE. EL: PAL: NEPT: IAC: I. REG: M. BRIT: *AE*   70   120
VIDVA. ERN: AVG: EL: BRVNS: ET. L. ANGLIAE. PRINCEPS. AD. SVCCESS: NOMINATA. MDCCI. *D.*
65 mm. By S. Lambelet. *MI ii,* 218/542; *v. Loon IV,* 335

Matilda (1156–89), daughter of Henry II, king of England. Sophia (1630–1714), daughter of Frederick V of the Palatinate
and Elizabeth; grand-daughter of James I.

386   Death of William III 1702

Obv. Bust r., laureate, armoured and draped. GULIELM: III. TRISTI DOLENDUS IN ÆVO. *Rev.*   *AR*   120   220
Eagle flying from the Temple of Janus, its doors open to reveal a smoking funeral pile. *Ex.*   *WM*   20   45
INVICTA VIRTUTE RESURGET. NAT. HAGAE COMITIS D. XIV. NOV. 1650. DENAT. KENGSINGTON D.
XIX. MARTII 1702. *D.* 48 mm. By M. Smeltzing. *MI ii,* 223/550; *v. Loon IV,* 339

387   William III, Memorial 1702

Obv. Bust r., laureate, armoured and draped. GULIELMUS. III. D.G. M. BR. FR. ET HIB. REX. *Rev.*   *AR*   27   55
ÆTERNITAS seated upon a pedestal, flanked by Britannia and Hercules. *Ex.* NAT. 4. NOV. 1650.   *AE*   4   9
CORONAT. 11. APR. 1689. MORT. 8. MART. 1702. *D.* 41 mm. By J. Dassier. *MI ii,* 225/554

Struck in 1731, from Dassier's series of English kings and queens. *See* No. 526.

ANNE, 1702–14

£   £

388*   **Accession of Anne 1702**
Obv. Bust l., crowned and draped. ANNA. D: G: MAG: BR: FR: ET. HIB: REGINA. *Rev.* A heart   AV   500   900
within branches of oak, resting on a pedestal inscribed ATAVIS REGIBVS, and threaded   AR   25   55
through a crown, above. ENTIRELY ENGLISH   *D.* 35 mm. [By J. Croker] *MI ii*, 227/1; *v. Loon*   AE   15   35
IV, 345. *See* **Plate 14**
Struck from more than one pair of dies.

389   ——
Obv. As No. 388. *Rev.* QVIS SEPARABIT, in the centre below a radiate heart, within a chained   AR   30   60
circle of roses each containing a heart; crown above. VNITED. BY. GOD. IN. LOVE. AND.   AE   15   35
INTEREST. *D.* 35 mm. [By J. Croker] *MI ii*, 228/3; *v. Loon IV*, 345

390   **Coronation of Anne 1702**
Obv. Bust l., draped. ANNA. D:G: MAG: BR: FR: ET. HIB: REGINA. *Rev.* Pallas standing, l.,   AV   350   750
hurling thunder at a two-headed monster. VICEM. GERIT. ILLA. TONANTIS. *Ex.* INAVGVRAT.   AR   28   60
XXIII. AP. MDCCII. *D.* 35 mm. [By J. Croker] *MI ii*, 228/4; *v. Loon IV*, 347, *Wollaston* 10   AE   15   35
The official coronation issue; struck from more than one pair of dies.

391   ——
Obv. Bust l., draped. ANNA: D. GRA. *Rev.* Similar to No. 390. VICEM. GERIT ILLA   AE   8   15
TONANTI   *Ex.* INAVGVRAT XXIII AP MDCCII. *D.* 26 mm. (By?) *MI ii*, 229/6–9; *v. Loon IV*, 347
A coarse copy of No. 390; there are several minor varieties.

392   **Prince George, Lord High Admiral 1702**
Obv. Bust l., draped. ANNA. D:G: MAG: BR: FRA: ET. HIB. REGINA. *Rev.* Bust l., armoured and   AR   60   110
draped. GEO: DAN: PR: M: ADM: ET. DVX. SVP: ANGLIÆ. *D.* 42 mm. [By J. Croker] *MI ii*,   AE   25   45
233/14; *MH* 1919, 118; *v. Loon IV*, 346
Struck from two obverse dies.

393*   **Expedition to Vigo Bay 1702**
Obv. Bust l., draped. ANNA. D G. MAG. BR. FR. ET. HIB. REGINA   *Rev.* Fleet attacking a fort and   AR   150   270
ships in a harbour. GALL: HISP. Q. CLASS. EXPUG. COMB. CAPT. *Ex.* BRIT. BATAV. Q. EXPEO. AD.
VIGOS. MDCCII   *D.* 44 mm. By J. Boskam. *MI ii*, 237/20; *MH* 1919, 122; *Betts* 96. *See* **Plate
14**
At least eight medals commemorate the capture of French and Spanish fleets by those of Britain and Holland at this action
on Spain's north-west coast.

394*   ——
Obv. Victory decorating a naval trophy, implements of war at her feet. SPES ET VIRES HOSTIUM   AR   140   260
FRACTAE   *Ex.* INCENSA GALLOR CLASSE. HISPAN. OPES AMERIC. INTERCEPT. *Rev.* Ships in
harbour entrance, some of which are burning; areas around the harbour of BOCES, CANGAS,
REDONDELLE and VIGOS identified. ANGLORVM ET BATAVORVM VIRTVTE   *Ex.* AD VIGOS PORT.
GALLICIÆ. 1702. *Edge.* DECIDIT IN CASSES PRÆDA PETITA MEOS. OVID. *D.* 40 mm. (By P. H.
Müller?) *MI ii*, 238/22; *MH* 1919, 124; *Betts* 101. *See* **Plate 14**

395   ——
Obv. Similar to No. 388. ANNA. DEI. GRA: MAG: BR: FRA: ET. HIB: REGINA. *Rev.* Ships burning   AV   550 1000
within a harbour, a fleet lying at its mouth near a fort. CAPTA. ET. INCENSA. GAL: ET. HISP: AR   55   95
CLASSE   *Ex.* AD. VIGVM. XII. OCT. MDCCII. *D.* 37 mm. [By J. Croker] *MI ii*, 236/18; *MH* 1919,   AE   20   40
120; *Betts* 97
Struck from more than one pair of dies.

396   **Capitulation of Towns on the River Meuse 1702**
Obv. As No. 395. *Rev.* Columns of soldiers near artillery bombarding a fortified city. VIRES.   AR   30   60
ANIMVMQVE. MINISTRAT. *Ex.* CAPTIS. COLONIA. TRAJANA. VENLOA. RVREMVNDA.   AE   20   35
STEPHANOVERDA. LEODIO. MDCCII. *D.* 37 mm. [By J. Croker] *MI ii*, 241/26; *v. Loon IV*, 358
Struck from more than one pair of dies.

397*   **Victories of the Earl of Athlone 1702**
Obv. Bust r., armoured. GODARDUS ATHLON: COM: EXERC: FOED: BELG: IMPERATOR. *Rev.*   AR   120   220
Obelisk decorated with twelve shields, inscribed KEYSWERDI VENLO. STEVWAERDT.   WM   25   55
ROERMOND LUYCK. STOCKHEM GREV.BROEC HAMMOND BRY VISET NAVAR PEER; four captives
chained to the base, inscribed SIC BATAVIS CONTINGIT AB HERCULE THESEUS. MDCCII. *D.*
49 mm. By M. Smeltzing. *MI ii*, 242/27; *v. Loon IV*, 366. *See* **Plate 14**
Godert de Ginkel, 1st Earl of Athlone (1630–1703), commander of the Dutch troops.

398*   **Siege and Capture of Bonn 1703**
Obv. Bust three-quarters r., armoured and draped. MENNO. BARO. DE. COEHOORN. SVMMVS.   AR   180   350
APVD. BATAVOS. ARMORVM. PRÆFECTVS. &   *Rev.* Fortified city of Bonn, seen from across the   WM   30   65

PLATE 13

369

372

373

380

381

383

PLATE 14

388

393

394

397

398

405

406

407

411

Rhine. sIC. IGNE. DoMata. FEROCI. (chronogrammatic date). *Ex.* UT TONUS EVERTIT   £   £
TUBARUM MOENIA QUONDAM SICQ. TONANS COEHORN, MOENIA BONNA TUA. *Edge.* E MALA
BONNA DIU, SIC BONA FACTA BREVI   *D.* 47 mm. By G. Hautsch / G. F. Nürnberger. *MI ii*,
245/34; *v. Loon IV*, 395. *See* **Plate 14**

Baron Mennoe van Cohorn (1641–1704), Dutch soldier and military engineer.

399   ——
Obv. As No. 393. *Rev.* Equestrian figure of Marlborough, commanding; bombardment of   *AR*   150   290
Bonn seen from across the Rhine. BONA A MALIS EREPTA   *Ex.* COCIALIBUS ARMIS IDIB. MAII.
MDCCIII   *D.* 44 mm. By J. Boskam. *MI ii*, 245/33; *v. Loon IV*, 395

John Churchill, 1st Duke of Marlborough (1650–1722), military commander.

400   **Duke of Marlborough, Cities Captured 1703**
Obv. As No. 392. *Rev.* Equestrian figure of Marlborough receives three keys offered on a   *AV*   700   1300
salver by a kneeling female figure. SINE. CLADE. VICTOR. *Ex.* CAPTIS. BONNA. HVO. LIMBVRGO.   *AR*   80   150
1703. *D.* 42 mm. [By J. Croker] *MI ii*, 246/35; *v. Loon IV*, 399   *AE*   30   55

401   **John Oriot** *c.*1703
Obv. Bust r. IOHANNES ORIOT. *Rev.* Hand issuing from clouds holds a balance over a barren   *AE*   60   —
landscape. NEC. NIMIUM NEC PARUM. *D.* 52 mm. Cast. [By B. Richter] *cf. MI ii*, 247/37–40

One of a group of personal medals by B. Richter. *See* C. Eimer, 'Johannes Oriot, The second of three unpublished medals',
SCMB September 1980, 275–6; M. Jones, 'Richter's medals for the Swedish Club', *NC* 1985, 249–54.

402   **Samuel Pepys, Memorial 1703**
Obv. Bust of Pepys l., draped; his signature (incuse) in field. *Rev.* A dandified figure   *AE*   —   22
standing, facing, holding plumed hat and cane. SAMUEL PEPYS ESQᴿ 1633–1703 (incuse). *D.*
70 mm. Cast. By R. Searle. *The Medal 6*, 45

Issued by the British Art Medal Society in 1985; *see* No. 2141. Samuel Pepys (1633–1703), diarist and official in the navy
office.

403   **Charles III, Departure from England for Portugal 1703**
Obv. Bust r., laureate. CAROLVS. III. HISPANIAR. INDIAR. REX. CATHOL. *Rev.* Eagle with olive-   *AR*   120   220
branch and thunder hovers over a fleet under sail. LIBERATOR. ET. ULTOR   *Ex.* CAROL. III.
HISPAN. REX BRITAN. BATAVQ. CLAS. IN LUSIT. PROFICISC. MDCCIII   *D.* 44 mm. By J. Boskam.
MI ii, 251/42; *v. Loon IV*, 406

Charles III (1685–1740), King of Hungary; as Charles VI, 1711–40, Holy Roman Emperor.

404   **Queen Anne's Bounty 1704**
Obv. Bust l., laureate and draped. ANNA. D:G: MAG: BRI: FR: ET. HIB: REG: *Rev.* Anne seated,   *AV*   700   1300
r., presents a charter to kneeling clergy. PIETAS. AVGVSTÆ. *Ex.* PRIMITIIS. ET. DECIMIS.   *AR*   65   110
ECCLESIÆ. CONCESSIS. MDCCIV. *D.* 44 mm. By J. Croker. *MI ii*, 251/43; *Farquhar* 1913/217   *AE*   20   35

This medal was also struck from another obverse die (No. 450). Refers to an act introduced by Anne, whereby monies
which the crown had received from the Church were reinvested for the benefit of the poorer clergy.

405*   **Battle of Schellenberg 1704**
Obv. Bust r., armoured. LVD. WILH. M. BADEN. EX. CAES. GEN. LOC. *Rev.* View of a military   *AR*   90   160
encampment; river god in foreground displays a crown. HOSTE CAESO FVGATO CASTRIS
DIREPTIS. *Ex.* AD SCHELLENBERGAM DONAWERDAE. 1704. *Edge.* VIRTVTE PRINCIPIS ET SOCIORVM
VIA VICTORIIS INSEQVENTIBVS APERTA   *D.* 37 mm. By G. Hautsch. *MI ii*, 252/45; *W & Z* 49;
v. Loon IV, 418. *See* **Plate 14**

406*   **Battle of Blenheim 1704**
Obv. Busts, armoured, facing each other. EUGENIUS D. SABAUDIAE IOH. D. MARLEBOROW. *Ex.*   *AR*   400   700
HIC POLLUX. HIC CASTOR ADEST. QUOS GLORIA FRATRES HOOGSTETTEQUE FACIT. NUNC QUOQUE.   *WM*   45   100
GALLE. TUMES? *Rev.* Panoramic view of a large battle, Fame hovering above. PIACULA
TEMERITATIS GALLICAE. *Ex.* GALLE, RETRO PROPERA, VULTUS PERFERRE DECOROS NON POTES,
AUT TUMULUM SERVITIUMVE VIDE. XIII. AUG. MDCCIIII. *D.* 57 mm. [By M. Smeltzing] *MI ii*,
260/55; *v. Loon IV*, 424. *See* **Plate 14**

Francis Eugène, Prince of Savoy (1663–1736), Austrian general; victorious with Marlborough in several campaigns. More
than twelve medals commemorate the battle of Blenheim.

407*   ——
Obv. Bust r., armoured. IOH. D. MARLEBVRG. ANG. EXER. CAPIT. GENER. *Rev.* Mars seated, l.,   *AV*   500   900
leaning on his shield, inscribed MARS VLTOR, watches a scene of battle. MIRATVR TELIS   *AR*   90   160
AEMVLA TELA SVIS. *Ex.* OB GALLOS ET BAVAROS DEVICTOS. TALLARDO DVC. AD HOCHSTAD. CAPTO   *AE*   35   55
1704. *Edge.* FORTVNÆ OBSEQVENTI DVCIS FORTISSIMI POST PRIMITIAS SCHELLENBERGICAS   *D.*
37 mm. By G. Hautsch. *MI ii*, 256/50; *v. Loon IV*, 427. *See* **Plate 14**

This medal also occurs with the obverse of No. 420. Camille de Tallard (1652–1728), French marshal; defeated by
Marlborough at Hochstädt.

			£	£
408	*Obv.* Bust r., armoured and draped. EVGENIVS FRANC. DVX SAB. CÆS. EXER. GENER. COMM. *Rev.*	AV	500	900
	Army routed within an encampment; above, angel with a flaming sword. GENIIE VIRTVTE	AR	90	160
	BONI. II. REG. 19. *Ex.* GALLIS BARAVISQ. CÆSIS TALLARDO CUM X. MILI. AD HOCHSTAD. CAPT.	WM	15	30

408

Obv. Bust r., armoured and draped. EVGENIVS FRANC. DVX SAB. CÆS. EXER. GENER. COMM. *Rev.* Army routed within an encampment; above, angel with a flaming sword. GENIIE VIRTVTE BONI. II. REG. 19. *Ex.* GALLIS BARAVISQ. CÆSIS TALLARDO CUM X. MILI. AD HOCHSTAD. CAPT. 1704. *Edge.* GLORIA AD TIBISCVM HVNGARIÆ PARTA, RENOVATVR AD DANVBIVM GERMANIÆ   *D.* 37 mm. [By G. Hautsch.] *MI ii*, 258/53–4; *v. Loon IV*, 427   AV 500 900 / AR 90 160 / WM 15 30

Struck from more than one pair of dies.

409

Obv. Bust l., draped. ANNA. D:G: MAG: BR: FRA: ET. HIB: REG. *Rev.* Britannia seated upon a globe, r., Victory in her hand, regards a captive seated on military trophies. DE. GALL: ET. BAV: AD. BLENHEIM. *Ex.* CAPT: ET. CAES: XXXM. SIGN. RELAT. CLXIII. MDCCIV. *D.* 34 mm. By J. Croker. *MI ii*, 256/49; *v. Loon IV*, 427   AV 400 700 / AR 28 55 / AE 15 30

Struck from more than one pair of dies.

410   **Capture of Gibraltar; Naval Engagement off Malaga 1704**

Obv. Bust l., draped. ANNA. D:G: MAG: BRI: FRA: ET. HIB: REG: *Rev.* Neptune in his marine car offers his trident and crown to Britannia. VICTORIÆ. NAVALES. *Ex.* CALPE. EXPVG. ET. GALL. VICT. MDCCIV. *D.* 40 mm. By J. Croker. *MI ii*, 266/64; *MH 1919*, 132; *v. Loon IV*, 454   AV 400 750 / AR 35 65 / AE 15 30

411*   **British Victories 1704**

Obv. Bust l., draped. ANNA. D.G. MAG. BR. FR. ET. HIB. REGINA. *Rev.* Britannia seated beneath a palm tree decorated with three shields, inscribed DE GALL ET BAVA AD DONAWERD / DE GALL. ET BAVA ITER. AD HOCHSTAD / GERMANIA LIBERATA HOSTIB FVGAT. Beyond, GIBRALTAR, and a fleet. DIVES TRIVMPHIS ANGLIA. *Ex.* FRETO. GADITAN. OCCVPAT. CLASSE. GALL. FVGATA. MDCCIV. *Edge.* IN OMNI GENTE, QVAE AVDIERIT NOMEN TVVM, MAGNIFICABITVR SVPER TE DEVS ISRAEL. IVDITH. XIII 31   *D.* 40 mm. By G. Hautsch. *MI ii*, 270/70; *MH 1919*, 135; *v. Loon IV*, 454. *See* **Plate 14**   AR 100 180 / WM 15 30

Commemorating military and naval victories at Donauwerth, Gibraltar, and Hochstädt.

412*   **Prince James (III), Legitimacy of Succession 1704**

Obv. Bust l. IAC. III. D.G. MAG. BRIT. REX   *Rev.* Radiate sun dispelling clouds above sea. VIRTUS. MOX. NUBILA. PELLET. *Ex.* 1704   *D.* 29 mm. By N. Roettiers. *MI ii*, 270/71; *CP* 60/33. *See* **Plate 15**   AR 80 150 / AE 35 65

413   **John Locke, Memorial 1704**

Obv. Bust almost facing, draped. IOHANNES LOCKE. *Rev.* Justice and Liberty seated upon a sarcophagus, an infant at their feet reading. *Ex.* M. 1704. *D.* 41 mm. By J. Dassier. *MI ii*, 271/72; *Storer* 2245   AR 45 80 / AE 7 15 / WM 3 7

Struck *c.*1740. John Locke (1632–1704), philosopher.

414   **Dr. Giorgio Baglivi 1704**

Obv. Bust r., draped. G. BAGLIVUS. MED. IN. ROM. ARCHIL. P. ET. SOC. REG. LOND. COLL   *Rev.* Tripod between medical implements, encircled by a serpent. .VNAM. FACIEMVS. VTRAMQVE. *Ex.* MDCCIIII. *D.* 40 mm. By F. St. Urbain. *MI ii*, 272/75; *Storer* 141   AR 130 200 / AE 70 110

A variety occurs without the date. Giorgio Baglivi F.R.S. (1669?–1707), Italian physician.

415*   **John Ray, Memorial 1705**

Obv. Bust of Ray three-quarters, l., draped. ÆT. 77. *Ex.* INO RAY: FRS. NAT 1627. OBT. 1704   *D.* 42 mm. by 53 mm. Oval, cast. (By G. D. Gaab?) *MI ii*, 273/76. *See* **Plate 15**   AE 70 —

Made *c.*1750; dated in the old style. Examples also occur without a reverse. John Ray (1627–1705), naturalist.

416   **Marriage of George Augustus and Caroline 1705**

Obv. Bust r., armoured and draped. GEORG. AVG. PRINC. ELECTORAL. BR & L. *Ex.* FLAMMAE FELICES   *Rev.* Bust r., draped. WILHEL. CAROL. MARCH. BRAND. *Ex.* QVAS MVTVVS EXCITAT ARDOR. *Edge.* CONNVBIO IVNCTI HERNHVSAE. ANN. MDCCV. II. SEPT. *D.* 65 mm. By E. Hannibal. *MI ii*, 277/82   AV 1500 2800 / AR 180 350

George Augustus, Electoral Prince of Hanover (1683–1760), George II 1727–60; Queen Caroline Wilhelmina Charlotte of Anspach (1683–1737).

417   **Barcelona Taken 1705**

Obv. Bust r., laureate, armoured and draped. CAROLVS. III. D.G. HISPANIARVM. REX. *Rev.* Fleet before a city under bombardment. MAGNORVM. HAEC. PORTA. LABORVM. *Ex.* BARCINO. CAPTA. PRID. EID. OCT. CIƆIƆCCV. *D.* 44 mm. By J. Boskam. *MI ii*, 279/84; *v. Loon V*, 19   AR 120 220

418   **Barcelona Relieved 1706**

Obv. As No. 409. *Rev.* Sun eclipsed above city and harbour. BARCELONA. LIB. GALLIS. FVG. *Ex.* I. MAII. MDCCVI. *D.* 35 mm. By J. Croker. *MI ii*, 280/86; *MH 1919*, 136; *v. Loon V*, 22   AR 28 55 / AE 15 30

Struck from more than one pair of dies.

			£	£

419 **Battle of Ramillies 1706**
Obv. As No. 409. *Rev.* Map of the conquered provinces displayed by two Fames; town in
the distance. GALLIS. AD. RAMELLIES. VICTIS. XII. MAII. MDCCVI. *Ex.* FLANDR: ET. BRABANT:
RECEPT: *D.* 34 mm. By J. Croker. *MI ii*, 284/92; *v. Loon V*, 33; *Forrer* I/475
Struck from more than one pair of dies.

AV	350	650
AR	28	55
AE	15	30

420 **Battle of Ramillies; Conquest of Brabant 1706**
Obv. Bust almost facing, armoured and draped. IOH. D.G. S.R.I. PR. D. MARL. EXERC. ANGL. C.
G. *Rev.* Mars bearing shields of Brabant, Flanders and Antwerp, and captured trophies,
strides over the enemy lying prostrate. PRETIVM NON VILE LABORVM *Ex.* GALLIS ACIE
DEVICTIS. BRABANTIA. FLANDR, ET. ANTWERP. XV. DIER. SP. EREPT. 1706. *Edge.* MARTE FEROX, ET
VINCI NESCIVS ARMIS. VIRG. *D.* 38 mm. By G. Hautsch. *MI ii*, 287/95; *v. Loon V*, 33

AV	500	900
AR	90	160
WM	15	30

421 **Victories over Louis XIV 1706**
Obv. Anne, as Minerva, subdues Louis XIV armed as a Roman warrior. LVDOVICVS MAGNVS
ANNA MAIOR. *Rev.* Victory advancing, l.; behind, a military trophy inscribed CLADES GALLOR.
IN BRAB. 23. MAI on a shield. CVRA PVGNACIS FACTA MINERVAE *Ex.* XII. VRBES CVM PROVINCIIS
INTRA XV. D: RECEPTÆ. 1706 Border of twelve shields inscribed BRVSSELLA, MECHLINA,
LIERA, ANTVERPIA, FVRNA, ALOSTVM, ATHVM, ALDENARDA, BRVGÆ, GANDAVIVM, DAMIVM, and
LOVANIVM *Edge.* DOMINVS TRADIDIT EVM IN MANVS FOEMINÆ. IVDITH.XVI.C. *D.* 43 mm. (By
P. H. Müller?) *MI ii*, 288/97; *v. Loon V*, 39

AR	100	170
WM	15	30

422 ——
Obv. As No. 421. *Rev.* A woman in a besieged tower casts stones down on the enemy.
PERCVTE ME NE DICATVR QVOD A FEMINA INTERFECTVS SIM. IVDIC.C. 9. *Edge.* As No. 421. *D.*
43 mm. (By P. H. Müller?) *MI ii*, 289/98; *v. Loon V*, 39

AR	90	160
AE	30	50
WM	15	30

423 **Union of England and Scotland 1707**
Obv. Bust l., crowned and draped. ANNA. DEI. GRATIA. MAG: BRITAN: FRA: ET. HIB: REGINA.
Rev. Statue of Anne, as Pallas. NOVÆ. PALLADIVM. TROIÆ. *D.* 69 mm. [By J. Croker] *MI ii*,
298/115; *v. Loon IV*, 349

AV	1200	1800
AR	170	300
AE	40	75

424* ——
Obv. Bust l., crowned and draped. ANNA. D:G: MAG: BRI: FR: ET. HIB: REG: *Rev.* British shield
within the Garter, crowned, upon a pedestal inscribed with the double cypher of A R;
supported by a lion and unicorn. MAII I. MDCCVII *D. a* 47 mm.; *b* 26 mm. By J. Croker. *MI
ii*, 295/107–10; *Farquhar* 1913/202, 1914–5/226. See **Plate 15**
Each was struck from more than one obverse die. Type *b* is on a thin flan.

a AV	700	1200
AR	65	140
AE	20	35
b AR	8	15

425 ——
Obv. As No. 409. *Rev.* Arms of Britain upon escutcheon, supported on a platform inscribed
SEMPER EADEM, and decorated with a rose and thistle; two infant genii support a crown above
the arms, and collar and George of the Garter below. *D.* 34 mm. By J. Croker/S. Bull. *MI ii*,
296/111–13; *Farquhar* 1913/260
Struck from several pairs of dies.

AV	350	650
AR	28	55
AE	15	30

426* **Brokers' Pass 1707**
Obv. Royal arms and motto. *Rev.* Arms and motto of the City of London; space below (for
holder's name). *Ex.* Double cornucopiae. *D.* 40 mm. Cast. (By?) *Caldecott* 1. See **Plate 15**
Given by the Corporation of the City of London to each sworn broker upon admission; it was to be produced if an anxious
client required evidence of their *bona fide* status. The frequency with which examples of this and No. 473 occur in a worn
state suggests that they saw considerable use, unlike those issued subsequently. *See also* Nos. 936, 1239 and 2126.

AR	85	—

427 **Prince James (III), Restoration of the Kingdom 1708**
Obv. Bust l., armoured and draped. IACOBVS. III. D.G. M. B. F. ET. H. REX. *Rev.* Map of Great
Britain and Ireland, marked ANGLIA. L, SCOT E, and HIB. D; ships around the coast. REDDITE
IGITVR. *D.* 51 mm. By N. Roettiers. *MI ii*, 314/136; *CP* 62/36 var.
This medal was struck with another obverse die, reading ∴ CVIVS EST ∴ (*MI ii*, 314/135).

AR	190	350
AE	90	150

428 ——
Obv. Bust of Prince James, r., laureate, armoured and draped. CVIVS. EST. *Rev.* Map of Great
Britain and Ireland, marked BRIT. L, SCOT. E, and HIB. D; ships around the coast. REDDITE. *D.*
38 mm. By N. Roettiers. *MI ii*, 312/133; *v. Loon V*, 98

AR	120	220
AE	55	90

429 ——
Obv. Bust of Prince James, l., laureate. .CUIUS. .EST. *Rev.* Map of Great Britain and Ireland,
marked BRIT, SCOT and HIE; ships around the coast. REDDITE. *D.* 30 mm. By N. Roettiers. *MI
ii*, 313/134; *v. Loon V*, 98
This medal was also struck with two similar reverse dies: one with only capital cities, D[ublin], E[dinburgh] and L[ondon]
identified; the other with an unmarked map.

AR	70	130
AE	30	55

430*   **Attempted Invasion of Scotland 1708**

         £   £

Obv. Bust l., laureate and draped. ANNA D.G. MAGN: BRIT: FRANC: ET HIB: REGINA. *Rev*.   *AR*   170   300

Sceptre of Providence entwined with a rose and thistle: to l., prisoners conducted to the   *WM*   35   65

Tower; to r., the ship SALISBURI amongst a fleet. QUIS NOS IMPUNE LACESSET UNITAS. *Ex*.

IRRITO SPURII IACOBI REDITU IN SCOTOS. CLASSE GALLICA EXTERNATA. M.DCCVIII. *D*. 47 mm. By

M. Smeltzing. *MI ii*, 318/143; *MH* 1919, 141. *See* **Plate 15**

At least six medals commemorate the attempted invasion.

431   ——

Obv. As No. 410. *Rev*. Britannia, armed, protects the crouching figure of Scotia from the   *AR*   55   95

French fleet in flight; one of their ships lying obstructed in the harbour. CLASSE. GALL. FVG.   *AE*   20   35

Ex. AD. FRETVM. EDENBVRG. XIV. MARTII. MDCCVIII. *D*. 40 mm. By J. Croker/S. Bull. *MI ii*,

316/141; *MH* 1919, 139; *v. Loon V*, 103; *CP* 27/7

432   ——

Obv. As No. 411. *Rev*. English fleet in pursuit of the French; coast of SCOTIA beyond. FVGERE   *AR*   90   160

NON FALLERE. TRIVMPHVS. *Ex*. GALLORVM. CONATVS. IN. SCOTIAM. ANNAE M. VIGILANTIA.   *AE*   30   55

ELVSI. CIƆIƆCCIIX *Edge*. SIC PVERI NASVM RHINOCEROTIS HABENT *D*. 40 mm. By G.   *WM*   15   30

Hautsch. *MI ii*, 317/142; *MH* 1919, 140; *CP* 23/2; *v. Loon V*, 100

433   **Battle of Oudenarde 1708**

Obv. Similar to 424 *a*. *Rev*. Two captives at the base of a column, surmounted by Victory   *AR*   85   180

and decorated with captured French standards. GALLIS. AD. ALDENARD. VICTIS   *Ex*. XXX.   *AE*   25   45

IUNII. MDCCVIII. *D*. 44 mm. By J. Croker. *MI ii*, 322/148; *v. Loon V*, 106

At least six medals commemorate this battle.

434   **Capture of Sardinia and Minorca 1708**

Obv. As No. 410. *Rev*. Victory standing on a conch floating in the sea; on either side,   *AV*   400   750

beyond, are two islands. SARDINIA. ET. BALEARIS. MINOR. CAPTÆ   *Ex*. MDCCVIII. *D*. 40 mm.   *AR*   55   95

By J. Croker. *MI ii*, 329/157; *MH* 1919, 146; *v. Loon V*, 95   *AE*   15   30

435   **Capture of the Citadel of Lille 1708**

Obv. Similar to No. 424a. *Rev*. Victory holding the shield of Lille above a plan of its   *AV*   700   1200

fortifications. INSVLÆ. CAPTÆ. MDCCVIII. *D*. 44 mm. By J. Croker. *MI ii*, 338/169; *v. Loon V*,   *AR*   75   170

119   *AE*   25   45

At least eight medals record the actions at Lille.

436   **Capture of Tournay 1709**

Obv. A Spanish ship, with French colours, in heavy seas on which are bales, one marked   *AR*   120   190

DORNIK, of jettisoned cargo. NE PEREAT PERDIT. *Rev*. City under bombardment. SOLVTA   *AE*   35   60

CATENIS INSVRGIT. *Ex*. TORNACVM CAPTVM. MDCCIX. *Edge* REGNI COLLAPSA RVVNT IMMANIA   *WM*   15   25

MEMBRA. VIRGIL   *D*. 44 mm. (By P. H. Müller?) *MI ii*, 356/193; *v. Loon V*, 141

This medal also occurs with the standing figures of the Genius of Tournay and Victory on the obverse. At least six medals

commemorate the capture of Tournay.

437   ——

Obv. As No. 410. *Rev*. Pallas seated, r., beside military trophies; town in the distance.   *AR*   35   65

TORNACO. EXPVGNATO. *Ex*. MDCCIX. *D*. 40 mm. By J. Croker. *MI ii*, 354/190; *v. Loon V*, 141   *AE*   15   30

  WM   10   20

438   **Battle of Malplaquet 1709**

Obv. Similar to 424 *A*. *Rev*. Battle scene in a wood; Victory hovering with two laurel   *AR*   75   170

wreaths. CONCORDIA. ET. VIRTVTE. *Ex*. GALLIS. AD. TAISNIERE. DEVICTIS. AVG: XXXI. MDCCIX.   *AE*   25   45

D. 47 mm. By J. Croker. *MI ii*, 359/197; *v. Loon V*, 145

This battle is commemorated by at least five medals.

439*   ——

Obv. Busts face to face, armoured and draped. EVGENIVS. FRANC. DVX. SABAVD. IOHANNES.   *AR*   90   160

DVX. D. MARLB. S.R.I.P. *Rev*. Sun, partially obscured by clouds, above an open landscape.   *WM*   15   30

CRVENTVS OCCIDIT. *Ex*. GALLI AD. MONTES HAN. VICTI. A. MDCCIX. D. XI. SEPT. *D*. 44 mm. By G.

Hautsch. *MI ii* 360/198; *v. Loon V*, 145. *See* **Plate 15**

This medal was also struck from an unsigned obverse die.

440   **Capture of Mons 1709**

Obv. As No. 410. *Rev*. Victory flying, l.; a city, beyond. MONTIBVS. IN. HANNONIA. CAPTIS.   *AR*   35   65

Ex. MDCCIX. *D*. 40 mm. By J. Croker/S. Bull. *MI ii*, 362/202; *v. Loon V*, 149   *AE*   15   30

			VF	EF
			£	£

441 Henry Newton 1709
Obv. Bust r., draped; 1709, below. HEN. NEWTON. ABLEG. EXT. BRIT. AD. M. ETRVR. D. ET. R.P.   *AE*   450   800
GEN. *Rev.* Pallas and Prudence stand in a landscape, embracing; cities in the distance.
ALTERIVS. ALTERA. POSCIT. OPEM   *D.* 86 mm. Cast. By M. Soldani-Benzi. *MI ii*, 367/209;
Johnson 133

Sir Henry Newton (1651–1715), Italian scholar; Queen Anne's ambassador in Genoa, and envoy for the Grand Duke of
Tuscany.

442 Trial of Dr. Henry Sacheverell 1710
Obv. Bust almost facing, in clerical robes. H: SACH. D:D: *Rev.* A mitre. :IS: FIRM: :TO: THEE: *AR*   50   90
D. 35 mm. Cast. (By?) *MI ii*, 367/210

This medal also occurs with a bust of Pope Innocent XI on the reverse. Henry Sacheverell (1674?–1724), political
preacher.

443* Capture of Douay 1710
Obv. Bust l., laureate and draped. ANNA AVGVSTA   *Rev.* Victory attaches a shield, inscribed   *AR*   75   170
SALVS PROVIN, to column standing amongst captured French trophies; beyond, enemy in   *AE*   25   45
flight. VALLO. GALLORVM. DIRVTO. *Ex.* ET. DVACO. CAPTO. MDCCX. *D.* 48 mm. By J. Croker.
MI ii, 369/213; *v. Loon V*, 165. *See* **Plate 15**

This medal was struck from two obverse dies. At least four medals commemorate the capture of Douay.

444 ——
Obv. Sun disappearing behind a terrestrial globe. DEFECTVM LVMINE VIDIT. *Rev.* Two   *AR*   90   160
soldiers seated playing dice, with counters labelled MONS, RUSEL, DORNIC, ARRAS, PARIS and   *AE*   35   60
DOVAY, the last of which they exchange. SPES PERDENS. *Ex.* DVACVM GALLIS PACEM SPERN.   *WM*   15   30
EREPTVM. MDCCX. *D.* 44 mm. (By M. Brunner?) *MI ii*, 371/216; *v. Loon V*, 165

445 Battle of Almenara 1710
Obv. As No. 443. *Rev.* A heated cavalry engagement. PVGNA. EQVESTRIS. *Ex.* HISPANIS. AD.   *AR*   85   180
ALMENARAM. VICT. IVLII. XVI. MDCCX. *D.* 48 mm. By J. Croker. *MI ii*, 373/218; *v. Loon V*,   *AE*   30   55
157; *Forrer* I/476

This medal was struck from two obverse dies.

446* Battle of Saragossa 1710
Obv. As No. 443. *Rev.* Victory presents captured Spanish standards to Anne, enthroned.   *AV*   750   1300
HISPANIS. PROFLIGATIS. *Ex.* AD. CÆSARIAM. AVGVSTAM. AVG. IX. MDCCX. *D.* 48 mm. By J.   *AR*   75   170
Croker. *MI ii*, 373/219; *v. Loon V*, 159. *See* **Plate 15**   *AE*   20   40

This medal was struck from two obverse dies.

447 Capture of Bethune, St. Venant, and Aire 1710
Obv. As No. 443. *Rev.* A trophy of captured French arms and standards. BETHVNIA. FANO.   *AR*   75   170
S^TI. VENANTII. ET. ARIA. CAPTIS. *Ex.* INSPECTANT. GALL. CENT. MILL. MDCCX. *D.* 48 mm. By J.   *AE*   20   35
Croker. *MI ii*, 374/220; *v. Loon V*, 171

This medal was struck from two obverse dies.

448* Successes of the Dukes of Marlborough and Savoy 1710
Obv. As No. 439. *Rev.* Five compartments containing views of DOVAY. / S. VENANT. /   *AR*   90   160
BETHVNE. / ARIEN., that at the top containing a general view of passing troops. MVNIMENTA   *WM*   15   30
OCCVPATA. *Ex.* MDCCX. *Edge.* ARMORVM FOEDERATORVM FRVCTVS   *D.* 44 mm. By G. Hautsch.
MI ii, 377/223; *v. Loon V*, 171. *See* **Plate 15**

This medal was also struck from an unsigned obverse die.

449* Prince James (III), Legitimacy of Succession 1710
Obv. Bust of Prince James, laureate, l. DOMINUM. COGNOSCITE. VESTRUM .·.   *Rev.* Sheep in a   *AR*   80   140
landscape. COGNOSCUNT. ME. MEÆ   *Ex.* 1710. *Edge.* Grained. *D.* 30 mm. By N. Roettiers.   *AE*   35   60
MI ii, 380/229; *CP* 63/38. *See* **Plate 15**

This medal also occurs with the same obverse as No. 455.

450 French Lines Passed, Bouchain Taken 1711
Obv. Bust l., laureate and draped. ANNA. AVGVSTA. *Rev.* French soldier surrenders his sword   *AR*   75   170
to a female figure seated amongst captured arms and holding a shield inscribed FORTVNA   *AE*   20   35
MANENS; town in distance. HOSTES. AD. DEDITIONEM. COACTI. *Ex.* VALLO. GALLORVM.
SVPERATO. ET. BVCHEMIO. CAPTO. MDCCXI. *D.* 44 mm. By J. Croker/S. Bull. *MI ii*, 385/237;
v. Loon V, 188

451 Concord of Britain 1711
Obv. Bust l., draped. ANNA. D.G. MAG. BR. FR. ET. HIB. REGINA. *Rev.* A harp. DVLCE MELOS   *AR*   85   160
VNITA SONNAT (chronogrammatic date). *Ex.* CONCORDIA BRITANNORVM. *D.* 44 mm. By P. H.   *WM*   12   25
Müller. *MI ii*, 386/238

			£	£

452   **John Molesworth 1712**
Obv. Bust r., draped; MDCCXII below. IO. MOLESWORTH. ABLEG. EXT. BRIT. AD. M. ETRVR. D.   *AE*   450   800
Rev. Prudence and Plenty, attended by Peace and Commerce, hold a wreath over a blazing   *Pb.*   80   —
altar decorated with an armorial shield. GLORIÆ. PRINCIPVM   *D.* 92 mm. Cast. By A. Selvi.
MI ii, 390/244

John Molesworth, 2nd Viscount Molesworth (1679–1726), diplomat; ambassador to the European courts, most notably that of Tuscany.

453   **Richard Molesworth 1712**
Obv. Bust r., helmeted, armoured and draped. RICCARD. MOLESWORTH. BRIT. TRIB. MIL. *Rev.*   *AE*   450   800
Bellona, rushing across a rocky landscape strewn with armour, withholds the advance of
Fortune. PER ARDVA   *D.* 89 mm. Cast. [By A. Selvi] *MI ii*, 391/245; *Forrer* V/473

Richard Molesworth, 3rd Viscount Molesworth (1680–1758), Field Marshal and Marlborough's aide-de-camp; brother of John.

454   **Prince James (III) and Princess Louisa, Memorial 1712**
Obv. Similar to No. 427. *Rev.* Bust l., draped. PRINCEPS. LVD. SER. M. B. REGIS. SOROR.   *a AR*   130   250
1712   *D.* 51 mm. By N. Roettiers. *MI ii*, 388/241; *CP* 63/40   *AE*   60   110

Type *b* is cast, unsigned, undated, and with stippled fields. Princess Louisa Mary (1692–1712), sister of Prince James.   *b AR*   220   —

455*   ——
Obv. Bust l., laureate. IACOBVS. III. D.G. M. B. F. ET. H. REX   *Rev.* Bust l. PRINCEPS. LVD. SER.   *AR*   70   130
MAG. BRI. REGIS. SOROR. *Edge.* Grained. *D.* 30 mm. By N. Roettiers. *MI ii*, 389/243; *CP*   *AE*   40   70
65/43. *See* **Plate 15**

456   **Prince James (III), Legitimacy of Succession c.1712**
Obv. Busts, r., of James II and Mary, conjoined, he laureate. IACOBUS. II. ET. MARIA. D.G.   *AR*   220   —
MAG. BRI. FRAN. ET. HIB. REX. ET. REGIN. *Rev.* Similar to the obverse of No. 427. *D.* 51 mm.   *AE*   80   —
Cast. [By N. Roettiers] *MI ii*, 216/540; *CP* 64/61

The medal has a stippled field; it also occurs without an obverse legend. The portraits are after G. Bower, No. 285.

457   ——
Obv. Similar to No. 443. *Rev.* Bust l. armoured and draped; similar to *obv.* of No. 427. CVIVS   *AE*   70   —
EST   *D.* 47 mm. Cast. [By N. Roettiers] *MI ii*, 382/232; *Farquhar* 1914–15, 267

458   **Peace of Utrecht 1713**
Obv. Bust l., laureate and draped. ANNA. D:G: MAG: BRI: FR: ET. HIB: REG: *Rev.* Britannia   *AV*   900   1500
seated l., with olive-branch, spear and shield; beyond, l., ships, and r., farming scene.   *AR*   100   180
COMPOSITIS. VENERANTVR. ARMIS. *Ex.* MDCCXIII. *D.* 58 mm. By J. Croker. *MI ii*, 399/256;   *AE*   40   75
v. Loon V, 230

459   ——
Obv. As No. 371, but temple door inscribed ANNO MDCCXIII: and in *Ex.* TRAIECTUM   *Rev.*   *AV*   800   1200
As No. 371. *D.* 48 mm. By D. Drappentier. *MI ii*, 402/262; *v. Loon V*, 227   *AR*   150   280

The amendment to this medal may have been made by D. Drappentier's son Jan.

460*   ——
Obv. Bust l., laureate and draped. ANNA. D.G. MAG. BRI. FR. ET. HIB: REG. *Rev.* Britannia   *AV*   350   650
standing l., holding olive-branch, shield and spear; beyond, l., ships, and r., farming scene.   *AR*   25   55
COMPOSITIS. VENERANTVR. ARMIS. *Ex.* MDCCXIII. *D.* 35 mm. By J. Croker. *MI ii*, 400/257;   *AE*   15   30
v. Loon V, 230. *See* **Plate 16**

Struck from several pairs of dies. A less common reverse has a different legend and Britannia without a shield.

461   **Death of Sophia, Electress of Hanover 1714**
Obv. Bust r., veiled and draped. SOPHIA. D.G. EX. STIRPE. EL: PAL: ELECT: VID: BR: ET. LVN: *AR*   180   350
MAG. BRIT: HAERES. *Rev.* Trees growing in a well-ordered garden; sun, radiate, setting over
distant mountains. TRANSMISSA LVCE REFVLGET   *Ex.* OBIIT. VIII. IVN. M.D.CC.XIV. *D.* 66 mm.
By E. Hannibal. *MI ii*, 410/274

462   **Anne, Memorial 1714**
Obv. Bust l., wearing a bandeau and draped. ANNA D.G. M. BR. FR. ET HIB. REGINA. *Rev.* Fame   *AR*   27   55
reveals a medallion of Prince George on an obelisk, decorated with military trophies,   *AE*   4   9
inscribed NATA 6. FEBR. 1665. CORONAT. 23. APR. 1702. MORT. I. AVG. 1714. *D.* 41 mm. By J.
Dassier. *MI ii*, 417/292

Struck in 1731, from Dassier's series of English kings and queens. *See* No. 526.

PLATE 15

412

415

424

426

430

439

443

446

448

449

455

PLATE 16

460

464

467

469

470

476

484

489

493

GEORGE I, 1714–27

                                                        £   £

463   **George I Proclaimed King 1714**

Obv. Bust r., armoured and draped. GEORGIVS. D.G. MAG. BRIT. FR. ET. HIB. REX. *Rev.* George standing, r., attended by Religion, is crowned with a laurel wreath by Liberty and offered symbols of sovereignty by Britannia. PRINC: OPT: RELIGIONIS ET LIBERTATIS CVSTODI *Ex.* PVBLICA AVCTORITATE PROCLAMATO $\frac{1}{12}$ AVG. ANNO MDCCXIIII. *D.* 67 mm. By E. Hannibal. *MI ii*, 420/2; *v. Loon V*, 251

	AV	—	—
	AR	400	750
	AE	90	160

464*   **Accession of George I 1714**

Obv. Bust r., laureate and draped. GEORG LVD. D.G. M. BRIT. FR. ET HIB. REX DVX B & L, S.R.I. ELEC. *Rev.* A star in the midst of the constellation of Leo. REGNORVM ALBIONIS NVNC IVRA GEORGIVS INTRAT. ANNO MDCCXIV. D. XII. AVGVSTI. *D.* 44 mm. [By G. Vestner] *MI ii*, 421/4. *See* **Plate 16**

AR	160	300

465   ——

Obv. As No. 464. *Rev.* Map of north-west Europe over which a horse leaps from HANOVER to LONDON. Other countries and cities identified. aCCeDens DIgnVs DIVIsos orbe brItannos. (chronogrammatic date). *Ex.* VNVS NON SVFFICIT ORBIS. *D.* 44 mm. [By G. Vestner] *MI ii*, 422/5

AV	900	1600
AR	170	330

466   **George I, Arrival in England 1714**

Obv. Bust r., laureate, armoured and draped. GEORGIVS. D:G. MAG. BRI. FRA. ET HIB REX. F. D. *Rev.* The King, as Neptune, approaches the coast in his marine car. RECTOR. MARIVM. *Ex.* ADVENTVS. REGIS. IN. BRITANNIAM. 18. SEPTEMB: 1714. *D.* 67 mm. By J. Croker. *MI ii*, 422/6; *v. Loon V*, 252

AR	170	320
AE	60	110

467*   **George I, Entry into London 1714**

Obv. Bust r., laureate, armoured and draped. GEORGIVS. D.G. MAG. BRI. FRA. ET. HIB. REX. F. D. *Rev.* The King, in a carriage, before the Royal Exchange, is presented with the City keys by Londinia. LÆTITIA PVBLICA *Ex.* ADVENTVS. REGIS. IN. VRBEM. 20. SEPT: 1714. *D.* 47 mm. By J. Croker. *MI ii*, 423/7; *v. Loon V*, 253. *See* **Plate 16**

AR	85	160
AE	25	45

468   **Coronation of George I 1714**

Obv. Bust r., laureate, armoured and draped. GEORGIVS. D.G. MAG. BRIT. FR. ET. HIB. REX. *Rev.* The King, enthroned beneath a canopy, is crowned by Britannia. *Ex.* INAVGVRAT. $\frac{31}{20}$ OCT. MDCCXIIII *D.* 51 mm. By E. Hannibal. *MI ii*, 423/8

AV	1200	2000
AR	170	320

469*   ——

Obv. As No. 464. *Rev.* Equestrian figure of St. George, l., slaying the Dragon, while Victory, hovering above, crowns him. FIDEI DEFENSOR ET AEQVI. *Ex.* CORONATVS 31. OCT. MDCCXIIII *D.* 44 mm. By G. Vestner. *MI ii*, 425/12. *See* **Plate 16**

AR	150	290
AE	50	90

470*   ——

Obv. Bust r., laureate, armoured and draped. GEORGIVS. D:G. MAG. BR. FR. ET. HIB. REX. *Rev.* The King enthroned, r., is crowned by Britannia. *Ex.* INAVGVRAT. XX. OCT. MDCCXIIII. *D.* 34 mm. By J. Croker. *MI ii*, 424/9; *v. Loon V*, 255; *Wollaston* 11. *See* **Plate 16**

AV	350	750
AR	25	65
AE	15	35

The official coronation issue; struck from several pairs of dies.

471   **George I** *c.*1714

Obv. Bust r., laureate, armoured and draped. GEORGIVS. D: G: M: B: F: ET: H: REX. F: D: *Rev.* Royal shield within the Garter. *Ex.* DIEV. ET. MON. DROIT., on a scroll. *D.* 25 mm. (By?) *MI ii*, 428/18

AR	8	15

Struck from several pairs of dies.

472   **North American Indian Chiefs' Medal** *c.*1714

Obv. Bust r., laureate, armoured and draped. GEORGE. KING. OF. BRITAIN. *Rev.* An American Indian firing an arrow at a deer standing on a hill beneath a tree; radiate sun, above. *D.* 41 mm. (By?) *Jamieson* l; *Betts* 163

AE	600	—

There are several variations of this piece, one of which is signed T.C. From time to time the British Government presented medals to North American Indian chiefs: as tokens of friendship; rewards for loyalty; and to signify the conclusion of treaties. *See* Nos. 514, 654, 707, 736, 1061, 1141, 1347, 1590, 1610.

473   **Brokers' Pass** *c.*1714

Obv. Royal Arms and motto DIEU ET MON DROIT *Rev.* Arms and motto of the City of London; below, a plaque (blank, for holder's name). *Ex.* Double cornucopiae. *D.* 39 mm. (By?) *Caldecott* 2

AR	65	—

Issues of this piece, formerly cast and latterly struck, were used up to *c.*1800. *See* No. 426

			£	£

474   **Sir Andrew Fountaine 1715**

Obv. Bust r., draped. ANDREAS. FOVNTAINE. EQVES. AVRATVS. ANGLVS. 1715. *Rev.* Pallas standing, l., amongst classical ruins and works of art, points to medals lying upon a tomb. *D.* 87 mm. Cast. By A. Selvi. *MI ii*, 433/30; *Johnson* 165

        AR   —   —
        AE   400   700
        Pb.   70   —

The obverse occurs with the reverse of No. 453. Andrew Fountaine (1676–1753), Warden of the Mint; connoisseur and collector.

475   **Battle of Sheriffmuir (Dunblain) 1715**

Obv. Bust r., laureate, armoured and draped. GEORGIVS. D:G: MAG: BR: FR: ET. HIB: REX. F: D. *Rev.* Victory, wielding a sword, hotly pursues fleeing cavalry. PERJURII. ULTRIX. *Ex.* AD. DVNBLAINVM. 13. NOV: 1715. *D.* 45 mm. By J. Croker. *MI ii*, 434/33; *CP* 29/1

        AR   85   180
        AE   25   45

This medal was struck from more than one pair of dies.

476*   **Capture of Preston 1715**

Obv. Similar to No. 475. *Rev.* Two captives chained to the base of an ornamental pedestal decorated by military trophies. FIDES MILITVM. *Ex.* REBELL: AD. PRESTON. CAPT: 13. NOV: 1715   *D.* 45 mm. By J. Croker. *MI ii*, 435/34; *CP* 29/2. *See* **Plate 16**

        AR   85   180
        AE   30   55

477   **James (III), Failure to Recover the Throne in 1708 and 1716**

Obv. Bust of Prince James, r., laureate, armoured and draped. NIHIL EFFICIENS   *Rev.* Map of Great Britain, marked SCOTIA 1708. M. MART. 1716. M. FEBR. BRITANNIA, HIBERNIA; ships around the coast. BIS VENIT VIDIT NON VICIT FLENSQVE RECESSIT * *D.* 33 mm. (By G. Vestner?) *MI ii*, 436/35; *MH* 1919, 149; *CP* 65/44

        AR   220   400

478   **Passing of the Act of Grace and Free Pardon 1717**

Obv. Similar to No. 475. *Rev.* Winged figure of Clemency standing, l., leaning against a column, touches a serpent's head with a caduceus. CLEMENTIA. AVGVSTI. *Ex.* MDCCXVII   *D.* 45 mm. By J. Croker. *MI ii*, 437/37; *CP* 30/3

        AR   85   160
        AE   20   35

An amnesty was offered to those engaged in recent rebellions. This medal was struck from two obverse dies.

479   **Treaty of Passarowitz 1718**

Obv. Similar to No. 475. *Rev.* The King, in Roman dress, stands beneath an ornamental tent and indicates the area of Morea on a globe. PACIS. ARBITER. *Ex.* INTER. GERMAN: TURC: ET. VENET: AD. PASSAROWITZ. 1718. *D.* 45 mm. By J. Croker. *MI ii*, 437/39

        AR   75   140
        AE   20   35

This medal was struck from more than one pair of dies. George I acted as mediator between Austria, Turkey and Venice.

480   **Alliance between George I and Emperor Charles VI 1718**

Obv. Bust r., laureate, armoured and draped. GEORG. D.G. MAG. BR. FR. ET. HIB. REX. *Rev.* Bust r., laureate, armoured and draped. CAROLVS. VI. D.G. ROM. IMP. SEMP. AVG. *D.* 31 mm. By J. Dassier. *MI ii*, 442/46

        AR   25   45
        AE   8   15

481   **Spanish Fleet Destroyed off Cape Passaro 1718**

Obv. Similar to No. 475. *Rev.* Statue of the King, as Neptune, upon a rostral column amidst captured naval trophies. SOCIORVM PROTECTOR. *Ex.* CLASSE. HISP: DELETA. AD. ORAS. SICILÆ. 1718. *D.* 45 mm. By J. Croker. *MI ii*, 439/42; *MH* 1919, 150

        AV   750   1400
        AR   75   140
        AE   20   35

This medal was struck from more than one obverse die.

482   **William Penn, Memorial 1718**

Obv. Bust r., draped. WILLIAM PENN. B. 1644. D. 1718. *Rev.* Penn and a North American Indian clasp hands. BY DEEDS OF PEACE   *Ex.* PENSYLVANIA SETLED 1681   *D.* 40 mm. By L. Pingo. *MI ii*, 438/40; *BHM* 201; *Betts* 531

        AR   180   350
        AE   80   140

Struck c.1780. More recent strikings from a new die have been noted; these omit the flaw at two o'clock on the obverse which is present on the original die. William Penn (1644–1718), founder of the proprietary colony of Pennsylvania.

483   **Joseph Addison, Memorial 1719**

Obv. Bust r., draped. JOSEPHUS ADDISON   *Rev.* NATUS AN. M.DC.LXII. MISTON VILTONIAE IN ANGLIA OBIIT AN M.DCC.XIX. *Ex.* SERIES NUMISMATICA UNIVERSALIS VIRORUM ILLUSTRIUM M.DCCC.XXIII. DURAND EDIDIT   *D.* 41 mm. By E. Rogat. *MI ii*, 444/50

        AR   16   35
        AE   3   7

Struck in Paris in 1823, from a series commemorating famous people of all countries. Joseph Addison (1672–1719), essayist, poet and statesman.

484*   **Princess Clementina, Escape from Innsbruck 1719**

Obv. Bust l., draped. CLEMENTINA. M. BRITAN. FR. ET. HIB. REGINA. *Rev.* Clementina hurriedly departing in a carriage; Rome in the distance. FORTVNAM. CAVSAMQVE. SEQVOR   *Ex.* DECEPTIS. CVSTODIBVS. MDCCXIX. *D.* 48 mm. By O. Hamerani. *MI ii*, 444/49; *CP* 65/45. *See* **Plate 16**

        AR   120   220
        AE   35   65

George I was against the marriage between Princess Maria Clementina (?–1735), (grand-daughter of John Sobieski, king of Poland), and James (III). She was arrested by Charles VI on her way to Rome and confined to Innsbruck Castle, from where she managed to escape.

485   **Marriage of James (III) and Princess Clementina 1719**

		£	£
Obv. Bust r., armoured and draped. IACOBVS. III. D.G. M. B. F. ET. H. REX *Rev.* Bust l.,	*AR*	120	220
draped. CLEMENTINA. MAGNAE. BRITANNIAE. ET. C. REG. *D.* 48 mm. By O. Hamerani. *MI ii,*	*AE*	40	75
446/52; *Farquhar 1923–24,* 219			

486   ————

Obv. Busts r., conjoined and draped, he armoured and she wearing a bandeau. IACOB. III. R.	*AR*	80	150
CLEMENTINA. R. *Rev.* Hercules takes the hand of Venus, attended by Cupid. REGIVM	*AE*	30	55
CONNVBIVM *Ex.* KAL. SEPTEMBER MDCCXIX. *D.* 41 mm. By O. Hamerani. *MI ii,* 445/51; *CP*			
66/47			

487   **Birth of Prince Charles 1720**

Obv. Busts r., conjoined and draped, James laureate and armoured. IAC. III. ET CLEM. D.G.	*AR*	90	180
MAG. BRIT. REG. *Rev.* Providence holds an infant wearing a badge on a ribbon. SPES	*AE*	35	70
BRITANNIÆ *Ex.* CAR. WALL. PR. NATUS. DIE. ULT. A. 1720 *D.* 43 mm. [By N. Roettiers] *MI*			
ii, 453/61; *Farquhar 1923–24,* 220			

Some examples exhibit speckling and flaws, and may be later strikings from rusted dies. Prince Charles Edward Louis Philip Casimir Stuart (1720–88), born in Rome; commonly referred to as the 'Young Pretender', 'Young Chevalier', or 'Bonnie Prince Charlie'.

488   ————

Obv. As No. 486. *Rev.* Providence, leaning against a column, indicates to an infant in her	*AR*	80	150
arms the territories of Britain and Ireland, labelled ING. SC. and IRL. on a globe. PROVIDENTIA	*AE*	30	50
OBSTETRIX *Ex.* CAROLO. PRINC: VALLIÆ NAT: DIE. VLTIMA A: MDCCXX. *D.* 41 mm. By O.			
Hamerani. *MI ii,* 452/60; *CP* 68/49			

489*   **John Law 1720**

Obv. Standing figure of Law holding a ship, and scroll, inscribed LOVISIANA EST EST BANCO	*AR*	350	650
ET MONETA: above, Fame blows two trumpets out of which issue LAVS IN ASTRIS. and LAVS IN	*WM*	45	80
TERRIS. To l., Envy seated in a cave. *Ex.* INVIDIAM VIRTVTE PARTAM GLORIAM NON INVIDIAM			
IVDICO. CIC.P.CAT.I. C.12. *Rev.* INVIDIA LVCRIPETAS ALLICIS VANAE VENDITIONE SPEI. LAVS			
QVOD VERVM EST. LATEAT QVAMIS. ALIQVANDO PATEBIT. INVIDIA AVRIFEROS VENDIS MONTES:			
POTIERIS AHENIS! LAWS QVICQVID SVB TERRA EST, IN APRICVM PROFERET AETAS. HORAT. I. EP. 6.			
AVTOR PASCITVR IN VIVIS LIVOR: POST FATA QVIESCIT: TVNC SVVS EX MERITO QVOQVE TVETVR			
HONOS. OVID. I. AMOR. 15. ARG. STRANSB. F. 1720. *D.* 44 mm. (By C. Wermuth?) *MI plates*			
CXLIV/1; *Betts* 114; *Law 2. See* **Plate 16**			

At least thirty medals, mostly of a satirical nature, commemorate Law and the collapse of his financial scheme, the 'Mississippi System'. John Law (1671–1729), Scottish financier and speculator.

490   ————

Obv. A windmill, its sails issuing objects, banknotes BILLETS, stock certificates ACTIEN, and	*AR*	170	300
coins. LES RICHESSES DE FRANCE *Ex.* 1720. *Rev.* EN MAGNAS DAT OPES CELEBER LAVV	*WM*	35	65
FOENORE QVESTVS, in the centre. KOMT SEHT DAS FRANTZ VOLCK AN! HERR LAVV THVT			
GROSSE THATEN! (chronogrammatic date). *D.* 32 mm. (By C. Wermuth?) *MI plates,*			
CLXIV/4–5; *Betts* 130; *Law 3*			

See No. 489.

491   ————

Obv. Half-length rear view of figure wearing a tricorn; MDCCII on their belt. VISIBILIS.	*AR*	90	150
INVISIBILIS. BANQVERODT IFT A LA MODE *Rev.* Prostrate figure of an old man holds a packet	*AE*	45	85
inscribed WEXL BRIEFE. and a caduceus. CREDIT IST MAUSE-TODT *D.* 26 mm. (By C.	*WM*	20	45
Wermuth?) *MI ii,* 451/59; *Betts* 115; *Law 27*			

See No. 489.

492   **Caroline, Princess of Wales** *c.*1720

Obv. Bust r., draped. WILHELMINA: CHARLOTTA: PRIN. WALLIÆ. *Rev.* A rosebush. ROSA:	*AE*	18	35
SINE: SPINA. *D.* 36 mm. (By J. Croker?) *MI ii,* 443/47			

Precisely what occasion this medal commemorates is unclear. The Princess of Wales, wife of George II, was usually known as Wilhelmina Charlotta until she ascended the throne in 1727.

493*   **Jacobite Appeal against the House of Hanover 1721**

Obv. Bust of Prince James r., armoured and draped. VNICA SALVS *Rev.* Hanoverian Horse	*AR*	100	180
tramples upon the British Lion and Unicorn; beyond, view of London. QVID. GRAVIVS.	*AE*	35	60
CAPTA *Ex.* MDCCXXI *D.* 50 mm. [By O. Hamerani] *MI ii,* 454/63; *CP* 68/51. *See* **Plate 16**			

494   **Death of the Duke of Marlborough 1722**

Obv. Bust r., armoured and draped. IOHANNES CHVRCHIL. S.R.I. P. DVX DE MARLBOROVGH.	*AR*	120	220
Rev. Victory, bearing two wreaths, walks over Mars and Death. MARS ALTER MARLBROVGH DE	*AE*	35	65
MARTE ET MORTE TRIVMPHAT. *Ex.* MDCCXXII. *D.* 49 mm. By G. Vestner. *MI ii,* 456/67			

			£	£

495 ——
Obv. Bust three-quarters, r., armoured and draped. IOHAN. CHURC. DUX MARLB. *Rev.*   AR   35   65
Victory, bearing a wreath and palm, stands between military trophies. VBI ADERAT IBI   AE   15   25
VICTORIA. *Ex.* OB. 27. JUN. 1722. NAT. ANN. 74. *D.* 42 mm. By J. Dassier. *MI ii*, 457/68   WM   3   9
Struck *c*.1740.

496* **Jacobite Conspiracy Discovered 1723**
Obv. A bishop holding a document, facing, seated in discussion with four others at a round   Pb.   250   —
table. DeCretVM est regno brIto restItVatVr abaCtVs (chronogrammatic date). *Ex.*
CONSPIRATIO = *Rev.* The same group are taken by surprise, observed by the celestial Eye
of Providence and smitten by lightning. ConspIrate aperIt DeVs et Vos fVLMIne
pVLsat (chronogrammatic date). *Ex.* BRITANNICA. *D.* 39 mm. (By C. Wermuth?) *MI ii*,
459/70. *See* **Plate 17**
A conspiracy to restore the Stuarts to the English throne.

497 **Christopher Wren, Memorial 1723**
Obv. Bust l., draped. CHRISTOP. WREN. EQVES. AVR &. ARCHITECT. .OBIIT. A.D. 1723. ÆT. 91.   AE   450   800
Rev. View of the main front of St. Paul's Cathedral. VNVM. PRO. CVNCTIS. .FAMA. LOQVATVR.
OPVS. .INCEPTA. AD. 1675 PERFECT. A.D. 1711. *Ex.* AEDES. S. PAVLI. LOND. *D.* 96 mm. Cast. By
G. D. Gaab. *MI ii*, 458/69; *Eidlitz* 1927, 1073. *See* frontispiece.
Christopher Wren (1632–1723), architect; professor of astronomy.

498 **Conyers Middleton 1724**
Obv. Bust r., draped; 1724 below. CONYERS. MIDDLETON. S. T. P. *Rev.* Curtain opened to   AE   180   330
reveal books on shelves and on a table. ACADEMIÆ. CANTABRIGIENSIS. PROTO.
BIBLIOTHECARIVS. *D.* 86 mm. Cast. By G. Pozzo. *MI ii*, 460/71; *Johnson* 209; *Storer* 2441
Conyers Middleton (1683–1750), divine; chief librarian at Cambridge. The medal records the eminence of Cambridge and
its library as a seat of learning.

499 **Starkey Myddelton 1724**
Obv. Naked boy and girl standing side by side, hands joined, upon a pedestal. .STARKEY   AR   100   —
MYDDELTON. MAN. MIDWIFE LONDON .1724. *Rev.* Armorial shield on an escutcheon with   Br.   55   —
motto, SPES IN DEO, and crest. *D.* 37 mm. Cast. (By?) *MI ii*, 461/72; *Storer* 2579
Starkey Myddelton (1688–1768), practised surgery in London. He published two papers in the *Philosophical Transactions*:
an account of an extra-uterine conception, 1744–5, vol. 43, pp. 336–40; an account of a child being taken out of the
abdomen after having lain there for upwards of sixteen years, during which time the woman had four children, all born
alive, 1747, vol. 44, pp. 617–21.

500 **William Wake 1725**
Obv. Bust r., in clerical robes. GUILIELMUS WAKE ARCH. CANT. *Rev.* JLLUSTRIUM VIRORUM QUI   AR   24   50
VERÆ RELIGIONI CHRISTIANÆ BONISQUE LITTERIS JN EUROPA RENOVANDIS RESTAURANDISQUE   AE   7   15
ADLABORARUNT JCONES VERISSIMAS REVERENDISSIMO IN CHRISTO PATRI GUILIELMO WAKE
ARCHIEPISCOPO CANTUARIENSI TOTIUS ANGLIÆ PRIMATI ET METROPOLITANO OFFERT, DICAT
DEDICATQUE JOANNES DASSIER GENEVENSIS. M.DCC.XXV. *D.* 42 mm. By J. Dassier. *MI ii*,
462/73
William Wake (1657–1737), Archbishop of Canterbury. Dassier's dedicatory medal for his series of Protestant Reformers.
See Nos. 34 and 361.

501 **Order of the Bath Revived 1725**
Obv. Head r., laureate. GEORGIVS. D.G. MAG. BR. FR. ET. HIB. REX. F. D. *Rev.* Standing figure of   AV   800   1400
Prince William, facing, dressed as Knight of the Bath. SPES. ALTERA. *Ex.* ORD. EQVIT. BALN.   AR   85   160
REST. ET. INSIG. AVCT. MDCCXXV. *D.* 46 mm. By J. Croker. *MI ii*, 463/75   AE   25   45
Prince William Augustus, Duke of Cumberland (1721–65), military commander; 3rd son of George II and Caroline. The
Most Honourable Order of the Bath (motto: 'Tria juncta in uno', Three joined in one; that is, England, Ireland and
Scotland) was formally constructed by Henry IV in 1399; after the coronation of Charles II it was neglected until being
revived by George I.

502 **Daniel Wray 1726**
Obv. Bust r., draped; 1726 on truncation. DANIEL. WRAY. ANGLVS. AET. XXIV. *Rev.* NIL ACTVM   AE   150   250
REPVTANS CVM QVID SVPERESSET AGENDVM   *D.* 70 mm. Cast. By G. Pozzo. *MI ii*, 465/78
Daniel Wray (1710–83), antiquary.

503* **Gibraltar Besieged by the Spanish Fleet 1727**
Obv. Bombardment between a fleet and land forces. VINCERE AVT MORI. *Ex.* GIBRALTAR   AR   170   330
OBSESSA D. XXII. FEBR. MDCCXXVII. *Rev.* SED DATVR TERTIVM. MINVS PERICVLOSVM ABIRE. *D.*   AE   70   120
41 mm. (By G. Vestner?) *MI ii*, 468/82; *MH* 1919, 155. *See* **Plate 17**

504 **Death of Isaac Newton 1727**
Obv. Bust l., draped. ISAACVS. NEWTONVS. *Rev.* Science, seated against a table, displays a   AV   700   1100
diagram of the planetary system. FELIX. COGNOSCERE. CAVSAS   *Ex.* M.DCC.XXVI   *D.* 51 mm.   AR   80   140

		VF	EF
By J. Croker. *MI ii*, 469/83; *Hocking* 234/7	AE	18	35

Dated in the old style. Sir Isaac Newton (1642–1727), natural philosopher and mathematician; Master of the Mint, 1699–1727.

505 ——

Obv. Bust almost facing, draped, head three-quarters r. ISAACUS NEWTONIUS. *Rev.* Newton's monument (in Westminster Abbey), the base inscribed NAT. 1642. M. 1726. *D.* 43 mm. By J. Dassier. *MI ii*, 470/85; *Hocking* 234/8

	AR	45	80
	AE	7	15

Dated in the old style.

506 ——

Obv. Bust three-quarters r., draped. ISAACUS NEWTONIUS *Rev.* EQ. AUR. PHILOSOPHUS. OBIIT 31. MART. 1727. NATUS ANNOS 85., within a wreath. *D.* 33 mm. [By J. Dassier] *MI ii*, 470/84; *Hocking* 234/9

	AR	25	40
	AE	8	15

507 Death of George I 1727

Obv. As No. 480. *Rev.* Britannia seated mournfully, l., holding a medallion of GEORG[E] II. D.G. M. B. F. H. R.; beyond, a fleet. MAGNI SOLATIA LUCTUS *Ex.* .1727. *D.* 31 mm. By J. Dassier. *MI ii*, 474/92

	AR	25	45
	AE	8	15

508 George I, Memorial 1727

Obv. Bust r., laureate and armoured. GEORGIUS. I. D.G. MAG. BR. FR. ET. HIB. REX. *Rev.* Monument flanked by Justice and Religion, inscribed NAT. 18. MAI. 1660. CORONAT. 21. OCT. 1714. M. 12. IUN. 1727. *D.* 41 mm. By J. Dassier. *MI ii*, 475/94

	AR	27	55
	AE	4	9

Struck in 1731, from Dassier's series of English kings and queens. *See* No. 526.

GEORGE II, 1727–60

509 Accession of George II 1727

Obv. Bust l., laureate, armoured and draped. GEORGIVS. II. D.G. MAG. BRIT. FR. ET. HIB. REX. F. D. *Rev.* Hanoverian Horse advancing, l., over rugged ground. NEC ASPERA TERRENT *Ex.* SVCCESSIO ELECTORALIS MDCCXXVII *D.* 63 mm. By E. Hannibal. *MI ii*, 476/1; *Forrer* II/422

	AR	500	900

510 Coronation of George II 1727

Obv. Bust l., laureate, armoured and draped. GEORGIVS. II. D.G. MAG. BR. FR. ET. HIB. REX. *Rev.* The King enthroned, r., is crowned by Britannia. VOLENTES. PER. POPULOS. *Ex.* CORON. XI. OCTOB. MDCCXXVII. *D.* 34 mm. By J. Croker. *MI ii*, 479/4; *Wollaston* 12

	AV	400	900
	AR	30	65
	AE	20	40

The official coronation issue; struck from more than one pair of dies.

511 ——

Obv. Bust l., laureate, armoured and draped. GEORGIVS II. D.G. MAG. BR. FR. ET. HIB REX. *Rev.* The King enthroned, r., is crowned by Britannia. VOLENTES. PER. POPVLOS. *Ex.* CORON. XI. OCTOB. MDCCXXVII. *D.* 34 mm. By T. Tibs. *MI ii*, 479/5

	AE	12	25

A coarse copy of No. 510.

512 Coronation of Caroline 1727

Obv. Bust l., wearing a bandeau, draped. CAROLINA. D:G. MAG. BR. FR. ET. HIB. REGINA. *Rev.* The Queen stands, facing, between Religion and Britannia. HIC. AMOR HÆC. PATRIA. *Ex.* CORON. XI. OCTOB. MDCCXXVII *D.* 34 mm. By J. Croker. *MI ii*, 480/8; *Wollaston* 14

	AV	450	1000
	AR	30	65
	AE	25	45

The official coronation issue; struck from more than one pair of dies.

513 ——

Obv. Bust l., draped. CAROLINA. D.G. MAG. BR. FR. ET. HIB. REGINA *Rev.* The Queen stands, facing, attended by Religion and Britannia. HIC. AMOR HÆC. PATRIA *Ex.* CORON. XI. OCTO MDCCXXVII *D.* 24 mm. By T. Tibs. *MI ii*, 481/9

	AE	8	15

A coarse copy of No. 512, with several varieties.

514* North American Indian Chiefs' Medal c.1727

Obv. Bust l., laureate, armoured and draped. GEORGIVS. II. DG. MAG. BR. FR. ET. HIB. REX. *Rev.* A deer in flight, l., from an arrow fired by an American Indian standing beneath a tree. *D.* 25 mm. (By?) *Jamieson* 5. *See* **Plate 17**

	AE	600	—

The portrait is based on that of No. 510. *See* No. 472.

515 Death of John Freind 1728

Obv. Bust l. IOANNES. FREIND. COLL. MED. LOND. ET. REG. S.S. *Rev.* An ancient and a contemporary physician (Freind?) stand facing each other, their hands clasped; medical

	AE	45	75

implements at their feet. MEDICINA. VETVS. ET. NOVA. *Ex.* VNAM FACIMVS VTRAMQVE. *D.* 57 mm. By F. St. Urbain. *MI ii*, 488/28; *Storer* 1122

John Freind (1675–1728), physician and politician.

			£	£

516   **Frederick, Prince of Wales 1729**
Obv. Bust of Frederick upon a pedestal, flanked by Fame and Britannia; above, infant genius bearing Prince's plumes and motto. FRIDERICUS WALLIÆ PRINCEPS ÆT. XXII. *Ex.* MDCCXXIX. *Rev.* An eagle trains her young one to fly towards the meridian sun from a rocky summit; beyond, ships at sea. VIRTUTE INGENITA FORTIS DUCTUQUE PARENTIS. *Ex.* SIC ITUR AD ASTRA. *D.* 40 mm. By J. Dassier. *MI ii*, 489/29

Frederick Lewis (1707–51), eldest son of George II and Caroline; father of George III.

AR   24   50
AE   7   15

517   **William Congreve, Memorial 1729**
Obv. Bust r., draped GULIELMUS CONGREVE. *Rev.* NATUS AN. M.DC.LXXII. BANDSAE IN COMITATU EBORACENSI APUD ANGLOS OBIIT AN. M.DCC.XXIX. *Ex.* SERIES NUMISMATICA UNIVERSALIS VIRORUM ILLUSTRIUM. M.DCC.XIX. DURAND EDIDIT. *D.* 41 mm. By A. Caqué. *MI ii*, 490/30

Struck in Paris in 1819, from a series commemorating famous people of all countries. William Congreve (1670–1729), dramatist.

AR   15   28
AE   3   7

518   **Death of Samuel Clarke 1729**
Obv. Bust almost facing, draped. SAMUEL CLARKE. *Rev.* A robed figure ascends a rocky mount, on the summit of which stands Truth pointing to heaven. QUO VERITAS VOCAT. *D.* 43 mm. By J. Dassier. *MI ii*, 490/31

Samuel Clarke (1675–1729), divine; mathematician and philosopher.

AR   24   50
AE   7   15

519   **George II, First Visit to Hanover 1729**
Obv. Bust l., laureate, armoured and draped. GEORGIVS sECVnDVs pRIMo BRVnsVICenses TERRAS REPETIt (chronogrammatic date). *Rev.* Mining activity in a landscape; Hanoverian Horse on a distant mound, with the motto NEC ASPERA TERRENT above. VND DA DIE SONNE AVFGING LEVCHTETE DAS GANTZE GEBIRGE DAVON. I. MACCAB.VI. 39. *Ex.* VERVM ERAT HOC DICTVM REGIS NON ASPERA TERRENT VERIVS HERCINIAM CVM VENIT ILLVD ERIT. *D.* 53 mm. By R. Wahl. *MI ii*, 491/32; *Müseler* 10.6.2/5

AR   400   700

520   **George II, Visit to the Hartz Mines 1729**
Obv. Bust r., laureate, armoured and draped. GEORGIVS. II. D G MAG. BRIT. FR. ET. HIB. REX. *Rev.* Wildman stands beside a pine-tree pouring coins from a cornucopia. NON SIBI SERVAT OPES IN PVBLICA COMMODA FVNDIT   *Ex.* Astronomical symbols of the Sun, Moon, Venus, Mars and Saturn, representing gold, silver, copper, iron and lead, between HERCYNIA DIVES   *D.* 50 mm. By E. Hannibal. *MI ii*, 492/33; *Müseler* 10.6.2/2

AR   300   550

521 *   **Jacobite Princes, Charles and Henry; Legitimacy of Succession** *c.*1730
Obv. Bust of Charles, r., armoured and draped, a star before him in the field. MICAT. INTER. OMNES   *Rev.* Bust of Henry, l., armoured and draped. ALTER. AB. ILLO. *Edge.* DIE. XXXI. DECEMBR. MDCCXX. EXTVLIT. OS. SACRVM. COELO   *D.* 41 mm. By O. Hamerani. *MI ii* 492/34; *CP* 69/52. *See* **Plate 17**

Examples also occur without a lettered edge. Prince Henry Benedict Maria Clement (1725–1807), Cardinal York; brother of Charles and last direct male descendant of the Stuart royal line.

AV   900   1600
AR   80   150
AE   25   40
WM   15   30

522   **State of Britain 1731**
Obv. Busts r., conjoined, laureate and draped, George II armoured and Caroline wears a bandeau. GEORGIVS II. & CAROLINA D.G. MAG. BR. FR & HIB. REX & REG. *Rev.* Britannia on a podium, enthroned, flanked by seated figures of Hanover and Germany. IMPERIVM SINE FINE DEDI. *Ex.* FELIX BRITANNIA. *D.* 44 mm. By P. P. Werner. *MI ii*, 499/46

AR   130   250

523   **Second Treaty of Vienna 1731**
Obv. Bust l., laureate. GEORGIVS. II. D:G: MAG: BRI: FRA: ET. H: REX. F. D. *Rev.* Neptune in his marine car commands tranquillity from the winds. PRÆSTAT. COMPONERE   *Ex.* FOEDVS. VIENNENSE M.DCC.XXXI. *D.* 47 mm. By J. Croker. *MI ii*, 496/39; *v. Loon suppl.* 58

The treaty concluded between England, France, Holland, Spain and the Holy Roman Empire, settled disputes arising from the Spanish Succession.

AV   800   1300
AR   85   160
AE   25   40

524   **Queen Caroline 1731**
Obv. Bust r., wearing a bandeau, draped. CAROLINA. D.G. MAG. BR. FR. ET. HIB. REG. *Rev.* Charity, seated, with four children. DILECTA DEO ET HOMINIBUS. *D.* 41 mm. By J. Dassier. *MI ii*, 499/44

From Dassier's series of English kings and queens. *See* No. 526.

AR   27   55
AE   6   14

525 **George II** 1731
    Obv. Bust l., laureate, armoured and draped. GEORGIUS. II. D.G. MAG. BR. FR. ET. HIB. REX.   *AR*   35   65
    Rev. NUMISMATA REGUM ANGLIAE A GULIELMO PRIMO AD HAEC USQUE TEMPORA GEORGIO II.   *AE*   8   18
    MAGNAE BRITANNIAE FRANCIAE ET HIBERNIAE REGI SERENISSIMO ETC. DICATA A JOANNE DASSIER
    GENEVENSIS REIPUB. CÆLATORE MONETALI ANNO M.DCC.XXXI. *D*. 41 mm. By J. Dassier. *MI ii*,
    498/43

    The dedicatory medal of Dassier's series of English kings and queens. *See* No. 526.

526 **Kings and Queens of England** 1731

William I (No. 1)	Richard II (No. 13)	James I (No. 104)
William II (No. 2)	Henry IV (No. 15)	Charles I (No. 164)
Henry I (No. 3)	Henry V (No. 16)	Cromwell (No. 203)
Stephen (No. 4)	Henry VI (No. 17)	Charles II (No. 271)
Henry II (No. 5)	Edward IV (No. 20)	Mary (No. 364)
Richard I (No. 6)	Edward V (No. 21)	James II (No. 384)
John (No. 7)	Richard III (No. 22)	William III (No. 387)
Henry III (No. 8)	Henry VII (No. 25)	Anne (No. 462)
Edward I (No. 10)	Henry VIII (No. 27)	George I (No. 508)
Edward II (No. 11)	Edward VI (No. 30)	Caroline (No. 524)
Edward III (No. 12)	Mary (No. 38)	George II (No. 525)
	Elizabeth I (No. 79)	

    D. 41 mm. (except No. 203, which is 38 mm.) By J. Dassier.

    Type *a* consists of the thirty-four medals; they were issued by subscription, available in silver at fifteen guineas and in   *a AR*   — 2000
    bronze at six guineas. *See* Jean Dassier, *A Sett of Medals of all the Kings of England*, London, 1731. Bronze medals are   *AE*   — 400
    occasionally found damascened, whereby the relief is gilt and the field 'bronzed'.
    Type *b* is a set struck a little later from the original dies, and includes the memorial medal of George II (No. 681), making   *b AR*   — 1600
    thirty-five pieces altogether. They sometimes occur on wooden trays. Some of the later strikings have less definition and   *AE*   — 250
    exhibit minor traces of die-disorder; they have not been valued separately under the individual entries. On some medals
    the 1 in the date has been struck with a J; these have not been transcribed in the entry. *See* No. 1236.

527 **Royal Dublin Society, Boyle Medal** 1731
    Obv. Bust r., draped; ROBERTVS BOYLE behind head. IN HONOREM ROBERTI BOYLE ET   *AR*   35   55
    AUGMENTUM SCIENTIARUM. FELIX QUI POTUIT RERUM COGNOSCERE CAUSAS. *Rev*. Minerva   *AE*   15   28
    seated, l., holding trident and cornucopia. REGALIS: SOCIETAS: DUBLINENSIS: CONDITA: A:S:
    MDCCXXXI *D*. 72 mm. By A. Wyon. *BHM* 3652; *Went* 1973, 42

    Struck from 1899 and usually found awarded in bronze. The Royal Dublin Society was founded in 1731 for the
    improvement of husbandry, manufactures and other useful applications of arts and sciences; since *c*.1760 they have issued
    more than forty various medals, mostly as prizes. Robert Boyle (1627–91), natural philosopher and chemist.

528 **Royal Family** 1732
    Obv. Busts face to face, draped; he armoured. GEORGIVS. II. REX. ET. CAROLINA. REGINA. *Ex*.   *AV*   1800 3200
    MDCCXXXII   *Rev*. Busts of the seven royal children. FELICITAS. IMPERII *Ex*. FREDERICVS P: *AR*   270   500
    WALLIÆ. GVLIELMVS. D: CVMBRIÆ. ANNA. AMELIA. CAROLINA. MARIA. LVDOVICA. PRINCIPES. *D*.   *AE*   80   150
    69 mm. By J. Croker/J. S. Tanner. *MI ii*, 500/47   *WM*   30   65

    Frederick Lewis, Prince of Wales (1707–51); Anne, Princess Royal (1709–59); Amelia Sophia Eleonora (1710–86);
    Caroline Elizabeth (1713–57); William Augustus, Duke of Cumberland (1721–65); Mary (1722–72); Louisa (1724–51).
    Another child, George William (1717), died in infancy.

529 **Charles Sackville** 1733
    Obv. Bust r., draped CAROLVS. SACKVILLE. MAGISTER. FLº: 1733   *Rev*. Harpocrates, finger on   *AR*   160   280
    his mouth, leans against a column and holds a cornucopia; masonic implements on the   *AE*   80   150
    ground. .AB. ORIGINE. *D*. 44 mm. By L. Natter. *MI ii*, 504/51; *Shackles* 114; *Nau* 137

    Charles Sackville, Earl of Middlesex, 2nd Duke of Dorset (1711–69), politician and privy councillor; Master of a masonic
    lodge in Florence.

530 **Marriage of Princess Anne and William** 1734
    Obv. Busts r., conjoined and draped, William armoured and Anne wearing a bandeau.   *AV*   600 1000
    WILH. CAR. HENR. FRIS. AR. ET. NASS. PR. ANNA REG. M. BR. F. N. MAX. *Rev*. Two winged genii,   *AR*   90   150
    their hands clasped, support the shields of the two Houses before an orange-tree. FRONDOSA
    TVTIOR VLMO. *Ex*. FEL. PR. AR. C. PR. F. R. M. BR. CONI. A. 1734. *D*. 44 mm. By P. P. Werner. *MI*
    ii, 508/56; *v. Loon suppl*. 88

    William (IV) of Orange, Charles Henry Friso (1711–51), Stadholder of Holland.

531 **Anne and William, Arrival in Leeuwarden,** 1734
    Obv. Busts r., conjoined and draped, William armoured. W.C.H.F. PRINC. AVR. ET ANNA MAG.   *AR*   25   45
    BRIT. *Rev*. The couple in a marine car steered by Cupid, l. ADVENTVS PRINCIPVM AVRIAC. *Ex*.
    EX ANGL. IN FRIS. MDCCXXXIV. *D*. 29 mm. By M. Holtzhey. *MI ii*, 510/61; *v. Loon suppl*. 91

    This medal also occurs with three other reverses commemorating the occasion.

532　University of Göttingen Instituted 1734　　　　　　　　　　　　　　　£　£
Obv. Bust l., laureate, armoured and draped. GEORG. II. D.G. M. BRIT. F. ET. H. REX. F.D. B. ET.　*AR*　120　230
L. D. S.R.I. A. T. ET. E. *Rev.* Göttingen seated, r., amongst symbols of learning; an infant
genius, hovering above, crowns her with a wreath. Beyond, a canal winds its way towards a
city. IN PVBLICA COMMODA　*Ex.* ACADEMIA GEORGIA AVGVSTA GOTTINGAE FVNDATA
MDCCXXXIIII　*D.* 49 mm. By E. Hannibal. *MI ii*, 513/67; *Erlander* 66–7
Commemorates the foundation by George II and served as a prize. It was subsequently replaced by a medal of George III
(No. 816).

533　Weir Built at Hameln 1734
Obv. Similar to No. 532. *Rev.* Ships on the river Weser approach a weir; a town beyond.　*AR*　200　350
COMMERCIVM VISVRGIS RESTITVTVM　*Ex.* VNDAR. IMPETV CATARACTIS TEMPERATO PROPE
HAMELAM. MDCCXXXIIII　*D.* 49 mm. By E. Hannibal. *MI ii*, 512/66

534　Prince Charles and Prince Henry, Legitimacy of Succession *c.*1735
Obv. Bust of Charles r., armoured and draped; Wolf and Twins on truncation. HVNC.　*AR*　90　170
SALTEM EVERSO. IVVNEM　*Rev.* Bust of Henry, r., armoured and draped. TRIPLICIS. SPES　*AE*　30　55
TERTIA. GENTIS　*D.* 45 mm. [By O. Hamerani] *MI ii*, 493/35; *Farquhar* 1923–24, 218
The bust of Charles is almost fully draped, whilst that of Henry is almost fully armoured. The issue of this medal may be
connected with the death in 1735 of Princess Clementina, the Princes' mother. *See* No. 570.

535　Marriage of Frederick, Prince of Wales and Princess Augusta 1736
Obv. Busts face to face. FRIDERICVS LVDOV. WALLIÆ PRINCEPS. AVGVSTA SAXONIÆ. *Ex.*　*AR*　70　130
SPONSI　*Rev.* Crowned female figure standing, r., displays the united shields of England,
Hanover and Saxony, which she decorates with a wreath. AVSPICATVM MATRIMON. TRIVM
SAXONIAR. CONIVNCT. *Ex.* A. MDCCXXXVI. *D.* 42 mm. [By G. Vestner] *MI ii*, 514/69
Princess Augusta (1719–72), daughter of Frederick II, Duke of Saxe-Coburg-Gotha.

536　Princess Anne of Orange 1736
Obv. Armorial shields of Britain and Nassau, crowned and with supporters. WILH. CAR.　*AR*　70　130
HENR. FRIS. PRINC. AVR. ET. ANNA MAG. BRIT. *Rev.* Mother seated, r., ready to suckle a new-
born baby; beyond, wind blows an orange off a tree. SPES ALTERA SURGIT. *Ex.* OB PVERPERIVM
XVIIII DECEMB. MDCCXXXVI　*D.* 42 mm. By N. v. Swinderen. *MI ii*, 516/71; *v. Loon suppl.*
101
The child whose birth is recorded here, died within half an hour of the birth, as signified by the falling orange.

537　Jernegan's Lottery 1736
Obv. Minerva standing between military trophies and emblems of the Arts and Sciences.　*AR*　8　15
BOTH HANDS FILL'D FOR BRITAIN. *Ex.* GEORGE REIGNING. *Rev.* Caroline, royally robed, waters
a grove of young palm-trees. GROWING ARTS ADORN EMPIRE. *Ex.* CAROLINE PROTECTING.
1736　*D.* 39 mm. By J. S. Tanner. *MI ii*, 517/72; *Betts* 169
Given to purchasers of a lottery ticket for a silver cistern made by Henry Jernegan (?–1761), a London goldsmith and
banker.

538　Death of John Conduitt 1737
Obv. Bust r., draped. IOHANNES CONDUITT. REI MONET: PRÆF: *Rev.* Truth introduces　*AR*　80　150
Conduitt, standing r., to Hampden, holding staff with cap of liberty, and Newton, seated,　*AE*　30　55
leaning on a diagram of the planetary system. MEMORES FECERE MERENDO. *Ex.* M.DCC.XXXVII.
D. 58 mm. By J. S. Tanner [after H. F. Gravelot] *MI ii*, 518/73; *Forrer* VI, 16
John Conduitt (1688–1737), Master of the Mint; succeeded Isaac Newton in the post in 1727.

539　Breda Restored to the House of Orange 1737
Obv. As No. 536. *Rev.* Princess Anne and Prince William of Orange in a car, r., drawn by　*AV*　450　700
lion and unicorn; above, two Fames bear the shield of Breda, s c beneath. VIRTUS ET FAMA　*AR*　60　110
TRIUMPHANT. *Ex.* INAUGURATIO BREDÆ. XII: SEPT. 1737　*D.* 42 mm. By N. v. Swinderen. *MI*
ii, 518/74; *v. Loon suppl.* 117
The Restoration ended a long-running dispute with Prussia.

540　The Royal Society [of London], Copley Medal 1737
Obv. Pallas seated l., amongst symbols of learning, holds a wreath in an outstretched hand　*AV*　550　750
and embraces the figure of Nature. G. COPLEY BARᵀ DIGNISSIMO. *Ex.* Blank (for recipient's　*AR*　30　50
name). *Rev.* Armorial shield of the Royal Society. SOCIETAS REG. LONDINI. *Ex.* NULLUS IN　*AE*　20　30
VERBA (motto). *D.* 43 mm. By J. S. Tanner. *MI ii*, 522/81; *D & W* 160/456; *Brettauer* 2543
Sir Godfrey Copley, Baronet (1653?–1709), M.P.; controller of the army's accounts. In 1736 funds from Copley's bequest
were converted into a gold medal, presented annually for the most significant contribution to the advancement of natural
science; it is the Royal Society's highest award. A new design, prepared by M. Gillick, was introduced *c.*1950 and is
presented in gilt silver. *See* No. 1186.

541 James Oglethorpe, 'The Christian Hero' 1737

Obv. Bust almost facing, draped. IACOBUS. OGLETHORPIUS. ARMIGER. ADHUC VIVUS. 1737. *Ex.* NESCIT CEDERE *Rev.* Bust three-quarters r., in clerical robes. REV̄DISSIMUS. IOHĒS. TILLOTSONUS. CANT: ARCHIĒPUS. OB: 1694. *Ex.* ANGLIA MUNDO *D.* 42 mm. (By J. S. Tanner?) *MI ii*, 523/82; *Betts* 170

	£	£
AV	—	—
AR	300	550
AE	130	250

James Edward Oglethorpe (1696–1785), philanthropist and founder of Georgia, USA, where persecuted Protestants from central Europe sought asylum. The medal was intended as a prize of ten guineas in gold for the writer of a poem, entitled *The Christian Hero*. The exergue inscription on the obverse is sometimes missing.

542 Monument to John Milton 1737

Obv. Bust r., draped. IOHANNES. MILTONUS. *Rev.* E MARMORE IN ECCLESIA SANCTI PETRI APUD WESTMONASTERIUM ERECTORE GULIELMO BENSONO ARM. ANNO SALUTIS HUMANÆ MDCCXXXVII. RYSBRACHIUS SCULPSIT. *D.* 52 mm. By J. S. Tanner. *MI ii*, 524/83

AR	30	55
AE	15	25

William Benson (1682–1754), critic and politician; commissioned the monument from the Flemish sculptor John Michael Rysbrack (1693?–1770), and engaged Tanner to engrave the medal.

543 25th Anniversary of the Peace of Utrecht 1738

Obv. Belgium seated, r., before the Temple of Janus; a captive nearby, holding a book inscribed EUANGELIUM. Above, Fame blows two trumpets inscribed IUBILATE XXV on banners. V. LUSTR: FOED: BELG: PACE STABIL. *Ex.* XI. APRIL. MDCCXXXVIII *Rev.* Seven crowned shields of Britain, Denmark, France, Germany, Poland, Portugal and Spain suspended from a ribbon. ORBIS CHRISTIAN: QUIETE INTER SE COMPOSITA. *D.* 56 mm. By N. v. Swinderen. *MI ii*, 525/85; *v. Loon suppl.* 127

AR	100	180

544* Jonathan Swift 1738

Obv. In the centre, an oval frame containing a clerically robed bust, almost facing, attended by Hibernia, History and two winged figures; below, a scroll inscribed REV. I. SWIFT. DSPD *Rev.* Hibernia seated, l., in a pastoral landscape, leans upon her harp and holds an olive-branch; ships beyond. *Ex.* MDCCXXXVIII. *D.* 38 mm. Cast. By J. Roche. *MI ii*, 525/86; *Frazer* 1887/313. *See* **Plate 17**

AR	220	—

Rev. Jonathan Swift (1667–1745), Dean of St. Patrick's, Dublin; satirist and author of *Gulliver's Travels*. Champion of the people and promoter of Irish trade and commerce.

545* Beggars' Benison Club 1739

Obv. Adam and Eve, their hands joined, walk towards a bower. BE. FRUITFULL. AND. MULTIPLY *Rev.* Adonis, with spear and dog, stands behind a recumbent Venus attended by Cupid. LOSE. NO. OPPORTUNITY With integral suspension loop. *D.* 29 mm. by 40 mm. Oval. (By?) *MI ii*, 526/87. *See* **Plate 17**

AV	300	550
AR	50	90

Struck *c.*1820, possibly for use as an admission ticket or pass. It is usually gilt and with a suspension loop. The club was established in Anstruther, Scotland, as a place of frivolity for men of all classes. Two similar medals, both circular, were also struck.

546 Convention of Prado 1739

Obv. A man standing, in Spanish dress, holds a purse in his outstretched hand; beyond, two armed men pursue a third towards some ships. I. DON. BENIAMIN. MADE. THE. CONVENTION. *Ex.* BRAVEO. *Rev.* A Spaniard leans against a column, a full purse at his feet. ALL'S. UNDONE. NO. SEARCH *Ex.* 95.000 £. *D.* 30 mm. [By J. Roche] *MI ii*, 528/90

AE	25	45

Spain had agreed to pay compensation of £95,000 for damages to British shipping by marauding Spanish coastal patrol vessels. Benjamin Keene (1697–1757), diplomat, 'Don Benjamin', was the British signatory of the Convention. A similar piece was also struck.

547* Capture of Portobello 1739

Obv. Bust three-quarters l., draped. THE HON^BLE. EDW^D. ESQR. VICE ADMIRAL OF THE BLUE *Rev.* A large fleet of ships; above, Fame heralds their passage. *D.* 39 mm. Cast. (By?) *MI ii*, 530/92; *MH* 1919, 156; *Betts* 92. *See* **Plate 17**

AR	160	—
AE	90	—

Spain refused to pay Britain compensation as agreed at Prado (No. 546). In response to this and continuing attacks on British shipping, war was declared. Edward Vernon (1684–1757) was the commander of one of two squadrons despatched to the Spanish-American colonies. His victories at Portobello, and those at Fort Chagre and Carthagena (*see* Nos. 554 and 558), made him a popular hero. More than eighty medals, many with die varieties, commemorate Vernon's successes. Most were struck in an alloy of copper and zinc, produced by Christopher Pinchbeck (1670?–1732), inventor, toy and clock maker, after whom the metal has come to be known. Pinchbeck's sons, Edward and Christopher, may have manufactured these medals. Most are either anonymous or signed with just initials, such as: I.M.; I.W.; P.E.; T.B.; T.M. *See* L. McCormick-Goodhart, 'Admiral Vernon Medals', *Numismatic Review*, N. York, 1945.

548 ———

Obv. Half-length figures of Vernon, r., and Brown, three-quarters l., each in a frock-coat and holding a staff. ADMIRAL VERNON AND COMMODORE BROWN *Ex.* TOOK PORTO BELLO *Rev.* Six ships entering Portobello harbour. WITH. SIX. SHIPS. ONLY. NOV. 22. 1739 *D.* 38 mm. (By?) *MI ii*, 532/97; *MH* 1919, 259; *Betts* 266

Br.	20	45

Charles Brown (1685?–1753), naval officer; Vernon's second in command. *See* No. 547.

			£	£

549 ——

Obv. Shield of Britain, within the Garter, crowned, with supporters, motto and crest; G R above. *Rev.* Six ships entering Portobello harbour. PORTO. BELLO. TAKEИ. BY. ADMIRAL. VERИOИ. WITH. SIX. SHIPS. ИOV. 22. 1739. *D.* 38 mm. By I.W.(?) *MI ii*, 539/125; *MH* 1919, 264; *Betts* 270   *Br.*   15   32

See No. 547.

550* ——

Obv. Half-length bust, three-quarters l., in frock-coat and holding staff. THE. BRITISH. GLORY. REVIV.D. BY. ADMIRAL. VERNON   *Rev.* Six ships entering Portobello harbour. HE. TOOK. PORTO. BELLO. WITH. SIX. SHIPS. ONLY. *Ex.* BY. COURAGE. AND CONDUCT. *D.* 37 mm. (By?) *MI ii*, 536/110; *MH* 1919, 193; *Betts* 212. *See* **Plate 17**   *AR*   60   110   *Br.*   18   40

See No. 547.

551 ——

Obv. Bust r., armoured and draped. EDW. VERNON. ESQ: VICE. ADMIRAL. 1739. *Rev.* Vernon's ship (Burford) in full sail. .SUCCESS. TO. THE. BRITISH. FLEET. *D.* 33 mm. (By?) *MI plates* CLIV/13; *MH* 1919, 157   *AE*   55   —

See No. 547.

552 ——

Obv. Half-length bust, three-quarters l., in frock-coat and holding staff. ADMIRAL. VERNON. TOOK. PORTO. BELLO. *Rev.* Six ships entering Portobello harbour. .WITH. SIX. SHIPS. ONLY. NOV 22. 1739. *D.* 26 mm. (By?) *MI ii*, 540/127; *Betts* 191   *Br.*   10   25

See No. 547.

553 **Admiral Vernon: Duke of Argyle 1739**

Obv. Three-quarter length figure in frock-coat, almost facing, his hand resting on a cannon; beyond, ship at sea. NON. DORMIT. QUI. VINCIT   *Ex.* ADMIRAL. VERNON. 1739. *Rev.* Full-length draped figure, almost facing, leaning against a column on which rests a ducal coronet; behind, trophy of arms and standards. IN. HUNC. INTUENS. CLARUS. ESTO. *Ex.* DUKE OF ARGYLE   *D.* 40 mm. By I.M.(?) *MI ii*, 560/188; *MH* 1919, 323; *Betts* 245   *Br.*   28   65

John Campbell, 2nd Duke of Argyle (1678–1743), soldier and politician. *See* No. 547.

554 **Fort Chagre Taken 1740**

Obv. Half-length figure of Vernon, facing, in frock-coat and holding a staff: a tree, l.; A VIEW OF FORT CHAGRE above a ship, r. THE. BRITISH. GLORY. REVIV.D. BY. ADMIRAL. VERNON. *Rev.* Six ships entering Portobello harbour. HE. TOOK. PORTO. BELLO. WITH. SIX. SHIPS. ONLY. *Ex.* NOV. 22. 1739   *D.* 37 mm. (By?) *MI ii*, 546/150; *MH* 1919, 271; *Betts* 283   *AR*   60   110   *Br.*   18   40

See No. 547.

555 **John Frederick Ostervald 1740**

Obv. Bust l., in clerical robes. IOH. FRID. AB OSTERVALD. *Rev.* ECCL: NEOCOM: PASTOR SOCIET: REG: IN ANGLIA AD PROPAG: EVANG: INSTITUTÆ SOCIUS UT ET SOCIET: AD PROMOT: COGNIT: CHRISTIANÆ NAT: XXIV NOV: AN: MDCLXIII. / 1740. Above, sun dispersing clouds; below, palm branches. *D.* 43 mm. By J. Dassier. *MI ii*, 557/184   *AR*   45   75   *AE*   12   20

John Frederick Ostervald F.R.S. (1663–1747), Swiss pastor.

556 **Martin Folkes 1740**

Obv. Bust r., wearing a cap and draped. MARTINUS FOLKES ARMᴿ. *Rev.* SOCIETATIS REGALIS LONDINI SODALIS. M.DCC.XL. within an ornamental device. *D.* 54 mm. By J. A. Dassier. *MI ii*, 558/185; *Forrer* I/511   *AR*   80   150   *AE*   20   45

Martin Folkes (1690–1754), antiquary and man of science. From J. A. Dassier's series of celebrated contemporaries. *See* Nos. 563–4, 8, 577, 580, 583–90.

557 **Birth of Princess Elizabeth Caroline 1740**

Obv. Busts r., conjoined and draped, Frederick armoured and Augusta wearing a coronet. FRIDERICVS WALLIAE PRINC. ET AVGVSTA D.S. *Rev.* Eternity seated, l., a figure of Palladium on her outstretched hand. AETERNITAS IMPERII BRITANNICI   *Ex.* FECVNDITATE AVGVSTAE DOMVS. MDCCXXXXI. *D.* 41 mm. By J. C. Koch. *MI ii*, 559/186   *AR*   65   110

Dated in the new style. Elizabeth Caroline (1740–59), daughter of Frederick, Prince of Wales and Augusta.

558 **Carthagena Taken 1741**

Obv. Full-length figure, three-quarters l., in a frock-coat and holding a staff, points to a city and ships entering its harbour. ADMIRAL: VERNON: VEIWING: THE: TOWN: OF: CARTHAGANA. *Ex.* 1740:1   *Rev.* Two ships entering the harbour of CARTHAGENA pass the forts of S. IAGO and S. IOSEPH at its mouth. THE FORTS OF CARTHAGENA DESTROYD BY ADᴹ. VERNON 1741   *D.* 37 mm. (By?) *MI ii*, 548/155; *MH* 1919, 307; *Betts* 334   *Br.*   22   50   *Pb.*   12   25

See No. 547.

559 ——
Obv. Full-length figures in frock-coats of Vernon, wearing a hat, facing, and Ogle, l.,   *Br.*   22   50
holding a staff. ADM^L VERNON AND S^R CHALONER OGLE *Ex.* WE LOOK FOR DON BLASS. *Rev.* *Pb.* 12 25
Ships entering Carthagena harbour in which a boat, marked DON BLASS, lies within a chain
boom. TOOK. CARTHAGENA APRIL 1741 *D.* 37 mm. (By?) *MI ii*, 550/160; *MH* 1919, 314;
Betts 324

Admiral Don Blas(s) de Leso, Governor of Carthagena. Chaloner Ogle (1681?–1750), admiral; the attack was mounted
jointly with Vernon. *See* No. 547.

560 Proposed Attack on Havana 1741
Obv. Full-length figure, l., sword raised, standing behind a cannon. Beyond, l., city of   *Br.*   25   55
HAVANAH, and r., a ship. ED: VERNON ESQ: VICE ADMIRAL OF THE BLUE *Rev.* Four ships
entering a harbour. VERNON: CONQUERD: CARTAGENA *Ex.* APRIL 1: 1741 *D.* 37mm. (By?)
MI ii, 555/177; *MH* 1919, 334; *Betts* 315

See No. 547.

561 Duke of Argyle: Robert Walpole 1741
Obv. Full-length draped figure, facing, leans against a column on which rests a ducal crown; *AR* 60   —
behind, a trophy of arms and standards. . THE GENEROUSE: DUKE: OF: ARGYLE *Ex.* NO. *AE* 18 32
.PENTIONER *Rev.* Devil advancing, l., leads Walpole by a leash towards the mouth of a
fantastic beast. MAKE. ROOM. FOR. SIR: ROBERT *Ex.* NO: EXCISE *D.* 37 mm. (By?) *MI ii*,
561/190; *MH* 1919, 327; *Betts* 247; *CP* 102/13

There are varieties of this piece. Examples in silver are sometimes cast. Sir Robert Walpole, 1st Earl of Orford
(1676–1745), statesman.

562 Robert Walpole 1741
Obv. Bust r., draped ROBERTUS. WALPOLE. ORD: PERISCELIDIS. EQVES. *Rev.* Statue of Cicero. *AR* 100 180
REGIT. DICTIS. ANIMOS. *Ex.* M.T.C. (Marcus Tullius Cicero) on ribbon. *D.* 49 mm. By L. *AE* 60 110
Natter [after J. M. Rysbrack] *MI ii*, 562/193; *Nau* 139   *Pb.* 25 45

563 Abraham de Moivre 1741
Obv. Bust r., draped. ABRAHAMUS DE MOIVRE. *Rev.* UTRIUSQUE SOCIETATIS REGALIS LOND. ET *AR* 80 150
BEROL. SODALIS. M.DCC.XLI. within an ornamental device. *D.* 54 mm. By J. A. Dassier. *MI ii*, *AE* 20 45
565/197

Abraham de Moivre (1667–1754), French mathematician. *See* No. 556.

564 Alexander Pope 1741
Obv. Bust r., draped. ALEXANDER POPE. *Rev.* POETA ANGLUS. M.DCC.XLI. within an ornamental *AR* 80 150
device. *D.* 54 mm. By J. A. Dassier. *MI ii*, 565/198   *AE* 20 45

Alexander Pope (1688–1744), poet. *See* No. 556.

565 George II, Protector of the Arts 1741
Obv. Bust r., hair bound with a fillet. GEORGIVS. II. D:G: MAG. BRI: FRA: ET. H: REX. F:D. *Rev.* *AR* 130 250
Statue of Minerva, facing, within a tetrastyle temple. OPTIMO PRINCIPI *Ex.* CIƆIƆ
CCXXXXI *D.* 51 mm. By L. Natter. *MI ii*, 566/199; *Nau* 138

566 Resignation of Robert Walpole 1742
Obv. Walpole seated, l., on a balcony overlooking a landscape; he holds a scroll, dated IAN. *AE* 25   —
18 1742 and leans on a money-bag. I AM KICKD OUT OF DOORS *Rev.* A pole bearing a human *Pb.* 20   —
head upon a walled gateway. NO SCREEN *D.* 37 mm. (By J. Roche?) *MI ii*, 566/200

Walpole's resignation followed accusations of bribery and corruption, and an adverse vote by Parliament on 28 January,
ten days after its re-assembly. The pole (of a traitor) on a wall is a pun on his name.

567 Robert Walpole, Earl of Orford 1742
Obv. Bust r., draped, as No. 562. THE RIGHT HON: ROBERT EARL OF ORFORD *Rev.* Britannia, *AE* 30 55
r., tramples upon Envy and places a coronet on Walpole. ENVY SHALL NOT PREVAIL AGAINST *Br.* 20 35
THEE *Ex.* MDCCXLII *D.* 39 mm. (By? after L. Natter) *MI ii*, 567/201

568 Duke of Marlborough 1742
Obv. Bust r., armoured. CAROLUS SPENCER. *Rev.* DUX DE MARLBOROUGH. M.DCC.XLII. *D.* *AR* 80 150
55 mm. By J. A. Dassier. *MI ii*, 568/202   *AE* 20 45

Charles Spencer, 3rd Duke of Marlborough (1706–1758), soldier. *See* No. 556.

569 Spanish Galleons Destroyed 1742
Obv. Kneeling officer receives a medal from the King, in Roman dress. PRO TALIBUS *AV*   —   —
AUSIS *Rev.* A ship, close to other members of a squadron, launches an attack on galleons *AR* 400 700
moored in port. *Ex.* OB. V. TRIREM. HISPAN. A.S. CALLIS. COMBVST. V. IVLII. MDCCXLII. *D.* *AE* 90 150
53 mm. By T. Pingo. *MI ii*, 568/203; *MH* 1919, 340

Captain Smith Callis led the attack off the French Mediterranean coast near St. Tropez, and was presented with the medal
. in gold; examples in silver were awarded to officers who took part in the action.

			£	£

570 Monument to Princess Clementina 1742
Obv. Bust r., in Papal robes and cap. BENED. XIV PONT. M. A. III. *Rev.* Clementina's monument (in St. Peter's, Rome). MEMORIÆ. M. CLEM. M. BRIT. REGINÆ   *D.* 34 mm. [By O. Hamerani] *MI ii*, 570/204; *Bartolotti* 743

     AV   600   1100
     AR   100   180
     AE   18   35

Clementina was much lamented by Pope Clement XII who erected a monument on her death in 1735. His successor, Pope Benedict XIV, ordered the striking of this medal which forms part of the series of papal medals struck annually since 1605.

571 William Windham 1742
Obv. Bust r., draped. GULIELMUS WINDHAM ARMIGER. *Rev.* OFFICII ET AUGURII CAUSA FECIT I. DASSIER MDCCXLII. within an ornamental device. *D.* 41 mm. By J. Dassier. *MI ii*, 570/205

     AR   35   60
     AE   10   22

William Windham (1716–61), soldier and European traveller. The medallist's dedicatory medal.

572* Martin Folkes 1742 (?)
Obv. Bust r. MARTINVS FOLKES   *Rev.* A sphinx in the foreground decorated with a crescent; beyond, the Pyramid tomb of Caius Cestius between two Corinthian pillars and, in the distance, walls partly in ruins. A meridian sun, above. SVA SIDERA NORVNT   *Ex.* ROMÆ. A.L. s742   *D.* 37 mm. (By?) *MI ii*, 571/206; *Shackles* 115. *See* **Plate 17**

     AR   50   90
     AE   18   30

The date of this medal is somewhat conjectural. If the *s* is an engraver's error and should represent a 5, the masonic date (5742) would then correspond to either 1738 or 1742 in the Christian calendar. Both dates have been questioned, however, as Folkes is not known to have been in Rome at the time suggested (At Rome in the year of light, s742). Folkes, who was Deputy Grand Master of the Freemasons in 1724, had visited Rome in 1733. In the same year Lorenz Natter made a medal of Thomas Sackville in Florence as Master of that masonic lodge (No. 529). The modelling of the portrait and the bust line of Folkes is not unlike that on Natter's medal of George II (No. 565).

573 Birth of Princess Caroline 1743
Obv. Busts face to face, draped. W.C. HENR. FR. PRINC. NASS. ET AR. ANNA. ANGL. PR. HÆR. PR. NASS. ET AR. *Rev.* Mother with infant standing in a landscape beneath celestial radiance; Dutch town in the distance. CARA DEÛM SOBOLES. *Ex.* LEOVARDIÆ. D. 28 FEBR 1743   *D.* 47 mm. By N. v. Swinderen. *MI ii*, 571/207; *v. Loon suppl.* 176

     AV   600   900
     AR   70   130

Daughter of Princess Anne and William IV of Orange.

574 Death of Ralph Brideoake 1743
Obv. Bust r., draped. RADULPH. BRIDEOAKE ARCHIDIACONUS WINTON. *Rev.* Exterior view of church. ECCLESIA BEATÆ MARIÆ SOUTHTON RESTITUTA 1722   *Ex.* NAT. 13 IUN. 1665. OB. 19 MART. 1742/3   *D.* 55 mm. By J. A. Dassier. *MI ii*, 573/209

     AR   60   110
     AE   18   35

Dated in both old and new style. A variety occurs of less fine work. Ralph Brideoake (1665–1743), archdeacon of Winchester.

575 Battle of Dettingen 1743
Obv. Bust l., armoured and draped. GEORGIVS II D.G. MAGN. BRIT. FR. ET HIB. REX FID. DEF. *Rev.* Equestrian figure of the King, l.; battle scene in landscape, beyond. LIBERTAS FAVORE DEI ET VIRTVTE MILITIS RESTITVTA. *Ex.* AD DETTINGAM D. XXVII IVN. MDCCXLIII. *D.* 65 mm. By D. Haesling. *MI ii*, 575/211

     AV   2000   3400
     AR   400   700

576 ——
Obv. Bust l., laureate, armoured and draped. GEORGIUS SECUNDUS DEI GRATIA. REX. *Rev.* Justice seated, facing, trampling upon Tyranny. PARCERE. SUBIECTIS. ET. DEBELLARE. SUPERBOS   *Ex.* OB GALLOS VICTOS APUD DETTINGEN PER EXER : FÆD : SUB AUSPICIO GEO : II. IUN : 16. 1743. *D.* 36 mm. By T. (T. Tibs?) *MI ii*, 578/215

     AE   18   35

577 Duke of Argyle, Memorial 1743
Obv. Bust r., armoured. IOHANN. CAMPBELL. *Rev.* DUX DE ARGYLE ET DE GREENWICH. MDCCXLIII within an ornamental device decorated with military standards. *D.* 55 mm. By J. A. Dassier. *MI ii*, 579/216; *CP* 101/12

     AR   80   150
     AE   20   45

See No. 556.

578 Marriage of Princess Louisa and Prince Frederick 1743
Obv. Bust of Frederick, r., draped. SPES ET AMOR PATRIÆ MAGNVM BOREÆ INCREMENTVM *Rev.* Bust of Louisa, l., draped. MAGNORVM SOBOLES REGVM PARITVRAQVE REGES. *D.* 44 mm. By M. G. Arbien. *MI ii*, 581/220

     AR   60   110

Frederick V (1723–66), King of Denmark 1746–66.

579 Alexander Pope 1743
Obv. Similar to No. 564. *Rev.* POETA ANGLUS. M.DCC.XLIII. within an ornamental device decorated with a lyre and the head of Apollo. *D.* 28 mm. [By J. A. Dassier] *MI ii*, 581/221

     AR   35   65
     AE   12   30

580 Earl of Chesterfield 1743
Obv. Bust l., draped. PHILIPPUS STANHOPE *Rev.* COMES DE CHESTERFIELD. MDCCXLIII within an ornamental device. *D.* 55 mm. By J. A. Dassier. *MI ii*, 582/222

     AR   80   150
     AE   20   45

Philip Dormer Stanhope, 4th Earl of Chesterfield (1694–1773), politician and wit; *see* No. 556.

PLATE 17

496

503

521

514

544

545

547

550

572

589

588

PLATE 18

594

595

602

603

604

610

616

623

625

626

			£	£
581	**French and Spanish Fleets Defeated off Toulon 1744**			
	Obv. Bust l., laureate, armoured and draped. GEORG. II D.G. MAG. BRI. FRA. ET. H. REX F. D.	*AR*	150	280
	Rev. Neptune, holding up two naval crowns, stands in a conch decorated with the English shield and drawn by two sea-horses; beyond, French and Spanish ships sinking. A DVOBVS *Ex.* CLASSIS. HISP. GAL. AB. ANG. VICTA. 1744. *D.* 44 mm. By A. R. Werner. *MI ii*, 583/223; *MH* 1919, 341			
582	——			
	Obv. A human body suspended from a gibbet; beyond, aftermath of a naval action. Around are the letters A B C D, each against a different aspect. *Ex.* 1743/4. *Rev.* Column of troops stand before a lion subduing a cock; beyond, ships approach a fortified coastal position. Around are the letters E F G H I, each against a different aspect. *D.* 38 mm. (By?) *MI ii*, 584/224; *MH* 1919, 342	*Br.*	30	55
	A pamphlet was probably issued with this piece, identifying its various aspects.			
583	**Robert Walpole 1744**			
	Obv. Bust l., draped. ROBERTUS WALPOLE. *Rev.* COMES DE ORFORD. M.DCC.XLIV. within an	*AR*	80	150
	ornamental device. *D.* 55 mm. By J. A. Dassier. *MI ii*, 585/226	*AE*	20	45
	See No. 556.			
584	**Lord Carteret 1744**			
	Obv. Bust r., draped. IOHANNES CARTERET. *Rev.* BARO DE CARTERET. M.DCC.XLIV. within an	*AR*	80	150
	ornamental device. *D.* 55 mm. By J. A. Dassier. *MI ii*, 586/228	*AE*	20	45
	John Carteret, 1st Earl Granville (1690–1763), orator and statesman. *See* No. 556.			
585	**William Pulteney 1744**			
	Obv. Bust r., draped. GUILIELMUS PULTENEY. *Rev.* COMES DE BATH. MDCCXLIV. within a	*AR*	80	150
	wreath. *D.* 55 mm. By J. A. Dassier. *MI ii*, 586/229	*AE*	20	45
	William Pulteney, Earl of Bath (1684–1764), statesman. *See* No. 556.			
586	**John Barnard 1744**			
	Obv. Bust r., draped. IOHANNES BERNARD EQUES. *Rev.* ALDERMANUS CIVITATIS LONDINI	*AR*	80	150
	MDCCXLIV. within an ornamental device. *D.* 55 mm. By J. A. Dassier. *MI ii*, 587/230	*AE*	20	45
	Sir John Barnard (1685–1764), merchant; Lord Mayor of London. *See* No. 556.			
587	**Robert Barker 1744**			
	Obv. Bust r. ROBERTUS BARKER. *Rev.* DOCTOR MEDICUS SOCIUS REGIÆ SOCIET. LONDINENSIS	*AR*	100	180
	MDCCXLIV. within an ornamental device decorated with the heads of Salus and Aesculapius.	*AE*	30	65
	D. 55 mm. By J. A. Dassier. *MI ii*, 588/232; *Storer* 162			
	Robert Barker (?–1745), physician. This obverse occurs coupled with the reverse of No. 588. *See* No. 556.			
588*	**Hans Sloane 1744**			
	Obv. Bust l., wearing a cap and draped. HANS SLOANE EQU. BARONETTUS. *Rev.* PRÆSES	*AR*	100	180
	SOCIETATIS REGIÆ LONDINENSIS. MDCCXLIV. between festoons of flowers and branches of oak.	*AE*	30	65
	D. 55 mm. By J. A. Dassier. *MI ii*, 589/234; *Storer* 3382. See **Plate 17**			
	The reverse occurs coupled with the obverse of No. 587. Sir Hans Sloane (1660–1753), physician; his collection of natural history specimens was purchased by the nation and formed the beginnings of the British Museum. *See* No. 556.			
589*	**Edmund Halley 1744**			
	Obv. Bust r., draped. EDMUNDUS HALLEY. *Rev.* ASTRONOMUS REGIS MAGNÆ BRITANNIÆ.	*AR*	100	180
	MDCCXLIV. within an ornamental device. *D.* 55 mm. By J. A. Dassier. *MI ii*, 589/235. *See*	*AE*	30	65
	Plate 17			
	Sir Edmund Halley (1656–1742), astronomer and mathematician. *See* No. 556.			
590	**Andrew Fountaine 1744**			
	Obv. Bust r., draped. ANDREAS FOUNTAINE EQ. AURAT. *Rev.* A.A.A. F.F. IIIVIR. *Ex.* M.DCC.XLIV.	*AR*	80	150
	D. 56 mm. By J. A. Dassier. *MI ii*, 590/236; *Hocking* 235/12	*AE*	20	45
	The reverse inscription [= Auro, Argento, Aere, Flando, Feriundo, Triumviri], which occurs on Roman coins, is an allusion to Fountaine's wardenship of the Mint (1727–53). *See* No. 556.			
591	**Recapture of Prague 1744**			
	Obv. Bust almost facing, armoured and draped. CAR: LOT: PRI * PERFIDIÆ VINDEX Below,	*AR*	65	120
	on a scroll NATUS DEC XII. MDCCXII *Rev.* Cavalry approach a fortified city. SUBSIDIO	*AE*	25	45
	BRITANNIÆ *Ex.* PRAGA RECUPERATA NO 26 MDCCXLIV *D.* 44 mm. By J. Kirk. *MI ii*, 590/237			
	Duke Karl Alexander (1712–80), Prince of Lorraine.			
592	——			
	Obv. Equestrian figure, armed, r.; a city beyond. CAR: LOR: PR: PERFIDORUM VINDEX *Ex.*	*AR*	50	90
	MDCCXLIV *Rev.* Cavalry approach a fortified city. SUBSIDIO BRITANNIÆ *Ex.* PRAGA	*Br.*	20	35
	RECAPTA NO 26 MDCCXLIV *D.* 43 mm. By J. Kirk. *MI ii*, 592/239			
	A coarse unsigned copy was made.			

593   **Expulsion of Jews from Bohemia, Decree Rescinded 1745**

Obv. Maria Theresa enthroned, l., attended by Charity and Justice, receives Mars who mediates on behalf of a rabbi standing behind him. XIII TEBETH. XVIII DECEMB on the cornice of the palace interior. EXILIO. MINATO. on a ribbon, above. *Ex.* NE. SVSPICETVR. REGINA. VERSVS. SERVOS. SVOS. RES. HVIVSCEMODI (chronogrammatic date). 1.REG.22.VS.15. *Rev.* Worshippers kneeling inside a synagogue, its walls displaying the arms of England, Holland, Poland and Sweden. DECRETO ABOLITO XIII. YYAR. XV MAII. Arms of Bohemia below. *Ex.* IstI. sVnt. DIes. qVos. nVLLa. VMqVaM. DeLeBIt. obLIVIo. et per. sIngVLas. generatIones. CVnCtæ. In toto. orbe. proVInCIae. CeLebrabVnt (chronogrammatic date). ESTHER.9.VS.28. *D.* 64 mm. By N. v. Swinderen. *MI ii*, 594/243; *Friedenberg* 1970/34–6; *v. Loon suppl.* 205

		£	£
	AR	900	1600
	WM	120	220

The combined dates total 5505 in the Jewish calendar, corresponding to 1745 in the Christian era. Maria Theresa (1717–80), Archduchess of Austria, Queen of Hungary and Bohemia.

594*   **Capture of the French Treasure Ships** *Marquis d'Antin* **and** *Louis Erasmé* **1745**

Obv. Five ships engaged in battle, identified: ND D LE PF MA   *Ex.* IULII. X. MDCCXLV. *Rev.* Two infant fames, each displaying an oval frame with uniformed busts of IAC. TALBOT. and IOHA. MORECOCK. Below, a procession of horse-drawn treasure wagons, marked 44 and 45. *Ex.* VENIEBUNT LONDⓄ. OCTO. I. ET. II. MDCCXLV   *D.* 38 mm. By J. Kirk. *MI ii*, 597/246; *MH* 1919, 343; *Betts* 381. *See* **Plate 18**

	AR	150	250
	AE	60	110

James Talbot and John Morecock, captains of the *Prince Frederick* and the *Duke*, captured, in the North Atlantic, treasure valued at £800,000, which was conveyed to the Tower in forty-five wagons on 1 and 2 October. The *Notre Dame* was the only French ship to escape. (*MI* and *Betts* both speak of these ships, in error, as Spanish).

595*   **Expected Arrival of Prince Charles, the Young Pretender 1745**

Obv. Bust r. CAROLUS WALLIÆ PRINCEPS 1745   *Rev.* Britannia standing on the shore regards an approaching fleet, her hand resting on the shield of St. George which partially reveals a globe marked with the British Isles. AMOR ET SPES   *Ex.* BRITANNIA   *D. a* 41 mm. *b* 31 mm. (By C. N. Roettiers?) *MI ii*, 600/251–2; *Farquhar* 1923–24, 178, 184. *See* **Plate 18**

	a AR	40	70
	AE	20	35
	b AR	45	75

Type *b* is on a thinner flan and has a grained edge.

596   **Anti-Gallican Society 1745**

Obv. Two men standing, wearing frock-coats and a medal on a ribbon, their hands clasped. WHERE HEARTS ARE RIGHT, LET HANDS UNITE. *Ex.* FOUNDED IN THE FRENCH WAR 1745   *Rev.* St. George spearing the French shield, on an escutcheon supported by lion and double-headed eagle : crest of Britannia; motto below FOR OUR COUNTRY on a ribbon (the Society's Arms). THESE BANNERS SPREAD, ARE GALLIA'S DREAD   *D.* 35 mm. By J. Kirk. *MI ii*, 603/256

	AR	40	75
	AE	20	30

The Society was formed to discourage the importation of French produce and encourage consumption of British goods; their device also occurs on contemporary engravings and ceramics.

597   **Carlisle Taken, The Rebels Repulsed 1745**

Obv. Bust r., draped. GUL: DUX. CUMB: DELICIÆ. MILITUM NATVS. 15. APR: 1721   *Rev.* The Duke of Cumberland, as a warrior, shield decorated with bust of the King, attacks a hydra; city in the distance. PRO. PATRE. ET. PATRIA   *Ex.* REB: EX. ANG. PULLSI. & CARL: REDACTUM. DEC. 1745. *D.* 37 mm. By (J.H.?) Wolff. *MI ii*, 604/258; *CP* 83/4

	AV	400	750
	AR	60	110
	AE	25	45

Struck from two pairs of dies. A coarse unsigned copy was also made.

598   ——

Obv. Equestrian figure of the Duke, l., sword drawn; city beyond. GUL. AUG: DUX CUMBERLANDIÆ   *Ex.* NAT. 15. APR. 1721   *Rev.* Anglia seated, l., receives an olive-branch from the Duke, as a warrior; at his feet lies a rebel, prostrate, with a papal shield. SPEM REDUCIS MENTIBUS ANXIIS   *Ex.* MDCCXLV   *D.* 35 mm. By A. Kirk/J. Kirk. *MI ii*, 606/264

	AR	28	55
	AE	20	35

599   ——

Obv. Bust r., draped. WILL: DUKE: CUMB: BRITISH: HERO. BORN. 15. APR. 1721: *Rev.* Equestrian figure of the Duke directs a soldier escorting two captive Highlanders. REBELLION: JUSTLY: REWARDED   *Ex.* AT. CARLILE. DEC: 1745   *D.* 34 mm. (By?) *MI ii*, 605/262

	Br.	15	30

Struck from more than one pair of dies.

600   ——

Obv. Bust r., armoured. GVLIELMVS. DVX. CVMBRIÆ. *Rev.* Lion subdues a wolf. IVSTITIA. TRIVMPHANS   *Ex.* MDCCXLV   *D.* 33 mm. By T. Pingo. *MI ii*, 607/265; *CP* 85/6

	AR	25	48
	AE	15	30

A brass unsigned copy of this medal was made.

601   ——

Obv. Bust l., laureate, armoured and draped. GEORGIUS. II. D.G. REX. *Rev.* Celestial hand holding a flaming sword guards a map of the British Isles marked with the positions of

	AR	70	130
	AE	35	55

L[ondon], D[ublin], E[dinburgh], C[arlisle] and D[unblain]; ships around the coast.   £   £
PERFICIT MIRACULA 1745   *D*. 29 mm. By J. Kirk. *MI ii*, 609/270; *CP* 30/2
<small>Another reverse has a Hydra – heads of the Pope, Devil, Pretender, cardinal, bishop and Louis XV – overcome by Truth.</small>

602*   **Prince Charles, The Young Pretender** *c*.1745
Obv. The Prince in decorative Highland dress standing, l., his right arm pointing the way   *Br.*   50   80
forward; behind, an attendant waits in readiness. CAROLUS. PRINCEPS   *Rev*. Fame bears a
crown, l., her trumpet issuing a pennant inscribed SUUM CUIQUE; city in the distance. *D*.
36 mm. (By?) *MI ii*, 601/254; *Farquhar* 1923–4, 200. *See* **Plate 18**

603*   **Thomas Birch** *c*.1745
Obv. A man, with two assistants, amputating a leg with a saw. THOMAS. BIRCH.   *AE*   50   —
SURGEON   *Rev*. A man leaning against a table, his hand on a skull, holds a pointer at a naked
figure standing upon a pedestal, to which he indicates various aspects; below, an infant with
its placenta attached. AND. MAN. MIDWIFE. BIRMINGHAM   *D*. 38 mm. (By?) *Storer* 376;
Brettauer 5493. *See* **Plate 18**
<small>This piece may have served as an entrance or advertising ticket.</small>

604*   **Battle of Culloden** 1746
Obv. Bust r., armoured. GULIELMUS. GEOR. II. R. FIL. DUX. CUMBRIÆ. *Rev*. Britannia seated, l.,   *AV*   900   1500
is assisted by the Duke, as Hercules, who tramples upon Discord. *Ex*. PERDVELLIB. EX. ANG.   *AR*   90   170
FVGAT. AD CULLOD. DEBELLAT 16. APR. 1746. *D*. 51 mm. By R. Yeo. *MI ii*, 613/278; *CP* 82/2;   *AE*   40   75
Forrer VI/702. *See* **Plate 18.**
<small>More than twelve medals commemorate the battle of Culloden.</small>

605   ——————
Obv. Equestrian figure of the Duke, l., sword drawn; city beyond. WILL: DUKE   *Br.*   12   25
CUMBERLAND   *Ex*. BORN. 15. AP. 1721   *Rev*. Battle scene. REBELION. JUSTLY.
REWARDED   *Ex*. CULLODEN 16 AP. 1746   *D*. 42 mm. (By?) *MI ii*, 612/277; *CP* 88/14
<small>The obverse is copied from No. 598. There are several varieties of this medal.</small>

606   ——————
Obv. Bust l., uniformed. GUL: DUX. CUMBRIÆ PRO. PATRIA. NA: XV. AP: MDCCXXI   *Rev*.   *AR*   70   130
Equestrian figure of the Duke commanding, l.; beyond, scene of battle. HORÆ. MOMENTO.   *AE*   30   55
Ex. COMPRESSUS. FUROR. CIVILIS. AD. CULLODEN. APR: XVI. MDCCXLVI. *D*. 41 mm. By (J.H.?)   *Br.*   15   30
Wolff. *MI ii*, 609/271; *CP* 83/3

607   ——————
Obv. Head of the Duke, r. CUMBERLAND   *Rev*. Apollo standing, l., leaning upon his bow,   *AV*   1500   2500
points to a wounded dragon. ACTUM EST ILLICET PERIIT   *Ex*. PROEL. COLOD. AP. XVI.   *AR*   500   850
MDCCXLVI   Integral suspension loop upon an ornamental scrolled border. *D*. 37 mm. by   *AE*   150   250
56 mm. Oval. By R. Yeo. *MI ii*, 615/283; *CP* 82/1; *Gordon* 14; *Payne* 34; *Tancred* 41–3
<small>Despite its appearance, there is no apparent record of this medal having been conferred as an honorary award.</small>

608   ——————
Obv. Bust r., similar to No. 604. GULIELMUS. DUX. CUMBRIÆ. *Rev*. Fame bearing an olive-   *AR*   70   130
branch, a banner on her trumpet inscribed VENIT VIDIT VINCIT, flies over a map of the British   *AE*   30   50
Isles with HIB[ernia], ANG[lia] and SCO[tia] identified. INSULA. CHARA. DEIS. HEROUM.   *WM*   12   28
INCLYTA. MATER   *Ex*. 16. AP. I. DIE. 26. ANNI. ÆT. SUÆ. REB. CULLODENICIS. CAMPIS. DOMUIT.
VIGILANTIA. SUA. MDCCXLVI   *D*. 36 mm. By J. Kirk/A. Kirk. *MI ii*, 613/279; *CP* 86/10

609   **Rebellion Defeated** 1746
Obv. Bust r., armoured. GVLIELMVS. DVX. CVMBRIÆ. *Rev*. A Highlander kneeling, r., before a   *Br.*   15   30
crowned rampant lion. *Ex*. 1746   *D*. 31 mm. (By?) *MI ii*, 616/286; *CP* 92/25

610*   **Failure of Prince Charles** 1746
Obv. Equestrian figure, l., wielding a sword. DUKE. OF. CUMBER: *Rev*. Charles, r., attempts to   *AE*   30   55
seize a crown upon a column but is held back by the Duke, who runs a sword through him.   *Br.*   25   45
COME BACK AGAIN   *Ex*. PRETENTER   *D*. 33 mm. (By?) *MI ii*, 618/290; *CP* 91/24. *See* **Plate
18**
<small>Another reverse, entitled MORE REBELS A COMEING, depicts an execution on the gallows..</small>

611   **Death of Professor Hutcheson** 1746
Obv. Bust almost facing, draped. FRANC. HVTCHESON. PHIL. MOR. IN. ACAD. GLASGVÆ. PVB.   *AE*   400   700
PROF. *Rev*. Female figure seated, mournfully, upon a sarcophagus. NON. SVO. SED. PVBLICO.
LVGET. DAMNO. *Ex*. POST. OB. MDCCXLVI. *D*. 107 mm. Cast. [By A. Selvi]. *MI ii*, 620/293; *CP*
102/14; *EPM* 1892, 320
<small>Francis Hutcheson (1694–1746), philosopher.</small>

			£	£
612	**George II: Duke of Cumberland** *c*.1746	*AR*	20	35

Obv. Bust l., armoured, GEORGIUS. II. REX. *Rev.* Bust r., armoured and draped. GULIELMUS DUX CUMBRIÆ *D*. 25 mm. By J. Kirk. *MI ii*, 622/295–6

The obverse occurs with a number of different reverses. One of a uniform group expressing harmony and stability; *see* Nos. 613–14.

613 Augusta, Princess of Wales *c*.1746   *AR*   20   35

Obv. Bust r., wearing a bandeau, draped. AUGUSTA WALLIÆ. PRINCIPISSA *Rev.* Moths hover above a candlelit table at which Cupid sleeps. POUR UN PLAISIR MILLE DE PEINE *D*. 25 mm. [By J. Kirk] *MI ii*, 623/299

A further eleven reverses each depict Cupid in a different attitude. See No. 612.

614 Frederick, Prince of Wales *c*.1746   *AR*   20   35

Obv. Bust l., armoured. FREDERICUS WALLIÆ. PRINCEPS *Rev.* Prince's plumes, coronet and motto. *D*. 25 mm. [By J. Kirk] *MI ii*, 623/297

The obverse also occurs coupled with that of No. 613. See No. 612.

615 William of Orange, Stadholder 1747   *AR*   40   70

Obv. Bust r., draped. WILH. CAR. HENR. FRISO. PRINC. NASS. ET AR. *Rev.* Belgic lion, l., rests its paw on a pedestal, inscribed HONY SOIT QVI MAL Y PENSE, and decorated with an orange branch. GLADIVS DOMINI ET GEDEONIS. *Ex.* HOLLANDIA PROCLAM: GVBERN. 3 MAII. 1747 With integral suspension loop. *D*. 38 mm. By N. v. Swinderen. *MI ii*, 629/317; *v. Loon suppl.* 227

More than ten medals commemorate his election and installation as Governor of Holland.

616* French Fleet Defeated off Cape Finisterre 1747   *AV*   800   1400

Obv. Bust l., crowned by Victory, her foot on the prow of a galley. GEORGE LORD ANSON VICT.   *AR*   80   150
MAY III MDCCXLVII *Rev.* Victory, holding a wreath and trident, stands upon a sea-monster   *AE*   35   60
over a globe. CIRCVMNAVIGATION, all within a central beaded circle. Outer border of six
laurel wreaths, inscribed BRETT DENNIS CAMPBEL KEPPEL SAVMAREZ SAVNDERS; below,
MDCCXL MDCCXLIV *D*. 43 mm. By T. Pingo. *MI ii*, 634/325; *MH 1919*, 345; *Betts* 382. See
Plate 18

George, Lord Anson (1697–1762), admiral; the reverse commemorates his four-year circumnavigation. Percy Brett (1709–81), admiral; John Campbell (1720?–90), vice-admiral; Peter Denis (d.1778), vice-admiral; Augustus Keppel, Admiral Viscount Keppel (1725–86), served under Anson; Philip Suamarez (1710–47), captain; Charles Saunders (1713?–75), admiral. The reverse of this medal was struck from two dies.

617 ——   *Br.*   25   45

Obv. Half-length figures wearing frock-coats, almost facing, each holding a staff. BY THE COVRAGE OF ADMIRAL ANSON & WARREN *Rev.* Fleet assembled off a coast. THE FRENCH FLEET DESTROYD MAY 4 1747 *D*. 36 mm. (By?) *MI plates* CLXXI/7; *MH 1919*, 346

Sir Peter Warren (1703–52), vice-admiral.

618 John Taylor 1747   *AR*   80   150

Obv. Bust r., draped. IOAN. TAYLOR EQVES MED. DOCT. IMP. REG. ET PRINC. PLVR.   *WM*   25   45
OPHTHALMIATER PLVRIMARVMQ. ACAD. SOC. *Rev.* EN VIRUM SCIENTIA MEDICA INSIGNEM
TOTAQVE EVROPA CELEBREM NAT. NORWICH. IN ANGLIA MDCCVIII D. XIII OCTOBR. HORA XI
NATVT. QVI COECIS INNVMERIS RESTITVENDO SE TOTVM BONO PVBLICO CONSECRAT *D*. 41 mm.
By A. Vestner. *MI ii*, 636/329; *Storer* 3490

John Taylor (1703–72), itinerant oculist. His year of birth is incorrectly stated.

619 Birth of William of Orange 1748   *AR*   70   130

Obv. Busts r., conjoined, William armoured and Anne draped. W.C.H. FRISO ET ANNA D.G. ARAVS. ET NASS. PRINC. *Rev.* Kneeling figures of Holland and Nassau receive the infant from a descending angel. TANDEM EXORATVS DEDIT *Ex.* WILHELMVS NATVS HAGÆ. COM. ANN. LIB. IVBIL. D. VIII. MART. *D*. 49 mm. By M. Holtzhey. *MI ii*, 639/333; *v. Loon suppl.* 262

Prince William (1748–1806), became William V and succeeded his father as Stadholder in 1751.

620 Peace of Aix-La-Chapelle Concluded 1749   *Br.*   15   30

Obv. Bust l., laureate. GEORGIUS. II. D.G. REX *Rev.* Britannia seated, r., with olive-branch, regards an approaching ship. PEACE. NOURISHES. TRADE *Ex.* PROCLAM'D. 2. FEB. 1748 *D*. 41 mm. (By?) *MI ii*, 652/355

A copy of No. 621; dated in the old style.

621 ——   *AV*   350   650

Obv. Bust l., laureate. GEORGIUS II. D.G. REX *Rev.* Similar to No. 620. PAX COMMERCII   *AR*   35   65
NUTRIX *Ex.* PROCLAM. 2 FEB. MDCCXLVIII. *D*. 35 mm. By J. Kirk. *MI ii*, 651/354   *AE*   15   25

Dated in the old style.

622   Freemasons of Minorca 1749

Obv. Harpocrates standing, l., finger on his mouth, compass and square in hand, leans against a column. TVTA. EST. FIDELI. SILENTIO. MERCES *Rev.* Two hands clasped. CONCORDIA. FRATRVM INSVLA. MINOR. BALEARI   *Ex.* 5749   *D.* 49 mm. By R. Yeo. *MI ii*, 652/356; *Shackles* 113

	VF (£)	EF (£)
AR	180	330
AE	90	140

The Masonic calendar places the creation of the world 4000 or 4004 years before the Christian calendar.

623*   Dissensions between Dr. Charles Lucas and the Corporation of Dublin 1749

Obv. Justice prevents Anarchy from stabbing the subdued figure of Liberty. MAY GEORGE PROTECT WHAT JUSTICE TRYS TO SAVE   *Rev.* THE GLORIOUS ATTEMPT OF LXIV TO PRESERVE THE CONSTITVTION MDCCXLIX. Above, Irish harp with broken strings; below, shield and regalia of Dublin. *D.* 40 mm. By T. Pingo. *MI ii*, 653/357; *Storer* 2273. See **Plate 18**

	VF	EF
AR	65	120
AE	20	35
Br.	15	25

With an integral suspension loop. Dr. Charles Lucas (1713–71), Irish patriot.

624   Jacobite Legitimacy of Succession 1749

Obv. A Highlander stands, facing, with a shield inscribed QUIS CONTENDAT MECUM, and drawn sword. NULLUM NON MOVEBO LAPIDEM UT ILLUD ADIPISCAR 1749   *Rev.* An expanded rose. MEA. RES. AGITUR. *D.* 33 mm. (By?) *MI ii*, 655/358; *Farquhar* 1923–24, 202

	VF	EF
AR	250	450
AE	70	130

Struck from more than one pair of dies.

625*   Prince Charles, Oak Society 1750

Obv. Bust of Charles, r. *Rev.* A leafless oak-tree, near the base of which sprouts a sapling. REVIRESCIT   *Ex.* 1750   *D.* 34 mm. [By T. Pingo] *MI ii*, 655/359; *Farquhar* 1923–24, 186. See **Plate 18**

	VF	EF
AV	600	1000
AR	70	130
AE	25	45

The portrait is after No. 595. This Jacobite Society met at the Crown and Anchor Tavern in the Strand. Members were entitled to a bronze medal; other metals were charged at their intrinsic value.

626*   Prince Charles, Legitimacy of Succession 1750

Obv. Bust r. PRINCE CHARLES EDWARD STUART   *Rev.* The Prince, as a Highlander, approaches Scotia standing beside a pedestal decorated with a thistle; beyond, ships and a castle. *Ex.* SEMPER ARMIS NUNC ET INDUSTRIA. *D.* 51 mm. (By T. Pingo?) *MI ii*, 656/360; *Farquhar* 1923–24, 191. See **Plate 18**

	VF	EF
AV	—	—
AR	170	320
AE	80	150
WM	30	55

This portrait is after No. 595. This medal usually exhibits rust marks and flaws, and was probably struck some years later.

627*   Jacobite Meeting in London 1750

Obv. Shield of St. George amidst a military trophy. CON. R. C. S. HOC NUM. D. EX PRÆ. JAC. 1750   *Rev.* A thistle. FLORESCAT ET PUNGAT   *D.* 34 mm. (By?) *MI ii*, 656/361; *D & W* 139/295. See **Plate 19**

	VF	EF
AR	450	—

628   Academy of Ancient Music, prize 1750

Obv. Student standing, playing a harpsichord, is crowned with a laurel wreath by Apollo. *Rev.* IN ACKNOWLEDGMENT OF. MERIT. ACADEMY. OF. ANTIENT. MUSIC. LONDON. MDCCL. PEPUSCH. PRÆSES., within the serpent of Eternity from which hangs a ribbon, inscribed STATE SVPER VIAS ANTIQVAS   *D.* 49 mm. By R. Yeo. *MI ii*, 657/362; *Erlanger* 105

	VF	EF
AR	45	85
AE	20	35

John Christopher Pepusch (1667–1752), German composer; founding member of the Academy.

629   Formation of the Free British Fishery Society 1750

Obv. Bust r., armoured and draped. FREDERICK PRINCE OF WALES. GOVERNOR OF THE SOCIETY. *Rev.* Fishermen on the shore with nets and barrels; trawler at sea hauls in nets. FOR THE ADVANTAGE OF GREAT BRITAIN. *Ex.* FREE BRIT. FISHERY BY A SOCIETY ESTABL. 1750. *D.* 40 mm. By L. Koch. *MI ii*, 659/365

	VF	EF
AV	350	650
AR	35	65
AE	20	35

630   George II 1750

Obv. Bust l., laureate and armoured. GEORGIUS II. D.G. MAG. BR. FR. ET HIB. REX. *Rev.* Britannia, seated on the sea-shore, regards Mercury who pours out an abundant cornucopia. HÆ TIBI SUNT ARTES   *Ex.* MDCCL. *D.* 55 mm. By J. A. Dassier. *MI ii*, 658/363

	VF	EF
AR	100	180
AE	25	55

This medal refers to the prosperity enjoyed after the Peace of Aix-La-Chapelle.

631   Frederick, Prince of Wales *c*.1750

Obv. Bust l., armoured. FREDERIC. WALLIÆ PRINCEPS. *Rev.* Two infant genii support the Prince's coronet, with plumes and motto, above clouds. *D.* 55 mm. By J. A. Dassier. *MI ii*, 660/366

	VF	EF
AR	100	180
AE	25	55

The exact occasion commemorated is unclear; it may record the Prince's death in 1751.

632   Prince Charles and Prince Henry, Cardinal York *c*.1750

Obv. Bust r., armoured and draped. CAROLVS VALIÆ PRINCEPS   *Rev.* Bust r., armoured and draped. HENRIC. DVX EBORACENSIS   *D.* 47 mm. By A.F (A. Franchi?) *Farquhar* 1923–4, 219

	VF	EF
AE	65	100

Henry was created Cardinal York by Pope Benedict XIV in 1747.

633   **Calendar Medal 1751**
Obv. Table of dates on which specific days fall throughout 1751. *Rev.* Table showing phases of the sun and moon. *D.* 38 mm. By J. Powell.
See No. 268.

Br.   £ 8   £ 15

634   **Death of Frederick, Prince of Wales 1751**
Obv. Bust l. FREDERICUS. WALLIÆ PRINCEPS   *Rev.* Britannia seated mournfully, r., beside the Prince's sarcophagus. LUCTUS NON IUSTIOR ULLUS. *Ex.* NATUS XX IAN: MDCCVI OBIIT XX MAR: MDCCL. *D.* 36 mm. By J. Kirk. *MI ii*, 661/367

AR   35   65
AE   15   30

635   **Duke of Montagu, Memorial 1751**
Obv. Bust l., armoured. JOANNES DVX DE MONTAGV. *Rev.* The Good Samaritan tends the wounds of a weary traveller. TV FAC SIMILITER. *Ex.* MDCCLI. *D.* 55 mm. By J. A. Dassier. *MI ii*, 663/369; *Brettauer* 3744

AR   80   150
AE   20   45

John, 2nd Duke of Montagu (1688?–1749), courtier and philanthropist.

636   **Death of Louisa, Queen of Denmark 1751**
Obv. Bust r., draped. LOVISA. D.G. DAN. NORV. VAND. GOTH. REGINA. *Rev.* Female figures of Denmark and Norway seated mournfully beside a tomb, inscribed DUO MORIUNTUR IN UNA   Two urns, inscribed MATRI DESIDERATISS and PRINC. FILIO. stand upon the tomb. ANTE DIEM   *Ex.* CORONAM MUTAVIT D. XIX DECEMB. MDCCLI. *D.* 50 mm. By M. G. Arbien/P. C. Winslöw. *MI ii*, 666/376

AR   60   100

637   **Cambridge University, Chancellor's Medal 1752**
Obv. Bust l., laureate, armoured and draped. GEORGIVS. II. PIVS. FELIX. PATER. PATRIAE. *Rev.* Figure of Cambridge enthroned, l., points to a student standing before her to whom Liberality makes a presentation; beyond, façade of the Senate House. STVDIIS HVMANITATIS   *Ex.* LIBERALITAS. T. HOLLES DVC. NOVOCASTR. ACAD. CANCELL. *D.* 52 mm. By R. Yeo. *MI ii*, 667/377; *Erlanger* 61

AV   700   900
AR   60   100
AE   20   35

A prize inaugurated by Thomas Pelham-Holles, Duke of Newcastle (1693–1768), elected Chancellor in 1748.

638*   **St. Thomas's Hospital, Cheselden Medal 1752**
Obv. Bust r., in surgeon's cap, draped. CHESELDEN. *Rev.* A cadaver on a table, awaiting examination; beyond, skull, book and two bell-glasses upon a table decorated with the arms of the hospital. MORS VIVIS SALVS. *Ex.* ST. THOMAS'S HOSPITAL   *D.* 72 mm. By W. Wyon. *MI ii*, 668/378; *BHM* 1339; *Storer* 618. See **Plate 19**

AR   70   120
AE   35   65

First struck in 1829 and awarded annually from *c.*1845 in silver, and sometimes in bronze, for surgical anatomy, it occurs frosted and set within a watch-style glass bound with a silver frame. William Cheselden (1688–1752), surgeon and anatomist.

639   **Prince Charles, Visit to London 1752**
Obv. Bust of Prince Charles, r. REDEAT MAGNUS ILLE GENIUS BRITANNIÆ   *Rev.* Britannia awaits the arrival of an approaching fleet. O DIU DESIDERATA NAVIS   *Ex.* LÆTAMINI CIVES SEPT XXIII MDCCLII   *D.* 43 mm. (By T. Pingo?) *MI ii*, 670/380; *Farquhar* 1923–24, 199
This medal is after No. 595.

AR   60   110

640   **Edinburgh Revolution Club 1753**
Obv. Tyranny and Popery take flight from William III, in Roman dress, who presents a scroll inscribed M. CHA [Magna Charta] to the seated figures of Justice and Religion. *Ex.* MEMINISSE JUVABIT   *Rev.* THE EDINBURGH REVOLUTION CLUB IN COMEMORATION OF THE RECOVERY OF THEIR RELIGION AND LIBERTY BY K. WILLIAM & Q. MARY AN 1688 ORDERED THIS MEDAL TO BE STRUCK ANNO 1753   *D.* 36 mm. (By?) *MI ii*, 672/384; *CP* 135/1
With an integral suspension loop.

AR   35   60

641   **Irish Surplus Revenue Dispute 1753**
Obv. The Speaker of the Irish Parliament, holding a bag inscribed VINDICATA, places a cap of Liberty on Hibernia attended by Industry and Law, who holds a document labelled LEGES. Fame, with a banner on her trumpet inscribed CXXIV, and a ribbon inscribed ERGO TVA JURA MANEBVNT, above. VTCVNQVE FERENT EA FACTA MINORES VINCIT AMOR PATRIAE   *Ex.* Vulture and wolf scramble for gold. *Rev.* SACRVM SENATORIBVS CXXIV QVI TENACES PROPOSITI FORTITER AC PRVDENTER JURA PATRIAE RITE VINDICARVNT XVII DIE DECEMBRIS AERAE CHRISTIANAE MDCCLIII QVOCIRCA VIVITE FORTES in the centre. QVIQVE SVI MEMORES ALIOS FECERE MERENDO   *D.* 44 mm. (By?) *MI ii*, 673/385
See Nos. 642 and 650.

AV   500   850
AR   65   110
AE   25   45

642   ——
Obv. Bust of the Speaker, almost facing. THE. SPEAKER AND LIBERTY   *Rev.* Irish harp, crowned. THE 124 PATRIOTS OF IRELAND & c. *Ex.* DECEMBER 17 1753   *D.* 36 mm. (By J.

Br.   25   45

                                                                   £   £

Roche?) *MI ii*, 674/386; *Went* 1978, 100

A similar but smaller medal was also struck. Henry Boyle, Earl of Shannon (1682–1764), Speaker in the Irish Parliament; opposed a government proposal for appropriating a surplus in the Irish exchequer. *See* Nos. 641 and 650.

643   **Society of Arts, Mercury and Minerva Medal 1753**
Obv. Busts r., conjoined, of Mercury and Minerva; below, a spray of rose, thistle and   *AV*   300   450
shamrock. ARTS AND COMMERCE PROMOTED   *Rev.* A wreath (space within, for recipient's   *AR*   25   40
name, subject and date). Below, SOC.Y INS.D LONDON 1753. *D.* 43 mm. By G. F. Pidgeon [*obv.*
after J. Flaxman]. *Allen* 12; *Jones* 1979, 277

Struck in 1807 and awarded thereafter until 1818. The Society of Arts (designated 'Royal' in 1908) awarded prize medals in gold and silver from 1758, and latterly in silver and bronze, for design and application in arts, manufactures and commerce: Nos. 644–8, 1420, 1566–7, 1863, 1917, 2074, and 2082. *See* H. T. Wood, *A History of the Royal Society of Arts*, London, 1913.

644*   **Society of Arts, Isis Medal 1753**
Obv. Head of Isis, l. ARTS AND COMMERCE PROMOTED   *Rev.* Similar to No. 643. *D.* 40 mm.   *AV*   250   350
By T. Wyon Jr. *Allen* 13; *D & W* 148/363. *See* **Plate 19**   *AR*   25   35
Awarded from 1810 for fine arts. *See* No. 643.

645   **Society of Arts, Ceres Medal 1753**
Obv. Head of Ceres, r. ARTS AND COMMERCE PROMOTED   *Rev.* Similar to No. 643. *D.* 39 mm.   *AV*   250   350
By W. Wyon. *Allen* 14; *D & W* 148/364   *AR*   25   35
Awarded from 1813 for agriculture. *See* No. 643.

646   **Society of Arts, Vulcan Medal 1753**
Obv. Head of Vulcan, l. ARTS AND COMMERCE PROMOTED   *Rev.* Similar to No. 643. *D.*   *AV*   250   350
41 mm. By G. Mills. *Allen* 15; *D & W* 148/365   *AR*   25   35
Awarded from 1818 for mechanics. *See* No. 643.

647   **Society of Arts, Mercury and Minerva Medal 1753**
Obv. Busts l., conjoined, of Mercury and Minerva. ARTS AND COMMERCE PROMOTED   *Rev.*   *AV*   450   550
Similar to No. 643. *D.* 52 mm. By W. Wyon. *Allen* 16; *Jones* 1979, 278 (sim).   *AR*   25   35
Awarded from 1820 until 1849. *See* No. 643.

648   **Society of Arts, Mercury and Minerva Medal 1754**
Obv. Britannia seated, l., is conferred with honours by Mercury and Minerva standing   *AV*   300   400
before her. ARTS. AND. COMMERCE. PROMOTED. *Ex.* SOCIETY INST. LONDON MDCCLIIII   *Rev.* A   *AR*   35   45
wreath (space within and around, for recipient's name, subject and date). *D.* 44 mm. By T.
Pingo [*obv.* after J. Stuart] *MI ii*, 684/401; *Allen* 2
Awarded from 1758 until *c.*1807. *See* No. 643.

649*   **Richard Mead, Memorial 1754**
Obv. Bust r., draped. RICHARDVS MEAD. MED. REG. ET S.R.S.   *Rev.* An infant strangling a   *AR*   65   100
serpent; above, sun and moon. LABOR EST ANGVES SVPERARE   *Ex.* Armorial shield, dividing   *AE*   30   55
N. AV. XI. MDCLXXIII. O. F. XVI. MDCCLIV   *D.* 40 mm. By L. Pingo. *MI ii*, 675/388; *Storer*
2407. *See* **Plate 19**
Struck *c.*1770. Richard Mead (1673–1754), physician; the reverse alludes to his work on snake poisons.

650   **Irish Surplus Revenue Dispute 1755**
Obv. Irish harp, crowned. PROSPERITY TO OLD IRELAND 1754   *Rev.* Standing figure of the   *Br.*   15   30
Earl of Kildare, l., sword drawn, prevents a hand from snatching money off a table. TOUCH.
NOT SAYS. KILDARE   *Ex.* MDCCLV   *D.* 36 mm. (By J. Roche?) *MI ii*, 676/391
James Fitzgerald, 1st Duke of Leinster (1722–73), statesman; supported the right to appropriate surplus revenue without Crown consent.

651   **The Louth Election 1755**
Obv. Hibernia standing upon an island rock, assailed by the zephyrs. FIRM TO OUR COUNTRY   *AR*   75   120
AS THE ROCK IN THE SEA   *Rev.* BY OUR STRICT UNION IN LOUTH WE DISAPPOINTED THE HOPES OF
OUR ENEMIES ON THE 1 OF NOVEM 1755 IN THE 29 YEAR OF THE REIGN OF K. GEO. THE II WHOM
GOD LONG PRESERVE   Above, a heart over clasped hands. MAY THE LOVERS OF LIBERTY NEVER
LOSE IT   *D.* 44 mm. (By T. Pingo?) *MI ii*, 677/392; *Frazer* 1887/314
The medal occurs with a suspension loop.

652   **French-American Colonies, Condition of Affairs 1755**
Obv. Mercury standing upon a sea-shore, facing, hand capped to ear listening; beyond, an   *AR*   70   130
Irish and a French frigate flying their colours. SALVS IN FLVCTIBVS   *Ex.* STATVS
RERVM   *Rev.* A North American Indian warrior, crowned and standing, r., foot on alligator,
holding a bow and an arrow; female figure seated upon a sea-horse, l., holds a temple. An
open sea beyond. SED MOTOS PRAESTAT COMPONERE FLVCTVS   *Ex.* SVB EXITVM ANNI
MDCCLV   *D.* 35 mm. By P. P. Werner. *Betts* 392

653   Loss of Minorca 1756
Obv. Half-length figure facing, holding staff and British flag: a fort firing cannon, l; a ship, r. BRAVE. BLAKNEY. REWARD *Ex.* BUT. TO. B. GIVE A. CORD. *Rev.* Half-length figure of Byng, l., receiving a purse; a ship, r. WAS MINORCA SOLD BY. B.[yng] *Ex.* FOR. FRENCH GOLD. D. 35 mm. (By?) *MI ii*, 679/394; *MH* 1919, 348 — Br. 25 45

John Byng (1704–57), admiral; gave up Minorca to the French after little resistance and was court-martialled and shot. William Blakeney (1672–1761), Deputy-Governor of Minorca; acclaimed on his return to England and given a baronetcy. The medal was struck from two dies; examples vary only slightly.

654* North American Indian Chiefs' Medal 1757
Obv. Bust l., laureate, armoured and draped. GEORGIVS. II. DEI. GRATIA. *Rev.* A European seated beneath a tree offers a pipe to an Indian seated opposite; a fire between them. LET US LOOK TO THE MOST HIGH WHO BLESSED OUR FATHERS WITH PEACE. *Ex.* J757. A narrow crenellated border. D. 44 mm. [By E. Duffield] *MI ii*, 682/399; *Betts* 401; *Jamieson* 8. See **Plate 19** — *a AR* 1200 —; *b AR* 80 150; *AE* 25 45; *WM* 18 35

At the outbreak of the French war England formed alliances with some American Indian Chiefs who were presented with examples of this medal. Type *a*: an original striking which usually occurs holed and showing some wear. Type *b* is a restrike made in the first half of the nineteenth century; the narrow crenellated border is often missing from these pieces and they usually have a fresh and unworn appearance. Both types show traces of a die crack in various stages of development. New dies were subsequently made (*Julian* IP 49) in the late nineteenth century. *See* No. 472.

655* Victory of Plassy 1757
Obv. Victory mounted upon an elephant, l. VICTORY. AT. PLASSY. CLIVE. COMMANDER *Ex.* MDCCLVIII SOC. P.A.C. *Rev.* Clive, as a Roman general, holds one staff, surmounted by the British lion, and presents another, surmounted by a dolphin, to Soobah Meer Jaafar. INIVRIES. ATTONED. PRIVILEGE. AVGMENTED. TERRITORY. ACQVIRED. *Ex.* A. SOVBAH. GIVEN. TO. BENGAL. MDCCLVIII D. 40 mm. [By J. Pingo] *MI ii*, 683/400; *Allen* 11. See **Plate 19** — AR 80 150; AE 30 55

Robert Clive, Lord Clive (1725–74), soldier and Governor of Bengal. This medal is one of a group sponsored by the [Royal] Society of Arts (styled on this medal 'Society Promoting Arts and Commerce') which commemorate British victories. Their edges are sometimes inscribed WILL. PITT. ADMINISTRING. Nos. 658, 661,5,9, 673,6,9, 680,5. *See also* No. 643.

656   Battle of Lissa, Surrender of Breslau 1757
Obv. Equestrian figure, l., sword drawn; beyond, an encampment. FREDERIC KING OF PRUSSIA *Ex.* LISSA DEC. 5 *Rev.* Infantry attacking a fortress. WE SUBMIT PRISONERS OF WAR *Ex.* DEC. 19 1757 D. 28 mm. (By?) *MI ii*, 685/403 — Br. 10 20

Frederick II, or Frederick the Great (1712–86), King of Prussia 1740–86; formed an alliance with England in 1756 marking the beginning of the Seven Years War. A number of similar medals were struck.

657* Louisburg Taken 1758
Obv. Globe, with areas of CANADA and AMERICA identified, decorated with the Union flag and a scroll inscribed PARITER. IN. BELLA, is flanked by soldier and sailor; above, Fame hovering. In foreground, female figure drops a lily into the sea. *Rev.* Shore-line batteries firing at a fleet. LOVISBOVRG. TAKEN. MDCCLVIII D. 44 mm. By T. Pingo. *MI ii*, 685/404; *MH* 1919, 350; *Betts* 410. *See* **Plate 19** — AV 3500 6000; AR 350 650; AE 120 240

Examples in gold and silver usually occur with a suspension loop.

658   ——
Obv. Bust of Britannia, l., trident projecting from behind her neck. O. FAIR. BRITANNIA. HAIL *Rev.* Victory walking, r., on the prow of a galley. LOVISBOVRG TAKEN. MDCCLVIII D. 40 mm. [By J. Pingo, after J. Stuart] *MI ii*, 686/405–6; *MH* 1919, 351; *Betts* 413 — AR 100 180; AE 40 70

A similar version by J. Kirk has a running figure of Victory on the reverse. *See* No. 655.

659   ——
Obv. Bust r., armoured and draped. ADM^L. BOSCAWEN. TOOK. CAPE. BRETON *Rev.* Ships in harbour; a castle under fire, r. LOUISBOURG *Ex.* IUL 26 1758 D. 40 mm. (By?) *MI ii*, 689/411; *MH* 1919, 356; *Betts* 403 — Br. 35 60

Varieties occur of both this and No. 660. The Hon. Edward Boscawen (1711–61), admiral.

660   ——
Obv. Bust r., draped and holding a baton. ADM^L BOSCAWEN TOOK CAPE BRETON *Rev.* Ships entering harbour, castle on l. LOUISBURG HARBOUR *Ex.* IUL 26 1758 D. 37 mm. (By?) *MI ii*, 688/408–9; *MH* 1919, 353; *Betts* 406 — Br. 30 55

See No. 659.

661   Goree Taken 1758
Obv. As No. 658. *Rev.* Victory walking, r., on the prow of a galley. GOREE. TAKEN. MDCCLVIII D. 40 mm. [By J. Pingo, after J. Stuart] *MI ii*, 691/415; *MH* 1919, 359 — AR 80 150; AE 30 55

The edge is sometimes inscribed AVGVSTVS KEPPEL COMMANDING. *See* No. 655.

PLATE 19

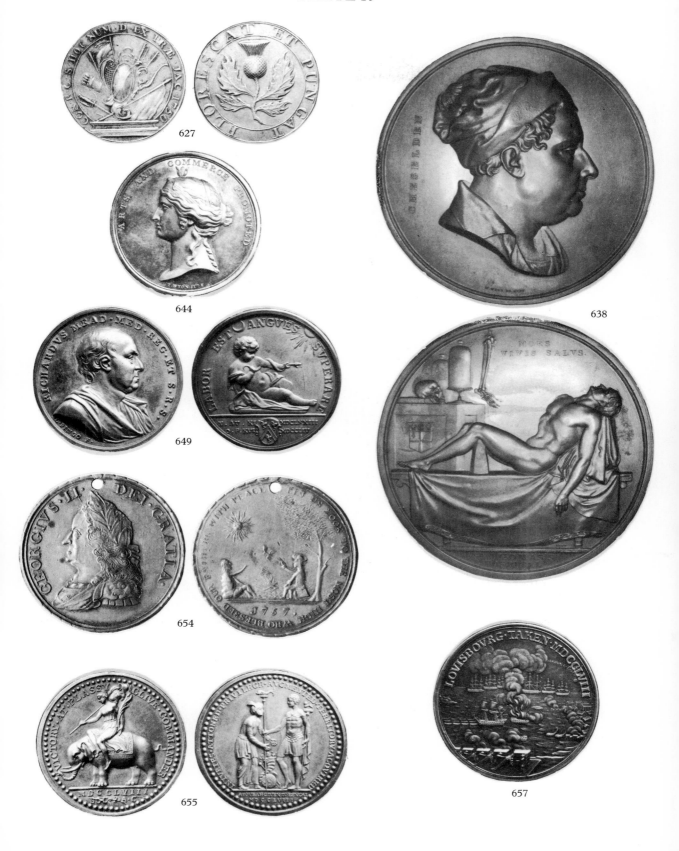

627

644

638

649

654

655

657

PLATE 20

670

674

683

685

687

694

695

696

708 (× ⅔)

707

			VF	EF
			£	£

662 British Victories 1758
Obv. Bust l., laureate and armoured. GEORGIVS. II. REX. *Rev.* Britannia, in a car drawn by a lion, drives over French lilies; Justice and Liberty in attendance. Above, FŒDUS INVICTUM on a ribbon. Around, campaigns with the respective commanders: SENEGAL. MAI. 2. MARSH. MASON / S. MALO^S. IUN. 16. MARLBRO. / CHERBOURG. AU. 16. HOW. / LOUISBOURG. IUL. 27. BOSCAWEN – AMHERST. / FRONTI^C. AUG. 27. BRADSTREET. / DUQUESNE. NOV. 24. FORBES. / GOREE. DEC. 29. KEPPEL. *Ex.* MDCCLVIII. *D.* 44 mm. (By J. Kirk?) *MI ii*, 692/416; *MH* 1919, 361; *Betts* 416   AR 120 220 / AE 25 45 / Br. 15 30

Jeffrey Amherst, Baron Amherst (1717–97), general. The reverse sometimes occurs coupled with that of No. 677.

663 Death of Anne, Princess of Orange 1759
Obv. Bust l., veiled and draped; above, a halo of stars. ANNA D.G. M. BR. PR. REG. TOT. BELG. FOED. GVB. MINORENNI PRINCIPE *Rev.* Sarcophagus decorated with a shield; below, symbols of Art and Science. NEC MAIESTATE NEC ÆTATE NEC VIRTVTE MOVETVR *Ex.* NATA 2 NOV. 1709. DENAT. 12 JAN. 1759. *D.* 41 mm. By J. G. Holtzhey. *MI ii*, 692/417; *v. Loon suppl.* 349   AR 45 85

664 George Frederick Handel, Memorial 1759
Obv. Bust l., draped. G. FRIDERICUS HAENDEL. *Rev.* NATUS HALAE IN MAGDEBURGICA AN. M.DC.LXXXIV. OBIIT AN. M.DCC.LIX. *Ex.* SERIES NUMISMATICA UNIVERSALIS VIRORUM ILLUSTRIUM. M.DCCC.XXIII. DURAND EDIDIT. *D.* 41 mm. By B. Wolff. *MI ii*, 696/424; *Niggl* 811   AR 16 35 / AE 3 7

Struck in Paris in 1823, from a series commemorating famous people from all countries. George Frederick Handel (1685–1759), composer.

665 Guadaloupe Taken 1759
Obv. Pallas, l., one foot on a galley's prow, holding a trident and military standard: MOORE, l.; BARRINGTON, r. *Ex.* SOC. PROM. ARTS AND. COMMERCE *Rev.* Britannia standing, l., raises a female figure holding sugar-canes. GVADALVPE. SVRRENDERS *Ex.* MAY. I. MDCCLIX *D.* 40 mm. [By L. Pingo, after J. Stuart] *MI ii*, 697/427; *MH* 1919, 362; *Betts* 417   AR 80 150 / AE 30 55

Struck c.1764. Samuel Barrington (1729–1800), admiral. Sir John Moore (1718–79), admiral. *See* No. 655.

666 Majority of George, Prince of Wales 1759
Obv. Bust l., armoured and draped. GEORGIVS. WALLIÆ. PRINCEPS. *Rev.* Female figure of Tellus seated, l., between two lions, couchant, plays a cymbal while four females dance around an oak-tree; a ribbon, inscribed ROBVR BRITANNIÆ, below. TELLVS JACTABIT ALVMNO. *Ex.* ADVLTÆ ÆTATIS DIES FAVSTISSIMVS IV. JVN. MDCCLIX *D.* 55 mm. By T. Pingo. *MI ii*, 698/428   AV 900 1600 / AR 170 320 / AE 60 110

George William Frederick (1738–1820), George III 1760–1820; eldest son of Frederick, Prince of Wales and Augusta.

667 ——
Obv. Bust almost facing, draped. GEORGIUS PRINCEPS WALLIAE *Rev.* The Prince standing, three-quarters l., crowned with a wreath by Victory. PRINCIPI OPTIMO *Ex.* MAY 24 1759 *D.* 42 mm. (By?) *MI ii*, 699/429   Br. 20 45

Dated in the old style.

668 George, Prince of Wales and Prince Edward 1759
Obv. Bust l., draped. GEORGIUS. WALLIÆ. PRINCEPS. Bust r., draped. EDWARDUS. GEO. WAL. PR. FRATER. *D.* 50 mm. By A. Vere. *MI ii*, 699/430   AR 130 240 / AE 40 70

Edward Augustus, Duke of York and Albany (1739–67), 2nd son of Frederick, Prince of Wales and Augusta.

669 Battle of Minden 1759
Obv. A British and a German soldier support Victory on a globe, who crowns each with a wreath. CONCORD. OF. THE. ALLIES *Ex.* AVG. I. MDCCLIX *Rev.* Victory seated, r., with captured French shields, supports a shield on her knee inscribed MINDEN *Ex.* SOCIETY. PROM. ARTS AND. COMMERCE *D.* 40 mm. [By J. Pingo, after J. Stuart] *MI ii*, 700/431; *Allen* 9   AR 80 150 / AE 30 55

Struck in 1763; *see* No. 655.

670* ——**
Obv. Bust r., armoured and draped. FERD: OF. BRVNSWICK *Rev.* Equestrian figure commanding cavalry; battle scene, beyond. PROTESTANTS. REIOICING *Ex.* THE. FRENCH. BEATEN. AT. MINDEN MDCCLIX *D.* 36 mm. By J. Kirk. *MI ii*, 702/433. See **Plate 20**   AR 90 160 / AE 35 65

Ferdinand, Duke of Brunswick-Wolfenbüttel K.G. (1721–92), Prussian Field marshal.

671 ——
Obv. Bust r., armoured. THE BRITISH HERO. THE MARQUIS OF GRANBY. *Rev.* Heart, crowned, within a wreath. *D.* 27 mm. (By?) *MI ii*, 703/436; *EPM* 1891, 388   Br. 10 20

John Manners, Marquis of Granby (1721–70), soldier.

672 **George II, Frederick of Prussia and the Allied Leaders 1759**
Obv. Busts face to face, laureate and armoured; crown above. KING. GEORGE. THE. II. FRED.
KING. OF PRUSSIA. 1759. *Rev.* Six portrait medallions of PRINCE FERDINAND, PRINCE HENRY,
DUKE BRUNSWIG, GEN. L. AMHERST, COL. CLIVE, ADM BOSCAWEN and H. W. M. PITT *D.* 46 mm.
(By?) *MI ii*, 704/438; *Betts* 425
William Pitt, 1st Earl of Chatham (1708–78), statesman.
Br. | 25 | 45

673 **Quebec Taken 1759**
Obv. Bust of BRITANNIA, l. Below, a trident and standard, marked SAVNDERS and WOLFE,
crossed and decorated with a wreath. *Rev.* Captive chained to the base of captured French
arms, which Victory crowns with a wreath. QVEBEC. TAKEN. MDCCLIX *Ex.* SOC. P.A.C. *D.*
40 mm. [By J. Pingo] *MI ii*, 705/439; *MH* 1919, 363; *Betts* 421
James Wolfe (1727–59), major-general. *See* No. 655.
AR 120 220 / *AE* 50 85

674* **Death of James Wolfe 1759**
Obv. Bust l., armoured and draped. IACOBUS WOLFE ANGLUS *Rev.* A funerary urn, its base
inscribed PRO PATRIA, amidst arms and standards. IN VICTORIA CÆSVS *Ex.* QVEBECÆ SEPT.
XIII. MDCCLIX *D.* 37 mm. By J. Kirk, *obv.* after I. Gosset. *MI ii*, 706/440; *Betts* 422. *See*
Plate 20
AR 120 220 / *AE* 40 75

675 ——
Obv. Half-length bust, r., draped, holding a raised sword. THE BRAVE GENERAL WOLF WAS
KILLED *Ex.* SEP. 18 1759 *Rev.* Ships before a harbour. BEFORE QUEBEC *D.* 37 mm. (By?)
Br. 35 65

676 **Battle of Quiberon Bay, Belleisle 1759**
Obv. Britannia armed with a trident, seated upon a sea-horse, is crowned by Victory.
BRITAIN. TRIVMPHED. HAWKE. COMMANDED *Ex.* OFF. BELLEISLE NOV. XX. MDCCLIX *Rev.*
Figures of NIGHT and TEMPEST shield FRANCE from the thunder of BRITAIN. *Ex.* FRANCE.
RELINQVISHES THE SEA S.P.A.C *D.* 40 mm. [By J. Kirk] *MI ii*, 706/441; *MH* 1919, 364; *Allen*
7
See No. 655. Edward Hawke, Baron Hawke (1705–81), admiral.
AR 80 150 / *AE* 30 55

677 **British Victories 1759**
Obv. As No. 662. *Rev.* Central shield with an inverted lily inscribed around garter PERFIDIA
EVERSA; below, a ribbon inscribed W. PITT AUSP. GEO. II PR. MI. Around, campaigns and
respective commanders: QUEBEC WOLFE MONCKN. TOWNSP SEP. 13 & 18 / CROWN POINT
AMHERST AUG. 4 / LAGOS BOSCAWEN AUG. 19 / MINDEN FERDINAND AUG. 1. / GUADALOUPE BARING
. MOORE MAY. 1 / NIAGARA IOHNSON IULY. 25 / HAWKE QUIBERON NOV. 20 *Ex.* MDCCLIX *D.*
44 mm. (By J. Kirk?) *MI ii*, 708/444; *MH* 1919, 367; *Betts* 418
Sir William Johnson (1715–74), superintendent of Indian affairs in North America. Robert Monckton (1726–82),
lieutenant-general. George Townshend, 4th Viscount (1724–1807), soldier. The reverse occurs coupled with that of
No. 662.
AR 120 220 / *AE* 25 45 / *Br.* 15 30

678 **Captain Wilson's Voyage to China 1760**
Obv. Neptune seated upon a rock, r., indicates a route to Mercury standing before him;
beyond, expanse of sea with islands. ITERARE CVRSVS RELICTOS *Ex.* MDCCLX. *Rev.* THE. GIFT.
OF. THE. ENG. EAST. INDIA. COMP. TO. CAPTAIN. WILLIAM. WILSON. COMMANDER. OF. THE. SHIP.
PITT. AS. AN. ACKNOWLEDGEMENT. OF. HIS. SERVICES. IN. HAVING. MADE. HIS. PASSAGE. TO. AND.
FROM. CHINA. BY. AN. UNUSUAL. COURSE. AND. THEREBY. EVINCING. THAT. NAVIGATION. TO. BE.
PRACTICABLE. AT. ANY. SEASON. OF. THE. YEAR. *D.* 68 mm. By R. Yeo. *MI ii*, 709/446; *MH*
1919, 369; *Erlanger* 179
Captain Wilson received an example of the medal in gold.
AV — — / *AR* 220 400 / *AE* 80 150

679 **Montreal Taken 1760**
Obv. Female figure seated mournfully beneath a pine-tree, r., beside a French shield.
MONTREAL TAKEN MDCCLX *Ex.* SOC. PROMOTING ARTS AND COMMERCE. *Rev.* River god, St.
Lawrence, reclining against the prow of a galley, a beaver walking on his leg; beyond, a
standard decorated with a wreath, inscribed AMHERST, and surmounted by a lion. THE
CONQVEST OF CANADA COMPLEATED *Ex.* Captured French and North American Indian
arms. *D.* 41 mm. [By J. Kirk] *MI ii*, 711/447; *Betts* 429; *Allen* 8
See No. 655.
AR 120 220 / *AE* 50 85

680 **Canada Subdued 1760**
Obv. Bust l., laureate. GEORGE. II. KING *Rev.* Female seated mournfully beneath a pine-
tree, r.; a beaver behind her. CANADA SUBDUED *Ex.* MDCCLX S.P.A.C *D.* 39 mm. [By L.
Pingo, after J. Stuart] *MI ii*, 711/448; *Betts* 430; *Allen* 5
See No. 655.
AR 120 220 / *AE* 50 85

			£	£

681 George II, Tribute and Memorial 1760
Obv. As No. 525. *Rev.* Victory, inscribing a shield ASIA AFRICA AMERI and EUR, seated amidst arms and standards, upon a sarcophagus inscribed NATUS. 10 NOV: 1683 COR: 22 OCT: 1727 OBIIT 25 OCT: 1760 Above, Fame reveals a portrait medallion of GU: PITT DICTATOR on an obelisk. TRIUMPHA UBIQUE *D.* 41 mm. By J. Dassier. *MI ii*, 714/454; *Betts* 427
See No. 526.

AR	60	110
AE	20	35

GEORGE III, 1760–1820

682 Accession of George III 1760
Obv. Bust l., armoured and draped. GEORGIVS. TERTIVS. REX IN. REG. XXV. OCT. MDCCLX *Rev.* As No. 666. *D.* 55 mm. By T. Pingo. *BHM* 1

AR	170	320
AE	60	110

683* ———
Obv. Bust l., armoured and draped. GEORGIVS. TERTIVS. REX *Rev.* Britannia standing, facing, beside a lion and objects. FELICITAS BRITANNIÆ *Ex.* INEUNTE REGNO OCT. XXV MDCCLX *D.* 41 mm. (By J. Kirk?) *BHM* 3. *See* **Plate 20**

AR	60	110
AE	25	40

684 ———
Obv. Bust l., draped. GEORGIUS. III. REX. *Rev.* Heart within a wreath, upon a base inscribed BORN MAY. 24 1738 PROCLAIMED OCTᴿ. 26. 1760 on its facia. ENTIRELY BRITISH *D.* 36 mm. By J. Kirk. *BHM* 4; *Forrer* III/164
Some examples have a grained edge.

AR	30	55
AE	15	25

685* George III, Protector of the Arts 1760
Obv. Head l., laureate. GEORGE III *Rev.* George III, in Roman dress, receives 'Mother of the Arts', who implores protection of her children, Sculpture, Poetry and Architecture. ARTS. PROTECTED *Ex.* MDCCLX SOC. P.A.C. *D.* 39 mm. [By J. Pingo] *BHM* 6; *Allen* 5. *See* **Plate 20**
See No. 655.

AR	45	85
AE	15	30

686 Pondicherry Taken 1761
Obv. Bust r., laureate, within a beaded circle. GEORGE. THE. THIRD *Rev.* Victory inscribing a shield COOTE STEEVENS, standing, r., between palms, rudders, and the spilt urns of the INDVS and GANGES rivers. TOTAL. EXPVLSION. OF. THE. FRENCH. FROM. INDIA *Ex.* PONDICHERRY TAKEN MDCCLXI *D.* 39 mm. By T. Pingo. *BHM* 72.
Sir Eyre Coote (1726–83), general; Charles Steevens (1705–61), rear-admiral.

AR	80	150
AE	30	55

687* Belleisle Taken 1761
Obv. As No. 683. *Rev.* Ships around an island. INSTAT. VI. PATRIA *Ex.* CALONESUS. CAPTA. VII. IUNII MDCCLXI *D.* 41 mm. (By J. Kirk?) *BHM* 71; *MH* 1919, 371. *See* **Plate 20**

AR	140	270
AE	50	90
Br.	30	55

688 ———
Obv. Bust of Britannia, l., between cap of liberty and trident. O. FAIR. BRITANNIA. HAIL *Rev.* Victory advancing, r., carrying captured French trophies. BELLEISLE. TAKEN. MDCCLXI *D.* 41 mm. By J. Kirk, [after J. Stuart]. *BHM* 70; *MH* 1919, 370
This medal is after No. 658. Edges of some examples are inscribed WILLIAM. PITT. ADMINISTRING.

AR	80	150
AE	30	55

689 Marriage of George III and Charlotte 1761
Obv. Busts r., conjoined. GEORG. III. SOPH. CAROL. M. B. F. ET H. REX ET REGINA *Rev.* Britannia holds the cap of liberty and burns incense at a tripod. VOTA BRITANNIÆ *Ex.* FELICI VINCULO IUNCTI D. X. SEPT. MDCCLXI *D.* 43 mm. By J. Abraham. *BHM* 11
Charlotte Sophia (1744–1818), niece of the duke of Mecklenburg-Strelitz.

AV	450	850
AR	80	150
AE	35	65

690 ———
Obv. Busts r., conjoined and draped, he laureate and armoured. GEORGE III & CHARLOTTE KING & QVEEN *Rev.* Eros standing, r., fans the flames of two hearts upon an altar. THE FELICITY OF BRITAIN *Ex.* MARRIED SEPT. THE VIII MDCCLXI *D.* 36 mm. By J. Kirk. *BHM* 10

AV	380	650
AR	35	65
AE	15	30

691 ———
Obv. Busts r., conjoined. GEORGIVS. III. ET. CHARLOTTA. REX: *Rev.* Two cherubs carry a scroll, inscribed FELICITAS. BRITANNIÆ *Ex.* DIIS AUSPICIBUS MDCCLXI *D.* 26 mm. (By?) *BHM* 17
Struck from more than one pair of dies.

AR	15	30
AE	8	15
WM	4	8

			£	£

692 Coronation of George III 1761
Obv. As No. 683. *Rev.* Bust r., draped. .CHARLOTTA. BRITANNIÆ. REGINA. NUPT: SEP: VIII *AR* 60 110
CORO: XXII MDCCLXI *D.* 41 mm. (By J. Kirk?) *BHM* 30 *AE* 25 40
More than forty medals commemorate the coronation.

693 ——
Obv. The King, enthroned, crowned by an archbishop. GEORGE. THE. III. KING. OF. ENGLAND. *AR* 45 —
CROWND Sᴾ 22. 1761. *Rev.* The Queen, enthroned, holding orb and sceptre. CHARLOTTE. *AE* 15 25
QUEEN. OF. ENGLAND. CROWND. Sᴾ. 22. 1761. *D.* 40 mm. (By?) *BHM* 36 *Br.* 10 20
Examples in silver have all been found to be cast.

694* ——
Obv. Bust r., laureate and armoured. GEORGIVS. III. D.G. M. BRI. FRA. ET. HIB. REX. F.D. *Rev.* *AV* 550 1100
The King enthroned, l., crowned by Britannia standing before him. PATRIAE. OVANTI *Ex.* *AR* 100 170
CORONAT. XXII. SEPT CIƆIƆCCLXI *D.* 34 mm. By L. Natter. *BHM* 23; *Wollaston* 16; *Nau* *AE* 45 95
151–4. *See* **Plate 20**
The official coronation issue; struck from several pairs of dies, and with many varieties. The obverse also occurs coupled with that of No. 696. Various contemporary copies were made.

695* ——
Obv. Head r., laureate. GEORGIVS. TERTIVS. REX INEUNTE REGNO. OCT. 25 *Rev.* Bust l., *AR* 20 35
crowned and draped. CHARLOTTA. REGINA. NUPT. SEP. 8. CORO. 22. 1761 *D.* 26 mm. (By?)
BHM 42. *See* **Plate 20**

696* Coronation of Charlotte 1761
Obv. Bust r., draped. CHARLOTTA. D.G. M. BR. FR. ET. HIB. REGINA. *Rev.* The Queen standing, *AV* 750 1500
facing, crowned by Fame hovering above. QVAESITVM. MERITIS *Ex.* CORON. XXII. SEPT *AR* 110 180
MDCCLXI *D.* 34 mm. By L. Natter. *BHM* 65–6; *Wollaston* 22; *Nau* 155–7. *See* **Plate 20** *AE* 55 100
The official coronation issue; struck from more than one pair of dies. The obverse occurs coupled with that of No. 694.

697 Death of Benjamin Hoadley 1761
Obv. Bust r., clerically robed. BENJ: HOADLEY. EPISCOPUS. VINTON. *Rev.* Bishop's mitre and *AR* 30 55
crozier upon a plinth near a tree, against which rests an armorial shield within the Garter. *AE* 15 25
VIGET. AD. EXTREMUM *Ex.* NAT: NOV: XIV. MDCLXXVI MORT: APR: XVII. MDCCLXI *D.* 37 mm.
By J. Kirk, *obv.* after I. Gosset. *BHM* 68; *EPM* 1892, 241
Benjamin Hoadley (1676–1761), Bishop of Winchester.

698 Charlotte, 18th Birthday 1762
Obv. Bust r., in a coronet, draped. CHARLOTTA BRITANNIÆ REGINA *Rev.* Two hands hold an *AR* 55 90
upright staff. UNITED TO IMMORTALIZE HER NAME IAN. XVIII. MDCCLXII *D.* 29 mm. (By T. *AE* 15 30
Pingo?) *BHM* 74

699 Birth of George, Prince of Wales 1762
Obv. Busts face to face, a star below. GEORGIVS. III. REX. CHARLOTTA. REGINA *Rev.* Britannia *AR* 70 120
seated, l., receives an infant, a star over its head, from Mercury. PACATVMQVE. REGET. *AE* 30 55
PATRIIS. VIRTVTIBVS. ORBEM *Ex.* XII. AVG. MDCCLXII *D.* 40 mm. By T. Pingo. *BHM* 77
The star symbolises the infant's princely origin. George Augustus Frederick, Prince of Wales (1762–1830), George IV 1820–30.

700 ——
Obv. As No. 698. *Rev.* Cherub rising from a cornucopia; 12. AUG 1762 on ribbon in the field. *AR* 55 90
PACATUMQUE. REGET. PATRIIS. VIRTUTIBUS. ORBEM *D.* 29 mm. (By T. Pingo?) *BHM* 78 *AE* 15 30

701 Royal Birth & British Victories 1762
Obv. As No. 683. *Rev.* In the centre PAX AUSPICATA NOV. 3 between a balance and anchor, *AV* 900 1600
within a Serpent of Eternity. Above, PR OF WALES BO AUG. 12 Around, naval campaigns and *AR* 170 320
the respective commanders: HERMIONE MAY 31 / THE HAVANNAH ALBEMᴸ. & POCOCK. AUG 14 / *AE* 55 100
NEWFOUNDLAND SEP 18 AMHERST ALCANᴬ. CASSEL &c &c / GRÆBENSTEIN FERDᴰ. & GRANBY IUNE *Br.* 30 55
24 / MARTINICO MONCKᴺ. & RODNEY FEB. 4. Sᵀ. LUCIA Sᵀ. VINCENT TOBAGO GRANADA &c MARCH 1.
5 &c. *Ex.* MDCCLXII *D.* 41 mm. (By J. Kirk?) *BHM* 82; *MH* 1919, 372; *Betts* 441
George Keppel, Earl of Albemarle (1724–72), general. Sir George Pocock (1706–92), admiral. George Brydges Rodney, 1st Baron Rodney (1719–92), admiral.

702 Seven Years War 1762
Obv. An American Indian, with bow and quiver, supports Cupid who places a figure of *AR* 70 130
Peace upon a column surmounted with the German eagle; at the base, shields of England *AE* 30 55
and France. EVROPAE ALMAM NE TARDET PACEM *Ex.* MDCCLXII *Rev.* Commerce seated,
upon a Belgic lion, leans upon bales and supports staff with cap of liberty; beyond, ship at
sea. DVRET VSQVE AD EXTREMVM *Ex.* BELG. FOED. *D.* 43 mm. By J. G. Holtzhey. *Betts* 442; *v.*
Loon suppl. 365; *Forrer* II/536

			£	£

703   **Peace of Paris 1763**
Obv. Bust r., laureate. LUDOVICUS XV. REX CHRISTIANISS. *Rev.* Peace standing, l., before a   *AR*   90   160
captive seated upon arms and trophies. PAX UBIQUE VICTRIX *Ex.* GALLORUM ET   *AE*   30   55
BRITANNORUM CONCORDIA MDCCLXIII. *D.* 41 mm. By B. P. S. Duvivier / J. G. Holtzhey. *Betts*
444; *Leroux* 309

By this treaty, between England, France, Portugal and Spain, French possessions in North America, to the Mississippi, were ceded to Britain. Louis XV of France (1710–74) king of France 1715–74. Restrikes of this medal may have been made.

704   **Capture of Morro Castle, Havana 1763**
Obv. Busts r., conjoined and uniformed. LVDOVICO DE VELASCO ET VINCENTIO   *AR*   170   320
GONZALEZ *Rev.* Assault on Morro Castle seen from harbour, and explosion of its   *AE*   55   90
magazine; soldiers storm a breach in the castle wall. In harbour are three large frigates and
longboats amongst bodies in the water. IN MORRO. VIT. GLOR. FVNCT. *Ex.* ARTIVM ACADEMIA
CAROLO REGE CATHOL ANNVENTE CONS. A. MDCCLXIII *D.* 48 mm. By D. T. F. Prieto. *MH*
1921, 680; *Betts* 443; *Medina* 12

Two large fleets under Admiral Pocock and the Earl of Albemarle besieged and bombarded the castle. The medal was struck by the Spanish Academy of Arts in memory of the men who lost their lives, including Commander Velasco and his deputy Vincentio Gonzales.

705   **Births of George, Prince of Wales 1762 and Prince Frederick 1763**
Obv. Bust l., laureate; above, Prince's plumes within coronet. GEORGIUS WAL: PRIN: NAT.   *AV*   170   300
AUG. 12. 1762 SPES. REGIS ET. PATRIÆ   *Rev.* Bust r.; above, a mitre. FREDERICUS. EPISC. OSNA.   *AR*   25   45
NAT. AUG. 16. 1763. SUMMUS. SINE. LABE. SACERDOS   *D.* 29 mm. (By?) *BHM* 84   *AE*   12   18
      Br.   5   8
Struck *c.*1765. Frederick Augustus, Duke of York and Albany (1763–1827), second son of George III and Charlotte.

706   **Prince Frederick elected Bishop of Osnabrück 1764**
Obv. Britannia seated, almost facing, leaning against the British shield at a table on which   *a,b AR*   45   75
rest a mitre and crozier. SPES PVBLICA   *Rev.* FREDERICVS M. BRITT. PR. EPISCOPVS OSNABRVG.   *AE*   20   30
D. BR. ET LVN. ANNVENTE GEORGIO TERTIO M. BRIT. FR. H. R. F. D. BRVNSW. ET LVNEB. S.R.I. A.
TH. ET ELECT. PATRE ET REGE OPT. POSTVLATVS EPISC. XXVII FEBRVARII MDCCLXIV *D. a*   *c AV*   150   250
43 mm.; *b* 40 mm.; *c* 31 mm. By T. Pingo. *BHM* 90   *AR*   25   45

707*   **North American Indian Chiefs' Medal 1764**
Obv. Bust r., laureate, armoured and draped. GEORGIUS III. D.G. M. BRI. FRA. ET. HIB. REX. F.D.   *AR*   3700   —
Rev. An American Indian and a uniformed officer, seated beneath a tree, pass a pipe between
them. Beyond, shipping on a river. HAPPY WHILE UNITED   *Ex.* 1764   *D.* 56 mm. Cast. (By
D. C. Fueter?) *Jamieson* 12; *Tancred* 49; *Betts* 511. *See* **Plate 20**

Sometimes mounted on the edge with a peace pipe and bird's wing, to which is attached a suspension loop. Some examples bear two punch marks N. YORK / D.C.F. (D. C. Fueter) in the field of the reverse. There are several varieties of this medal; *see* No. 472.

708*   **Death of William Stukeley 1765**
Obv. Bust r., a wreath of clover in hair. REV. GVL. STVKELEY. M.D. SR & AS   Below, ÆT 54   *AE*   170   320
(incuse). *Rev.* View of Stonehenge. *Ex.* OB. MAR. 4. 1765 Æ: 84   *D.* 89 mm. Cast. (By G. D.
Gaab?) *BHM* 94; *Storer* 3453. *See* **Plate 20**

William Stukeley (1687–1765), physician, rector, antiquarian and numismatist; author of a work on Stonehenge, published in 1740 when he was 54. His age at death as stated in the exergue is incorrect.

709   **Death of the Duke of Cumberland 1765**
Obv. Bust r., armoured and draped. WILL. D. OF. CUMBERLAND   *Rev.* A tomb, inscribed NAT.   *AR*   70   130
XV. APRIL. MDCCXXI OB. XXXI OCTO. R MDCCLXV, flanked by Cupid, as Hercules, and a   *AE*   25   45
mournful Britannia; a scroll inscribed CULLODEN at her feet. SWEET. WILL.S BLOOM. IS.
CLOSD. *D.* 38 mm. By J. v. Nost. *BHM* 91

710   **Royal Military Academy 1765**
Obv. Bust r., laureate. AVSPICIIS GEORG. III OPT. PRINC. P.P. *Rev.* Athena stands holding a   *AV*   300   450
spear and palm branch. PRAEMIA LAVDI   *Ex.* D.M. GRANBY MAG. GEN. ORD. MDCCLXV   *D.*   *AR*   90   170
36 mm. By T. Pingo. *BHM* 93; *Grimshaw* 17   *AE*   20   30

Marquis of Granby was governor of the Academy; prizes in gold and silver were awarded to gentlemen cadets.

711   **Royal College of Physicians, Browne Medal 1765**
Obv. Bust l., draped. ESSE ET VIDERI D. GVLIELMVS BROWNE, EQVES. NAT. III. NON. IAN. A. I.   *AV*   250   350
MDCXCII. *Rev.* Kneeling figure, r., being crowned by Apollo, seated. SVNT SVA PRAEMIA   *AR*   35   65
LAVDI   *Ex.* ELECTVS COLL. MED. LOND. PRAESES A. S. MDCCLXV   *D.* 37 mm. By L. Pingo.   *AE*   20   30
BHM 92; *Storer* 500

Awarded annually in gold, from 1774, for Greek and Latin studies. Sir William Browne (1692–1774), physician; became president of the College in 1765.

712   **Notts. and W. Riding of Yorkshire Agricultural Society 1765**
Obv. Ceres standing, l., holding a cornucopia and plough. SOCIETY FOR IMPROVEMENT OF   *AR*   30   45
AGRICULTURE   *Ex.* INST. NOTTS. & W.R. YORKS. MDCCLXV   *Rev.* A wreath (space within for   *AE*   8   15

recipient's name). *D.* 40 mm. By T. Pingo. *D & W* 170/531 £ £

An early agricultural society prize, awarded in silver. Other societies who issued medals at this time include the Salford Hundred in 1767; Glamorganshire, 1772; Richmondshire, 1778; Essex, 1793; and Staffordshire, 1800. The greatest number of agricultural prize medals were issued during the nineteenth century.

713 **Repeal of the Stamp Act 1766**
Obv. Bust l., draped GVLIELMVS PITT *Rev.* THE MAN WHO. HAVING SAVED THE PARENT.
PLEADED WITH SUCCESS FOR HER CHILDREN *D.* 40 mm. By T. Pingo. *BHM* 100; *Betts* 516

AR	45	80
AE	25	40
Pb.	12	25

Struck from more than one pair of dies. A similar medal is signed I.W. (John Westwood Sr.?).

714 ——
Obv. Bust three-quarters r., draped. GUL'. PITT. LIBERTATIS VINDEX *Rev.* Upright sword surmounted by cap of liberty between two clasped hands, within a wreath. BRITANNIA ET AMERICA IVNCTÆ. *D.* 33 mm. (By?) *BHM* 102; *Betts* 521

Br.	180	330

715 **Death of James (III), The Old Pretender 1766**
Obv. Bust of Prince Henry r., in clerical cap and robes. HENRICVS. M. D. EP. TVSC. CARD. DVX.
EBOR. S. R. E. V. CANC *Rev.* Religion standing in foreground holding cross and bible; lion, couchant, cardinal's hat and crown at her feet. View of St. Peter's, Rome, beyond. NON.
DESIDERIIS. HOMINVM. SED. VOLVNTATE. DEI. *Ex.* * AN. MDCCLXVI *D.* 53 mm. By F.
Cropanese. *BHM* 99; *CP* 75/63

AR	140	270
AE	65	110
WM	25	45

Struck on flans of slightly varying diameter.

716 **Lord Camden, Lord Chancellor 1766**
Obv. Bust r., draped. CHARLES LORD CAMDEN CHANCELLOR OF BRITAIN *Rev.* Standing figures of Liberty and Equality. LIBERTY EQVITY *Ex.* MDCCLXVI *D.* 40 mm. By T. Pingo.
BHM 97; *EPM* 1888, 263

AR	55	95
AE	20	35

Charles Pratt, Earl Camden (1714–94), Chief Justice.

717 **Restoration of Alnwick Castle 1766**
Obv. Bust r., draped. HU. PERCY DUKE OF NOR. *Rev.* View of castle. ALNWICK CASTLE RESTORED *Ex.* MDCCLXVI *D.* 44 mm. By J. Kirk. *BHM* 106.

AR	45	75
AE	15	30

Hugh Percy, 1st Duke of Northumberland (1715–86).

718* **Lord Robert Clive 1766**
Obv. Bust three-quarters l., draped. ROBERT. CLIVE. BARON. OF. PLASSY. *Rev.* An obelisk inscribed 1757 FEB. 5 NABOES. CAMP. DESTROYED JUNE 23 VICTORIOUS. AT PLASSEY. 1763.
ESTABLISHED. PEACE. IN. BENGAL. AND. MADE. OMRA. OF. THE EMPIRE., which Fame, standing, indicates. HONOUR. THE. REWARD. OF. MERIT. *Ex.* ANNO. 1766 *D.* 42 mm. By J. v. Nost.
BHM 95; *EPM* 1890, 60; *Forrer* II/302. *See* **Plate 21**

AR	70	130
AE	30	55

The reverse of this medal is signed C.G (?) in the exergue.

719 **Lodge L'Immortalité de l'Ordre Constituted, London 1766**
Obv. A man chisels IMMORTALITATI ORDINIS IVIƆCLXVI on a plinth; masonic implements at its base. LONDINENS. LIBER. FRAT. ARCHITECTONIC. *Rev.* A globe, radiate; below, sprig of acacia upon a tablet within the Serpent of Eternity. NON EST MORTALE QUOD OPT. *D.* 40 mm.
By J. Kirk. *BHM* 108; *Shackles* 2

AR	45	85
AE	20	35

720 **Royal College of Surgeons 1767**
Obv. Armorial shield and crest, within a wreath. QVÆ PROSVNT OMNIBVS ARTES *Ex.*
MDCCLXVII *Rev.* Galen standing, r., contemplates a human skeleton on the ground. *D.*
48 mm. By T. Pingo. *BHM* 110; *Storer* 5928

AV	550	700
AR	80	130
AE	35	60

This was awarded annually in gold to the professor of anatomy. The reverse composition has been taken from the frontispiece of William Cheselden's *Osteographia* of 1733. Galen (*fl.*165 AD), Greek physician.

721 **Visit of Christian VII 1768**
Obv. Bust r., draped. CHRISTIANVS VII D.G. DAN. NORV. V.G. REX *Rev.* A double cornucopiae around clasped hands holding a winged caduceus; MDCCLXVIII ADV. IN. BRITANN., below.
CONCORDIA REGVM SALVS POPVLORVM *D.* 40 mm. By T. Pingo. *BHM* 129

AR	50	85
AE	20	35

Christian VII (1749–66–1808), of Denmark and Norway. At least four other medals commemorate the visit.

722 **Westmeath Election 1768**
Obv. Hibernia stands beside a pillar supporting an Irish shield. VINCIT AMOR PATRIAE *Rev.*
Hand holding a wreath. PRESENTED TO THE RIGHT HON. ANTHONY MALONE BY THE FREE INDEPENDANT ELECTORS OF WESTMEATH IN ACKNOWLEDGMENT OF HIS STRENVOVS SVCCESSFVL SVPPORT OF THEIR INTEREST ON IVLY XXV MDCCLXVIII *D.* 48 mm. By T. Pingo. *BHM* 126;
Frazer 1887/314

AR	70	120
AE	35	60

Anthony Malone (1700–76), Chancellor of the Irish Exchequer; Privy Councillor.

			£	£

723*   **Royal Academy of Arts 1768**
Obv. Bust r., hair bound with a fillet. GEORGIVS III D.G. MAGN. BRIT. FR. ET HIB. REX   *Rev.*   *AV*   850   1200
Minerva seated beside a young artist to whom she indicates a temple on a hill, beyond. HAVD   *AR*   100   180
FACILEM ESSE VIAM VOLVIT   *Ex.* R. AC. INSTITVTED 1768   *D.* 55 mm. By T. Pingo. [after G. B.
Cipriani & E. Penny] *BHM* 132. *See* **Plate 21**
Awarded annually in gold until 1772, and biennially thereafter, in the three disciplines of Architecture, Painting and
Sculpture. A new type (No. 1228*b*) was introduced in 1830 and similarly awarded until 1936. *See* No. 724.

724   **Royal Academy of Arts 1768**
Obv. As No. 723. *Rev.* A Torso. STVDY   *Ex.* R. AC. INSTITVTED 1768   *D.* 55 mm. By T.   *AR*   60   110
Pingo. *BHM* 133; *D & W* 146/345; *Erlanger* 89–90
A number of these medals in silver, and latterly bronze, were awarded annually by the R.A. Schools to students, the reverse
based on the Belvedere torso in the Vatican. *See* Nos. 1228*a*, 1306, 1862, 1916. In 1936 a standard medal (bust of George
III wearing a tricorn/inscription divided by laurel branch, by E. Gillick) was introduced and replaced all the other Royal
Academy prize medals. *See* S. C. Huchinson, *History of the Royal Academy 1768–1968*, London, 1968.

725*   **John Wilkes 1768**
Obv. Bust almost facing, draped, head r. JOHN WILKES. ESQ. *Rev.* Figure of Time inscribes a   *AR*   90   150
pyramid 45 NORTH BRITON MAGNA CHARTA   *Ex.* IN MEMORY OF THE YEAR MDCCLXVIII   *D.*   *AE*   45   85
45 mm. (By?) *BHM* 117. *See* **Plate 21**
John Wilkes (1727–97), political agitator and reformer; M.P. for Middlesex. Issue 45 of his paper, *The North Briton*,
libelled Government ministers and he was subsequently arrested. More than twelve medals commemorate Wilkes.

726   ——
Obv. Bust r., draped. IOHN WILKES ESQ. *Rev.* Infant genius advancing, l., holds a staff with   *AR*   50   90
the cap of liberty. GENIUS OF LIBERTY. *Ex.* ELECTED KNIGHT OF THE SHIRE FOR MIDDLESEX   *AE*   20   35
MDCCLXVIII   *D.* 34 mm. By J. Kirk. *BHM* 115; *D & W* 198/765   *WM*   10   20

727   ——
Obv. Bust l., draped. IOHANNES WILKES   *Rev.* Britannia seated, r., holding a staff with the   *Br.*   8   15
cap of liberty, an olive-branch, and a shield inscribed 45   *D.* 24 mm. (By?) *BHM* 123; *D &*
W 198/772

728   **Cambridge University, Chancellor's Medal 1768**
Obv. Bust r., laureate, armoured and draped. GEORGIVS III PIVS FELIX PATER PATRIAE   *Rev.*   *AV*   700   900
Apollo confers a wreath upon a scholar; above, infant genius bearing a trumpet and ribbon,   *AR*   60   100
inscribed DETUR DIGNISSIMO   *Ex.* AUSP: AUG: HEN: DUC: DE GRAFTON ACAD: CANTAB: *AE*   20   35
CANCELL: *D.* 54 mm. By J. Kirk. *BHM* 112; *Erlanger* 61
Awarded in gold. Augustus Henry Fitzroy, 3rd Duke of Grafton (1735–1811), politician; became Chancellor of
Cambridge University in 1768.

729   **Prince Henry, Cardinal York: Sede Vacante 1769**
Obv. Armorial shield and crest. *Rev.* HENRICVS. CARDINALIS DVX. EBOR. S.R.E. VICECAN.   *AR*   80   150
CELLARIVS SEDE VACAN. 1769   *D.* 29 mm. Italian? (by?) *BHM* 135; *CP* 76/64   *WM*   20   35
The Sede Vacante followed the death of Pope Clement XIII, and lasted from 2 February until 19 May 1769.

730   **Viscount Chetwynd 1769**
Obv. Bust r., laureate, armoured and draped. GEORGIVS. III DEI GRA. REX. *Rev.* EX. DONO.   *AR*   90   170
WILHELMI. VICECOMITIS. CHETWYND. MDCCLXIX. *D.* 37 mm. (By?) [after J. S. Tanner] *BHM*   *AE*   45   80
134; *EPM* 1890, 54/1   *WM*   20   35
William Richard, 3rd Viscount Chetwynd (1685–1770), politician; Master of the Mint. This medal also occurs with a
dedicatory inscription on the reverse, which was struck after his death.

731   **William Shakespeare 1769**
Obv. Bust of Shakespeare, r., draped. WE SHALL NOT LOOK UPON HIS LIKE AGAIN. *Rev.* JUBILEE   *AR*   20   35
AT STRATFORD IN HONOUR AND TO THE MEMORY OF SHAKESPEARE. SEPT^R 1769 D.G. STEWARD. *D.*
32 mm. By J. Westwood Sr. *MI* i, 208/43; *BHM* 136; *Ogden* 45
Occurs with a suspension clasp. David Garrick (1717–79), actor-manager.

732   **Death of William Beckford 1770**
Obv. Bust almost facing, draped; a sword and mace to l. WILL^M BECKFORD. ESQ^R *Rev.* THE.   *AR*   60   110
ZEALOUS. ADVOCATE. & INVARIABLE. PROTECTOR OF. THE. RIGHTS. PRIVILEGES & LIBERTIES OF.   *AE*   20   35
THE. PEOPLE. *Ex.* OBIIT. 21. JUN. 1770 ANNO. ÆTATIS 65. *D.* 43 mm. (By?) *BHM* 141; *EPM*   *Br.*   15   30
1888, 269/2
William Beckford (1705–70), politician and Lord Mayor of London; collector.

733   **Death of the Marquis of Granby 1770**
Obv. Bust l., draped. GRANBY   *Rev.* Mars seated, l., beside a shield and military trophy.   *AR*   60   110
MILITVM DVX ET AMICVS   *Ex.* NAT. MDCCXX M. MDCCLXX *D.* 41 mm. By L. Pingo. *BHM*   *AE*   25   40
145; *EPM* 1891, 391/6

			£	£
734	**Death of Reverend George Whitefield 1770**			

Obv. Bust three-quarters r., draped. GEORGE WHITEFIELD *Rev.* AN ISRAELITE INDEED. A GOOD SOLDIER OF JESUS CHRIST. *Ex.* DIED 30 SEP. 1770 IN YE 56 YEAR OF HIS AGE *D.* 40 mm. By I.W. (J. Westwood Sr.?) *BHM* 149

AR 70 120
AE 25 45

A similar medal occurs of 38 mm. George Whitefield (1714–70), one of the founders of Methodism; he is commemorated on several medals.

735* ——

Obv. Bust almost facing, draped. THE REV. GEORGE WHITEFIELD A.M. *Rev.* Cherub seated upon a funerary urn leaning against a skull. *Ex.* B. 16 D. 1714 D. 30 S. 1770 *D.* 36 mm. By T. Pingo. *BHM* 147; *Betts* 527. *See* **Plate 21**

AR 50 90
AE 25 40

736* **North American Indian Chiefs' Medal** *c.*1770

Obv. Bust r., armoured and draped. GEORGIVS III DEI GRATIA. *Rev.* Royal arms, crest, supporters and motto. *D.* 77 mm. (By?) *Jamieson* 14; *Betts* 435. *See* **Plate 21**

AR 1200 —

Suspension clasp near edge. There are a number of variations: in the diameter; number of rivets on the King's armour; in the treatment of his hair. The medal occurs both struck and in the form of two repoussé plates united at the rim to form a hollow medal. *See* No. 472.

737 **William and Mary College, Virginia** *c.*1770

Obv. Bust of George III, r. REGNANTE GEORGIO TERTIO MVSIS AMICO QVÆSITVM MERITIS *Rev.* William III, attended by Mary, presents a charter to a kneeling figure of James Blair. GVL. ET MAR. TRADVNT BLARO CHART. COL. *Ex.* ANNO REGNI QVARTO *D.* 43 mm. By T. Pingo. *BHM* 154; *Betts* 528

AV — —
AR — —
AE 250 400

A prize endowed by Lord Botetourt, Governor of Virginia 1768–70; it was awarded annually in gold from 1772, for classics and philosophy. James Blair D.D. (1656–1743), Scottish episcopalian divine. Commissary and councillor in the colonial government of Virginia; received the Charter of the college in 1692. Restrikes of this medal have been made in the present century.

738 **Worshipful Company of Coopers** *c.*1770

Obv. Arms of the Company: shield supported by two animals, and with a crest of a bird. *Rev.* Plain (for member's name and date). *D.* 33 mm. (By?) *Garnett pl.* 1, 1

AR 35 50

The date inscribed often refers to the member's admission to the Company, which may be earlier than the date of the medal's manufacture. Some medals are hallmarked and allow for a more precise dating. Those which are silver-gilt may indicate that the holder had risen above the rank of Liveryman. Most of the medals issued by Companies in the City of London date from the nineteenth century, and some Companies changed the dies for their medals at least once. Medals of Companies which have been noted include those of the Apothecaries, Armourers and Braziers, Bakers, Barber Surgeons, Bowyers, Carpenters, Clothworkers, Coachmakers, Cooks, Cordwainers, Cutlers, Distillers, Drapers, Fanmakers, Farriers, Fishmongers, Free Watermen, Fruiterers, Gardeners, Glass Sellers, Haberdashers, Innholders, Joiners, Master Mariners, Musicians, Needlemakers, Painters & Stainers, Pattenmakers, Plumbers, Poulterers, Saddlers, Shipwrights, Stationers, Tallow-Chandlers, Tinplate Workers, Turners, Tylers and Bricklayers, Vintners, and Weavers. *See* Nos. 739–40, 924–5, 2033.

739* **Worshipful Company of Distillers** *c.*1770

Obv. Arms of the Company: shield supported by a Highlander and an American Indian; motto below, DROP. AS. RAIN DISTIL. AS. DEW *Rev.* Plain (for member's name and date). *D.* 50 mm. (By?) *Garnett pl.* 1, 7; *Guest* 919. *See* **Plate 21**

AR 40 55

See No. 738.

740 **Worshipful Company of Vintners** *c.*1770

Obv. Arms of the Company: an escutcheon decorated with a chevron and three tuns. *Rev.* Plain (for member's name and date). *D.* 38 mm. (By?) *Garnett pl.* 1, 6; *Guest* 923

AR 30 45

Usually found with a suspension loop. *See* No. 738.

741 **Opening of Armagh Library 1771**

Obv. Bust r., draped. RICH: HIBERN: PRIMAS. BARO. ROKEBY. DE. ARMAGH *Rev.* Façade of building. TO ΤΗΣ ΨΥΧΗΣ ΙΑΤΡΕΙΟΝ. *Ex.* BIBLIOTH. ARMAC. M.D.CC.LXXI. *D.* 37 mm. By J. Kirk, *obv.* after I. Gosset. *BHM* 157; *Frazer* 1887/316

AR 50 90
AE 20 35

Richard Robinson, Baron Rokeby (1709–94), Archbishop of Armagh; public benefactor.

742 **Death of Princess Augusta 1772**

Obv. Bust r., wearing a bandeau and draped. AUGUSTA PRINCESS OF WALES. BORN. NOV. 30. 1719. *Rev.* Phoenix rising. A MUCH INJURED VICTIM. *Ex.* DIED 8 FEB 1772 *D.* 33 mm. (By T. Lyng?) *BHM* 159

AR 35 65
AE 20 35

Contemporary brass copies were made with a diameter of 28 mm.

743* **Marriage of Prince Charles and Princess Louisa, 1772**

Obv. Bust l., armoured and draped. CAROLVS. III. N. 1720. M. B. F. ET. H. REX. 1766. *Rev.* Bust l., draped. LVDOVICA. M. B. F. ET. H. REGINA. 1772 *D.* 32 mm. (By?) *BHM* 163; *Farquhar* 1923–4, 201. *See* **Plate 21**

AV 1000 1800
AR 85 150
AE 35 65

Louisa, Duchess of Albany (1753–1824), daughter of Prince Gustav Adolph of Stolberg-Gedern.

			VF	*EF*
			£	£

744*   Voyage of the *Resolution* and the *Adventure* 1772
Obv. Bust r., laureate. GEORGE. III. KING. OF. GR. BRITAIN. FRANCE. AND. IRELAND ETC. *Rev.* Two ships at sea. RESOLVTION ADVENTURE. *Ex.* SAILED. FROM. ENGLAND MARCH. MDCCLXXII   *D. a* 44 mm.; *b* 43 mm. [By J. Westwood Sr.] *BHM* 165; *MH* 1919, 373; *Betts* 552. See **Plate 21**

a AV   —   —
AR   1300   2400
AE   —   —

Examples of the silver medals sometimes exhibit the speckling of rust marks from the die and may have been struck some years later. Brass medals were struck with a different reverse die which exhibits a flaw in the exergue; the ship's (l.) anchor is in a 'home' position, and they are usually struck on a thinner flan. This type was issued with a loop mount on the edge and was intended for distribution to natives in the Pacific islands during Captain Cook's voyage; examples have been found on the coast of some of these islands, including New Zealand. James Cook (1728–79), mariner and explorer. The obverse is signed B:F (Boulton, fecit?) on the truncation. *See* A. Wedgewood, *Matthew Boulton's 'Otaheite' Medal*, Birmingham, 1926.

b Br.   800   1500

745   Marine Society 1772
Obv. Britannia seated beside a young sailor; beyond, ships at sea. MARINE SOCIETY INSTITUTED MDCCLVI *Ex.* INCORPORATED MDCCLXXII   *Rev.* REWARD OF MERIT TO (space, for recipient's name) within a wreath. *D.* 42 mm. (By?) *D & W* 251/362–4; *Payne* 326; *MH* 1919, 80.

AR   20   35

The Society was formed in 1756 on the outbreak of the Seven Years War in order to encourage men to volunteer for service in the fleet. In 1786 they established the first nautical training ship (the *Warspite*) in Britain. Medals were presented in silver from *c.*1791 to boys who had completed five years service at sea with good conduct. They were struck from more than one pair of dies. Examples examined seem to be made of a base silver, or to be silver-plated bronze. *See* J. C. Prior, 'The Marine Society Medals', *OMRS* 1969, 28–30.

746   David Garrick 1772
Obv. Bust r., draped. DAVID GARRICK   *Rev.* Three Muses, standing. HE UNITED ALL YOUR POWERS *Ex.* MDCCLXXII   *D.* 40 mm. By L. Pingo. *BHM* 160; *EPM* 1891, 379/1; *Svarstad* 73

AR   55   100
AE   25   40

747*   Joshua Reynolds 1773
Obv. Bust l., draped. SIR JOSHUA REYNOLDS   *Rev.* Female seated at an easel, painting a portrait of Reynolds. PRESIDENT OF THE ROYAL ACADEMY *Ex.* MDCCLXXIII   *D.* 31 mm. By J. Kirk. *BHM* 177. See **Plate 21**

AR   50   90
AE   15   30

Sir Joshua Reynolds (1723–92), portrait painter; first President of the Royal Academy of Arts.

748   Death of the Earl of Chesterfield 1773
Obv. Bust l., draped. PHIL. STANHOPE. COM: DE. CHESTERFIELD. *Rev.* Hibernia stands holding an Irish shield. MEMINISSE JUVAT   *Ex.* HIB: PROREX AB AN. 1745 AD A. 1747 OB. 1773 *D.* 37 mm. By J. Kirk, *obv.* after I. Gosset. *BHM* 181

AR   45   85
AE   20   35

749*   Death of Thomas Snelling 1773
Obv. Bust r., draped. THOMAS SNELLING   *Rev.* OBIIT DIE II MAII MDCCLXXIII ÆTAT LXI within a wreath. MERVISTI above. *D.* 40 mm. By L. Pingo. *BHM* 180. *See* **Plate 21**

AR   60   110
AE   25   40

Thomas Snelling (1712–73), numismatist and antiquary.

750   Treaty of St. Vincent 1773
Obv. Bust r., hair bound with a fillet, and armoured. GEORGIVS. III. MB. REX   *Rev.* Britannia standing, r., holds an olive-branch before a Carib who has laid down his arms. PEACE AND PROSPERITY TO Sᵀ VINCENTS   *Ex.* MDCCLXXIII   *D.* 55 mm. Cast. By G. M. Moser. *BHM* 183; *Betts* 529; *Gordon* 16; *Tancred* 47–8.

AR   350   650
AE   90   140
WM   40   70

The Caribs were unhappy when St. Vincent had been ceded to Britain by France at the Peace of Paris in 1763. Silver medals were presented, unnamed, to the militia and volunteers who helped to suppress the Carib rebellion against the English on the island; they often occur with a suspension loop. The quality of these medals varies quite considerably, both in the cast and in the 'finish' given to them; on some examples the signature is missing.

751   Medical Society of London 1773
Obv. Bust l., draped. CHARLOTTA. DEI. GRA. MAG. BRI. FRA. ET. HIB. REGINA   *Rev.* Hygeia feeding a serpent entwined around a smoking altar. SALUTI AUGUSTÆ *Ex.* SOC. MED. LOND. INSTITUTA MDCCLXXIII   *D.* 41 mm. by J. Kirk. *BHM* 184; *Storer* 6545

AR   45   85
AE   15   25

752   Medical Society of London, Fothergill Medal 1773
Obv. Bust r., draped. ANTONIUS FOTHERGILL. MD. LL. D. & c. *Rev.* Similar to No. 751, but altar not smoking. *D.* 46 mm. By J. Vining/W. Wilson [after J. Flaxman / J. Kirk] *BHM* 185; *Storer* 1088

AV   500   700
AR   80   150
AE   45   80
WM   20   40

Struck from *c.*1825 and awarded in gold and silver. Anthony Fothergill (1735?–1813), physician. *See* M. Jones, 'The Fothergillian Medal', *BNJ* 1984, 248–62.

753   Duke of Gloucester 1773
Obv. Bust of the Duke of Gloucester, draped, r. *Rev.* DUKE OF GLOCESTER 1773 *D.* 26 mm. By J. Kirk. *BHM* 169

AR   7   12
AE   —   2

William Henry, Duke of Gloucester (1743–1805), brother of George III. This medal is from a uniform series, issued *c.*1775 with the *Sentimental Magazine*, comprising: William Beckford, Queen Charlotte, Oliver Cromwell, Duchess of Cumberland, David Garrick, George II, George III, Duchess of Gloucester, William Pitt, Charles Pratt and John Wilkes.

			£	£

754* **William Hunter 1774**
Obv. Bust l., in surgeon's cap and robes. GVL. HVNTER. ANATOMICVS. *Rev.* Large vase decorated with the scene of a surgical operation, its stem dividing the date 1774. OLIM. MEMINISSE. IVVABIT. *D.* 81 mm. Cast. By E. Burch. *BHM* 188; *CP* 109/29; *Storer* 1721–2. *See* **Plate 21**

AR	200	350
AE	70	120
Fe.	60	100

Examples also occur unsigned and undated. Medals in silver were used as prizes in the nineteenth century by St. George's Hospital, London, and are sometimes found with edge inscriptions. William Hunter (1718–83), anatomist and obstetrician; collector of medals and benefactor (Hunterian Museum, Glasgow).

755 **Oliver Goldsmith, Memorial 1774**
Obv. Bust l., draped. OLIVER GOLDSMITH *Rev.* BORN 10TH NOVR 1728 DIED 4TH APRIL 1774 within a wreath. *D.* 43 mm. By W. Woodhouse. *BHM* 187a; *Frazer* 1886/611; *Storer* 1342

AR	50	90
AE	20	35
WM	12	25

Struck c.1840. Oliver Goldsmith (1728–74), author; doctor in Padua, 1745.

756 **Death of the Duke of Atholl 1774**
Obv. Bust r., draped. IOANNES. MURRAY. ATHOL. DUX *Rev.* Female seated, l., mournfully. QUIS. TEMPERET. A. LACHRYMIS *Ex.* NAT. VI. MAII. MDCCXXIX OB. V. NOV. MDCCLXXIV *D.* 37 mm. By J. Kirk. *BHM* 192; *EPM* 1887, 256

AR	50	90
AE	20	35

John Murray, 3rd Duke of Atholl (1729–74), succeeded to the title in 1764; sold the sovereignty of the Isle of Man to the Treasury in 1765.

757 **Religious Stability 1774**
Obv. Bust r., armoured and draped. GEORGIUS. III. DEI. GRA. MAG. BRI. FRA. ET. HIB. REX. *Rev.* Sword, sceptre and three crowns on cushion upon a column, inscribed DIEU ET MON DROIT, and decorated with shields of England, Ireland and Scotland; its base dated 1774, and decorated with rudder and trident. OPTIMUM STABILIMENTUM RELIGIO *D.* 42 mm. By J. Kirk. *BHM* 197

AR	50	90
AE	15	30

758 **Royal Humane Society Medal 1774**
Obv. Naked boy standing, r., attempts to breathe life in an extinguished torch which he holds. LATEAT SCINTILLVLA FORSAN *Ex.* SOC. LOND. IN RESVSCITAT. INTERMORTVORVM INSTIT. MDCCLXXIV *Rev.* A wreath (space within, for recipient's name). HOC PRETIVM CIVE SERVATO TVLIT *D.* 51 mm. By L. Pingo [after Dr. Watkinson]. *MH* 1919, 820; *Payne* 308–9

AR	100	160
AE	45	65

Awarded by the Society to those who saved or attempted to save life at personal risk. This medal was issued up to c.1820, when new dies were prepared by B. Pistrucci. Those in silver are sometimes found frosted and set within a watch-style glass bound with a silver frame. Examples in bronze were awarded from c.1850. *See* P. J. Bishop, *A Short History of the Royal Humane Society*, London, 1974. Local humane societies were established subsequently and many awarded medals, including those of Hundred of Salford; Northampton, 1789; Glasgow, 1790; Bristol, 1807; Plym, Tamar, Lynher and Tavy, 1831; Liverpool, 1839.

759 ——
Obv. A man rescues another from drowning in a river. NARE EST ALIENAM NOSSE SALUTEM *Ex.* Space (for inscription). *Rev.* ROYAL HUMANE SOCIETY INST : 1774 AWARDED FOR PROFICIENCY IN SWIMMING EXERCISE WITH REFERENCE TO SAVING LIFE FROM DROWNING *D.* 51 mm. (By?) *MH* 1919, 826; *Payne* 310

AR	25	40

Struck in 1882, and awarded annually in competitions at public schools and on training ships. The recipient's name is normally found on the edge, and that of the ship or school on the obverse.

760 **Prince Henry, Cardinal York: Sede Vacante 1774–1775**
Obv. Similar to No. 729. *Rev.* Similar to No. 729, but with star above inscription, and dated 1774. *D.* 29 mm. Italian? (By?) *BHM* 196; *CP* 76/65

AR	80	150

This Sede Vacante followed the death of Pope Clement XIV, and lasted from 22 September 1774 until 15 February 1775. The star intimates Henry's princely origins.

761 **Lord North, Chancellor of Oxford University 1775**
Obv. Bust l., draped. FRIDERICUS. BARO. NORTH ORD: PERISCEL: EQVES *Rev.* Arms upon a crowned mantle from which is suspended the Order of the Garter. SU: ÆRAR: PR: CANC: SCAAC: ET. ACAD: OXON: MDCCLXXV *D.* 37 mm. By J. Kirk, *obv.* after I. Gosset. *BHM* 200; *Betts* 551

AR	90	150
AE	35	65

Frederick, Lord North (1732–92), first Lord of the Treasury; Prime Minister.

762 **Gold Recoinage 1775**
Obv. Similar to No. 757. *Rev.* Britannia seated, l., holding scales. AVRI SACRVM PONDVS *Ex.* RE. NVMMARIA. BENE. CONSTITVTA MDCCLXXV *D.* 42 mm. By J. Kirk. *BHM* 202

AR	70	120
AE	25	45

763 **John Harrison c.1775**
Obv. Bust r., draped. IOANNES HARRISON. *Rev.* As No. 697 or 741. *D.* 36 mm. By J. Kirk, *obv.* after J. Tassie. *BHM* 156; *EPM* 1892, 231

AR	70	120
AE	25	45

John Harrison (1693–1776), horologist and inventor. The subject has no apparent connection with either reverse; possibly that which was intended was never finished.

PLATE 21

718

723

725

736 ($\times \frac{2}{3}$)

735

739

744b

743

747

749

754 ($\times \frac{2}{3}$)

PLATE 22

767

769

780

770

774

783

789

792

801

764   **John Smart** *c.*1775

Obv. Bust r., draped. IOH: SMART: PICT: EFFIG: MINUT: *Rev.* Plain. *D.* 37 mm. By J. Kirk, [after J. Smith]. *BHM* 153

	VF	EF
	£	£
AR	90	150
AE	30	55

John Smart (1741–1811), miniaturist.

765   **Retirement of David Garrick 1776**

Obv. Bust l., draped. DAVID GARRICK   *Rev.* Masks of Comedy and Tragedy amidst symbols of the Arts. ILLE HISTRIO ANGLICANUM   *Ex.* MDCCLXXVI   *D.* 37 mm. By J. Kirk, [*obv.* after I. Gosset] *BHM* 204

AR	55	100
AE	25	40
WM	15	30

766   **Lord Bathurst 1776**

Obv. Bust l., draped. HEN. COMES. BATHURST. ANGLIÆ CANCELL   *Rev.* Façade of the Chancery Court. ÆDES. SEX. CLER: CUR: CANCELL: *Ex.* EXTRUCTÆ MDCCLXXVI   *D.* 37 mm. By J. Kirk, *obv.* after I. Gosset. *BHM* 203; *EPM* 1887, 263

AR	45	85
AE	15	30

Henry, Lord Bathurst (1714–94), Attorney General and Lord Chancellor. The obverse is sometimes found coupled with the reverse of No. 771.

767*   **George Washington, Siege of Boston 1776**

Obv. Bust r. GEORGIO WASHINGTON SVPREMO DUCI EXERCITVVM ADSERTORI LIBERTATIS   *Ex.* COMITIA AMERICANA   *Rev.* Equestrian figures of Washington and officers on a hill-top from where they observe the evacuation of troops from Boston, beyond. HOSTIBUS PRIMO FUGATIS   *Ex.* BOSTONIUM RECUPERATUM XVII. MARTII MDCCLXXVI. *D.* 70 mm. By B. P. S. Duvivier [*obv.* after J. A. Houdon] *Baker* 47; *Betts* 542. See **Plate 22**

AR	—	—
AE	600	1000

Commemorating the evacuation of Boston by British troops after the siege by American forces. The medal was first struck in Paris *c.*1790, where restrikes were subsequently made from an altered die; these restrikes omit punctuation stops on the reverse, and often have the metal and a symbol on the edge. A second restrike was made by the United States Mint from *c.*1860; later examples of this copy usually have a much lighter patina. Medals struck from original dies usually exhibit flaws above the E's of 'Georgio' and 'Adsertori', and the M of 'Supremo'.

768   **Death of David Hume 1776**

Obv. Bust r., draped. DAVID. HUME. SCOTUS. *Rev.* Figure of Time seated, r., upon a cube. FELICITER. AUDET. *Ex.* NAT: MDCCXI. MORT: MDCCLXXVI   *D.* 39 mm. (By?) *BHM* 206; *CP* 104/20; *EPM* 1892, 312

AR	180	350
AE	120	220

David Hume (1711–76), historian, philosopher and statesman.

769*   **Benjamin Franklin 1777**

Obv. Bust almost facing, draped, head three-quarters l., wearing a cap. B. FRANKLIN OF PHILADELPHIA L.L.D. ◊ F.R.S. *Rev.* A yew-tree in an open landscape struck by lightning. NON IRRITA FULMINA CURAT   *Ex.* 1777   *D.* 44 mm. (By?) *Betts* 547; *EPM* 1891, 101. See **Plate 22**

AR	1200	1800
AE	200	380

Benjamin Franklin (1706–90), American statesman, scientist and philosopher. This medal may refer to an inquiry of the Privy Council, relating to political papers which Franklin received and forwarded to America where they were published.

770*   **'Madame' Chevalier De Beaumont D'Éon 1777**

Obv. Bust r., draped. MADAME D'EON   *Rev.* AVOCAT AU PARᵀ DE PARI[S] DOCTᴿ EN Dᵀ CAPITᴺ DE DRAGˢ CHEVALIE DE L. R. ET. M. DE Sᵀ LOˢ MINISTRE DE LA COU DE FRANCE EN ANGLETERRE. GENTILHOM D'AMBASSADE EN RUSSIE. 1777   *D.* 40 mm. (By?) *EPM* 1891, 78. See **Plate 22**

AR	270	500
AE	130	250

Charles Geneviève Louis Auguste André Timothée De Beaumont D'Éon (1728–1810), French ambassador and courtier; a transvestite of considerable renown. In 1777 a civil court action was fought by two men in respect of a wager concerning D'Éon's gender; a subject which had aroused much curiosity and financial speculation during the time he was in London. The affair was a minor *cause célèbre* and the matter only entirely resolved on his death. See *London Magazine*, September 1777.

771   **Earl of Mansfield 1777**

Obv. Bust r., draped. GULIELM: MURRAY. COM: DE. MANSFIELD   *Rev.* Justice standing, l., holding scales and an olive-branch. VTRIQVE FIDELIS. *Ex.* MDCCLXXVII   *D.* 37 mm. By J. Kirk, *obv.* after I. Gosset. *BHM* 209; *CP* 105/21

AR	45	85
AE	20	35

William Murray, 1st Earl of Mansfield (1705–93), Lord Chief Justice. *See* No. 766.

772   **Battle of German Town 1777**

Obv. GERMAN TOWN OCTᴿ 4. 1777 within a wreath. *Rev.* Battery of cannon fire upon a house in field. *D.* 44 mm. By J. Milton. *Betts* 556; *Gordon* 17; *Stainton* 6; *Tancred* 332

AR	1400	—
AE	450	800

Struck *c.*1790. Six companies of the 40th Regiment, under Colonel Sir Thomas Musgrave (1737–1817), threw themselves into a large stone house (belonging to Mr. Chew), which they defended against a large American force which was eventually repulsed. Examples of the medal were awarded, although few are found engraved. German Town is situated near Philadelphia; Chew's house is represented on the medal, and is also found in the background of an engraved portrait of Musgrave. A bronze restrike (nineteenth century?) of this medal has been noted.

773   **General Burgoyne, Surrender at Saratoga 1777**

Obv. Bust l., draped. HORATIO GATES DUCI STRENUO   *Ex.* COMITIA AMERICANA   *Rev.* Burgoyne presents sword of surrender to Gates, amidst captured military trophies; beyond, an army laying down their arms, l., before a column of armed soldiers, r., standing erect.

AV	—	—
AR	1200	2000
AE	150	250

SALUS REGIONUM SEPTENTRIONAL   *Ex.* HOSTE AD SARATOGAM IN DEDITION. ACCEPTO DIE XVII.   WM   40   70
OCT. MDCCLXXVII   *D.* 56 mm. By N. M. Gatteaux. *Betts* 557; *Julian* MI-2; *Loubat* 2

The dies of this medal, originally struck in France *c.*1785, were brought to the United States and examples restruck. John
Burgoyne (1722–92), British army officer and dramatist. Horatio Gates (1728–1806), born in Maldon, Essex; settled in
Virginia and was a major-general in the service of the United States.

774* Battle of Ushant 1778
Obv. Bust almost facing, uniformed. AUGUSTUS KEPPEL. *Rev.* JUDICIOUS BRAVE AND GALLANT   AR   70   120
within a wreath. *D.* 40 mm. By I.H.(?) *BHM* 214; *MH* 1919, 437. *See* **Plate 22**   AE   20   35

775 ——
Obv. Bust almost facing, draped. ADMIRAL AUGUSTUS KEPPEL   *Rev.* Naval engagement.   AE   15   30
VICTORY   *D.* 24 mm. (By?) *BHM* 216; *MH* 1919, 440

776 Death of William Pitt 1778
Obv. Bust r., draped. GVL. PITT. COMES. DE. CHATHAM. PATRIÆ. DECVS. ET. DELICIÆ   *Rev.*   AR   50   85
Britannia, standing, leans mournfully against a funerary urn. QVIS. DESIDERIO. SIT. PVDOR.   AE   20   35
AVT. MODVS. *Ex.* NAT. NOV. XV. MDCCVIII. OB. MAII. XI. MDCCLXXVIII. *D.* 37 mm. By J. Kirk
[*obv.* after I. Gosset] *BHM* 213; *Betts* 523; *EPM* 1890, 54/7

777 Admiral Keppel, Acquittal by Court Martial 1779
Obv. Bust three-quarters l., uniformed, head three-quarters r. THE HON^BLE AUGUSTUS KEPPEL   *Br.*   20   35
ADMI^RL OF § BLUE   *Rev.* Justice stands victorious over the prostrate figure of Envy; beyond,   WM   12   25
frigate at sea. JUSTICE TRIUMPHANT AND MALICE DEFEATED   *Ex.* FEB: 11: 1779   *D.* 34 mm.
(By T. Lyng?) *BHM* 221; *MH* 1919, 441; *Betts* 564

Admiral Keppel had been tried for misconduct after the action at Ushant.

778 Death of Captain Cook 1779
Obv. Bust three-quarters r., uniformed. CAPT: JAMES COOK. *Rev.* COURAGE AND   AR   700   1200
PERSEVERANCE   *Ex.* BORN 1728. DIED 1779. *D.* 37 mm. (By?) *BHM* 218; *MH* 1919, 375; *Betts*   AE   270   450
555   WM   100   180

779 ——
Obv. As No. 778. *Rev.* KILL'D. BY THE INDIANS. AT O'WHY'HEE. .FEBRUARY 14. .1779. *Ex.* Two   AE   400   700
oak branches. *D.* 37 mm. (By?) *BHM* 219; *MH* 1919, 376; *Betts* 554   WM   130   250

780* Captain Cook, Memorial 1779
Obv. Bust l., draped. IAC. COOK OCEANI INVESTIGATOR ACERRIMVS REG. SOC. LOND. SOCIO   AV   2700   5000
SVO   *Rev.* Fortune, leaning against a naval column, places a rudder upon a globe. NIL   AR   250   400
INTENTATVM NOSTRI LIQVERE   *Ex.* AVSPICIIS GEORGII III   *D.* 43 mm. By L. Pingo. *BHM*   AE   120   180
258; *MH* 1919, 374; *Betts* 553. *See* **Plate 22**

Sponsored in 1784 by The Royal Society for subscribers to a fund in Cook's memory.

781 ——
Obv. Bust l., uniformed. JACOBUS COOK   *Rev.* NATUS AN. M.DCC.XXVIII. MARTON IN CUMBRIA   AR   180   350
ANGLIÆ OBIIT AN. M.DCC.LXXIX. *Ex.* SERIES NUMISMATICA UNIVERSALIS VIRORUM ILLUSTRIUM   AE   80   150
M.DCCC.XXIII. DURAND EDIDIT   *D.* 41 mm. By T. Smith. *BHM* 1207; *MH* 1919, 377

Struck in Paris in 1823, from a series commemorating famous people of all countries.

782 Naval Action off Flamborough Head 1779
Obv. Bust r., uniformed. JOANNI PAVLO JONES CLASSIS PRAEFECTO. COMITIA AMERICANA. *Rev.*   AV   —   —
View of a naval engagement. HOSTIVM NAVIBVS CAPTIS AVT FVGATIS. *Ex.* AD ORAM SCOTIAE   AR   900   1700
XXIII. SEPT. M.DCCLXXVIIII. *D.* 57 mm. By A. Dupré, [*obv.* after J. A. Houdon]. *BHM* 222;   AE   150   250
MH 1928, 580; *Julian* NA-1; *Loubat* 17

John Paul Jones (1747–92), Scottish naval commodore who fought in the service of the United States; he captured the
English frigate *Serapis* at this action. The medal has been restruck from original dies in France, and those newly prepared
at the United States Mint.

783* Proposed Attack and Evacuation of Rhode Island 1779
Obv. Plan of Rhode Island; soldiers hurrying across towards boats moored off the coast.   *Br.*   350   650
D'VLUGTENDE AMERICAANE^N VAN ROHDE YLAND AUG^T 1778   *Rev.* Broadside view of a British   WM   200   500
frigate. DE ADMIRAALS FLAG VAN ADMIRAAL HOWE 1779   Wreath below. *D.* 32 mm. Dutch
(By?) *MH* 1919, 415; *Betts* 561. *See* **Plate 22**

The reverse die originally included the word VLUGTENDE below the ship. Very few examples were struck before that word
was erased and replaced with a wreath (as above) or left plain. Richard Howe, Earl Howe (1726–99), admiral of the fleet.

784 Peter Clare 1779
Obv. Bust r., draped. PETRUS CLARE. LOND: CHIRURG: SOC: *Rev.* ARTEM MEDENDI REMED: ORE   AR   55   90
ABSORPT: INV^T ET DIVULG^T A: D: 1779   *D.* 32 mm. By T. Holloway. *BHM* 217; *Storer* 648   AE   20   35

Peter Clare (1738–86), surgeon; author of medical treatises.

			VF	EF
			£	£

785 Victory of Cape St. Vincent 1780
Obv. Bust facing, uniformed, head r. ADMIRAL RODNEY *Rev.* ACTIVE BRAVE VICTORIOUS *Ex.* 1780 A wreath border. *D.* 38 mm. (By?) BHM 225; *MH* 1919, 378
AR 90 160
AE 20 35

786 Medical Society of London, Fothergill Medal 1780
Obv. Bust r., draped. IOHANNES FOTHERGILL MEDICVS EGREGIVS AMICIS CARVS OMNIVM AMICVS *Rev.* MEDICINÆ & SCIENTIÆ NATVRALIS INCREMENTO within a wreath. DON. SOC. MED. LOND. AN. SALVT. 1773. INSTIT. *Edge.* NAT MAR. 8. 1712. OB. DEC. 26. 1780. *D.* 48 mm. By L. Pingo. BHM 223; *Storer* 1091
AV 550 800
AR 110 180
AE 50 90

Awarded annually in gold or silver from *c.*1787. John Fothergill (1712–80), physician; assisted Benjamin Franklin in drafting the reconciliation between England and the American colonies.

787 Completion of Freemasons' Hall 1780
Obv. Winged female standing, l., inscribes a column IN HONOUR OF THE SUBSCRI; she holds a trumpet and a scroll on which appears an elevation of the building. Beyond, a building covered in scaffolding. *Ex.* MDCCLXXX *Rev.* GRAND LODGE OF FREE MASONS IN ENGLAND TO (space, for subscriber's name) IN GRATEFUL TESTIMONY OF A LIBERAL SUBSCRIPTION TOWARDS COMPLEATING THEIR HALL *D.* 47 mm. By L. Pingo. *Shackles* 3; *Poole* 10
AR 50 85
AE 20 35

Modern restrikes have been made.

788 Capture of St. Eustatius 1781
Obv. Bust three-quarters r., uniformed. ADMIRAL RODNEY *Rev.* Fleet of seven ships before a harbour town. ST. EUSTATIA. SABA. AND. ST. MARTINS. *Ex.* TAKEN FROM THE DUTCH IN 1781 *D.* 36 mm. (By?) BHM 235; *MH* 1919, 385
Br. 30 55

The action is commemorated on more than ten medals.

789* ——
Obv. Bust r., uniformed. G. B. RODNEY *Rev.* Two frigates, one on fire, sailing before a harbour fortress. RODNEY. FOR. EVER. *D.* 33 mm. (By?) BHM 233; *MH* 1919, 386. *See* **Plate 22**
Br. 20 40

This obverse occurs with four other reverses, each with narrative inscriptions recording the victory.

790 Trial of Lord George Gordon 1781
Obv. Bust l., draped. .L.G.G. .P.P.A. *Rev.* L. GEO. GORDON. TRIED AND HONOURABLY AQUITTED. BY A VIRTUOUS JURY FEB^RY 5 J78J, within an ornamental trefoil. *D.* 44 mm. (By?) BHM 240; *EPM* 1891, 387
AR 140 250
AE 60 110

Lord George Gordon (1751–93), fervent anti-Catholic; tried for treason after leading a rioting mob. Entered Parliament and was President of the Protestant Association; latterly, a convert to Judaism.

791 Battle of Dogger Bank 1781
Obv. Dutch ship, captioned HOEZEE! DE BRIT RUIMT ZEE, firing at a departing British ship. *Ex.* OP. DEN VYFDEN DER OOGSTM. 1781. *Rev.* O BATAVIER. GOD STAAFTUWREGT: DAAR ZOUTMAN MET ZIJN HELDEN VEGT. HERSTELT HIJDE EER DER VRIJE VLAG. TROTS OVERMAGT. IN ÉÉNEN SLAG. Above, a naval crown; below, a wreath. *D.* 30 mm. By A. V. Baerl. *MH* 1921, 627; *Betts* 588
AR 40 70

One of several Dutch medals struck for this action.

792* George III 1781
Obv. Bust l., laureate, armoured and draped. GEORGIUS III REX ANG. *Rev.* Lion tied up with rope attempts to break its bonds. INDOCILIS PATI. *Ex.* IN PERPET MEMOR. MDCCLXXXI. *D.* 54 mm. Swedish or German? (By?) BHM 239; *Betts* 584. *See* **Plate 22**
AR 450 800
AE 140 220

The frustrated lion may refer to resentment at the Treaty of Armed Neutrality, which resisted British claims and indirectly aided the American colonies. The King is dressed in readiness for war; the reverse composition has been taken from J. C. Hedlinger's medal (*Felder* 18) commemorating the death of Karl XII of Sweden in 1718.

793 Libertas Americana 1781
Obv. Youthful female bust of Liberty, l., with flowing hair, and staff with the Phrygian cap of liberty. LIBERTAS. AMERICANA. *Ex.* 4 JUIL. 1776. *Rev.* Infant figure of America, as Hercules, strangling two serpents, while France, as Minerva, repels the approach of an attacking British lion. NON SINE DIIS ANIMOSUS INFANS. *Ex.* $\frac{17}{19}$ OCT. $\frac{1777}{1781}$ *D.* 48 mm. Struck *c.*1790. By A. Dupré. *Betts* 615; *Loubat* 14
AR 1400 2500
AE 400 750

The two dates refer to American victories over Burgoyne at Saratoga, 1777, and Cornwallis at Yorktown in 1781. Charles Cornwallis, 1st Marquis Cornwallis (1738–1805), major-general in the American War of Independence; governor-general of India and lord-lieutenant of Ireland. Cast copies and restrikes of this medal have been made.

794 Siege of Gibraltar 1782
Obv. Bust l., draped. GEORGE AUGUSTUS ELIOTT GOVERNOR OF GIBRALTAR. *Rev.* Hercules stands between two pillars, separated by sea. FORTITER ET RECTE. *Ex.* XIII SEPT MDCCLXXXII. *D.* 59 mm. By J. P. Droz. BHM 247; *MH* 1919, 402
AE 100 180

Restrikes were made during the nineteenth century at the French Mint. George Augustus Eliott, 1st Baron Heathfield (1717–90), defender of Gibraltar.

                                                        £   £

795 ——. *Obv.* Bust l., armoured. GEORG. AVGVSTVS. ELLIOTT. GIBRALTARIÆ. IMP   *Rev.* Ships in action against harbour batteries. NON. MILLE. CARINAE   *Ex.* MDCCLXXXII   *D.* 51 mm. By G. Z. Weber. BHM 249; *MH* 1919, 403   AR 270 520   AE 130 250

796 ——. *Obv.* Fleet before Gibraltar. PER TOT DISCRIMINA RERUM   *Ex.* XIII SEPT. MDCCLXXXII   *Rev.* REDEN LAMOTTE SYDOW ELIOTT within a wreath. BRUDERSCHAFT   *D.* 49 mm. By L. Pingo. BHM 248; *MH* 1919, 408; *CP* 108/27; *Payne* 223/1   AV — —   AR 180 320   AE 70 120

General Eliott's medal presented in silver to members of the Hanoverian Brigade which took part in the defence of the fortress. Reden, La Motte and Sydow were the names of the regiments comprising the Brigade, named after the officers who raised them.

797 ——. *Obv.* Bust l., uniformed. GEO. AUGUSTUS. ELIOTT. GOVERNOR. OF. GIBRALTAR. AN. 1782. *Rev.* Naval assault on the Rock. *Ex.* VICTRIX IN FLAMIS VICTRIX IN VNDIS. *D.* 42 mm. By Terry. BHM 246; *MH* 1919, 401; *CP* 107/25   AR 80 150   AE 35 65

Struck from more than one pair of dies, one of which is unsigned.

798 Death of Daniel Solander 1782
Obv. Bust r.; behind, a flowering Solandra with its stem cut. DANIEL SOLANDER   *Rev.* IOSEPHO BANKS EFFIGEM AMICI MERITO D.D.D. CL. ET IOH. ALSTROEMER   *D.* 37 mm. By G. Ljunberger. BHM 252; *Hyckert I*, 282   AV 700 1100   AR 140 270   AE 70 120   WM 25 45

Daniel Charles Solander (1736–82), Swedish botanist. Joseph Banks (1743–1820), naturalist and benefactor. They both accompanied Cook in his circumnavigation in 1768. The medal was struck at the Swedish Royal Mint in 1783 and dedicated to Banks, who was Solander's benefactor and friend, by Klas and Johann Alströmer. Banks's grandfather Jacob Bancks was Swedish and became a naturalized Englishman, serving as a naval officer and M.P. for Minehead. A medal was struck of him by Benjamin Richter *c*.1703. *Hyckert I*, 136; *MI ii*, 248/38.

799 William Romaine 1782
Obv. Bust l., draped. THE. REVᴰ Wᴹ ROMAINE. A.M   *Rev.* Open bible, inscribed LIFE OF FAITH WALK OF FAITH   *Ex.* RECTOR OF Sᵀ ANN'S BLACK FRIARS & LECTURER OF Sᵀ DUNSTAN IN THE WEST LONDON 1782   *D.* 37 mm. (By?) BHM 241   AE 30 50   Br. 25 45

Reverend William Romaine (1714–95), divine.

800 Blockade of Gibraltar 1783
Obv. Ships in the bay of Gibraltar. 'T GEBLOQUEERDE GIBRALTAR 1783. *Rev.* Ship sinking. ROYAAL GEORGE ADMIRAAL KEMPENFELT   *Ex.* 1783   *D.* 33 mm. Dutch (By?) *MH* 1919, 412; *v. Loon suppl.* 584   AR 70 130   AE 25 38   WM 12 25

Rear-admiral Richard Kempenfelt (1718–82), British naval commander. The *Royal George* sank in 1782 whilst under repair at Spithead; it was one of a fleet assembling for the relief of Gibraltar.

801* Relief of Gibraltar 1783
Obv. BY A ZEALOUS EXERTION OF PATIENCE PERSEVERANCE AND INTREPIDITY AFTER CONTENDING WITH AN UNPARALLELED SUCCESSION OF DANGERS AND DIFFICULTIES IN THE DEFENCE OF GIBRALTAR DURING A BLOCKADE AND SIEGE OF ALMOST FOUR YEARS THE GARRISON UNDER THE AUSPICES OF GEORGE III TRIUMPHED OVER THE COMBINED POWERS OF FRANCE AND SPAIN, within a wreath. Below, a lion couchant, holding a shield of Gibraltar, upon a plinth inscribed BLOCKADE COMMENCED JUNE XXI MDCCLXXIX SIEGE TERMINATED FEBRUARY II MDCCLXXXIII   *Rev.* Plan of the bay of Gibraltar, showing positions of batteries and ships. BATTERING SHIPS DESTROYED   Below, a plinth inscribed SEPTEMBER XIII MDCCLXXXII   *D.* 59 mm. By L. Pingo. BHM 253; *MH* 1919, 410; *Tancred* 52–3; *Payne* 223/2. See **Plate 22**   AR 200 330   AE 80 150   WM 28 55

General Picton's medal, presented in silver to officers; it is occasionally found with a suspension loop and the edge inscribed.

802* ——. *Obv.* Bust r., wearing a cocked hat and uniformed. ELLIOT AN MARTIS SOCIVS NON: IVPITER IPSE EST   *Rev.* View of the bombardment. VICTRIX IN FLAMIS VICTRIX GIBRALTAR IN VNDIS. *Ex.* MDCCLXXXIII   *D.* 43 mm. By J. C. Reich. BHM 254; *MH* 1919, 409; *CP* 108/28. See **Plate 23**   AR 130 250   AE 70 130   WM 20 40

Struck from more than one pair of dies.

803 Peace of Versailles 1783
Obv. Seated figure of Louis XVI, swathed in robes decorated with lilies, points to a thirteen bar shield which Liberty attaches to a pillar surmounted by the cap of liberty. LIBERTAS AMERICANA   *Ex.* MDCCLXXXIII   *Rev.* Minerva standing, r., displays the shields of France, Britain, Holland and Spain suspended from a ribbon. COMMVNI CONSENSV   *D.* 45 mm. By J. L. Oexlein. *Betts* 608   AR 170 330   WM 45 80

		VF	EF
		£	£

804 ——

Obv. Peace and Liberty, as Britain and America, stand on the sea-shore shaking hands;   *AR*   160   300
between them, shields of France, Ireland and Gibraltar. Beyond, open sea and distant   *WM*   45   70
bombardments of MAHO[N], l., and GIBR[ALTAR], r. SIC. HOSTES CONCORDIA IVNGIT
AMICOS   *Ex.* View of fortified town and harbour. PRVDENTIA & FATIS   *Rev.* Peace stands
over the prostrate figure of War; above, Fame hovering, from whose trumpet issues FIAT
PAX   Beyond, fleet on open sea and distant bombardment. ENSIBVS EX MARTIS LVX PACIS
LÆTA RESVRGIT   *Ex.* OPE VULCANI 1783   *D.* 41 mm. By J. C. Reich. *BHM* 255; *MH* 1919,
411; *Betts* 255

805* ——

Obv. Britannia seated, l., shaking hands with an American Indian standing before her.   *WM*   250   —
FELICITAS: BRITANNIA: ET: AMERICA   Beyond, buildings symbolizing London.   *Ex.*
MDCCLXXXIII SEP.T 4   *Rev.* In the centre, two radiate circles, inscribed AMERICAN : CONGRESS.
WE ARE ONE. Around, a continuous chain of thirteen interlinked circles, inscribed MASSCHS,
N. HAMPS, CONNCT, R. ISLAND, N. IORKE, N. IERSEY, PENSILVA, DELAWARE, MARYLAND,
VIRGINIA, N. CAROLI, S. CAROLI, GEORGIA   *D.* 40 mm. (By J. C. Reich?) *BHM* 256; *Betts* 614.
See **Plate 23**

806   **Glasgow University, William Hunter Medal 1783**

Obv. Bust l., in surgeon's cap and gown. GULIELMUS HUNTER MDCCXVIII. MDCCLXXXIII   *Rev.*   *AR*   50   85
IN ACADEM. GLASGUENS. FACULTATE MEDICA DISCIPULUS INGENIO AC LABORE INSIGNIS   *AE*   15   28
PROEMIUM HOCCE MERITO CONSECUTUS EST   *D.* 70 mm. By N. Macphail. *CP* 153/11; *Storer*
1720

Struck *c.*1870; the portrait taken from No. 754. One of a group of memorial medals awarded by the University of
Glasgow's medical faculty for Anatomy, Pathology, Physiology and Surgery. *See* Nos. 832, 852, 911.

807*   **Joseph Priestley 1783**

Obv. Bust r., draped. JOSEPHUS PRIESTLEY   *Rev.* Priestley's scientific apparatus on a bench.   *AR*   60   110
Ex. MDCCLXXXIII. *D.* 36 mm. By J. G. Hancock. *BHM* 251; *Forrer* II/411; *Davis* 29. *See*   *AE*   25   40
Plate 23   *WM*   15   28

Joseph Priestley (1733–1804), chemist and theologian. The reverse was struck from two dies, differing in the arrangement
of the apparatus.

808   **Henry Quin 1783**

Obv. Bust r. HENRICVS QVIN. M.D.   *Rev.* Plain. *D.* 41 mm. By W. Mossop. *BHM* 281; *Frazer*   *AR*   70   120
1887/448; *Storer* 2908   *AE*   45   70

Henry Quin (1717–91), Irish physician; patron of William Mossop. Quin was presented with this medal by Robert Watson
Wade, of the Irish Treasury, on his recovery from illness. It is one of a uniform group, portraying figures in Irish political
and social circles; including William Alexander, Mr & Mrs Beresford, and William Deane. *See* No. 818.

809   **Society of Industry 1783**

Obv. Seated figures of Abundance and Peace, holding cornucopia and olive-branch;   *AR*   20   35
beyond, a beehive. PLENTY & PEACE ARE THE FRUITS OF INDUSTRY & SUBORDINATION. *Rev.*   *AE*   10   18
Central space (for recipient's name). SOCIETY OF INDUSTRY FOUNDED XXIX NOVEMBER
MDCCLXXXIII. *D.* 35 mm. By J. Milton. *Stainton* 1; *Erlanger* 178; *D & W* 137/285

Awarded in silver and bronze from 1785. Several parishes in Lincolnshire formed a scheme for the training of the children
of the poor, in crafts such as spinning. Medals were awarded from *c.*1785 as a form of encouragement; examples in silver
were sold to subscribers. *See* R. Bouyer, *An Account of the Origin, Proceedings and Intentions of the Society for the Promotion
of Industry . . . in the County of Lincoln, Louth, c.*1779.

810   **George Frederick Handel, Centenary of Birth 1784**

Obv. Bust l., draped. COMM. G.F. HANDEL MDCCLXXXIV   *Rev.* SUB. AUSP. G. III within a   *AV*   300   450
wreath. *D.* 32 mm. (By?) *BHM* 259; *Niggl* 813   *AR*   35   60
Possibly used as an entrance ticket at the centenary concerts.   *AE*   15   28

811*   **Lunardi's Aerial Ascent 1784**

Obv. Bust l., draped. VINCENT LUNARDI FIRST AERIAL TRAVELLER IN ENGLAND   *Rev.* Balloon   *AR*   130   220
above the clouds. ET SE PROTINIES ÆTHEREA TOLLIT INASTRA VIA   *Ex.* SEPTEMBUS 15   *AE*   70   120
MDCCLXXXIV   *D.* 35 mm. (By L. Pingo?) *BHM* 260; *D & W* 33/356–7. *See* **Plate 23**   *WM*   35   65
Struck from two reverse dies, varying in the inscription on the exergue. Vincenzo Lunardi (1759–1806), Italian working
for the Neapolitan Ambassador in England. *See* C. Eimer, 'With both feet off the ground', *SCMB* September 1984, 217–8.

812   **Samuel Johnson 1784**

Obv. Bust l., draped. SAMUEL JOHNSON   *Rev.* NATUS LISCHFELDIAE IN STRAFORDIA AN.   *AR*   16   35
M.DCC.IX. OBIIT AN. M.DCC.LXXXIV   *Ex.* SERIES NUMISMATICA UNIVERSALIS VIRORUM   *AE*   3   7
ILLUSTRIUM M.DCCC.XXIV DURAND EDIDIT   *D.* 41 mm. By T. Smith.

Struck in Paris in 1824, from a series commemorating famous people of all countries. Samuel Johnson, known as Dr.
Johnson (1709–84), lexicographer, critic and conversationalist.

		£	£

813 Highland and Agricultural Society 1784
Obv. Seated female figure crowns the heads of two figures holding agricultural implements. *AR* 15 25
Ex. SEMPER ARMIS NUNC ET INDUSTRIA *Rev.* A wreath (space within, for recipient's name).
HIGHLAND AND AGRICULTURAL SOCIETY OF SCOTLAND INST. MDCCLXXXIV. *D.* 45 mm. (By?) *CP*
177/1; *D & W* 136/272
A prize medal awarded from *c.*1830; it also occurs in two other sizes. Later medals based on this design were struck by
A. Kirkwood & Son.

814* Death of David Latouche 1785
Obv. Bust l., wearing a cap and draped. DAVID LATOUCHE ESQ BELVIEW. *Rev.* Liberty, Justice *AR* 90 160
and Plenty standing. QUI BENE PARTA MELIUS DISPENSAVIT. *Ex.* NAT 1704 OB 1785 *D.* 44 mm. *AE* 35 65
By W. Mossop. *BHM* 263; *Frazer* 1887/448. *See* **Plate 23**
David Digues Latouche (1704–85), member of a banking family; first Governor of the Bank of Ireland.

815 Foundation of the Medical Lyceum 1785
Obv. Busts l., conjoined. GEORGIVS. FORDYCE. ET. JOANNES. HVNTER. PATRONI. *Rev.* Snake *AR* 80 150
casting its skin. RENOVANDO VIGET below. LYCEUM. MEDICVM *D.* 42 mm. By J. Milton [after *AE* 30 55
J. Flaxman] *BHM* 262; *Stainton* 3; *Storer* 1083
Struck from more than one pair of dies. George Fordyce (1736–1802), physician and chemist. John Hunter (1728–93),
surgeon and anatomist; brother of William.

816 Göttingen University 1785
Obv. Head r., laureate. *Ex.* GEORGIVS III MDCCLXXXV *Rev.* Winged youth, standing beside a *AV* 500 700
plinth decorated with a medallion of George II, upon which he leans a shield inscribed *AR* 70 120
INGENIO ET STVDIO *Ex.* GEORGIA AVGVSTA ADIVDICANTE *D.* 50 mm. By E. Burch. *BHM* *AE* 25 40
266; *Erlanger* 67 *WM* 15 30
Awarded by the university in the name of the King as Elector of Hanover. *See* No. 532.

817 George III *c.*1785
Obv. Bust r., laureate and armoured. GEORGIVS III DEI GRATIA *Rev.* Liberty standing, *AR* 90 160
facing, holds the cap of liberty. SEMPER HONOS NOMENQVE TVVM *D.* 40 mm. By L. Pingo. *AE* 45 70
BHM 265
It is unclear what occasion is commemorated. *BHM* suggests that it may relate to an interview between John Adams, the
first American ambassador, and George III.

818 Edmund Sexton *c.*1785
Obv. Head r. EDM. SEX. VISCOVNT. PERY. *Rev.* Plain. *D.* 40 mm. By W. Mossop. *BHM* 264; *AR* 50 90
Frazer 1887/448 *AE* 25 45
Edmund Sexton, Viscount Pery (1719–1806), Irish lawyer and politician. *See* No. 808.

819 Royal Irish Academy 1786
Obv. Bust l., draped. IACOBVS. COMES. DE. CHARLEMONT. PRÆS *Rev.* Female figure of Art *AV* 700 1000
seated upon books, l., displaying the Irish shield. VETERES REVOCAVIT ARTES. *Ex.* ACAD. REG. *AR* 90 160
HIB. INST. IAN. 28 MDCCLXXXVI. *D.* 53 mm. By W. Mossop. *BHM* 267; *Frazer* 1887/449; *AE* 25 45
EPM 1888, 283
Struck *c.*1790 and awarded in gold. Another version by J. Woodhouse, based on this medal, was struck *c.*1785. James
Caulfield, 1st Earl of Charlemont (1728–99), Irish statesman.

820 Thomas Ryder 1786
Obv. Bust r., draped. THOMAS RYDER. *Rev.* NON. ALIENA UNQUAM RYDER VESTIGIA PRESSIT., *AR* 80 130
within a wreath; lyre and mask below. *D.* 43 mm. By W. Mossop. *BHM* 242; *Frazer* *AE* 30 55
1887/447
Thomas Ryder (1735–90), Irish actor. He took up an engagement at Covent Garden in 1786.

821* Death of Adam Smith 1787
Obv. Bust r. ADAM SMITH 1787 *Rev.* Minerva standing, l., leaning on a spear, empties a *AR* 110 180
bountiful cornucopia. *D.* 40 mm. Cast. (By?) *BHM* 268; *CP* 111/33. *See* **Plate 23** *AE* 45 80
Adam Smith (1723–87), political economist; author of *The Wealth of Nations*.

822 Hampstead Philomvestigists 1787
Obv. Seated figure of Christ, l., feeding lambs. SUNDAY. SCHOOLS. INSTITUTED. 1787. E. *AR* 55 90
MONTAGU. ESQ. PATRON *Ex.* FEED MY LAMBS. *Rev.* A book in the centre, between two *AE* 25 45
interlinked triangular devices, inscribed HAMPSTEAD PHILOMVESTIGISTS SOCIETY
HAMPSTEAD; symbols around. BROTHERS. DO. ALL. THE. GOOD. YOU. CAN. *D.* 44 mm. (By?)
BHM 270; *D & W* 133/249
Edward Montagu (1716–98), Master of Chancery; benefactor.

823* Death of Prince Charles 1788
Obv. Bust r., similar to No. 715. HEN. IX. MAG. BRIT. FR. ET. HIB. REX. FID. DEF. CARD. EP. TVSC. *AR* 100 170
Rev. Similar to No. 715, but dated in *Ex.* AN MDCCLXXXVIII *D.* 53 mm. By G. Hamerani *AE* 35 60

[after F. Cropanese]. *BHM* 282; *CP* 77/69. *See* **Plate 23**   £   £

Based on No. 715 and struck from more than one pair of dies; on some examples rust marks are evident and the signature is indiscernible. Prince Henry was then the last direct male descendant in the Stuart line.

824   Merlin's Temple of Music 1788

Obv. Magician holding a wand seated, l., at a table. AMBROSIUS. MERLIN. MDCCLXXXVIII. *Rev.* Pipe organ within a domed kiosk; above, meridian sun. TEMPLE OF MUSIC   *D.* 40 mm. By J. Milton. *BHM* 293; *Stainton* 5

AR	60	110
AE	30	55
WM	15	30

John Joseph Merlin (1735–1803), mechanical engineer and inventor.

825   George III, Recovery of Health 1789

Obv. Bust r., laureate. GEORGIVS III MAGN. BR. FR. ET HIB. REX   *Rev.* Main west front of St. Paul's Cathedral. LÆTITIA CVM PIETATE   *Ex.* DEO OPT. MAX. REX PIENTISS PRO SALVTE REST. V. S. L. M. AP. 23. 1789   *D.* 54 mm. (By L. Pingo?) *BHM* 313

AR	120	230
AE	55	90

This medal also occurs with another obverse legend and a lettered edge. More than twenty medals commemorate the King's recovery, which was celebrated by a thanksgiving at St. Paul's Cathedral.

826   ——

Obv. Hygeia standing, r., places a patera, from which a serpent in her arms feeds, upon a column decorated with an oval medallion of the King. GEORGIO III OPTIMO PRINCIPI. *Ex.* 1789   *Rev.* Representation of Cheltenham Well. OB SALUTEM RESTAURATAM. *Ex.* S. MOREAU ARBIT : ELEG : CHELTENHAM : EXCUD CUR : 1788   *D.* 43 mm. [By J. G. Hancock & T. Phipson] *BHM* 301; *Storer* 6176

AV	400	600
AR	65	110
AE	20	35

827   ——

Obv. Bust r., laureate. GEORGIVS III. D.G. MAG. BR. FR. ET. HIB. REX. *Rev.* Snake entwined around a tripod on which rests a burning altar. FELICITAS PUBLICA. *Ex.* SAL. REG. REST. 1789. *D.* 35 mm. By J. P. Droz. *BHM* 311; *Storer* 6173

AV	280	450
AR	25	45
AE	15	30

Struck from two pairs of dies.

828   Francis Willis 1789

Obv. Bust three-quarters l., draped. DOCTOR WILLIS. *Rev.* BRITONS REJOICE YOUR KING'S RESTORED. 1789   *D.* 33 mm. By C. James. *BHM* 333; *Storer* 3790; *D & H Middx.* 220

AR	60	110
AE	20	45
WM	10	20

Francis Willis (1718–1807), physician and clergyman; attended the King.

829   Wesleyan Methodism, 50th Anniversary 1789

Obv. Bust r., draped. THE REV. IOHN WESLEY. A.M. *Rev.* Wesley preaching to a congregation beneath a tree. BY GRACE ARE YE SAVED THROUGH FAITH. *Ex.* ANNO DOMINI 1789   *D.* 36 mm. [By W. Mainwaring] *BHM* 334

AE	38	70
WM	25	45

John Wesley (1703–91), founder of Methodism. The obverse occurs with a number of other reverses. Several medals commemorate the anniversary.

830   Baron Rokeby, Armagh Observatory 1789

Obv. Bust r., in clerical robes. RICH ROBINSON BARON ROKEBY LORD PRIMATE OF ALL IRELAND. *Rev.* Exterior view of the observatory. THE HEAVENS DECLARE THE GLORY OF GOD. *Ex.* MDCCLXXXIX   *D.* 53 mm. By W. Mossop. *BHM* 330; *Frazer* 1887/449

AR	80	140
AE	35	65

831   Society for Free Debate, Birmingham 1789

Obv. Bust of Demosthenes, l., draped. SOCIETY FOR FREE DEBATE INSTITUTED IN BIRMINGHAM 1789. *Rev.* TO RAISE THE GENIUS AND TO MEND THE HEART. *D.* 33 mm. By P. Wyon. *D & W* 110/80; *Davis* 44

AR	45	80
AE	20	35
WM	10	20

Demosthenes (385?–322 BC), Athenian orator and statesman.

832   Glasgow University, Cullen Medal 1790

Obv. Bust l., draped. GULIELMUS CULLEN MDCCX. MDCCXC   *Rev.* As No. 806. *D.* 70 mm. By N. Macphail. *BHM* 342; *Storer* 709

AR	40	75
AE	12	25

Struck *c.*1870. *See* No. 806. William Cullen (1710–90), physician.

833   Church and King Club, Manchester 1790

Obv. George III standing, facing, holds a scroll inscribed TESTA CORPO; church and pillar inscribed BILL OF RIGHTS and MAGNA CARTA, respectively. MAY OUR HAPPY CONSTITUTION IN CHURCH & STATE EVER CONTINUE UNIMPAIRED. *Ex.* CHURCH AND KING CLUB MANCHESTER   *Rev.* THE THIRD ATTEMPT OF THE DISSENTERS IN THE SHORT PERIOD OF THREE YEARS TO OBTAIN A REPEAL OF THE CORPORATION AND TEST ACTS THOSE BARRIERS OF THE BRITISH CONSTITUTION WAS FRUSTRATED IN THE HOUSE OF COMMONS BY A MAJORITY OF CLXXXIX MARCH 11 MDCCXC. *D.* 44 mm. (By L. Pingo?) *BHM* 344

AR	25	45
AE	12	20

Examples occur frosted and set within a watch-style glass bound with a silver frame.

834   Duke of Atholl's Medal 1790

Obv. Farming scene of ploughing and reaping. GOD. SPEED. THE. FIELD. D ATHOLE. PRIZE. MEDAL. 1790. *Rev.* Domestic scene of spinning, knitting etc. GOD SPEED THE HOUSE. D ATHOLE

AR	70	120
AE	20	35

PRIZE MEDAL 1790. *D*. 48 mm. By J. Milton. *Stainton* 8c   £   £

The obverse and reverse each occur coupled with the common reverse of a wreath, blank for the recipient's name.

835   **Richard Sheridan** *c*.1790

Obv. Bust three-quarters l., draped. R.B. SHERIDAN ESQ. M P. *Rev*. RESISTLESS WIT WHOSE   WM   25   45
POINTED DART PIERCES CORRUPTIONS DASTARD HEART above crossed branches. *D*. 36 mm. (By
W. Mainwaring?) BHM 346; *D & H* Middx. 217

Richard Brinsley Sheridan (1751–1816), dramatist and politician.

836*   **Anti-Slavery Society** *c*.1790

Obv. A chained negro slave, kneeling, r. AM I NOT A MAN AND A BROTHER   *Rev*. WHATSOEVER   AR   100   170
YE WOULD THAT MEN SHOULD DO UNTO YOU, DO YE EVEN SO TO THEM. *D*. 33 mm. (By?) BHM   AE   25   45
269; *D & H* Middx. 233–8. *See* **Plate 23**   WM   15   25

The obverse is after a design by William Hackwood. This piece was struck from several dies and there are many varieties.
Examples also occur gilt, with the figure of the slave enamelled, and with inscriptions in French and German. The only
example that has been noted with a signature (?) was marked WD on the ground below the slave's knee. The Society was
founded in 1787.

837*   **Northern Lighthouses** *c*.1790

Obv. A lighthouse between a buoy and a beacon. IN SALUTEM OMNIUM NORTHERN   AR   90   —
LIGHTHOUSES   *Rev*. MEDAL REFERRING TO ADMIRALTY PROTECTION AND A DESCRIPTION OF   Pb.   35   —
THE PERSON BY THE ENGINEER   *D*. 26 mm. (By?) *MH* 1919, 803*a*; Eimer, *SNC* April 1982,
86. *See* **Plate 23**

This piece occurs with a suspension loop. It was intended to afford protection to the wearer against being press-ganged
into naval service. A medal with a similar purpose, dated 1757, served the builders of Eddystone Lighthouse. *See*
D. Fearon, *SNC* December 1967, 328–9.

838   **Daniel Mendoza and William Warr** 1791

Obv. The heads of D. MENDOZA AND W. WARD. face to face. *Rev*. Two pugilists sparring;   AE   300   550
above, branch of oak. *Ex*. 1791   *D*. 36 mm. By W. Mainwaring. BHM 356; *D & H* Middx.   WM   100   170
35

Daniel Mendoza (1764–1836) and William Warr (1770?–1809) were both eminent boxers and met on several occasions. In
1791 Mendoza went on a sparring tour of England and Ireland and opened a boxing school at the Lyceum in the Strand,
London. Warr's name has been incorrectly spelt on the medal. *See* H. D. Miles, *Pugilistica, The History of British Boxing
1719–1863*, vol. I, 120–2, London, 1880.

839   **Death of John Wesley** 1791

Obv. Bust l., draped. REV. IOHN WESLEY. M.A BORN 21 JUNE 1703 DIED 2 MARCH 1791   *Rev*.   AE   25   45
WELL DONE GOOD AND FAITHFUL SERVANT ENTER THOU INTO THE JOY OF THY LORD., within a   WM   15   30
radiate wreath. *D*. 40 mm. By J. G. Hancock. BHM 357

Wesley's death is commemorated by a few medals.

840   ——

Obv. Bust r., draped. THE REV?. IOHN WESLEY A M   *Rev*. HOLY BIBLE upon a funerary urn   AE   30   55
festooned with flowers. HIS WORKS SHALL FOLLOW HIM   *Ex*. OB. MAR. 2. 1791. ÆT 88.   WM   20   40
D. 35 mm. By W. Mainwaring. BHM 359

841   **Death of Selina, Countess of Huntingdon** 1791

Obv. Bust almost facing, veiled and draped. SELINA COUN$ DOW? OF HUNTINGDON. *Rev*.   AE   25   45
WHOSE FAITH FOLLOW, CONSIDERING THE END OF THEIR CONVERSATION: JESUS CHRIST. *Ex*.   WM   10   18
DIED. JUNE: 17: 1791. AG? 86. *D*. 34 mm. By P. Kempson and S. Kindon. BHM 351; *EPM*
1892, 317

Selina Hastings, Countess of Huntingdon (1707–91), patron of Methodism. A similar medal has a different reverse
inscription.

842   **Death of Caleb Evans** 1791

Obv. Bust l., draped. THE REV. CALEB EVANS. D.D. *Rev*. BLESSED ARE THE DEAD WHICH DIE IN   AE   15   30
THE LORD. within a floral border. *Ex*. OBT. AUG. 9. 1791 ÆT. 54. *D*. 37 mm. By W. Mainwaring.   WM   10   20
BHM 350; *EPM* 1891, 82

William Caleb Evans (1737–91), Baptist minister.

843*   **Marriage of Duke of York and Frederica** 1791

Obv. Busts l., conjoined. FRIDERICVS PR. M. BRITAN. DVX EBORAC. EPISCOP. OSNABRVG.   AR   60   110
FRIDERIC. CAROL. VLRIC. CATHAR. PR. BORVSS. REG. FILIA PRIMOGENITA   *Rev*. Shields of the
two Houses united with a garland held by Hymen. IAM MARTE NVNC AMORE   *Ex*. CELEBRAT.
NUPTIAE D. XXIX. SEPT. MDCCXCI. *D*. 45 mm. By F. W. Loos Jr. BHM 348. *See* **Plate 23**

Princess Frederica Charlotte Ulrica Catherina (1767–1820), eldest daughter of Frederick William II of Prussia.

844*   **Death of Lord Effingham** 1791

Obv. Bust l. THO. HOWARD. COM. DE. EFFINGHAM. REI. MONET. PRÆF. 1784. *Rev*. Britannia   AV   400   750
seated, l., upon a globe over which she pours coinage from her cornucopia. PRO   AR   40   75

PLATE 23

PLATE 24

845

848

849

855

864

866

869

			VF	*EF*
PATRIÆ *Edge.* NATVS. XIII. JAN. MDCCXLVII. OB. XV. NOV. MDCCXCI. ÆT. XLIV *D.* 35 mm. By J. Milton. *BHM* 353; *Stainton* 9. *See* **Plate 23**		AE	20	35

Thomas Howard, Earl of Effingham (1747–91), Master of the Mint; Governor of Jamaica.

845*   **Defeat of Sultan Tippoo 1792**
Obv. Bust l., draped. CAR. MARCHIO CORNWALLIS STRATEGUS ACERRIMUS. *Rev.* Cornwallis, standing before his aides, receives Sultan Tippoo who presents his two sons. FAS SIT PARCERE HOSTI. *Ex.* SULTANO TIPPOO DEVICTO OBSIDES RECIPIT MDCCXCII. *D.* 48 mm. By C. H. Küchler. *BHM* 363; *Pollard* 5. *See* **Plate 24**

		VF	*EF*
	AR	90	170
	AE	20	45

Struck from two pairs of dies, one of which is incorrectly dated 1793. Küchler's medals were made at Matthew Boulton's Soho Manufactory; some were restruck in the nineteenth century after Boulton's death (*Pollard* pp. 314–6). Tippoo Sahib (1751–99), Sultan of Mysore; killed in action at the storming of Seringapatam in the fourth Mysore war.

846   **Death of Sir Robert Strange 1792**
Obv. Bust r., draped. ROBERTVS. STRANGE. *Rev.* An angel leaning on a column, r., holds a palm branch and wreath. FAMÆ ÆTERNÆ. *D.* 90 mm. Cast. By G. Z. Weber. *BHM* 362

		VF	*EF*
	AE	150	250

Examples occur within a circular brass frame. Robert Strange (1721–92), engraver.

847   **Society Promoting Religion and Virtue 1792**
Obv. Figures of Charity, Religion and Virtue, standing; beyond, l., temple on a hill. RIGHTEOUSNESS EXALTETH A NATION   *Rev.* ASSOCIATION FOR RELIGION AND VIRTUE INST OCT 9 1792, in the centre; space above (for recipient's name). ACQUAINT THYSELF WITH GOD & BE AT PEACE. *D.* 40 mm. By W. Mossop. *BHM* 364; *Frazer* 1886/452

		VF	*EF*
	AR	30	55
	AE	10	15

This medal was awarded in silver. It has an integral suspension loop.

848*   **George, Prince of Wales 1792**
Obv. Bust l., draped. GEORGIVS PRIN. GALL   *Rev.* Male figure standing, l., offers bread to a pilgrim. CORONAM MUNIFICENTIA SUPERAT   *Ex.* MDCCXCII   *D.* 48 mm. By W. Barnett. *BHM* 361. *See* **Plate 24**

		VF	*EF*
	AR	90	180
	AE	40	70
	WM	20	35

The precise occasion for this medal is unclear. The reverse illustrates the story of King Alfred and St. Cuthbert.

849*   **Capitulation of Valenciennes 1793**
Obv. Bust l., draped. FREDERICUS. DUX. EBOR: EPISC: OSNABURG. *Rev.* Equestrian figure of the Duke receives the surrender of the castle. SCELUS IMPAR VIRTUTI *Ex.* VALENTIANA. EXPUGNAT. IUL. XXVIII MDCCXCIII. *Edge.* AUGURIUM. FELIX. DEUS. ET. PAX. ALMA. SECUNDENT *D.* 41 mm. By W. Whitley. *BHM* 367. *See* **Plate 24**

		VF	*EF*
	AR	80	140
	AE	35	60
	WM	20	35

850   ——
Obv. Bust almost facing, laureate and uniformed. HIS ROYAL HIGHˢ FREDᴷ DUKE OF YORK. *Rev.* VALENCIENNES SURRENDERED TO HIS ROYAL HIGHNESS FREDᴷ DUKE OF YORK JULY 25. Below, military trophies. *Ex.* 1793 *D.* 39 mm. By W. Mainwaring. *BHM* 368; *Hennin* 524

		VF	*EF*
	AE	20	35
	WM	15	30

851   **Thomas Paine 1793**
Obv. Bust r., draped. THOMAS PAINE. *Rev.* Man standing, r., two others behind him, regards a mountain, on the side of which is a mouse. THE MOUNTAIN IN LABOUR *Ex.* 1793 *D.* 33 mm. (By W. Mainwaring?) *BHM* 365; *Hennin* 587; *D & H* Middx. 208

		VF	*EF*
	WM	55	90

Thomas Paine (1737–1809), political philosopher and author.

852   **Glasgow University, John Hunter Medal 1793**
Obv. Bust l. JOANNES HUNTER MDCCXXVIII. MDCCXCIII *Rev.* As No. 806. *D.* 70 mm. By N. Macphail. *CP* 153/12; *Storer* 1715

		VF	*EF*
	AR	50	85
	AE	15	28

Struck *c.*1870. *See* No. 806.

853   **Board of Agriculture 1793**
Obv. Head r., laureate. GEORGIUS III. D: G. MAG. BR. REX. BOARD OF AGRICULTURE ESTABL'D 23. AUG. 1793. *Rev.* Female figure standing, r., holds a spade entwined with a serpent; beyond, plough in a landscape. Above, a ribbon (blank, for inscription). *Ex.* VOTED (space, for the date). *D.* 48 mm. By C. H. Küchler. *Pollard* 6

		VF	*EF*
	AV	550	850
	AR	80	120
	AE	10	18

Awarded from *c.*1800 in gold and silver for thirty-one categories, e.g.: a leather substitute for shoes; instruments for husbandry; irrigation; ameliorating conditions of the labouring poor. See *Premiums offered by the Board of Agriculture*, 1801. Examples in bronze are probably later strikings. *See* No. 845.

854   **Naval Victory, First of June 1794**
Obv. Bust l., uniformed. RIC: COMES HOWE VICE-ADMIRALLUS ANGLIÆ & C. *Rev.* Britannia seated, r., receives a trident from Neptune who stands in a marine car pointing towards a burning fleet. Above, Victory inscribes commanders' names, HOWE GRAVES BRIDPORT BOWYER CALDWELL GARDNER and PASLEY on an obelisk. NON NOBIS SED PATRIÆ *Ex.* MDCCXCIIII 1ˢᵀ JUNE. *D.* 57 mm. By W. Barnett. *BHM* 382; *MH* 1919, 419

		VF	*EF*
	AR	120	200
	AE	45	85
	WM	25	55

This action is commemorated by at least six medals.

			£	£

855* ——
Obv. Bust r., uniformed. RIC. COMES HOWE THALASSIARCHA BRITAN. PATRIÆ DECUS ET
TUTAMEN. *Rev.* Naval engagement. NON SORTE SED VIRTUTE. *Ex.* GALLOR. CLASSIS PROFLIG.
DIE I JUNII. MDCCXCIV. *D.* 48 mm. By C. H. Küchler. *BHM* 383; *MH* 1919, 417. *See* **Plate
24**
Struck from more than one pair of dies. *See* No. 845.

AR 150 280
AE 35 65

856 ——
Obv. Bust r., uniformed. EARL HOWE ADM.ᴸ OF THE WHITE K: G: *Rev.* Neptune advancing, r.,
in a marine car. FRENCH FLEET DEFEATED OFF USHANT *Ex.* VII SAIL OF THE LINE CAPTURED 1
JUNE MDCCXCIV. *D.* 41 mm. By W. Wyon. *BHM* 387; *MH* 1919, 418; *Mudie* 3
Struck in 1820, from Mudie's series commemorating British Victories. *See* No. 1136.

AR 30 55
AE 9 15
WM 3 7

857   Joseph Priestley, Arrival in America 1794
Obv. Bust r., draped. JOSEPHUS PRIESTLEY. *Rev.* APR: VIII BRITTANNIÆ LITORA LINQUENS
COLUMBIAM ADVENIT JUNII IV MDCCXCIV, in the centre. MAGNUS CHRISTIANUS
PHILOSOPHUS * *D.* 54 mm. By T. Phipson. *BHM* 381.

AE 90 170
WM 40 70

858   Unification of Corsica with Great Britain 1794
Obv. Bust r., draped. GEORGIVS. III. DEI. GRATIA. *Rev.* CORSICA UNITED TO GREAT BRITAIN
MDCCXCIV *D.* 21 mm. By C. Twigg.
On 17 June 1794 the Corsican people acknowledged George III as King.

WM 20 35

859   Thomas Erskine and Vicary Gibbs 1794
Obv. Busts r., conjoined. HON. T. ERSKINE. V. GIBBS. ESQ. PATRIOTS WHO FOR SACRED FREEDOM
STOOD *Rev.* Justice assists the falling figure of Britannia. RETURNING JUSTICE LIFTS ALOFT
HER SCALE *Ex.* MDCCXCIV *D.* 44 mm. By J. Milton. *BHM* 376; *Stainton* 11
Thomas Erskine, 1st Baron Erskine (1750–1823), Lord Chancellor. Sir Vicary Gibbs (1751–1820), judge.

AR 60 110
AE 25 40

860   Hardy, Thelwall and Tooke: Acquitted of High Treason 1794
Obv. Busts r., conjoined and draped. T. HARDY. J. H. TOOKE. J. THELWALL. *Rev.* Busts l.,
conjoined and draped. V GIBBS and T ERSKINE COUNSEL, in the centre, within the Serpent of
Eternity. Around, names of the three defendants and respective jurors. *D.* 37 mm. (By?)
BHM 377; *EPM* 1891, 80/2
Thomas Hardy (1752–1832), radical politician and founder of the Corresponding Society. John Thelwall (1764–1834), political reformer. John Horne Tooke (1736–1812), politician; philologist.

AR 65 120
AE 25 45
WM 10 20

861   Charles, Marquis of Cornwallis 1794
Obv. Bust three-quarters r., wearing a cocked hat and uniformed. CHARLES MARQUIS
CORNWALLIS. *Rev.* Fame standing upon a military trophy blowing her trumpet. AB ORIENTE
AD OCCASUM *Ex.* 1794 *D.* 39 mm. By W. Mainwaring. *BHM* 373; *EPM* 1890, 80/2

WM 8 15

862   Opposition to the War with France 1794
Obv. Bust r., draped. CAROLUS JACOBUS FOX *Rev.* Envy, seated upon clouds obscuring the
sun, threatened with a flaming celestial sword. VIDET INVIDIA ET ÆGROTAT *D.* 31 mm. By
W. Whitley. *BHM* 388; *EPM* 1891, 96
Charles James Fox (1749–1806), statesman.

WM 15 30

863   Trinity College Dublin 1794
Obv. Three standing female figures of History, Oratory and Poetry; above, Pegasus. VOS
LENE CONSILIVM ET DATIS ET DATO GAVDETIS ALMÆ. *Ex.* INST. A.D. MDCCXCIV *Rev.* EGREGIE
MERENTI IN ARTE ORATORIA (space, for recipient's name) in the centre, within a band
inscribed NEC FACUNDIA DESERET HUNC A wreath, around. HISTORICA SOCIETAS COLLEGI
DVBLINIENSIS *D.* 52 mm. By W. Mossop. *Frazer* 1887/454 sim.; *D & W* 120/159
Awarded in silver for history, poetry and oratory; the die was made with three movable central portions for each of the subjects. The Historical Society was founded in 1770 for promoting the study of history and elocution.

AR 35 55

864* **Birthday of Queen Charlotte 1795**
Obv. Bust l., wearing a coronet and draped. CHARLOTTE REGINA. *Rev.* FROGMORE DIE XIX MAII.
M.DCC.XCV. Below, branches of oak. *D.* 35 mm. [By C. H. Küchler] *BHM* 389; *Pollard* 10.
See **Plate 24**
See No. 845.

AR 60 110
AE 20 35

865   Marriage of Prince of Wales and Caroline of Brunswick 1795
Obv. Busts r., conjoined and draped. GEORG. WALL. PRINC. ET CAROLIN. BRUNS. PR. *Rev.*
Hymen holds a ribbon uniting the shields of Britain and Brunswick-Wolfenbüttel; beyond,
skyline of London. JUNXIT HYMEN TAEDIS ILLUSTRIBUS AMBOS. *Ex.* NUPTIAE REGIAE LOND.
MDCCXCVII. *D.* 48 mm. By C. H. Küchler. *BHM* 392; *Pollard* 9
The medal is incorrectly dated. Princess Caroline Amelia Elizabeth (1768–1821), daughter of Duke Charles William Ferdinand of Brunswick. Another reverse just has the inscription FROGMORE MAY 19TH 1795, recording the Royal visit on the Queen's birthday. *See* No. 845.

AR 90 170
AE 25 55

			£	£

866* ——
Obv. Bust almost facing, draped. Wreath border, interlaced with a ribbon inscribed GEORGE   AR   70   130
PRINCE OF WALES   *Rev.* BORN THE XII OF AUGUST MDCCLXII. MARRIED TO CAROLINE PRINCESS   WM   25   45
OF BRUNSWICK ON THE VIII OF APRIL MDCCXCV. *D.* 47 mm. By W. Whitley. *BHM* 391. *See*
Plate 24

867   **Naval Action off Isle de Groix 1795**
Obv. Bust r., uniformed. A.A. HOOD LORD BRIDPORT ADMIRAL OF THE WHITE. *Rev.* Victory   AR   90   170
standing, facing, one foot on land, displays a naval crown and captured French standards;   AE   25   55
beyond, a fleet at sea. OFF PORT L'ORIENT & CLOSE TO THE FRENCH SHORE & BATTERIES WITH 22
SHIPS ATTACKED & DEFEATED THE FRENCH FLEET OF 32 SHIPS. THREE SHIPS & 228 GUNS
TAKEN   *Ex.* 23.ᴰ JUNE 1795   *D.* 49 mm. By J. G. Hancock. *BHM* 406; *MH* 1919, 539
Alexander Hood, 1st Viscount Bridport (1727–1814), admiral.

868   **Lord Stanhope 1795**
Obv. Bust of Stanhope, l., draped. THE MINORITY OF ONE 1795. *Rev.* STANHOPE THE FRIEND OF   WM   20   35
TRIAL BY JURY, LIBERTY OF THE PRESS, PARLIAMENTARY REFORM, ANNUAL PARLIAMENTS,
HABEAS CORPUS ACT, ABOLITION OF SINECURES, AND OF A SPEEDY PEACE WITH THE FRENCH
REPUBLIC. *D.* 42 mm. By W. Whitley. *BHM* 405
Charles Stanhope, 3rd Earl Stanhope (1753–1816), politician; man of science.

869*   **Monarchy and Constitution, Anti-Republican Sympathies 1795**
Obv. Domestic scene of family life, within a wreath; above, imperial crown. GOD SAVE THE   WM   20   35
KING THE LAND WE LIVE IN AND MAY THOSE WHO DONT LIKE IT LEAVE IT. *Rev.* A decapitated
French aristocrat, standing, points to his head on the ground. ABHOR EVIL CLEAVE TO THAT
WHICH IS GOOD. A PHILOSOPHICAL CURE FOR ALL EVILS. LICENTIOUS LIBERTY IS DESTRUCTION.
D. 49 mm. By W. Whitley. *BHM* 407; *Forrer* VI/465. *See* **Plate 24**

870   **St. Vincent's Black Corps 1795**
Obv. Victory steps over a fallen Carib. Sᵀ VINCENTS BLACK CORPS. *Rev.* Armed native soldier,   AE   170   320
barefoot, standing upon a mound. BOLD LOYAL OBEDIENT   *D.* 48 mm. By H.G.(?) *Gordon*
21; *Payne* 223
Awarded to native soldiers for the campaign against the French and Carib troops on the island of St. Vincent; named
examples have not been noted. *See* No. 750. *Stainton* (p. 153, B) suggests that the medallist may be Henry Gretton, an
engraver and member of the Goldsmiths' Company.

871   **Birth of Princess Charlotte 1796**
Obv. Bust r., diademed. H.R.H. THE PRINCESS CHARLOTTE. *Rev.* BORN JANʸ 7 1796 within a   *a* AR   10   18
wreath. *D.* 22 mm. (By?) *BHM* 409   AE   5   8
Struck *c.*1817; type *b* is a set of four uniform medals commemorating her birth; marriage 1816; death 1817; obsequies
1817; they sometimes occur in a rectangular cardboard case. Princess Charlotte Augusta (1796–1817), only child of   *b* AR   —   80
George, Prince of Wales and Caroline. Examples in bronze are gilt.   AE   —   40

872   **Anderson College 1796**
Obv. Bust l., draped. IOANNES. ANDERSON MDCCXXVI – MDCCXCVI   *Rev.* APVD. ACADEMIAN.   AE   15   25
IOANNIS. ANDERSON. IN. FACVLTATE. MEDICINAE. EXAMINATIONIBVS. HABITIS. QVI. PRAE.
CONDISCIPVLIS. EMINVIT. HOCCE. PRAEMIO. DONATVS. EST   *D.* 51 mm. By J. Macdonald.
BHM 410
A prize medal; struck and awarded from *c.*1870. John Anderson (1726–96), Scottish natural philosopher.

873*   **Edward Jenner 1796**
Obv. Bust l., draped. EDUARD JENNER ENTDECKER DER SCHUTZIMPFUNG D. 14 MAI 1796   *Rev.*   AR   50   90
Children, their hands linked, dancing around a cow. EHRE SEY GOTT IN DER HÖHE   *Ex.* UND   AE   25   40
FREUDE AUF ERDEN   *D.* 36 mm. By F. W. Loos. *BHM* 412; *Storer* 1798. *See* **Plate 25**
Edward Jenner (1749–1823), physician; discoverer of vaccination.

874   **Naval Engagement off Helvoetsluys 1796**
Obv. Bust l., uniformed. SIR HENRY TROLLOPE KNIGHT. *Rev.* Lion running amok in a   AR   90   170
dismasted ship; beyond, a fleet in retreat. IN THE GLATTON OF 54 GUNS ENGAGED AND BEAT OFF   AE   25   55
6 FRENCH FRIGATES CARRYING TWO HUNDRED & SIX GUNS. *Ex.* HELVOETSLUYS. JULY 16
1796   *D.* 49 mm. By J. G. Hancock. *BHM* 414; *MH* 1919, 541
Sir Henry Trollope (1756–1839), admiral.

875   **London Missionary Society 1796**
Obv. Ship in full sail. THE DUFF, CAPT: JAMES WILSON. *Ex.* SAIL'D 10ᵀᴴ AUG. 1796   *Rev.* WITH   AE   100   180
MISSIONARIES TO THE SOUTH SEAS FOR THE CONVERSION OF THE HEATHENS   *D.* 38 mm. (By?)   WM   45   85
BHM 416; *MH* 1919; 449*a*

		£	£

876*   **Stonehenge 1796**
Obv. View of Stonehenge within a wreath inscribed STONEHENGE 1796; above, druid's head over a ribbon, inscribed TANTUM RELIGIO POTUIT   *Rev.* Circular calendar with signs representing the orrery of the druids. Above, DUM TACENT CLAMANT and below, CHOIR GAVR   *D.* 50 mm. By T. Wyon Sr. *BHM* 417; *D & W* 190/707. *See* **Plate 25**

	AR	60	100
	AE	25	45
	WM	20	35

877   **York Minster 1796**
Obv. Exterior view of the Minster. *Ex.* YORK MINSTER 1796   *Rev.* Fortress on a mound from which troops cross, r., over a drawbridge. CLIFFORDS TOWER   *Ex.* BLOWN UP A.D. 1684   *D.* 45 mm. By T. Wyon Sr. *BHM* 418

	AR	50	90
	AE	20	35
	WM	10	18

878   **The Royal Society, Rumford Medal 1796**
Obv. Flaming crucible upon an ornamental tripod. NOSCERE QUÆ VIS ET CAUSSA   *Rev.* PRÆMIUM OPTIME MERENTI EX INSTITUTO BENJ. A RUMFORD S.R.I. COMITIS ADJUDICATUM A REG. SOC. LOND., within a wreath. *D.* 76 mm. By J. Milton. *Stainton* 22; *D & W* 161/465

	AV	—	—
	AR	80	140
	AE	30	50

Benjamin Thompson, Count Rumford (1753–1814), (born Woburn, Mass.), physicist; experimented with calorific heat. He endowed this medal which was awarded biennially from 1802, in gold and silver, for discoveries in fire, heat, light and colours. It was discontinued in 1863. *See* No. 879.

879   **Rumford Memorial Medal 1796**
Obv. Head l. BENIAMIN AB RUMFORD S. ROM. IMP. COMES INSTITVIT MDCCXCVI   *Rev.* OPTIME IN LVCIS CALORISQVE NATVRA EXQVIRENDA MERENTI ADIVDICAT SOC: REG: LOND., within a wreath. *D.* 78 mm. By C. Wiener. *BHM* 413; *Storer* 3522.

	AV	—	—
	AR	80	140
	AE	30	50

Struck *c.*1863; awarded by the Royal Society in gold and silver. *See* No. 878.

880   **French Expedition to Bantry Bay 1797**
Obv. FRIENDLY ASSOCIATION BANTRY GARRISON divided by a crown. A wreath border. *Rev.* Three ships in stormy waters, assailed by the zephyrs. AFFLAVIT DEUS ET DISSIPANTUR   *Ex.* JAN MDCCXCVII   *D.* 40 mm. By W. Mossop. *BHM* 425; *MH* 1919, 458; *Payne* 212.

| | AR | 110 | 190 |
| | AE | 40 | 70 |

Examples in silver were awarded to officers of the Bantry Garrison.

881*   **Battle of Cape St. Vincent 1797**
Obv. Bust l., uniformed. JOHN JERVIS EARL OF S.^T VINCENT ADMIRAL OF THE WHITE. BORN JANUARY 26 1735.   *Rev.* Hispania, reclining on the sea-shore, leans against a shield inscribed PLUS ULTRA; a naval engagement, r. WITH 22 SHIPS AND 1428 GUNS PERSUED & DEFEATED THE SPANISH FLEET OF 37 SHIPS AND 2600 GUNS FOUR SHIPS AND 382 GUNS TAKEN   *Ex.* FEBRUARY 14 1797. *D.* 49 mm. By J. G. Hancock. *BHM* 435; *MH* 1919, 450. *See* **Plate 25**

	AR	90	170
	AE	25	55
	WM	10	20

John Jervis (1735–1823), admiral of the fleet; created Earl St. Vincent on his victory. More than ten medals commemorate the battle.

882   ——
Obv. Bust l. ADMIRAL EARL S.^T VINCENT G.C.B.   *Rev.* Victory hovering above two Spanish ships at which she hurls thunderbolts. *Ex.* SPANISH FLEET DEFEATED. OFF CAPE S.^T VINCENT XIV. FEB.^Y MDCCLXXXXVII   *D.* 41 mm. By G. Mills/N. G. A. Brenet. *BHM* 438; *MH* 1919, 452; *Mudie* 4

	AR	45	85
	AE	18	28
	WM	6	10

Struck in 1820, from Mudie's series commemorating British Victories. *See* No. 1136.

883   ——
Obv. Bust almost facing, uniformed. EARL S.^T VINCENT DEFEATED THE SPANISH FLEET   *Rev.* Two infant genii display an earl's coronet and British ensign above the sea. VALOUR REWARDED   *Ex.* FEB 14 1797 FOUR SHIPS TAKEN OFF CAPE S.^T VINCENT   *D.* 38 mm. [By T. Wyon Sr.] *BHM* 433; *MH* 1919, 451

	AR	40	75
	AE	12	25
	WM	8	15

884   **Battle of Camperdown 1797**
Obv. Bust r., uniformed. ADAM LORD VISCOUNT DUNCAN ADMIRAL OF THE WHITE BORN JULY 1 1731   *Rev.* A sailor nailing the Royal Standard to a ship's gallant mast. OCTOBER 11 1797 WITH 24 SHIPS & 1198 GUNS DEFEATED THE DUTCH FLEET OF 26 SHIPS & 1259 GUNS 9 SHIPS & 592 GUNS TAKEN   *Ex.* HEROIC COURAGE PROTECTS THE BRITISH FLAG   *D.* 49 mm. By J. G. Hancock. *BHM* 426; *MH* 1919, 459

| | AR | 90 | 170 |
| | AE | 25 | 55 |

Adam Duncan, Viscount Duncan (1731–1804), admiral.

885*   ——
Obv. Bust almost facing, uniformed. SIR RICHARD ONSLOW BART ADMIRAL OF THE BLUE. BORN 23 JUNE 1741   *Rev.* A fleet in formation. SECOND IN COMMAND OCTO 11 1797   *Ex.* IN THE MONARCH OF 74 GUNS BROKE. THE. REAR. OF. THE. DUTCH. LINE & TOOK THE ADMIRAL.^S SHIP   *D.* 48 mm. By J. G. Hancock. *BHM* 427; *MH* 1919, 472. *See* **Plate 25**

| | AR | 90 | 170 |
| | AE | 25 | 55 |

Sir Richard Onslow (1741–1817), admiral.

886   ——

		£	£

Obv. Bust l., uniformed. ADM. VISC. DUNCAN   *Rev.* Duncan receives Admiral de Winter's sword in surrender. DUTCH FLEET DEFEATED 9 SHIPS OF THE LINE CAPTURED 11 OCT^R 1797   *D.* 41 mm. By T. Webb/W. Wyon. *BHM* 432; *MH* 1919, 460; *Mudie* 5

     AR   30   55
     AE   9   15
     WM   3   7

Struck in 1820, from Mudie's series commemorating British Victories. *See* No. 1136.

887   ——

Obv. Bust three-quarters r., uniformed. LORD VIS^T DUNCAN OF CAMPERDOWN ADMIRAL OF THE BLUE   *Rev.* Britannia seated, l., beside a lion, leans on a rudder and holds a wreath and ensign. BRITANNIA TRIUMPHANT   *Ex* DUTCH FLEET DEFEATE^D 11. SHIPS TAKEN OCT^R 11. 1797. *D.* 38 mm. [By T. Wyon Sr.] *BHM* 428; *MH* 1919, 461

     AR   55   100
     AE   15   25
     WM   10   18

888*   **John Philip Kemble 1798**

Obv. Bust facing, draped, head l. IOHANNES PHILIPPUS KEMBLE   *Rev.* TRAGOEDUS ANGLICUS ÆT. XLI. MDCCXCVIII in a wreath decorated with theatrical masks. *D.* 53 mm. By J. G. Hancock. *BHM* 446; *Svarstad* 124. *See* **Plate 25**

     AR   65   110
     AE   20   35

John Philip Kemble (1757–1823), actor. A similar medal, diameter 36 mm., was made by J. Westwood Jr.

889*   **Battle of the Nile 1798**

Obv. Bust three-quarters l., uniformed. HORATIO LORD NELSON REAR ADMIRAL OF THE RED BORN SEPTEMBER 29 1758. *Rev.* River god, Nilus, reclining l., surveys a naval engagement. AUGUST 1^T 1798 WITH 14 SHIPS & A BRIG DEFEATED THE FRENCH FLEET OF 15 SHIPS & 4 FRIGATES SUPPORTED BY GUN BOATS AND A BATTERY ON SHORE NINE SHIPS TAKEN AND 4 DESTROY'D   *D.* 48 mm. By J. G. Hancock/P. Kempson. *BHM* 448; *MH* 1919, 475. *See* **Plate 25**

     AR   110   200
     AE   40   75
     WM   20   35

Horatio Nelson, Viscount Nelson (1758–1805), naval hero.

890*   **Battle of the Nile, Davison's Medal 1798**

Obv. Hope standing on a rocky promontory, l., holding an oval medallion of Nelson, inscribed EUROPE'S HOPE AND BRITAIN'S GLORY; beyond, an open sea. REAR-ADMIRAL LORD NELSON OF THE NILE   *Rev.* British fleet assembled in Aboukir Bay prepare to engage the French. ALMIGHTY GOD HAS BLESSED HIS MAJESTY'S ARMS. *Ex.* VICTORY OF THE NILE AUGUST 1. 1798. *Edge.* A TRIBUTE OF REGARD = FROM ALEX^R DAVISON, ESQ^R ST. JAMES' SQUARE (incuse). *D.* 47 mm. By C. H. Küchler. *BHM* 447; *MH* 1919, 482; *Pollard* 15; *Gordon* 24. *See* **Plate 25**

     AV   1800   2800
     AR   180   350
     AE   40   70

A tribute award by Alexander Davison (1750–1829), Nelson's prize agent and confidant who had amassed a large fortune as a government contractor. Medals were given in gold (admirals and captains), silver (officers), gilt bronze (petty officers), bronze (all others). They are occasionally found in a watch-style glass, framed, with the recipient and ship's name engraved in the field.

891   **Battle of the Nile 1798**

Obv. Head l. R. ADMIRAL LORD NELSON. K.B. BORN NOVEMBER MDCCLIV   *Rev.* Victory standing, r., inscribes NELSON on a shield. INDIA SAV^D. MALTA REGAIN^D. EGYPT PRESERV^D. *Ex.* 1. OF AUGUST MDCCXCVIII. *D.* 41 mm. By N. A. Ponthon. *BHM* 449; *MH* 1919, 485

     AE   50   90

Nelson's year of birth is incorrectly stated.

892   ——

Obv. Victory holding a medallion of A. LD. NELSON, seated before a pyramid. VIRTUTE NIHIL OBSTAT & ARMIS   *Ex.* VICTORY OF THE NILE AUG^T 1. 1798. *Rev.* Ribbon, inscribed LAUS DEO NOV. 29 1798, decorating a shield and anchor. SUB HOC SIGNO VINCES   *D.* 38 mm. By T. Wyon Sr. *BHM* 450; *MH* 1919, 484

     AR   50   90
     AE   15   30
     WM   10   20

893   ——

Obv. Bust almost facing, uniformed, head three-quarters r. ADMIRAL LORD NELSON OF THE NILE BRITAINS GLORY & DEFENCE   *Rev.* Naval engagement. ALMIGHTY GOD HAS BLESSED HIS MAJESTY'S ARMS   *Ex.* FRENCH FLEET DEFEATED AUGUST. 1. 1798. *D.* 38 mm. [By T. Wyon Sr.] *BHM* 452; *MH* 1919, 476

     AR   70   130
     AE   30   50
     WM   15   30

A similar obverse has a bust of Nelson with his empty right sleeve pinned up.

894   ——

Obv. Bust r., uniformed. NELSON PRÆFECTUS CLASSIS ANGLICAE. Below, IETTON. *Rev.* Neptune attacking a sea-horse with his trident; ships on the horizon. TERROR TERRIBILIUM   *Ex.* I: AUGUSTI MDCCLXXXXVIII. *D.* 33 mm. French (By?) *MH* 1919, 480; *Hennin* 856

     AR   45   80
     WM   15   28

Struck from more than one obverse die.

895   **Naval Action off Tory Island 1798**

Obv. Bust r., uniformed. SIR I. BORLASE WARREN BART. K.B. REAR ADMIRAL OF THE BLUE. *Rev.* Hibernia seated upon arms, r., holds an olive-branch aloft; to r., a fleet at sea. ATTACKED & DEFEATED THE FRENCH SQUADRON ON THE COAST OF IRELAND   *Ex.* OCTO 12 1798   *D.* 49 mm. By J. G. Hancock. *BHM* 455; *MH* 1919, 542

     AR   90   170
     AE   25   55

Sir John Borlase Warren (1753–1822), admiral.

			£	£
896	—— *Obv.* Bust almost facing, uniformed. Sᴿ J.B. WARREN BARONET. K.B. THE LORD OF HOSTS IS WITH US *Rev.* A naval engagement. THE SISTER COUNTRY AGAIN RESCUED FROM INVASION *Ex.* BREST SQUADRON DEFEATᴰ OFF TORY ISLAND OCTOBER. 12. 1798. *D.* 38 mm. [By T. Wyon Sr.] *BHM* 456; *MH* 1919, 543	AR AE WM	55 15 10	90 30 20
897	**British Victories 1798** *Obv.* Bust l., armoured and draped. GEORGIUS III. D:G. M. BR. FR. ET H. REX. *Rev.* Britannia seated, r., amongst arms and trophies, holds up a figure of Victory. MARI VICTRIX TERRAQUE INVICTA. *Ex.* AVITUM TRANSCENDIT HONOREM MDCCXCVIII. *D.* 48 mm. By C. H. Küchler. *BHM* 458; *MH* 1919, 544; *Pollard* 16	AR AE	90 20	170 45

This and other Küchler medals were restruck during the nineteenth century; those of George III were struck from more than one obverse die. See *Pollard* pp. 291–2, 314–16.

898	**Minorcan Magistrates 1798** *Obv.* Head r., laureate. GEORGIVS. III. REX. *Rev.* Justice standing, facing; beyond, fort overlooking sea with ship. SALUS POPULI *Ex.* 15. NOV. 1798 *D.* 51 mm. By J. Milton. *BHM* 461; *Stainton* 18	AE	60	110

The date is missing from some examples. A note in the manuscript catalogue of Sarah Banks (whose collection was bequeathed to the British Museum in the early nineteenth century) suggests that this medal was awarded by the Magistrates in Minorca, which had been captured by the British on 15 November 1798, but was given up at the Peace of Amiens in 1802.

899	**Loyal Birmingham Light Horse Volunteers 1798** *Obv.* Female seated, her arm upon a plaque inscribed LBLHV BLA, presents Cupid with an olive-branch. DUCIT AMOR PATRIÆ *Ex.* INSTITUTED JUNE 10. 1797 *Rev.* Crowned plinth, inscribed STRUCK TO COMMEMORATE THE PRESENTATION OF COLOURS TO THE BIRMINGHAM LOYAL ASSOCIATIONS JUNE 4. 1798. *D.* 41 mm. By J. S. Jorden. *BHM* 459	AR AE WM	40 12 8	75 20 15
900	**Worlingworth (Suffolk) Volunteers 1798** *Obv.* An infantryman standing, facing; beyond, castle keep. *Rev.* A heart and palms and inscription WORLINGWORTH VOLUNTEERS within a crowned garter, inscribed FOR OUR KING AND OUR COUNTRY, in the centre. Around, a broad wreath. Below, IOHN HENNIKER MAJOR COMMᵀ *D.* 38 mm. By J. G. Hancock. *EPM* 1892, 234; *Tancred* 382	AV AR	350 55	500 85

John Henniker-Major, 2nd Baron Henniker (1752–1821), politician. One of a few struck medals of local volunteer regiments; some have a recipient's name on the edge. *See* Nos. 943–5.

901A[*]	**Matthew Boulton, Medallic Scale 1798** *Obv.* Bust r., draped. MATT. BOULTON ESQᴿ F.R.S.L. & ED. P.R.I.M.S.A. (incuse). *Rev.* In the centre, head of Science, radiate; around, striking specifications for coin and medal production, in concentric circles: M: BOULTON ERIGEA A SOHO ANGL: 1788 UNE MACH: A VAPEUR PR: FRAP: MONN: (incuse) (400)/1798. IL ER: UNE BIEN SUPERIEURE A 8. BALANCIERS NOUVEAUX. (480)/CES CERC: & CHIF: MARQ: LE DIAM: & NO: DE PIECES FRAP: P: MIN: (560)/P: 8 ENFANS SANS FATIG: DU PL: PET: OU PL: GR: VOLUME. (640)/OU DE 8. DIFF: GRAND: ENSEMBLE. ON PEUT (720)/(800) AUGM: L'EFF: AU DEG: NECESS. (920) *D.* 43 mm. (By R. Dumarest?) *Pollard* 27. See **Plate 25**	AE WM	45 15	85 30
901B	*Obv.* Bust as No. 901*A.* MATT. BOULTON ESQ F.R.S.L. & ED. F.R.I. & A.S. (incuse). *Rev.* Similar to No. 901*A.* *D.* 41 mm. (By R. Dumarest?) *BHM* 462; *Eidlitz* 1928, 1.	AE WM	45 15	85 30

Matthew Boulton (1728–1809), industrialist, engineer and inventor. These medals record the methods he employed for coin and medal production at his Soho Manufactory, Birmingham. Each numbered circle on the reverse indicates how many coins of that diameter could be struck in one minute by eight of Boulton's presses.

902	**Joseph Munden 1799** *Obv.* Bust r., draped. JOSEPH SHEPPARD MUNDEN *Rev.* ENGLISH COMEDIAN EXPOSER OF FOLLY AND DISPELLOR OF SPLEEN AGED 40 1799, within a wreath decorated with theatrical masks. TO CHEER THE SINKING HEART AND CREATE A MORAL LIFE IS ALL THAT PHILOSOPHY CAN TEACH THE MIND + *D.* 53 mm. By J. G. Hancock. *BHM* 469; *Svarstad* 170	AR AE	50 15	90 25

Joseph Munden (1758–1832), actor.

903	**Siege and Capture of Seringapatam 1799** *Obv.* Lion, r., subduing a tiger (the emblem of Tippoo Sultan's government). Beyond, a banner with the Union badge and an Arabic inscription [= the lion of God is the conqueror]. *Ex.* IV. MAY. MDCCXCIX *Rev.* Fortress of Seringapatam under attack. *Ex.* Persian inscription [= Seringapatam God bestowed 28th day of the month Thilkeïda, 1213, of the Hegira]. *D. a* 48 mm.; *b* 45 mm. By C. H. Küchler. *Pollard* 20; *Gordon* 25; *Payne* 65–7	aAV AR AE WM bAV AR	900 120 60 35 800 80	1400 200 110 65 1100 150

Type *a* was struck at Matthew Boulton's Soho Manufactory, Birmingham and is signed C.H.K.; *see* No. 845. Type *b* is an inferior contemporary copy made at the Calcutta Mint and erroneously signed C.ℵ.H; bronze and white metal medals of this type were not distributed. The medal was granted by the Hon. East India Co. and given from 1808 to European and native troops of the Bengal Presidency engaged in the siege: gold (generals and senior officers), gilt silver (field officers), silver (captains), bronze (native commissioned and European non-commissioned officers) and white metal (privates).

PLATE 25

873

876

881

888

885

889

890

901A

PLATE 26

908

919

923

958

929

925

959

			£	£

904 Capture of Seringapatam 1799

Obv. Head l. MARQ⁵ WELLESLEY GOV͞ᴿ AND CAPTᴺ GEN͞ᴸ OF INDIA   *Rev.* Two British soldiers:
one holding a standard, the other attacking a native. *Ex.* SERINGAPATAM MAY IVᵀᴴ
MDCCLXXXXIX   *D.* 41 mm. By G. Mills/N. G. A. Brenet. *BHM* 478

	AR	70	130
	AE	30	55

Struck *c.*1820 by J. Mudie, but not included in his medallic series of British Victories (*See* No. 1136). Richard Colley, Marquis Wellesley (1760–1842), sent to India as governor-general; elder brother of Arthur, Duke of Wellington.

905 Siege of Acre 1799

Obv. Bust l., uniformed. SIR WILLIAM SIDNEY SMITH K.S. OF SWEDEN   *Rev.* Youth standing
on the sea-shore displays a naval shield; beyond, a palm and distant view of Acre. *Ex.*
BONAPARTE REPULSED AND SIEGE OF ACRE RAISED 20 MAY 1799. *D.* 49 mm. By J. G. Hancock.
BHM 473; *MH* 1919, 546

	AR	80	150
	AE	25	55

Sir William Sidney Smith (1764–1840), admiral. Napoleon Bonaparte (1769–1821), French Emperor.

906 ——

Obv. Bust l., uniformed. ADMIRAL SIR S SMITH   *Rev.* Lion, within a rocky pass, protects
camel from menacing tiger. *Ex.* ACRE DEFENDED. BUONAPARTE REPULSED SYRIA SAVED. XXᵀᴴ
MAY MDCCLXXXXIX   *D.* 41 mm. By G. Mills/N. G. A. Brenet. *BHM* 476; *MH* 1919, 545;
Mudie 7

	AR	35	65
	AE	14	22
	WM	6	10

Struck in 1820, from Mudie's series commemorating British victories. *See* No. 1136.

907 ——

Obv. Bust three-quarters r., uniformed. Sᴿ W. SYDNEY SMITH CAPTAIN OF THE TIGRE OF 74
GUNS. *Rev.* British ships in the bay of Acre. *Ex.* REPULSED BUONAPARTE IN 11 ATTACKS, MADE
BY HIM, ON ACRE 1799   *D.* 38 mm. [By T. Wyon Sr.] *BHM* 474; *MH* 1919, 547

	AR	60	110
	AE	20	35
	WM	12	22

908* Restoration of Ferdinand IV 1799

Obv. Bust r., armoured and draped. FERDIN. IV D: G. SICILIAR. ET HIE. REX. *Rev.* Ship entering
the bay of Naples lined by people; above, Fame bearing a medallion of Nelson, inscribed
HOR. NELSON DUCA BRONTI   *Ex.* PER MEZZO DELLA DIVINA PROVVIDENZA DELLE DI LUI VIRTU
DELLA FEDE & ENERGIA DEL SUO POPOLO DEL VALORE DE' SUOI ALLEATI ED IN PARTICOLARE
GL'INGLESI GLORIOSTE RISTABILITO SUL TRONO. LI 10. IUGLIO. 1799. *D.* 48 mm. By
C. H. Küchler. *BHM* 479; *MH* 1919, 489; *Pollard* 18. See **Plate 26**

	AR	150	280
	AE	35	75

Ferdinand IV, king of Naples 1759–1806 and 1815–25; conferred the title of Duke of Bronte on Nelson in recognition of his services in assisting in the restoration of the Neapolitan royal family. *See* No. 845; *see also* A. Wedgewood, *Matthew Boulton's Medal on the Reconquest of Naples in 1799*, Birmingham, 1926.

909 Death of Earl Howe 1799

Obv. Bust l., uniformed. EARL HOWE ADMIRAL OF THE FLEET. MDCCXCIX   *Rev.* Military arms
and trophies around a rostral column, its base inscribed MEMORA͞ᴱ VICTORY JUNE 1ˢᵀ
MDCCXCIV   *Ex.* FRENCH FLEET DEFEATᴰ VII SHIPS TAKEN   *D.* 38 mm. [By T. Wyon Sr.] *BHM*
468; *MH* 1919, 420

	AR	45	85
	AE	12	22
	WM	8	15

910 Capture of Helder Point 1799

Obv. Bust facing, uniformed, head l. SIR RALPH ABERCROMBIE. K.B. LIEUTENANT GENERAL.
Rev. Column on rocks decorated with a crown and flags; sea and peninsula, beyond. PATRIÆ
INFELICI FIDELIS. *Ex.* LANDED IN HOLLAND. & TOOK HELDER POINT AUGᵀ 27 1799. *D.* 40 mm.
[By T. Halliday] *BHM* 477; *EPM* 1887, 247

	AR	55	100
	AE	20	38
	WM	12	22

The obverse occurs coupled with the reverse of No. 930. Sir Ralph Abercromby (1734–1801), general.

911 Glasgow University, Black Medal 1799

Obv. Bust l., draped. JOSEPHUS BLACK MDCCXXIII. MDCCXCIX   *Rev.* As No. 806. *D.* 70 mm.
By N. Macphail. *BHM* 466; *Storer* 383

	AR	40	75
	AE	12	25

Struck *c.*1870. Joseph Black (1728–99), chemist. His birth year is incorrectly stated. *See* No. 806.

912 William Pitt 1799

Obv. Bust l., draped. WILLIAM PITT APPOINTED FIRST LORD OF THE TREASURY AND
CHANCELLOR OF THE EXCHEQUER DEC: 1783   *Rev.* WITH FORTITUDE WISDOM AND INTEGRITY HE
SERVES A PROSPEROUS NATION AND A VIRTUOUS KING / 1799 AGED 40, within a wreath. *D.* 53 mm.
By J. G. Hancock. *BHM* 470

	AR	60	110
	AE	12	25

William Pitt (1759–1806), statesman; second son of William Pitt, 1st Earl of Chatham.

913 Earl Spencer, First Lord of the Admiralty 1799

Obv. Bust l., uniformed. EARL SPENCER FIRST LORD OF THE ADMIRALTY APPOINTED MAR. 2.
1795   *Rev.* Fame standing, r., beside an anchor and rudder. DECORI DECUS ADDIT AVITO. *Ex.*
UNDER WISE COUNSELS THE BRITISH NAVY TRIUMPHS. MDCCXCIX   *D.* 38 mm. By T. Wyon Sr.
BHM 471; *MH* 1919, 551

	AR	45	85
	AE	12	25
	WM	8	15

George John Spencer, 2nd Earl Spencer (1758–1834), politician; naval administrator.

			£	£

914   Masonic School, Dublin 1799
Obv. Female seated, upon a large cross and anchor, embraces three infants. *Rev.* Square and
compass, enclosing a triangle inscribed G, suspending a double equilateral triangle; above,
Eye of Providence. *D.* 52 mm. by 63 mm. Oval. By W. Mossop [after E. Smyth]. *Frazer*
1887/453; *Shackles* 93; *Forrer* IV/167
Possibly used as a prize by the school which was founded in 1790.

    AE   35   60

915   Charles James Fox 1800
Obv. Bust three-quarters r., draped. CHARLES JAMES FOX BORN JANUARY 13 1749 *Rev.* WITH
LEARNING ELOQUENCE AND ZEAL HE MAINTAINS THE RIGHTS OF A FREE AND LOYAL PEOPLE 1800
within a wreath. *D.* 53 mm. By J. G. Hancock. *BHM* 488; *EPM* 1891, 98/7

    AE   12   25
    WM   8   15

916   George III, Preserved from Assassination 1800
Obv. Bust l., armoured and draped. GEORGIUS III. D: G. MAGN. BRIT. FR. ET. HIB. REX. *Rev.* A
burning altar, inscribed D.O.M.; above, Eye of Providence. PERSPICIT ET PROTEGIT. *Ex.* A
SICARIO SERVATUS MAI. XV. MDCCC. *D.* 48 mm. By C. H. Küchler. *BHM* 483; *Pollard* 23i
Struck with a number of different obverse dies (*see* No. 897) and from one other reverse die. The attempted assassination of
the King took place at Drury Lane Theatre, where he was shot at by a madman as he entered his box. The King is reported
to have shown unconcern and to have 'slept as quietly as usual during the interval'.

    AR   90 170
    AE   20   45

917   Union of Great Britain and Ireland, Act Passed 1800
Obv. Lion reclining on an anchor. GREAT BRITAIN AND IRELAND UNITED MDCCC; above, an
open book inscribed ONE LAW Around, shamrock and oak. *Rev.* Britannia and Hibernia
stand before a pyramid. FRIENDSHIP UNION AND PEACE *Ex.* 1800 *D.* 38 mm. By J. G.
Hancock. *BHM* 494; *Frazer* 1887/316

    AR   35   65
    AE   12   25
    WM   4   9

918   Lord Nelson, Return to England 1800
Obv. Bust l., uniformed. ADMIRAL LORD NELSON *Rev.* Britannia standing on the shore
awaits an approaching ship; an altar, r., inscribed AUG. 1 1798, and a Union shield. HAIL!
VIRTUOUS HERO. THY VICTORIES WE ACKNOWLEDGE AND THY GOD. *Ex.* RETURNED TO ENGLAND
NOV 5 1800 *D.* 38 mm. By T. Halliday. *BHM* 490; *MH* 1919, 490

    AR   55 100
    AE   15   30
    WM   10   20

919*   Earl St. Vincent's Reward 1800
Obv. Bust l., uniformed, within a wreath. EARL ST VINCENT'S TESTIMONY OF APPROBATION.
1800 *Rev.* Naval officer and bluejacket, standing against a backdrop of the Union flag,
shaking hands; above, a crown. LOYAL AND TRUE Wreath border. *D.* 47 mm. By C. H.
Küchler [after J. Flaxman] *BHM* 489; *MH* 1919, 456; *Pollard* 19; *Payne* 298. See **Plate 26**
Given to those who had served him on his ships, *Victory* and *Ville de Paris.*

    AV 1600 2800
    AR 120 220
    AE   65 120

920   Samuel Tyssen 1800
Obv. Bust l. SAMUEL. TYSSEN. ARM. A. S. S. *Rev.* DE NARBOROUGH HALL IN AGRO NORFOLCIENSI
EFFIGIAVIT AMICA MANUS JOAN. MILTON MDCCC, within a wreath. *D.* 41 mm. By J. Milton.
BHM 491; *Stainton* 21
Samuel Tyssen (1750?–1800), numismatist; his large collection of coins was dispersed by Sotheby's in 1802.

    AR   50   90
    AE   20   35
    WM   10   18

921   Farming Society of Ireland 1800
Obv. Farm animals grazing. QUÆ CURA BOUM QUI CULTUS HABENDO SIT PECORI *Ex.* FARMING
SOCIETY OF IRELAND INSTITUTED MDCCC *Rev.* Farm implements; space around (for
recipient's name). STADIUM QUIBUS ARVA TUERI *D.* 51 mm. By W. Mossop. *Frazer*
1887/455
Awarded in silver. A large number of agricultural societies in Ireland issued prize medals during the nineteenth century,
such as those of Cork, Navan, Newry, N. Dublin & Fingal, Wexford and Waterford.

    AR   35   60
    AE   8   15

922   George III 1800
Obv. Bust r., laureate. GEORGIUS. III. DE. GR. MAG. BRITAN. FRAN. ET. HIB. REX. *Rev.* A
pumping station beside a waterway on which is a barge; an agricultural and industrial
landscape. *Ex.* MDCCC *D.* 41 mm. By G. V. Bauert. *BHM* 495; *Parkes Weber* 9
This may refer to Britain's industrial development at the beginning of a new century. The styling of the King's title on this
and No. 923 is less usual.

    AR   45   85
    AE   20   35

923*   George III c.1800
Obv. Bust r., laureate, armoured and draped. GEORGIUS. III. DE. GR. MAG. BRITAN. FRAN. ET.
HIB. REX. *Rev.* Sun, radiate. DIFFUSO LUMINE NITET *D.* 74 mm. By J. Colibert. *BHM* 2. See
Plate 26
The occasion for this medal is unclear; the reverse (the diffusion of light) may allude to the beginning of a new century.
Another reverse occurs with just the inscription: WHO REIGNS IN THE HEARTS OF HIS PEOPLE MDCCLXXXXIX.

    AR 300 650
    AE   80 150

924   Worshipful Company of Cooks c.1800
Obv. Arms of the Company: shield supported by a horse and stag, each pierced with an
arrow. Below, motto on ribbon, VULNERATI NON VICTI 1482 *Rev.* Plain (for member's name
and date). *D.* 44 mm. (By?) *Garnett pl.* 1, 4
See No. 738.

    AR   35   50

925*   **Worshipful Company of Cutlers** *c*.1800

      Obv. Arms of the Company, within wreath: elephant, l., its draped bodice decorated with crossed swords. *Rev.* Plain (for member's name and date). Integral suspension loop. *D.* 43 mm. by 63 mm. Oval. (By?) *Garnett pl.* 2, 2. See **Plate 26**

      <small>*See* No. 738.</small>

		£	£
	AR	55	75

926   **Union of Great Britain and Ireland 1801**

      Obv. Bust r., laureate, armoured and draped. GEORGIUS III. D.G BRITANNIARUM REX. F.D NATUS JUNII IV MDCCXXXVIII   *Rev.* Britannia seated upon an island rock, with rudder and the revised British shield; before her, a cherub displays an open book, inscribed XIX and illustrating the Irish harp. NULLA DIES PACEM NEC FOEDERA RUMPET   *D.* 49 mm. By J. G. Hancock. *BHM* 527

      <small>The Act of Union became law on 1 January 1801.</small>

	AR	70	130
	AE	20	35
	WM	10	18

927   ——

      Obv. Bust similar to No. 897. GEORGIUS III. D: G. BRITANNIARUM REX. FIDEI. DEF. &c   *Rev.* Britannia and Hibernia stand facing each other, their hands clasped. JUNGUNTUR OPES FIRMATUR IMPERIUM. *Ex.* 1. JAN MDCCCI. *D.* 48 mm. By C. H. Küchler. *BHM* 524; *Pollard* 24

      <small>Struck from at least two obverse dies. *See* No. 897.</small>

	AR	80	150
	AE	20	35

928   **George III, Recovery from Illness 1801**

      Obv. Bust r., draped. GEORGIUS III. D: G. BRITANNIARUM REX. FIDEI DEF. *Rev.* Cherub, illuminating the sky with a torch, kneels against an altar, inscribed GISBORN AND REYNOLDS, supporting an imperial crown; a staff of Aesculapius rests against the altar. THOU WILT PROLONG THE KINGS LIFE   *Ex.* RECOVERED FROM ILLNESS MARCH. 1801   *D.* 38 mm. By J. G. Hancock. *BHM* 503; *Storer* 6190

      <small>Thomas Gisborne (d.1806), physician in ordinary to the King. Henry Revell Reynolds (1745–1811), physician-extraordinary; attended the King in 1788 and again in 1801.</small>

	AR	45	85
	AE	12	25
	WM	8	15

929*   **English Army in Egypt 1801**

      Obv. Bust facing, uniformed. LIEUT: GENL: SIR R: ABERCROMBY   *Rev.* Horse standing, r.; beyond, three pyramids. ARRIVAL OF THE ENGLISH ARMY IN EGYPT   *Ex.* 8 MARCH 1801   *D.* 41 mm. By T. Webb. *BHM* 504; *Bramsen* 141; *Mudie* 8. See **Plate 26**

      <small>Struck in 1820, from Mudie's series commemorating British victories. *See* No. 1136.</small>

	AR	30	55
	AE	9	15
	WM	3	7

930   **Death of Sir Ralph Abercromby 1801**

      Obv. Bust l., wearing a cocked hat and uniformed; a quizzing glass held to his right eye. SIR RALPH ABERCROMBIE. K.B. *Rev.* Britannia lying mournfully before a tomb, inscribed WOUNDED MAR. 21. DIED MAR 28 1801; pyramids beyond. *Ex.* FRENCH DEFEATED MAR. 21. 1801   *D.* 40 mm. By T. Halliday. *BHM* 506; *Bramsen* 143

      <small>The reverse occurs coupled with the obverse of No. 910.</small>

	AR	45	85
	AE	15	30
	WM	8	15

931   **Lord Keith: Death of Abercromby 1801**

      Obv. Bust l., uniformed. LORD KEITH K.B. VICE ADMIRAL OF THE RED. *Rev.* Scottish soldier contemplates an urn decorated with a medallion of Abercromby; behind, an array of military trophies. SIR RALPH ABERCROMBY WOUNDED MARCH 21 DIED MARCH 28 1801. *D.* 49 mm. By J. G. Hancock. *BHM* 507; *MH* 1919, 552

      <small>George Elphinstone, Viscount Keith (1746–1823), admiral.</small>

	AR	80	150
	AE	20	45

932   **London Highland Society 1801**

      Obv. Head r. ABERCROMBIUS DUX IN EGYPTO CECIDIT VICTOR 28 MAR 1801   *Rev.* Highlander, sword raised, seizes a French standard from a resisting soldier. NA FIR A CHOISIN BUAIDH SAN EPHAIT. [= These are the heroes who won victory in Egypt] 21 MAR 1801   *Edge.* (running script, incuse) O'N CHOUMUN CHAELEACH D'ON FHREICEADAN DUBH NA XLII RT. [= From the London Highland Society to the Black Watch, or 42nd Regiment]   *D.* 49 mm. By G. F. Pidgeon, *rev.* after B. West. *BHM* 512; *Gordon* 29

      <small>Medals were given in silver and bronze for the regiment's action at Alexandria against Bonaparte's Invincible Legion. Examples also occur with the edge inscription in English, and without any lettering.</small>

	AV	—	—
	AR	70	130
	AE	30	55

933   **Battle of Copenhagen 1801**

      Obv. Justice standing, r., beside a column against which lean two portrait medallions of H. PARKER and L. NELSON; beyond, an open sea with a ship on the horizon. MARITIME JUSTICE AND BRITISH VALOR. *Rev.* View of a naval engagement. *Ex.* PASSED. THE. SOUND. AND DEFEATED. Y. DANISH FLEET. MAR. 30   *D.* 38 mm. (By T. Halliday?) *BHM* 510; *MH* 1919, 491

      <small>The illustration on the reverse is of the fleet entering Helsingör. Sir Hyde Parker (1739–1807), admiral.</small>

	AR	55	100
	AE	15	30
	WM	10	20

934   **Egypt Delivered 1801**

      Obv. Bust three-quarters l., uniformed. MAJOR GEN. LORD HUTCHINSON   *Rev.* Exchanging a treaty, Hutchinson stands facing the Bey of Egypt, who holds the reins of a rearing horse; a

	AR	30	55
	AE	9	15

pyramid beyond. EGYPT DELIVERED *Ex.* SEPT 11 MDCCCI *D.* 41 mm. By T. Webb/A. Dupré. *BHM* 509; *Bramsen* 2161; *Mudie* 9	WM	3	7

John Hely Hutchinson, Baron Hutchinson (1757–1832), soldier. Struck in 1820, from Mudie's series commemorating British victories. *See* No. 1136.

935   Preliminaries for the Treaty of Amiens 1801

Obv. Oval shield of the Union flag mounted on two crossed swords. PRELIMINARIES OF PEACE	AR	30	55
BETWEEN GREAT-BRITAIN AND FRANCE SIGNED OCTOBER 1ᶠᵗ 1801. *Rev.* Peace standing, facing,	AE	12	22
empties her cornucopia on a quay; beyond, ships at sea. THEY SHALL PROSPER THAT LOVE	WM	4	9
THEE *D.* 38 mm. (By?) *BHM* 516; *Bramsen* 162			

936   Brokers' Pass *c.*1801

Obv. Royal arms (as introduced after the Union) and motto DIEU ET MON DROIT. *Rev.* Arms	AR	25	40
and motto of the City of London; below, a plaque (blank, for holder's name). *Ex.* Double	AE	12	15
cornucopiae. *D.* 41 mm. By J. Milton. *Caldecott* 3; *Stainton* 49			

Used up to *c.*1830; on some examples the medallist's signature is indistinct. Examples in bronze are specimen strikings. *See* No. 426.

937   Prince of Wales and Duke of Clarence:
Grand Master and President of the Freemasons 1802

Obv. Busts r., conjoined and draped; on either side, G and TH, radiate. GEO : A : F : P : WALL : G :	AR	55	90
M GULI : H : D : CLARENT : G : P. *Rev.* Prince's plumes and Freemason's arms divide two oval	AE	15	28
vignettes containing masonic symbols; above, Fame. IN. PRINCIPIO. ERAT. SERMO. ET. SERMO.	WM	10	18
ILLE. ERAT. APUD. DEUM. ERATQUE. ILLE. SERMO. DEUS : ET. LUX. ISTA. IN. TENEBRIS. LUCIT. SED.			
TENEBRÆ. EAM. NON. COMPREHENDERUNT *Ex.* W. HOLLINS. P.M.L.N. 38. MDCCCII *D.*			
42 mm. By J. G. Hancock. *BHM* 530; *Shackles* 7			

William Henry, Duke of Clarence (1765–1837), William IV 1830–37; 3rd son of George III.

938   Duke of Bedford 1802

Obv. Bust r., draped. FRANCIS DUKE OF BEDFORD PRESIDENT 1802 *Rev.* Britannia seated, r.,	AR	55	90
awards prizes to two farmers. *Ex.* BATH AND WEST OF ENGLAND SOCIETY. A wreath border. *D.*	AE	20	35
59 mm. By J. Milton. *BHM* 547; *Stainton* 25	WM	10	18

Francis Russell, 5th Duke of Bedford (1765–1802), agriculturalist.

939   Duke of Kent, Governor of Gibraltar 1802

Obv. Bust l., uniformed. EDWARD DUKE OF KENT K.G. & K.S.P. GOVERNOR OF GIBRALTAR *Rev.*	AR	55	110
View of Gibraltar. TAKEN BY SIR GEORGE ROOKE 1704 *Ex.* NORTH VIEW OF GIBRALTAR ROCK	AE	30	55
1802 *D.* 38 mm. (By?) *BHM* 531; *MH* 1919, 133	WM	15	30

Edward Augustus, Duke of Kent and Strathearn (1767–1820), 4th son of George III. George Rooke (1650–1709), naval commander.

940   Peace of Amiens 1802

Obv. Victory crowning George III, in Roman dress, with a wreath. REGNO PACEM	AR	45	80
OBTULIT *Ex.* SUPER PACE RATA DIE 27 MARTII *Rev.* Façade of St. Paul's Cathedral. DEO	AE	15	30
GLORIAM REFERT *Ex.* PAX CELEBRATA DIE I JUNII MDCCCII *D.* 49 mm. By J. G. Hancock.	WM	8	15
BHM 541; *Bramsen* 209; *Taylor* 39a			

More than twenty medals commemorate the Treaty, by which England surrendered all her conquests except Ceylon and Trinidad, which Holland and Spain were compelled to cede.

941   ——

Obv. Similar to No. 897. *Rev.* Peace extinguishes a pile of arms; beyond, an open sea.	AR	90	170
TRIUMPHIS POTIOR *Ex.* PAX UBIQUE MDCCCII *D.* 48 mm. By C. H. Küchler. *BHM* 535;	AE	20	45
Pollard 25			

Struck from more than one obverse die. *See* No. 897.

942   ——

Obv. Bust l., uniformed. MARQUIS CORNWALLIS BRITISH PLENIPOTENTIARY AT AMIENS. *Rev.*	AR	45	85
Britannia seated beside a cherub, holds a tablet inscribed AD[dington] H[awksbury]	AE	15	25
COR[nwallis] BUO[naparte]. A medallion of George III on her lap. POST NUBILA	WM	8	15
PHOEBUS *Ex.* DEFINITIVE TREATY CONCLUDED 1802. *D.* 38 mm. By J. G. Hancock. *BHM*			
539; *Bramsen* 204			

Struck with two other reverse dies, varying in the inscription on the exergue. Henry Addington, 1st Viscount Sidmouth (1757–1844), politician. Robert Banks Jenkinson, 2nd Earl of Liverpool, (1770–1828), statesman; Master of the Mint.

943   Loyal Birmingham Light Horse Volunteers 1802

Obv. Peace presents a medal to a soldier in Roman dress. FOR TRUE PATRIOTISM *Ex.* PEACE	AR	40	75
MDCCCII *Rev.* PRESENTED TO (space, for recipient's name) BY THE TOWN OF BIRMINGHAM	AE	15	30
MAY XXVIII MDCCCII *D.* 48 mm. [By J. G. Hancock] *Payne* 213			

Awarded in silver and bronze. *See* No. 900.

		£	£

944   **Manchester and Salford Royal Light Horse Volunteers 1802**

Obv. Bust of George III, laureate, r.; G. R. in field. Chain border of hearts and hands. *Rev.* A TESTIMONY OF GRATITUDE FROM HIS FELLOW TOWNSMEN FOR SPIRITED AND PATRIOTIC SERVICES, 1802 (space, for recipient's name). MANCHESTER & SALFORD VOLUNTEERS *D.* 36 mm. (By?) *Payne* 217; *Tancred* 374

AV	280	380
AR	55	85
AE	12	25
WM	8	15

Awarded to officers in gold. *See* No. 900.

945   **Nottinghamshire Yeomanry 1802**

Obv. Head r., laureate. GEORGIVS. III. REX. MDCCCII *Rev.* A tree stump, inscribed FOI LOI ROI, from which grows a flourishing oak. NOTTS. YEOMANRY. GREEN DALE OAK *D.* 36 mm. By C. H. Küchler. *Pollard* 26; *Payne* 218; *Tancred* 377

AV	350	450
AR	55	90

Occurs with a suspension loop; awarded in gold to officers, and in silver to non-commissioned officers and privates. *See* No. 900.

946   **Henry Addington 1803**

Obv. Bust r., draped. HENRY ADDINGTON CHANCELLOR OF THE EXCHEQUER & FIRST LORD OF THE TREASURY *Rev.* Female holding a scroll, inscribed STATE OF THE NATION, kneels before Britannia, Justice and Time; beyond, Westminster Abbey. WHO CAN WITHOLD APPLAUSE *Ex.* MDCCCIII. *D.* 49 mm. By J. G. Hancock. *BHM* 550; *EPM* 1887, 251

AR	80	150
AE	25	50

947   **Robert Banks 1803**

Obv. Bust l., draped. ROBERT BANKS LORD HAWKESBURY SECRETARY OF STATE *Rev.* Britannia seated, l., despatches Mercury with a scroll across an open sea. INTEGRITY AIDS DISPATCH *Ex.* MDCCCIII *D.* 49 mm. By J. G. Hancock. *BHM* 548; *Hocking* 236/15

AR	80	150
AE	25	50

948   **Breaking of the Treaty of Amiens 1803**

Obv. Leopard destroys a scroll. LE TRAITÉ D'AMIENS ROMPU PAR L'ANGLETERRE EN MAI DE L'AN 1803 *Rev.* Equestrian figure of Victory, r., advancing. L'HANOVRE OCCUPÉ PAR L'ARMÉE FRANÇAISE EN JUIN DE L'AN 1803 *Ex.* FRAPPÉE AVEC L'ARGENT DES MINES D'HANOVRE L'AN 4 DE BONAPARTE *D.* 41 mm. By R. V. Jeuffroy. *Parkes Weber* 113; *Bramsen* 271

AR	45	85
AE	12	20

949   **Barber Beaumont, Volunteer Rifle Corps 1803**

Obv. Head l. BARBER BEAUMONT *Rev.* THE DUKE OF CUMBERLAND'S SHARP SHOOTERS. THE FIRST VOLUNTEER RIFLE CORPS IN GREAT BRITAIN WAS RAISED IN 1803 *D.* 41 mm. (By?) *BHM* 549; *EPM* 1887, 265

AE	15	25

John Thomas Barber Beaumont (1774–1841), founder of insurance offices, painter and author; responsible for raising the first volunteer rifle corps.

950   **National Edition of Shakespeare's Works 1803**

Obv. Shakespeare seated upon a rock, flanked by the Dramatic Muse and Genius of Painting. HE WAS A MAN TAKE HIM FOR ALL IN ALL I SHALL NOT LOOK UPON HIS LIKE AGAIN. *Rev.* THIS MEDAL REPRESENTING SHAKSPEARE BETWEEN THE DRAMATICK MUSE AND THE GENIUS OF PAINTING IS RESPECTFULLY PRESENTED TO THE PERSON WHOSE NAME IT BEARS IN GRATEFUL COMMEMORATION OF THE GENEROUS SUPPORT GIVEN BY THE SUBSCRIBERS TO THE GREAT NATIONAL EDITION OF THAT IMMORTAL POET BY I. I. & J. N. BOYDELL. AND G. & W. NICOL. 1803. Above, lyre and olive-branch, radiate. *D.* 48 mm. By C. H. Küchler [*obv.* after T. Banks] *BHM* 553; *Pollard* 28

AV	700	950
AR	30	55
AE	10	20

Subscribers' names are sometimes found on the edge. Another reverse enumerates Shakespeare's works. John Boydell (1719–1804), engraver and publisher. Josiah Boydell (1752–1817), painter and engraver; nephew of John. George and William Nicol were booksellers and publishers.

951   **Death of Joseph Priestley 1804**

Obv. Bust r., draped. JOSEPHUS PRIESTLEY. *Rev.* APR: VIII BRITTANNIÆ LITORA LINQUENS COLUMBIAM ADVENIT JUNII IV MDCCXCIV. NATUS 13 MART. 1733. MORT. 6. FEB. 1804., in the centre. MAGNUS CHRISTIANUS PHILOSOPHUS ★ *D.* 54 mm. By T. Phipson. *BHM* 565

AE	40	70
WM	12	25

Based on No. 857; three similar medals were struck on his death.

952   **Settlement of the British at Bombay; East India Company's Victory 1804**

Obv. Neptune reclining against a globe, l., holds the British ensign. SETTLEMENT OF THE BRITISH AT BOMBAY *Ex.* MDCLXII *Rev.* Neptune, radiate, seated upon a globe, holds the figure Victory. THE FRENCH FLEET REPULSED BY THE E.I. COMPY.ˢ XV. FEB. MDCCCIV *D.* 41 mm. By J. P. Droz/G. Mills. *BHM* 567; *MH* 1919, 555; *Mudie*

AR	35	65
AE	9	15
WM	3	7

Struck in 1820, from Mudie's series commemorating British victories. *See* No. 1136. The action of the East India Company's fleet against that of the French took place in the Straits of Malacca.

953   **William Betty 1804**

Obv. Bust r., draped. WILLIAM HENRY WEST BETTY. *Rev.* BRITISH TRAGEDIAN AGED 13 YEARS A.D 1804 within a wreath. *D.* 45 mm. By J. Westwood Jr. *BHM* 559; *EPM* 1888, 68/2; *Svarstad* 25

AE	20	35
WM	12	25

William Henry West Betty (1791–1874), Shakespearian actor known as the 'Young Roscius'. There are at least seven medals of Betty.

			£	£

954 ——

Obv. Bust of Betty r., draped. THE YOUNG ROSCIUS. *Rev.* Sword, trumpet, manuscript and goblet within a wreath. NOT YET MATURE YET MATCHLESS BORN SEPT^R 13TH 1791. Below, MDCCCIV D. 42 mm. By T. Webb. *BHM* 557–8; *EPM* 1888, 69/5–6; *Svarstad* 28–9
Struck from two obverse dies.

     AE   15   25
     WM   8   15

955 Horticultural Society of London, Foundation Medal 1804

Obv. A greenhouse in a garden setting. ALIENIS MENSIBUS ÆSTAS. *Rev.* God of gardens decked with flowers by Flora and being offered fruits by Pomona. Space around (for recipient's name). *Ex.* SOC. HORT. LOND. INST. 7. MART. 1804. D. 68 mm. By G. F. Pidgeon [after R. Batty]. *D & W* 155/422–3

     AV   —   —
     AR   45   70
     AE   12   20

Awarded from 1811 in gold and silver, and latterly in bronze, in recognition of services to the Society and for exhibits at meetings. The reverse of the medal was adapted for the seal of the Society, which was designated 'Royal' in 1861. They frequently used the medal to commemorate eminent members; *see* Nos. 1138, 1290, and 1580. Other horticultural societies who subsequently issued prizes include: Aylesbury, 1821; Cambridge, 1824; Berkshire, 1831; Guernsey, 1832, and Henley, 1833. See H. R. Fletcher, *The Story of the Royal Horticultural Society, 1804–1968*, London, 1969.

956 Death of Reverend James Wilkinson 1805

Obv. Bust l., in clerical robes. REV^D JAMES WILKINSON A M. BORN 5 AUG 1730 DIED 18 JAN 1805 *Rev.* Religion, standing, holds an open bible and scales. THE MEMORY OF THE JUST IS BLESSED PRO. 10. C.7.V. *Ex.* FAITH AND JUSTICE UNITED D. 49 mm. By J. Westwood Jr.

     AE   15   25

957 Battle of Trafalgar, Nelson Memorial 1805

Obv. Bust l. HOR. VICECOM. NELSON OB PATRIAM PVGNANDO MORT. OCT XXI. MDCCCV. *Rev.* Bellona advancing, r., across the sea towards galleys. IPSE BELLI FVLMEN. D. 53 mm. By T. Webb, [*rev.* after J. Flaxman] *BHM* 577; *MH* 1919, 507

     AR   90   170
     AE   25   60

More than twenty-five medals commemorate Nelson and the victory at Trafalgar.

958* ——

Obv. Seaman stands, mournfully, beside a tomb inscribed GALLANT NELSON DIED. IN THE HOUR OF VICTORY 21. OCT^R A D. 1805.; above, an obelisk decorated with a medallion of Nelson and military trophies. *Ex.* TRAFALGAR *Rev.* Britannia, grief-stricken, seated beside a pedestal inscribed BASTIA ABOVKIR COPENHAG; above, an urn covered with a veil which Neptune seated, r., reveals to expose the letters H N. Ships beyond. IN LIFE VICTORIOUS IN DEATH TRIUMPHANT *Ex.* MDCCCV D. 52 mm. By P. Wyon. *BHM* 579; *MH* 1919, 511; *Bramsen* 434. *See* **Plate 26**

     AR   110   190
     AE   40   70
     WM   15   30

The reverse was struck from more than one die.

959* ——

Obv. Small bust, l., draped, between palm and laurel branches; below, an oval shield within a ribbon inscribed TRIA. JUNCTA. IN. UNO, and motto. ADMIRAL LORD NELSON D. OF BRONTE ENGLAND EXPECTS EVERY MAN WILL DO HIS DUTY NATUS SEP. 29. 1758 HOSTE DEVICTO REQUIEVIT OCT. 21. 1805 *Rev.* Broadside view of ship. THE LORD IS A MAN OF WAR EXODUS C.15.V.3. VICTORY OFF TRAFALGAR OVER THE COMBINED FLEETS OF FRANCE & SPAIN OCT. 21. 1805 D. 51 mm. By T. Halliday. *BHM* 585; *MH* 1919, 498; *Gordon* 31. *See* **Plate 26**

     WM   160   290

This medal occurs in a circular brass frame with a suspension loop. It may have been sponsored by Alexander Davison. *See* No. 890.

960* ——

Obv. Bust l., uniformed. HORATIO VISCOUNT NELSON. K.B. DUKE OF BRONTE. & c. *Rev.* Panoramic view of the naval engagement. ENGLAND EXPECTS EVERY MAN WILL DO HIS DUTY *Ex.* TRAFALGAR OCT^R 21. 1805. *Edge.* TO THE HEROES OF TRAFALGAR FROM M. BOULTON (incuse). D. 48 mm. By C. H. Küchler [after C. Andras/R. Cleveley] *BHM* 584; *MH* 1919, 493; *Pollard* 30i; *Gordon* 30. *See* **Plate 27**

     AV   —   —
     AR   270   550
     AE   90   180
     WM   70   130

Boulton's private medal presented to captains and first-lieutenants in silver, and other ranks in pewter; examples occur with the names of the recipient and the ship engraved in the field, and set within a watch-style glass and framed. Examples in gold are probably special presentation pieces. It is unclear whether bronze medals were awarded; gilt examples also occur. This medal is sometimes found with a similar but unadopted portrait of Nelson. Restrikes were made during the nineteenth century, the edges of which are not always lettered. *See* No. 845. In 1966 Messrs J. Pinches made restrikes in gold and silver, hallmarked, and with slightly smaller diameters.

961* ——

Obv. Bust l., uniformed. NELSON ET BRONTI. VICTOR TRAFALGAR ET VICTIMA. PERIIT ET PERIIT. OCT. 21. 1805. *Rev.* Panoramic view of two fleets in battle formation; a wreath around. MEMORIÆ CONSECRAVIT. GUL. TURTON M.D. F.L.S. *Ex.* ESTO PERPETUA. D. 45 mm. By T. Wyon Sr. *BHM* 586; *MH* 1919, 496; *Storer* 3580. *See* **Plate 27**

     AR   160   320
     AE   80   150

William Turton (1735–1806), physician; sponsored this medal as a tribute to Nelson. Examples were presented to the authors of ten memorial poems which were published in 'Luctus Nelsoniani – Poems on the Death of Lord Nelson, in Latin and English and Dedicated by Command to His Royal Highness George Prince of Wales, 1807.' Restrikes in silver, sometimes hallmarked, were made in 1966 by Messrs J. Pinches.

		VF	EF
		£	£

962 ——
Obv. Bust three-quarters l., uniformed. ADM. LORD NELSON *Rev.* Bellona standing, r., on the prow of a galley. NILE 1 AUG 1798. COPENHAGEN 28 APR 1801. TRAFALGAR 21 OCT 1805 *D.* 41 mm. By T. Webb/J. P. Droz. *BHM* 595; *MH* 1919, 518; *Mudie* 6

		VF	EF
AR	65	120
AE	25	45
WM	9	20

Struck in 1820 by Mudie for his series commemorating British victories, but occurs less frequently than No. 963 in the set. *See* No. 1136.

963 ——
Obv. Bust l. ADM. VISC. NELSON K.B. D: OF BRONTE. *Rev.* As No. 962. *D.* 41 mm. By T. Webb/J. P. Droz. *BHM* 596; *MH* 1919, 520

	VF	EF
AR	55	100
AE	20	35
WM	7	15

Struck in 1820 by Mudie for his series commemorating British victories; *see* No. 1136. Although not included in Mudie's descriptive catalogue, this medal occurs more frequently than No. 962.

964 ——
Obv. Bust r., uniformed. HORATIVS NELSON *Rev.* Rostral column adorned with four prows, laurel wreaths and anchors; its base decorated with a figure of Victory. FAMAM QVI TERMINAT ASTRIS *Ex.* VINC. HISP. ET. GALL. CLASS. CECIDIT D. XXI OCT. MDCCCV *D.* 40 mm. By A. Abramson. *BHM* 574; *MH* 1919, 497

	VF	EF
AR	70	130
AE	35	60
WM	20	35

965 ——
Obv. Bust l., uniformed. H. VICECOM. NELSON. *Rev.* H. VICECOM. NELSON OB PATRIAM PVGNANDO MORT. OCT. XXI. MDCCCV. within a wreath. 39 mm. (By?) *BHM* 581; *MH* 1919, 505

	VF	EF
AR	50	90
AE	20	35
WM	8	15

Another reverse has the figure of Victory, standing upon a galley, displaying a medallion of Nelson.

966 ——
Obv. Bust l., uniformed. ADM. VISC. NELSON K.B. D. OF BRONTE. *Rev.* NILE 1. AUG.ᵗ 1798. COPENHAGEN 1. APRIL 1801. TRAFALGAR 21. OCT. 1805. *D.* 24 mm. (By?) *BHM* 597; *MH* 1919, 513

	VF	EF
a AE	5	8
b AE	—	55

Struck *c.*1820. Type *b* consists of six uniform medals portraying naval heroes: Earl Howe, 1794; Admiral Duncan, 1797; Earl St. Vincent, 1797; Sir Sydney Smith, 1799; Lord Nelson, 1805; and Lord Exmouth, 1816; each with reverses listing their respective victories. They are all gilt, and are sometimes found in a contemporary filigree brass box inscribed NAVAL VICTORIES on the lid.

967 ——
Obv. Bust l., uniformed, of Nelson. ENGLAND EXPECTS EVERY MAN WILL DO HIS DUTY. *Rev.* TRAFALGAR 27 ENG. DEFEATED 33 SP. & FR. & CAPTURED 19 OCT 21 1805 *Edge.* grained. *D.* 20 mm. (By?) *BHM* 591; *MH* 1919, 517

	VF	EF
a AR	12	20
WM	3	5
b AR	—	90
WM	—	25

Struck *c.*1810. Type *b* consists of four uniform medals, each with this obverse of Nelson, recording victories at Cape St. Vincent 1797; Nile 1798; Copenhagen 1801; and Trafalgar 1805. They are sometimes found in a contemporary silver box.

968 Battle of Trafalgar 1805
Obv. Bust three-quarters l., uniformed. ADMIRAL LORD COLLINGWOOD *Rev.* Panoramic view of two fleets in battle formation. HIS COUNTRY'S FUTURE HOPE *Ex.* TRAFALGAR VICTORY OCTOBER 21 1805 *D.* 38 mm. (By?) *BHM* 593; *MH* 558

	VF	EF
AR	70	130
AE	30	55
WM	15	28

Cuthbert Collingwood, Baron Collingwood (1750–1810), admiral; assumed command at Trafalgar after Nelson's death.

969 Miss Mudie 1805
Obv. Bust r., draped. MISS MUDIE THE THEATRICAL PHENOMENON AGED. 7. 1805 *Rev.* Theatrical mask, a serpent issuing from an eye, upon sword, torch, book (THE WILL) and wreath. THE PRIDE OF AGE THE ORNAMENT OF YOUTH. *D.* 39 mm. By T. Webb. *BHM* 572

	VF	EF
AE	20	35
WM	10	20

A. S. Mudie (1798–?), actress; her most celebrated role was in 1805 as Peggy in Garrick's *The Country Girl*.

970 Royal Visit to Weymouth 1805
Obv. Busts r., conjoined and draped. GEORGIUS III ET CHARLOTTE REX ET REGINA MDCCCV *Rev.* Crown within wreath. IN COMMEMORATION OF THE ROYAL VISIT Below, WEYMOUTH (incuse) on a scroll. *D.* 38 mm. (By?) *BHM* 569

	VF	EF
AE	15	25
WM	8	15

Some examples omit the word WEYMOUTH.

971 Sydney Smith, Promotion to Flag-Rank 1805
Obv. Bust r. GVLIELMVS SIDNEY SMITH. MDCCCV. *Rev.* COEUR DE LION. within a wreath. *D.* 53 mm. By T. Webb. *BHM* 573; *MH* 1919, 549

	VF	EF
AR	60	100
AE	15	25
WM	8	15

This portrait of Smith also occurs on a medal recording his Presidency of the Reunion of the Knights of the White Slaves in Africa, 1816.

972 Thomas Coram, Memorial 1805
Obv. Bust three-quarters l., of Coram, draped. .IN. MEMORY. OF. THE. FOUNDLING'S. FRIEND. 1805. *Rev.* FOUNDLING. HOSPITAL INSTITUTED. 17,ᵀᴴ OCTOBER. 1739. THOMAS. CORAM.

	VF	EF
AR	45	85
AE	15	28

FOUNDER. Above, three interlinked serpents. *D*. 39 mm. By J. Porter. *BHM* 571; *Storer*   £   £
5074; *EPM* 1890, 77
Thomas Coram (1668?–1751), philanthropist.

973   **George Cooke 1805**
Obv. Bust r. GEORGIUS COOKE. TRAGOEDUS COMOEDUSQUE ANGLICUS. *Rev.* VELUTI IN SPECULUM   *AR*   50   90
MDCCCV within a wreath. *D*. 54 mm. By T. Webb. *BHM* 570; *EPM* 1890, 76; *Svarstad* 45   *AE*   15   25
George Frederick Cooke (1756–1811), actor.

974   **Stockport Sunday School 1805**
Obv. Façade of building. STOCKPORT SUNDAY SCHOOL *Ex.* (Space for name)   *AR*   20   38
TRUSTEE *Rev.* ERECTED ANNO DOMINI 1805 BY VOLUNTARY SUBSCRIPTION FOR THE EDUCATION   *AE*   10   15
& RELIGIOUS INSTRUCTION OF THE CHILDREN OF THE LABOURING POOR, within a wreath. *D*.
51 mm. By B. R. Faulkner. *Taylor* 62a
Struck *c*.1820.

975   **Death of William Pitt 1806**
Obv. Bust l. GVLIELMO PITT R.P.Q.B. *Rev.* An island rock buffeted by heavy waves and   *AR*   40   75
lightning. PATRIAE COLVMEN DECVS. *Ex.* OB. A. MDCCCVI. *D*. 53 mm. By T. Webb. *BHM* 610   *AE*   12   22

976   ——
Obv. Bust l., draped. WILLIAM PITT HE WAS A MAN, TAKE HIM FOR ALL IN ALL. WE SHALL NOT   *AR*   45   80
LOOK UPON HIS LIKE AGAIN! *Rev.* Britannia weeping beside a tomb, inscribed IN MEMORY OF   *AE*   15   25
WILL^M PITT OB^T JANU[ary] 23 ÆTT 46. Above, 'OH MY COUNTRY' *Ex.* MDCCCVI *D*. 52 mm.   *WM*   8   15
By P. Wyon. *BHM* 617; *Hocking* 246/2

977   **Battle of Maida 1806**
Obv. Head l., laureate. GEORGIVS TERTIVS REX *Rev.* Britannia advancing, l., with raised   *AV*   —   —
shield and spear, is crowned by Victory hovering above; a triskeles in the field, behind.   *AR*   80   150
MAIDA IVL. IV MDCCCVI *D*. 36 mm. By G. F. Pidgeon. *BHM* 620; *Tancred* 69–70   *AE*   50   90
Awarded in gold to commanding officers. The action was fought in Calabria near Maida; the triskeles is the ancient symbol
of Sicily.

978   **British Attack on Buenos Aires Repulsed 1806**
Obv. Bust r., laureate, armoured and draped. LA. LEALTAD. DE. BUENOS-AIRES. A. SU. REI.   *AR*   90   150
CARLOS. IIII. *Rev.* Lion seated, in an open landscape near a river mouth, upholds the Spanish
flag; nearby lies a fallen British ensign. Above, the sun in partial eclipse. QUISO SER
VENCEDOR. YA ESTA VENCIDO. DIA XII DE AGOSTO DE M.DCCC.VI. *D*. 51 mm. By I. F. Arrabel.
MH 1928, 740
Charles IV (1748–88–1819) of Spain. Struck from two obverse dies; at least four other medals commemorate this action.

979   **Death of Charles James Fox 1806**
Obv. Bust r., draped. C.I. FOX OB. SEP. XIII MDCCCVI. *Rev.* Victory standing, facing, upon a   *AR*   45   80
globe marked with Britain. LIBERTATIS. HVMANITATISQVE VINDEX. *D*. 54 mm. By T. Webb.   *AE*   12   25
BHM 604; *EPM* 1891, 99/11
Struck from more than one obverse die.

980   **Royal Naval College 1806**
Obv. Bust r., laureate. ROYAL NAVAL COLLEGE FOUNDED BY KING GEORGE III. MDCCCVI *Rev.*   *AR*   25   40
AWARDED TO (space, for recipient's name) AT AN EXAMINATION, in the centre. SECOND   *AE*   8   15
MATHEMATICAL PRIZE *D*. 53 mm. By T. Wyon Jr. *MH* 1919, 560 (*obv.*)
One of several medals which the College presented from *c*.1815; it has been found awarded only in silver.

981 *   **Union of England and Scotland, Centenary 1807**
Obv. Busts l., conjoined, she wearing a bandeau and he laureate. GEORGIVS III. ET   *AR*   170   320
CHARLOTTA. REX ET REGINA BRITANNIARVM. Around, a band inscribed WITH GOD AND THE   *AE*   80   150
PEOPLE. THE THRONE IS IMMORTAL. Two outer decorative borders. *Rev.* Standing figures of
Hibernia, Anglia and Scotia, identified by shamrock, rose and thistle, their hands linked.
CONCORD IS THE SECURITY OF NATIONS *Ex.* 1807 below a bundle of arrows. A wreath border.
D. 84 mm. By T. Wyon Sr., after T. Martyn. *BHM* 628; *CP* 31/1. See **Plate 27**
Edges of some examples are inscribed with the name of a volunteer regiment.

982   **Lord Milton 1807**
Obv. LORD MILTON ELECTED M.P. FOR THE COUNTY OF YORK 1807 within a wreath; above,   *WM*   15   25
Fame. *Rev.* SUCCESS TO THE FRIENDS OF MILTON within a wreath. *Edge.* Obliquely grained.
D. 36 mm. (By?) *BHM* 623
Charles William Wentworth Fitzwilliam, Viscount Milton (1786–1857), whig politician. Similar pieces were issued by
Henry Lascelles (2nd Earl Harewood, 1767–1841, tory politician), William Roscoe, and William Wilberforce.

983* **Abolition of the Slave Trade, Royal Assent 1807**

Obv. Bust r. WILLIAM WILBERFORCE M.P. THE FRIEND OF AFRICA. *Rev.* Britannia seated upon a dais, inscribed I HAVE HEARD THEIR CRY, and attended by Mercury, Prudence and Justice, is crowned by Victory, hovering above. SLAVE TRADE ABOLISHED MDCCCVII. *D.* 53 mm. By T. Webb. *BHM* 627; *Hocking* 230/95. *See* **Plate 27**

	£	£
AR	90	170
AE	30	55

Examples with rust marks and speckling may have been struck some years later. William Wilberforce (1759–1833), slavery abolitionist; philanthropist.

984 **Abolition of the Slave Trade 1807**

Obv. A white man and a negro, standing, facing each other, their hands clasped; beyond, five negroes dancing around a tree. WE ARE ALL BRETHREN   *Ex.* SLAVE TRADE ABOLISHED BY GREAT BRITAIN 1807. *Rev.* Arabic inscription [= Sale of slaves prohibited in 1807, Christian era, in the reign of George the Third; verily, we are all brothers]. *D.* 36 mm. By G. F. Pidgeon/J. Phillp. *D & W* 188/694

a AE	15	32
b AR	—	180
AE	—	35

Type *a* was struck *c*.1814 and issued by Macauley & Babington for use as a token in Sierra Leone. Type *b* was struck *c*.1830–50; occurs on flans of varying thickness and with the medallist's initials sometimes omitted. They are sometimes gilt, and occur within a metallic case, in the form of two thin circular 'shells'. *See* D. Vice & F. Pridmore, 'Sierra Leone Penny Token 1814', *SNC* 1975, July/Aug. 278–81.

985 **William Roscoe** *c.*1807

Obv. Bust l., draped. WILLIAM ROSCOE THE FRIEND OF HUMANITY AND FREEDOM THE ENLIGHTENED ADVOCATE OF PEACE   *Rev.* Pegasus upon Mount Parnassus; below, a scroll, trumpet, and book entitled LEO X   *D.* 53 mm. By P. Wyon. *BHM* 618

AE	15	25
WM	8	15

William Roscoe (1753–1831), historian, politician and banker; published the *Life of Leo X* in 1805. Spoke in favour of the bill for the Abolition of Slavery; helped to found the African Institution in 1807.

986 **Nelsonic Crimson Oakes 1808**

Obv. Bust l., uniformed. GALLANT NELSON DIED OCTᴿ 21. OFF CAPE TRAFALGAR   *Rev.* Eye of Providence above compasses; around, a crescent moon, stars and other symbols. NELSONIC CRIMSON OAKES COMMENCED JANᵞ 19. 1808. *D.* 53 mm. By B.P (B. Patrick?) *BHM* 640; *MH* 1919, 526

AR	40	75
WM	10	20

Struck from more than one pair of dies. BP may have been a society formed to honour Nelson and to perpetuate his memory.

987 **Dunkeld Bridge Opened 1808**

Obv. View of a bridge. BRIDGE OF DUNKELD   *Ex.* LENGTH 685 Fᵀ BREADTH 27 AND CENTRE ARCH IS 90 FEET. *Rev.* BUILT BY THE MOST NOBLE JOHN DUKE OF ATHOLL. EXPENCE ABOVE £30,000, FOUNDED 24ᵀᴴ JUNE 1805, AND OPENED THE 7ᵀᴴ NOVᴿ 1808   *D.* 50 mm. (By?) *BHM* 639; *EPM* 1887, 256

AR	55	90
AE	20	35
WM	12	20

John Murray, 5th Duke of Atholl (1778–1846).

988* **English Army Arrives in the Peninsula 1808**

Obv. Bust r. ARTHUR DUKE OF WELLINGTON. *Rev.* Female figures of Spain and Portugal advancing, l., one deflecting thunderbolts from an eagle, seek assistance from a moored British ship. THE ENGLISH ARMY ARRIVES IN THE PENINSULA   *Ex.* MDCCCVIII. *D.* 41 mm. By N. G. A. Brenet. *BHM* 635; *Bramsen* 742; *Mudie* 12. *See* **Plate 27**

AR	30	55
AE	9	15
WM	3	7

Arthur Wellesley, 1st Duke of Wellington (1769–1852), Field-marshal and statesman. Struck in 1820, from Mudie's series commemorating British victories. *See* No. 1136.

989 **Battle of Vimiera; English Army Enters Lisbon 1808**

Obv. Triumphal car bearing military trophies, r., escorted by Victory, hovering above. *Ex.* BATTLE OF VIMIERA AUG XXI MDCCCVIII   *Rev.* British ships moored at a quayside. *Ex.* THE ENGLISH ARMY ENTERS LISBON SEPT. XI. MDCCCVIII   *D.* 41 mm. By J. J. Barre/G. Mills. *BHM* 637; *Bramsen* 2207; *Mudie* 13

AR	30	55
AE	9	15
WM	3	7

Struck in 1820, from Mudie's series commemorating British victories. *See* No. 1136.

990 **Covent Garden Theatre, Stone-laying 1808**

Obv. Bust of George, Prince of Wales, r. *Rev.* GEORGIUS. PRINCEPS. WALLIARUM. THEATRI. REGIIS. INSTAURANDI. AUSPICIIS. IN. HORTIS. BENEDICTINIS. LONDINI. FUNDAMENTA. SUA. MANU. LOCAVIT MDCCCVIII. *D.* 91 mm. By P. Rouw. *BHM* 638

AE	50	90

Made in two halves and joined by two fixings in the centre of the piece.

991 **Christ's College, Cambridge, Porteus Medal 1808**

Obv. Bust l., laureate, armoured and draped. GEORGIUS III. PIUS FORTIS DEFENSOR FIDEI. *Rev.* Gateway decorated with College arms. OB INSIGNE IN S.S. PUBLICE LEGENDIS ELOQUIUM   *Ex.* COLL. CHRISTI PIETATIS ERGO D. ALUMNUS OLIM BEILBY PORTEUS. EPISC. LOND. 1808. *D.* 43 mm. By J. Phillp [*obv.* after G. F. Pidgeon] *BHM* 632; *Taylor* 29c

AV	380	480
AR	35	65
AE	12	25

A prize awarded in gold; two similar medals, each 49 mm. in diameter, were also struck. Beilby Porteus (1731–1808), Bishop of London; fellow of Christ's College.

992   **George III, Jubilee 1809**
                                                                         £   £

		VF	EF

992   **George III, Jubilee 1809**
Obv. George III, enthroned, l., acclaimed by Britannia standing behind. BRITONS   *AR* 80 150
REJOICE   *Rev.* A trident, IUBILEE below, within a wreath tied by rose, thistle and shamrock.   *AE* 45 80
FIFTIETH YEAR OF KING GEORGE THE THIRD'S REIGN 1809   *D.* 70 mm. By J. Barber. *BHM* 641   *WM* 15 30
More than fifteen medals celebrate the commencement of the fiftieth year of the King's reign.

993   ———
Obv. Bust of George III, r., armoured and draped. GOD SAVE THE KING   *Rev.* GRAND   *AR* 45 80
NATIONAL JUBILEE OCT. 25. 1809 within a wreath, inscribed GOD GIVE PRAISE on a ribbon. THE   *AE* 15 25
50 YEAR HE HAS GOVERN'D & PRESERVED AN AFFECTIONATE & LOYAL PEOPLE. *D.* 42 mm. [By T.   *WM* 8 15
Wyon Sr.] *BHM* 653

994   **Death of Sir John Moore 1809**
Obv. Bust l. LIEUT. GENERAL SIR J. MOORE K.B.   *Rev.* A gladiator shields the fallen figure of   *AR* 30 55
Moore from the French eagle. DEATH OF. SIR JOHN MOORE   *Ex.* CORUNNA 16 JANUARY 1809.   *AE* 9 15
D. 41 mm. By G. Mills/J. A. Couriguer. *BHM* 666; *Bramsen* 2214; *Mudie* 14   *WM* 3 7
Sir John Moore (1761–1809), lieutenant-general. Struck in 1820, from Mudie's series commemorating British victories. *See No.* 1136.

995   **Action at Penaflor 1809**
Obv. Bust l. MAJ. GEN. SIR W. P. CARROL. KᵀC.B. &ᶜ   *Rev.* Mars standing, r., with sword and   *AR* 35 65
shield. PENAFLOR 1809   *D.* 41 mm. By T. I. Wells. *BHM* 664; *Bramsen* 2216   *AE* 15 30
Sir William Parker Carrol (1775?–1842), major-general.   *WM* 10 20

996   **Colonel Wardle 1809**
Obv. Bust r., draped. COL: G. L. WARDLE. M.P. MOVED THE ENQUIRY RELATIVE TO THE D: OF   *AR* 40 75
Yᴷ   *Rev.* MAY OUR GLORIOUS CONSTITUTION TRIUMPH OVER ALL ITS ENEMIES in the centre.   *AE* 15 30
"THE DUTY WHICH I OWE MY COUNTRY IS PARAMOUNT TO EVERY OTHER CONSIDERATION"   *WM* 8 15
MARCH. 1809   *D.* 40 mm. (By?) *BHM* 668
Gwyllym Lloyd Wardle (1762?–1833), soldier and politician.

997   **Passage of the Douro, Portugal 1809**
Obv. As No. 988. *Rev.* River god prevents passage of English ships. *Ex.* PASSAGE OF THE DURO   *AR* 30 55
1809   *D.* 41 mm. By N. G. A. Brenet/E. J. Dubois. *BHM* 671; *Bramsen* 843; *Mudie* 15   *AE* 9 15
Struck in 1820, from Mudie's series commemorating British victories. *See No.* 1136.   *WM* 3 7

998   **Captain J. Wooldridge 1809**
Obv. Fireships approach the French fleet; below, a label supported by a cable border. *Rev.*   *AV* — —
CAPTAIN JAMES WOOLDRIDGE LED THE BRITISH FIRESHIPS WHEN FOUR FRENCH SAIL OF THE LINE   *AR* 80 150
WERE BURNT UNDER THEIR OWN BATTERIES IN AIX ROADS., within a wreath. *D.* 40 mm. (By?)   *AE* 35 60
BHM 669; *MH* 1919, 562; *Payne* 300
Some examples are dated XI APRIL. MDCCCIX on the label. Specifically struck for Captain James Wooldridge, who received the medal in gold affixed to a gold chain.

999   **Battle of Talavera 1809**
Obv. Bust r., uniformed. ARTHUR DUKE OF WELLINGTON   *Rev.* Victory standing between the   *AR* 35 65
British lion and French eagle. *Ex.* BATTLE OF TALAVERA 1809. *D.* 41 mm. By G. Mills/La   *AE* 12 18
Fitte. *BHM* 673; *Bramsen* 867; *Mudie* 16   *WM* 6 10
Struck in 1820, from Mudie's series commemorating British victories. *See No.* 1136.

1000*   **Death of Matthew Boulton 1809**
Obv. Bust r., draped. MATTHEW BOULTON ESQᴿ F.R.S. Lᴺ & ED. F.R.I. & A.S. *Rev.* THE LIBERAL &   *AR* — —
ENLIGHTENED PATRON OF ARTS AND MANUFACTURES in the centre. BORN AT BIRMINGHAM SEP.   *AE* 180 400
III MDCCXXVIII. DIED AUG. XVII MDCCCIX AGED LXXXI. *D.* 102 mm. By P. Wyon, after P. Rouw.
BHM 660; *EPM* 1888, 84/2; *Eidlitz* 1928, 3. *See* **Plate 27**

1001   ———
Obv. Bust r., draped. MATTHEW BOULTON. ESQ. F.R.S. & c; below, a plain ribbon. *Rev.*   *AE* 45 70
FAREWEL within a wreath. BRIGHTER SCENES I SEEK ABOVE IN THE REALMS OF PEACE AND   *WM* 20 35
LOVE   *D.* 48 mm. (By C. H. Küchler?) *BHM* 661; *Pollard* 33i; *EPM* 1888, 85/3
Examples of this medal may been restruck some years after Boulton's death, as perhaps were the varieties and trial strikings which occur (*Pollard* 33ii–iii; pp. 314–16).

1002   ———
Obv. Bust r., draped. MATTHEW BOULTON 1792   *Rev.* MATTHEW BOULTON DIED AUGUST 17ᵀᴴ   *AE* 80 150
1809 AGED 81 YEARS. *D.* 35 mm. (By?) *BHM* 663
Examples examined have all exhibited numerous die cracks, and suggest that the die probably had a short life.

PLATE 27

960

981 (× ⅔)

961

983

988

1006

1000 (× ½)

PLATE 28

1007

1014

1017

1020

1027 (× ⅔)

1040

1031

1003   Matthew Boulton, Obsequies 1809
Obv. MATTHEW BOULTON DIED AUGUST 17TH 1809 AGED 81 YEARS. *Rev.* IN MEMORY OF HIS OBSEQUIES AUGST 24TH 1809. within a wreath. *D.* 41 mm. (By?) *BHM* 662; *EPM* 1888, 86/5; *Eidlitz* 1928, 8   AE   12   22
Struck for distribution amongst mourners at Boulton's funeral and workmen at his manufactory.

1004   British Attack on Antwerp 1809
Obv. Female standing, r., her foot on a galley; to r., a hand issuing from a castle. *Ex.* ANVERS ATTAQUEE PAR LES ANGLAIS MDCCCIX   *Rev.* Jupiter enthroned, facing. JUPITER STATOR   *Ex.* NAPOLEON A SCHOENBRUNN MDCCCIX. *D.* 41 mm. By A. J. Depaulis/J.F. Domard. *Bramsen* 870; *Parkes Weber* 64; *MH* 1921, 182   AR 35 65 / AE 10 20

1005   'Old Price' Riots, Covent Garden 1809
Obv. O P upon a trumpet decorated with laurel branches. GOD SAVE THE KING. MAY OUR RIGHTS & PRIVILEGES REMAIN UNCHANGED   *Rev.* Man seated, l., upon an ass with the face of Kemble as Shylock and the ears of Mephistopheles, holding two pennants, inscribed OLD PRICES and OPEN BOXES. which he waves. FROM N. TO O. JACK YOU MUST GO. *Ex.* JOHN BULL'S ADVICE TO YOU IS, GO: 'TIS BUT A STEP FROM N, TO – O., on a ribbon. *D.* 43 mm. (By P. Wyon?) *BHM* 675; *D & W* 17/184   AR 45 80 / AE 25 45 / WM 8 15
John Philip Kemble, actor-manager; reopened Covent Garden in 1809 with much higher prices, the initial cause of dissent and the O.P. ('Old Price') Riots. An effort to create an atmosphere of harmony by allowing free admission to certain parties such as Jews, from whose ranks came several prominent and popular members of the boxing fraternity, backfired to produce an isolated streak of anti-Semitism. *See* No. 1006.

1006* ——
Obv. Bust l., draped, of Kemble as Shylock with the pointed ears of Mephistopheles. THIS IS THE JEW, WHICH SHAKESPEARE DREW. V P (Vox Populi) NO PRIVATE BOXES AV'RICE AND TITLED LUST, ALONE WE BLAME. YET BLUSH WE MUST FOR 'TIS A NATIONS SHAME. *Rev.* WHAT D'YE WANT? OP OB & DPO (Old Prices, Old Boxes, Deference to Public Opinion) within a wreath. THE DRAMAS LAWS, THE DRAMAS PATRONS GIVE. AND HE WHO LIVES TO PLEASE, SHOULD PLEASE TO LIVE. *D.* 42 mm. (By?) *BHM* 676; *Friedenberg* 1970, 22–5. *See* **Plate 27**   WM 60 110
Examples sometimes occur within a circular brass frame. *See* No. 1005.

1007*   George III, Golden Jubilee 1810
Obv. Bust l., uniformed. GEO. III. BORN 4TH JUNE 1738. ASCENDD THE THRONE OCTR 25TH 1760. *Ex.* COMPLETED 50TH YEAR OF HIS REIGN OCTR 25TH 1810. *Rev.* Britannia, attended by three infants holding a flaming heart, amidst clouds, seated on a plinth inscribed FROGMORE; above, radiate sun. THE FIFTIETH YEAR   *D.* 48 mm. (By?) *BHM* 686; *Wollaston* 47. *See* **Plate 28**   AR 45 85 / AE 15 30 / WM 8 15
At least eight medals celebrate the King's Golden Jubilee.

1008   ——
Obv. Bust l., laureate and draped. GEORGIUS III. D: G. BRITANNIARUM REX. FID. DEFEN. 25 OCT. 1810. *Rev.* Arms of Salisbury. LUSTRA DECEM COMPLEVIT. REGNAT ADHUC, REGNETQUE DIU. *D.* 48 mm. [By C.H. Küchler] *BHM* 684; *Pollard* 34   AV — — / AR 90 170 / AE 25 55
Lord Radnor's medal for Salisbury's jubilee celebrations.

1009   British Victories 1810
Obv. Bust r., draped. GEORGIVS. III. D G BRITANNIARVM. REX   *Rev.* Fame kneeling, l., inscribes NIL EGYP COPEN [Gibr]ALTER S. VINCEN ACRE PORT TRAFAL TALAV, on a column. MATVROS LARGIMVR HONORES   *Ex.* L radiate, within the Serpent of Eternity. *D.* 43 mm. By W.S. Mossop. *BHM* 700; *MH* 1919, 563   AR 50 90 / AE 15 30
The L on the reverse refers to the Jubilee year.

1010   British Victories in the Peninsular War 1810
Obv. Bust r., LIEUT. GEN. LORD VISCOUNT WELLINGTON. K.B. MDCCCX   *Rev.* Victory standing, r., upon a rock, a fallen French standard at her feet. *D.* 50 mm. By T. Wyon Jr. [obv. after J. Nollekens] *BHM* 699; *Bramsen* 990; *Forrer* VI/641   AR 90 170 / AE 28 50 / WM 12 22

1011   Imprisonment of Francis Burdett 1810
Obv. Bust r., draped. SIR FRANCIS BURDETT BART MP. FOR WESTMINSTER. MDCCCX   *Rev.* THE INTREPID CHAMPION OF FREEDOM, THE ENLIGHTENED ADVOCATE OF THE RIGHTS & LIBERTIES OF THE PEOPLE., within a radiate circle. *D.* 48 mm. (By?) *BHM* 689; *EPM* 1888, 256/2   AE 18 30 / WM 10 18
Sir Francis Burdett (1770–1844), politician; public benefactor.

1012   Joseph Hanson 1810
Obv. Bust r. JOH HANSON ESQR THE WEAVERS FRIEND STRANGEWAYS MANCHESTER 1810. *Rev.* A loom, spinning wheel and printing machine, within a wreath. SPINNING WEAVING PRINTING;   AR 50 90 / AE 20 35

below, a shuttle inscribed 39600   *D.* 42 mm. By T. Wyon Sr., *obv.* after P. Rouw. *BHM* 693; *EPM* 1892, 228
WM   10   18

Joseph Hanson (1781–1811), industrial reformer. He was imprisoned and fined for acts on behalf of the Luddites; 39,600 subscribers each contributed one penny to a fund set up to help him.

1013   **Belfast Academical Institution 1810**
Obv. BELFAST ACADEMICAL INSTITUTION 1810   Above, QUÆRERE VERUM on a ribbon. Space around (for an engraved inscription). *Rev.* A young pupil standing, r., being conferred with a wreath by a seated female; view of building, beyond. *D.* 47 mm. By T. W. Ingram. *Guest* 928 sim.
AR   28   45
AE   8   15

A prize medal, usually found awarded in silver. Struck from more than one pair of dies.

1014*   **The Solar System** *c.*1810
Obv. Sun in the centre; around, the planets MERCURY VENUS EARTH MARS CERES PALLAS JUNO VESTA JUPITER SATURN HERSHEL, with their respective symbols and satellites, in a delineated orbit. Below, THE SOLAR SYSTEM   *Rev.* Sun in the centre; around are four globes designating the solstices, located on a circular band at their respective months. An outer border of the zodiac. *D.* 51 mm. (By?). *See* **Plate 28**
WM   40   70

Hershel (now known as Uranus) was discovered in 1781 by Sir William Herschel (1738–1822), mathematician and astronomer. Vesta, the last of the four largest minor planets, was discovered in 1807.

1015   **Prince of Wales, Prince Regent 1811**
Obv. Bust l.; below, a spray of rose, thistle and shamrock. HIS ROYAL HIGHNESS GEORGE PRINCE OF WALES   *Rev.* Prince Regent, enthroned, attended by Justice and Britannia. REGENT OF THE UNITED KINGDOM   *Ex.* FEBRUARY VI MDCCCXI   *D.* 49 mm. By T. Wyon Sr., after P. Rouw/T. Wyon Jr. *BHM* 706; *Hocking* 249/24
AR   70   130
AE   20   40
WM   12   25

The Prince of Wales was sworn in as Regent following a recurrence of the King's illness.

1016   **English Army on the Tagus 1811**
Obv. Duke of Wellington, as a Roman general, seated, l. *Ex.* FABIUS CUNCTATOR   *Rev.* River god reclining, before English tents. *Ex.* LINES OF TORRES VEDRAS THE ENGLISH ARMY ON THE TAGUS 1810. 1811   *D.* 41 mm. By L. M. Petit/E. J. Dubois. *BHM* 713; *Bramsen* 1138; *Mudie* 17
AR   30   55
AE   9   15
WM   3   7

Struck in 1820, from Mudie's series commemorating British victories. *See* No. 1136.

1017*   **Battle of Albuera 1811**
Obv. Bust r., uniformed. MARSHAL GEN. LORD BERESFORD. *Rev.* Polish lancer attacks a British infantryman. BATTLE OF ALBUERA XVI. MAY MDCCCXI   *D.* 41 mm. By T. Webb/N.G.A. Brenet. *BHM* 718; *Bramsen* 1123; *Mudie* 18. *See* **Plate 28**
AR   35   65
AE   12   18
WM   6   10

William Carr Beresford, Viscount Beresford (1768–1854). Struck in 1820, from Mudie's series commemorating British victories. *See* No. 1136.

1018   **Duke of Gloucester 1811**
Obv. Bust r., armoured and draped. H.R.H. WILLIAM FREDERICK DUKE OF GLOUCESTER. *Rev.* ELECTED MARCH 26. INSTALLED JUNE 29. MDCCCXI within a wreath. CHANCELLOR OF THE UNIVERSITY OF CAMBRIDGE. *D.* 48 mm. (By?) *BHM* 710
WM   7   15

William Frederick, 2nd Duke of Gloucester (1776–1834), soldier; provincial governor.

1019   **Thomas Crib 1811**
Obv. Pugilist standing upon a roped-off platform. IN HONOUR OF THE CHAMPION OF ENGLAND THOˢ CRIB   *Rev.* WITH MOLINEUX AT THISTLETON GAP within a wreath. SUCCESSFUL IN 10 BATTLES THE LAST SEPᴿ 28ᵀᴴ 1811   *D.* 40 mm. (By J. Porter?) *EPM* 1890, 82
WM   35   55

Thomas Crib, or Cribb (1781–1848), champion pugilist (formerly a coal-porter) nicknamed 'Black Diamond'. This, his second meeting with Tom Molineux, an American boxer, took place in Leicestershire before more than twenty thousand people. Molineux retired in the eleventh round with a fractured jaw. Large crowds greeted Crib on his return to London; his backer is reported to have made £10,000 from the contest and may have commissioned the medal.

1020*   **James Sadler 1811**
Obv. Bust l. JAMES SADLER. FIRST ENGLISH AERONAUT   *Rev.* A balloon with two men in its gondola. ASCENDED FROM BIRMINGHAM. TRAVERS'D UPWARDS OF 112 MILES, IN 1 HOUR & 20 MINUTES. THE 21 ASCENT OCTOBER. 7. 1811. *D.* 53 mm. By P. Wyon. *BHM* 712; *Forrer* VI/634. *See* **Plate 28**
AR   130   220
AE   80   140
WM   40   75

James Sadler (1753–1828), balloonist who made a number of flights; see *An Authentic Narrative of The Aerial Voyage of Mr. Sadler Across the Irish Channel*, October 1st 1812, Dublin, 1812.

1021   **Capture of Badajoz 1812**
Obv. Bust facing, uniformed. LIEUT. GEN. SIR T. PICTON. K.B.   *Rev.* Picton plants the British standard on a parapet. *Ex.* BADAJOZ APRᴸ VI MDCCCXII   *D.* 41 mm. By T. Webb/G. Mills.
AR   35   65
AE   12   20

BHM 730; *Bramsen* 2240; *Mudie* 19   *WM*   6   10

Sir Thomas Picton (1758–1815), promoted to lieutenant-general after Badajoz. Struck in 1820, from Mudie's series commemorating British victories. *See* No. 1136.

1022   Assassination of Spencer Perceval 1812

Obv. Bust l., draped. THE R.T HON.BLE SPENCER PERCEVAL CHANCELLOR OF THE EXCHEQUER   *AE*   15   28
&.C *Rev.* A tomb depicting an assassination scene, upon which stands Britannia, mourn-   *WM*   8   15
fully; a ribbon, inscribed BELLINGHAM, at her feet. HE LIVED BELOVED AND LAMENTED
FELL! *Ex.* ASSASSINATED MAY 11. 1812. *D.* 49 mm. By W. Turnpenny. *BHM* 729

Spencer Perceval (1762–1812), statesman; shot by John Bellingham as he entered the lobby of the House of Commons.

1023   Execution of John Bellingham 1812

Obv. Bust l., draped. JOHN BELLINGHAM EXECUTED MAY 18. 1812. AGED 42. YEARS. *Rev.*   *AE*   15   30
ASSASSINATED THE RIGHT HONOURABLE SPEN: PERCEVAL MAY 11. 1812., in the centre. Around, a   *WM*   10   18
garter inscribed "THOU SHALT DO NO MURDER" *D.* 40 mm. (By?) *BHM* 724; *EPM* 1888, 59

John Bellingham (1771?–1812), bankrupt merchant.

1024   Battle of Almarez 1812

Obv. Bust l. LIEUT. GENERAL LORD HILL. *Rev.* Victory, accompanied by Bellona, flies over a   *AR*   30   55
destroyed bridge. *Ex.* ALMARAZ MAY XIX MDCCCXII *D.* 41 mm. By G. Mills/R. Gayrard,   *AE*   9   15
obv. after H. Hopper. *BHM* 727; *Bramsen* 1155; *Mudie* 20   *WM*   3   7

Rowland Hill, 1st Viscount Hill (1772–1842), succeeded Wellington as Commander-in-Chief in 1828. Struck in 1820, from Mudie's series commemorating British victories. *See* No. 1136.

1025   British Army Enters Madrid 1812

Obv. Bust l. LIEUT. GEN. MARQUIS WELLINGTON. K.B. &c. &c. MDCCCXII *Rev.* Garlanded   *AR*   70   130
shields of Britain, Portugal and Spain upon a plinth, inscribed VIMEIRA TALAVERA BUSACO   *AE*   25   40
CIUDAD RODRIGO BADAJOZ SALAMANCA, amidst military trophies. ENTER'D MADRID AUGUST XII.   *WM*   10   20
D. 45 mm. By T. Wyon Sr./P. Wyon. *BHM* 737; *Bramsen* 1160

The reverse was struck from two dies.

1026   Battle of Salamanca 1812

Obv. British troops prepare an advance, r., towards the French in the mountains, at whom   *AR*   35   65
Bellona hurls thunder. JULY XXII. MDCCCXII SALAMANCA *Rev.* Equestrian figure of   *AE*   12   18
Wellington, l., is fêted by two Spaniards. *Ex.* THE BRITISH ARMY ENTERS MADRID AUG. XII.   *WM*   6   10
MDCCCXII *D.* 41 mm. By N.G.A. Brenet. *BHM* 735; *Bramsen* 1175; *Mudie* 21

Struck in 1820, from Mudie's series commemorating British victories. *See* No. 1136.

1027*   War with America 1812

Obv. Bust l., uniformed. ISAACUS HULL PERITOS ARTE SUPERAT JUL. MDCCCXII AUG. CERTAMINE   *AV*   —   —
FORTES *Rev.* Two frigates in a naval engagement. HORAE MOMENTO VICTORIA INTER CONST.   *AR*   1200   2200
NAV. AMER. ET GUER. ANGL. *D.* 65 mm. By J.M. Reich. *EPM* 1892, 311; *Julian* NA–12; *MH*   *AE*   100   180
1928, 594; *Loubat* 25. *See* **Plate 28**

This action saw the surrender of the English frigate *Guerrière*, under Captain J.R. Dracres, to Captain Isaac Hull (1773–1843), an American naval officer. This medal is one of a group of sixteen commemorating the Anglo-American War of 1812–15, all with specific reference to Britain; *see* No. 1065. They were first struck by the United States Mint *c.*1818 and have been subsequently restruck, in some cases with altered dies.

1028   Wellington, Parliamentary Tribute 1812

Obv. Bust l. ART. COMES DE WELLINGTON *Rev.* VOTA PVBLICA within a wreath. *D.* 54 mm. By   *AR*   60   110
T. Webb. *BHM* 746; *Bramsen* 1174   *AE*   15   30
                                                    WM   8   15

1029   Lord Wellington 1812

Obv. Bust three-quarters r., uniformed, head r. LORD WELLINGTON *Rev.* Ribbon entwined   *AR*   70   130
around a Corinthian helmet, shield and standard, inscribed RODRIGO BADAJOZ ALMEIDA;   *AE*   30   55
below, a captured standard of NAP[oleon]. All within a wreath. ASSYE. VIMIERA. TALAVERA.   *WM*   12   25
BUSACO *D.* 48 mm. By T. Halliday. *BHM* 744

1030   Death of Edward Smyth 1812

Obv. Bust three-quarters r., draped. EDWARD SMYTH ESQ.R *Rev.* SCULPTOR OF THE FIGURES &   *AR*   60   110
C WHICH ADORN MANY OF THE PUBLIC BUILDINGS IN THE CITY OF DUBLIN/BORN 1749 DIED   *AE*   35   55
1812 *D.* 44 mm. By W. Woodhouse. *BHM* 731; *Frazer* 1887/609

Struck *c.*1845, for the Royal Irish Art Union. Edward Smyth (1749–1812), sculptor.

1031*   Wellington, Duke of Ciudad Rodrigo 1813

Obv. Bust l. WELLINGTON DUQUE DE CIUDAD RODRIGO. *Rev.* Figure of Victory upon a short   *AR*   80   150
column, inscribed AÑO DE 1813; behind, captured arms and standards. TRIUNFO DE
VITORIA *Ex.* A NOMBRE Ð LAS CORTES EL DIP. POR CHARCAS *D.* 46 mm. By F. Sagau.
Bramsen 2251; *Medina* 19. *See* **Plate 28**

			£	£

1032 ———
Obv. As No. 1031. *Rev.* Victory advancing, l., stepping over fallen arms and standards.   *AR*   80   150
TRIUNFO DE VITORIA *Ex.* POR LA PROV. DE CHARCAS D. MARⓄ RODᶻ OLMEDO AÑO 1813
D. 46 mm. By F. Sagau. *Bramsen* 2250; *Medina* 20

1033 Battle of Vitoria 1813
Obv. As No. 999. *Rev.* Bellona advancing, l., driving a biga. *Ex.* BATTLE OF VITTORIA 1813.   *AR*   30   55
D. 41 mm. By G. Mills/Lefevre. BHM 756; *Bramsen* 1236; *Mudie* 22   *AE*   9   15
Struck in 1820, from Mudie's series commemorating British victories. *See* No. 1136.   *WM*   3   7

1034 English Army Pass the Pyrenees 1813
Obv. As No. 988. *Rev.* British lion subdues the French eagle. THE ENGLISH ARMY PASS THE   *AR*   30   55
PYRENEES *Ex.* MDCCCXIII *D.* 41 mm. By N. G. A. Brenet. BHM 760; *Bramsen* 1285;   *AE*   9   15
Mudie 23   *WM*   3   7
Struck in 1820, from Mudie's series commemorating British victories. *See* No. 1136.

1035 Royal Military Academy 1813
Obv. Bust l. FIELD MARSHAL F. DUKE OF YORK. *Rev.* Queen Charlotte presents colours, one   *AR*   30   55
inscribed VIRES ACQUIRIT EUNDO; beyond, College portico. PRESENTATION OF COLOURS BY HER   *AE*   9   15
MAJESTY AUGUST 1813. *Ex.* 1802; façade of the Academy, above. *D.* 41 mm. By T.   *WM*   3   7
Webb/N.G.A. Brenet. BHM 769; *Bramsen* 1246; *Mudie* 11
Struck in 1820, from Mudie's series commemorating British victories. *See* No. 1136.

1036 Battle of San Sebastian 1813
Obv. Bust r. LIEUT: GENERAL LORD LYNEDOCH *Rev.* Soldier in Roman dress, standing upon   *AR*   35   65
ramparts, holds a crown aloft; beyond, a castle burning. *Ex.* S. SEBASTIAN AUG XXXI   *AE*   12   18
MDCCCXIII *D.* 41 mm. By T. Webb, after P. Rouw/G.Mills. BHM 761; *Bramsen* 1244;   *WM*   6   10
Mudie 24
Thomas Graham, Baron Lynedoch (1748–1843), Scottish general. Struck in 1820, from Mudie's series commemorating
British victories. *See* No. 1136.

1037 Surrender of Pamplona 1813
Obv. As No. 988. *Rev.* Female figure of Pamplona surrenders her keys to an equestrian   *AR*   30   55
soldier in Roman dress. ENGLAND PROTECTS THE TOWN OF POMPEI. *Ex.* CAPITULATION OF   *AE*   9   15
PAMPELUNE OCTOBER THE 31 MDCCCXIII. *D.* 41 mm. By N.G.A. Brenet/J.P. Droz. BHM 765;   *WM*   3   7
Bramsen 2254; *Mudie* 25
Struck in 1820, from Mudie's series commemorating British victories. *See* No. 1136.

1038 Duke of Sussex 1813
Obv. Bust l. DUKE OF SUSSEX *Rev.* Two clasped hands within a triangle; 1813 below.   *AV*   —   40
D. 7 mm. By W. Wyon. BHM 754; *Shackles* 6   *AR*   —   20
Struck *c.*1820; commemorating the alliance of the Grand Lodges of the Antient and Modern Freemasons. Augustus
Frederick, Duke of Sussex (1773–1843), Grand Master of the Freemasons; 6th son of George III.

1039 Manchester Pitt Club 1813
Obv. Bust l., draped. Rᵀ HONᴮᴸᴱ WILLIAM PITT MANCHESTER PITT CLUB 1813 *Rev.* An   *AR*   25   45
allegory of Pitt rousing the Genius of Great Britain to resist the demons of Anarchy who   *AE*   15   25
have overthrown Religion and Royalty; the Virtues, l., await the result. *Ex.* HIMSELF AN   *WM*   8   15
HOST *D.* 50 mm. By T. Wyon Jr. [obv. after J. Nollekens] BHM 771; *Hocking* 247/10
After the death of William Pitt in 1806, clubs were formed throughout Britain to perpetuate his principles. Those which
issued medals include: Birmingham, 1814; Blackburn, 1814; Dudley, 1813; Leicester, 1814; Liverpool, 1814;
Northwich, 1814; Nottingham, 1814; Rochdale, 1813; Saddleworth, 1818; Sheffield, 1810; Stirling, 1814; Suffolk, 1821;
Warrington, 1814 and Wolverhampton, 1813. Medals of certain clubs occur frosted and set within a watch-style glass,
bound by a silver frame with a suspension loop.

1040* The General Agricultural Society 1813
Obv. Plough, scythe, flail, rake, etc in the centre. THE GENERAL AGRICULTURAL SOCIETY   *AR*   45   70
ASSEMBLING AT DONCASTER INSTITUTED 1813. *Rev.* Large bull standing, l., near three sheep.
PRIZE MEDAL *Ex.* (space, for value) GUINEAS *D.* 73 mm. By W. Turnpenny. *See* **Plate 28**

1041* Betrothal of Princess Charlotte 1814
Obv. Bust r. CAROLETTA AVGVSTA. *Rev.* Spes standing, facing, head l., holding olive-branch,   *AR*   55   100
cornucopia, and rudder resting on a globe. SPES PVBLICA. *Ex.* IAN. VII. MDCCCXIV *D.*   *AE*   15   30
54 mm. By T. Webb. BHM 778. *See* **Plate 29**   *WM*   8   15
The engagement between Princess Charlotte and Prince William of Orange was broken off after a few months.

1042* Battle of Toulouse 1814
Obv. Head of Britannia, l., in a Corinthian helmet. BRITANNIA *Rev.* The Duke of   *AR*   30   55
Wellington standing beside a military trophy holds a captured French standard and wreath.   *AE*   9   15

BATTLE OF TOULOUSE   *Ex.* X. APRIL MDCCCXIV   D. 41 mm. By R. Gayrard/N.G.A. Brenet.   WM   3   7
BHM 789; *Bramsen* 1384; *Mudie* 26. *See* **Plate 29**
<small>Struck c.1820, from Mudie's series commemorating British victories. *See* No. 1136.</small>

1043   **Treaty of Paris 1814**
     Obv. Bust r., laureate. GEORGIVS PRINCEPS WALLIÆ PATRIAM PRO PATRE REGENS   AR   130   250
     MDCCCXIIII   *Rev.* Britannia, supporting the fallen figure of EVROPA, is crowned by Victory.   AE   55   100
     SEIPSAM CONSTANTIA EUROPAM EXEMPLO   D. 69 mm. By J. Barber/T. Wyon Jr. [*rev.* after H.
     Howard] *BHM* 805; *Bramsen* 2277
     <small>More than twenty medals commemorate the peace.</small>

1044   ——
     Obv. Mars, in an attitude of war, restrained by Peace. TREATY OF PEACE SIGNED AT PARIS   *Ex.*   AR   55   90
     MAY 30TH 1814. *Rev.* THIS IS THE WORK OF JEHOVAH: IT IS MARVELLOUS IN OUR EYES. within a   AE   18   35
     wreath decorated with the shields of Great Britain, Prussia, Sweden, France, Austria and
     Russia. D. 56 mm. By T. Wyon Jr. *BHM* 818; *Bramsen* 1439
     <small>The obverse was prepared in 1811, and is dated accordingly beside the signature in the exergue.</small>

1045   ——
     Obv. Busts r., conjoined and laureate, of George, Prince Regent, Alexander I, Francis II   AE   25   40
     and Frederick William III. NVNQVAM VIDEBIMVS EIS SIMILES ITERVM. *Rev.* Peace standing, l.,   WM   10   20
     holding olive-branch and cornucopia. AVSPICIVM MELIORIS AEVI   *Ex.* PAX. PER. EVROPAM
     MDCCCXIV. MAI. XXX   D. 48 mm. [By E. Thomason] *BHM* 802; *Bramsen* 1459
     <small>Alexander I (1777–1825), emperor of Russia 1801–25. Francis II (1768–1835), emperor of Austria 1804–35. Frederick
     William III (1770–1840), emperor of Prussia 1797–1840.</small>

1046   **Peace in Europe 1814**
     Obv. As No. 1042. *Rev.* Hercules standing upon a fallen French standard. THE REPOSE OF   AR   30   55
     HERCULES MDCCCXIIII. D. 41 mm. By R. Gayrard/J.P. Droz. *BHM* 825; *Bramsen* 1441;   AE   9   15
     Mudie 27   WM   3   7
     <small>Struck in 1820, from Mudie's series commemorating British victories. *See* No. 1136. Gayrard's signature on some
     examples is indistinct.</small>

1047   **England Gives Peace to the World 1814**
     Obv. Bust facing, head laureate, l. GEORGE PRINCE REGENT MDCCCXVI   *Rev.* Britannia seated,   AR   30   55
     l., adorns a globe, held by Victory, with an olive-branch. *Ex.* ENGLAND GIVES PEACE TO THE   AE   9   15
     WORLD 1814   D. 41 mm. By G. Mills/E.J. Dubois. *BHM* 776; *Bramsen* 1438; *Mudie* 28   WM   3   7
     <small>Struck in 1820, from Mudie's series commemorating British victories. *See* No. 1136. The date on the obverse, apparently a
     mistake by the medallist, should read MDCCCXIV.</small>

1048   **Wellington Created Duke 1814**
     Obv. Bust l. WELLINGTON MDCCCXIV   *Rev.* Breast Star of the Order of the Garter. VIRTUTIS   AE   20   35
     FORTUNA COMES   *Edge.* Grained. D. 22 mm. (By?)

1049   **Duke of Wellington, Victories 1814**
     Obv. Bust l. ARTHURUS DUX DE WELLINGTON   *Rev.* Hibernia seated, l., indicates a plinth,   AR   75   140
     inscribed VIMEIRA TALAVERA BUSACO CIU. RODRIGO BADAIOZ SALAMANCA VITTORIA TOULOUSE,   AE   35   65
     decorated with a ducal crown, radiate. EUROPÆ LIBERATOR BRIT. PRÆSIDIUM HIB. DECUS   *Ex.*   WM   15   25
     A.D. 1814. PACATO VICTORIIS TERRARUM ORBE   D. 56 mm. By I. Parkes. *BHM* 791; *Frazer*
     1893/8

1050   **Visit of the Allied Sovereigns to England 1814**
     Obv. As No. 1042. *Rev.* Neptune standing on the sea-shore, before the TEMPLVM. JANI   AR   30   55
     (Temple of Janus), welcomes a foreign ship. VISIT OF THE SOVEREIGNS OF RUSSIA AND   AE   9   15
     PRUSSIA   *Ex.* JUNE VI MDCCCXIV   D. 41 mm. By R. Gayrard/J.J. Barre. *BHM* 854; *Bramsen*   WM   3   7
     1474; *Mudie* 30
     <small>Struck in 1820, from Mudie's series commemorating British victories. *See* No. 1136. On some examples Gayrard's
     signature is indistinct.</small>

1051   **Visit of Frederick William III 1814**
     Obv. Bust r., laureate. FREDERICK WILLIAM III. KING OF PRUSSIA. *Rev.* HOSPES BRITANNIARUM   AR   50   90
     MDCCCXIV   D. 53 mm. By T. Halliday. *BHM* 853; *Bramsen* 1473   AE   25   45

1052   **Visit of Alexander I 1814**
     Obv. Bust r., laureate. ALEXANDER. IMP. ROSSICI. AVTOCRATOR. *Rev.* ORBIS TE LAVDAT   AR   60   100
     PACATVS. MDCCCXIV. within a wreath. D. 54 mm. By T. Webb. *BHM* 848; *Bramsen* 1470   AE   20   35
        WM   8   15

			£	£
1053*	**Visit of Alexander I and Catherine, Grand Duchess of Oldenburg 1814**			
	Obv. Bust r., laureate. ALEXANDER RUSSIARUM IMPERATOR. *Rev.* Britannia seated, l., holding	AV	350	500
	olive-branch and trident. OB. ADVENT. M.D. CATHARINÆ. HOSP. GRATISSIMA. *Ex.* GAUDENS	AR	45	80
	BRITANNIA MDCCCXIV *D.* 35 mm. By T. Wyon Sr. BHM 845; *Bramsen* 1481. *See* **Plate 29**	AE	20	35
	Catherine, Grand Duchess of Oldenburg, sister of Alexander I.			
1054	**Bethnal Green Volunteers 1814**			
	Obv. ENROLLED 13TH AUG. 1803, AND DISEMBODIED AT THE GENERAL PEACE OF EUROPE, 24TH	AR	55	90
	JUNE, 1814 within a wreath. BETHNAL GREEN VOLUNTEER INFANTRY. L.T COL. CARRICK. *Rev.*	AE	20	35
	Britannia standing beside a broken column holds an olive-branch aloft. ENGLAND'S			
	PERSEVERANCE DETHRONED BUONAPARTE. *D.* 50 mm. By P. Wyon. BHM 833; *Payne* 212			
	Presented in silver to members of the corps by Lieutenant-Colonel Carrick.			
1055*	**Hanoverian Accession, Centenary: Peace of Paris 1814**			
	Obv. Bust l., laureate and draped. GEORGE PRINCE OF WALES. REGENT. *Rev.* Britannia seated,	AR	130	250
	flanked by Peace and Victory. JUBILEE IN HONOUR OF THE PEACE 1 AUG: 1814. *Ex.* Hanoverian	AE	55	100
	Horse; below, CENTENARY between a spray of rose, thistle and shamrock, and a lis.			
	D. 69 mm. By T. Wyon Jr. [after T. Lawrence] BHM 829; *Hocking* 248/16. *See* **Plate 29**			
1056	**Brunswick Accession, Centenary 1814**			
	Obv. Bust r., laureate, of the Prince Regent. THE ILLUST.S HOUSE OF BRUNSWICK ASC.D THE	AR	75	130
	THRONE OF G.T BRITAIN AUG.T 1.T 1714. *Rev.* Britannia standing, facing, upon an island rock,	AE	30	55
	beside the Royal shield, lion, and crown, holding trident and Victory upon a globe. EUROPE'S			
	PROTECTING GENIUS *Ex.* CENTENARY COMPLETED IN THE 54H Y.R OF K: GEO: 3.R AUG.T 1.T			
	1814 *D.* 50 mm. By T. Wyon Jr. [*obv.* after N. Marchant] BHM 779; *Hocking* 248/14			
	Another reverse records the Centenary celebrated by the Corporation of Cork.			
1057	——			
	Obv. Busts r., conjoined and laureate, of George I, armoured and draped, George II,	AR	80	150
	uniformed, and George III. THE. ILLUSTRIOUS. HOUSE. OF. HANOVER. 100. YEARS. ON. THE.	AE	35	60
	THRONE. OF G.T BRITAIN. AUG. 12. 1814. N.S. *Rev.* Peace, seated on the sea-shore, holds an	WM	15	30
	olive-branch and a portrait medallion inscribed G.P.R. (George, Prince Regent). Beyond, a			
	ship at sea. NUNC FELICES. *D.* 50 mm. By W.S. Mossop. BHM 781; *Frazer* 1887/460			
1058	**English Army Re-enters Hanover 1814**			
	Obv. Bust facing, uniformed. H.R.H. DUKE OF CAMBRIDGE *Rev.* Britannia seated, r., feeds	AR	30	55
	two horses. THE ENGLISH RE-ENTER HANOVER *Ex.* MDCCCXIV. *D.* 41mm. By T. Webb/J.J.	AE	9	15
	Barre. BHM 777; *Bramsen* 1489; *Mudie* 31	WM	3	7
	Adolphus Frederick, Duke of Cambridge (1774–1850), 7th son of George III. Struck in 1820, from Mudie's series commemorating British victories. *See* No. 1136.			
1059	**Treaty of Ghent between Great Britain and the United States 1814**			
	Obv. Peace standing upon a globe, facing, holds olive-branch and cornucopia. ON EARTH	AE	20	35
	PEACE GOOD WILL TO MEN *Rev.* TREATY OF PEACE & AMITY BETWEEN GREAT BRITAIN AND THE	WM	10	20
	UNITED STATES OF AMERICA SIGNED AT GHENT DEC. 24. 1814, within a wreath. *D.* 46 mm. (By?)			
	BHM 841; *Leroux* 875			
1060	**Apprentice Boys of Derry 1814**			
	Obv. Bust almost facing, draped. GEORGE WALKER, DEFENDER OF DERRY 1688. *Rev.* Soldiers	AR	25	40
	before a coastal garrison flying the British flag; beyond, ship at sea. NO SURRENDER *Ex.*	AE	10	20
	APPRENTICE. BOYS. OF. DERRY CLUB FOUNDED 1814 *D.* 41 mm. By W.S. Mossop. BHM 855;			
	Frazer 1887/465			
1061*	**North American Indian Chiefs' Medal 1814**			
	Obv. Bust r., laureate and draped, wearing the collar of the Great George. GEORGIVS III DEI	*a* AR	800	—
	GRATIA BRITANNIARVM REX. F: D: *Rev.* Royal arms, crest, supporters and motto; 1814	AE	80	120
	below. *D. a* 75 mm.; *b* 60 mm.; *c* 38 mm. By T. Wyon Jr. BHM 844; *Jamieson* 24–6. *See*			
	Plate 29	*b* AR	800	—
	These medals often occur with a suspension loop. Examples in bronze are specimen strikings. *See* No. 472.	*c* AR	600	—
1062	**Chronology of Sovereigns c.1814**			
	Obv. Bust l., uniformed. HIS ROYAL HIGHNESS GEORGE PRINCE REGENT. *Rev.* CHRONOLOGY OF		40	70
	THE SOVEREIGNS OF ENGLAND, within a chained circle of six shields, each with a rose in a			
	Garter. *D.* 48 mm. (By?) BHM 783			
	A bronze box medal containing sixteen engraved monochrome card discs, a portrait and dates of a sovereign on each side: William I, William II, Henry I, Stephen, Henry II, Richard I, John, Henry III, Edward I, Edward II, Edward III, Richard II, Henry IV, Henry V, Henry VI, Edward IV, Edward V, Richard III, Henry VII, Henry VIII, Edward VI, Mary, Elizabeth I, James I, Charles I, Charles II, James II, William III, Anne, George I, George II and George III.			

PLATE 29

1041

1042

1055

1061 ($\times \frac{2}{3}$)

1053

1066

1067 ($\times \frac{2}{3}$)

PLATE 30

1073

1078

1085

1084

1086

1088

1092

1103

1063   **Opposition to the Corn Bill 1815**
        Obv. Bust r., draped, of Samuel Birch. THE RT. HON. THE. LORD MAYOR OF LONDON   *Rev.* A   WM   20   35
        wheatsheaf, radiate. A FREE IMPORTATION + PEACE & PLENTY +   *D.* 39 mm. By W.
        (T. Webb?) *BHM* 858; *EPM* 1888, 71
        Samuel Birch (1757–1841), dramatist and pastry cook; Lord Mayor 1814–15.

The prices shown above are: £ (VF) and £ (EF).

1064   **Congress of Vienna 1815**
        Obv. French eagle with thunderbolt approaches the coast; to l., TEMPLVM. JANI (Temple of   AR   30   55
        Janus), its doors lying broken. XXVI. FEBRUARY MDCCCXV. *Rev.* Mercury, displaying a scroll   AE   9   15
        inscribed TO ARMS, flying over the globe. DECLARATION OF THE CONGRESS OF VIENNA   *Ex.* XIII   WM   3   7
        MARCH. *D.* 41 mm. By N.G.A. Brenet/A.J. Depaulis. *BHM* 869; *Bramsen* 1597; *Mudie* 32
        This also commemorates Napoleon's flight from Elba. Struck in 1820, from Mudie's series commemorating British
        victories. *See* No. 1136.

1065   **Naval Action off Tristan da Cunha 1815**
        Obv. Bust r., uniformed. THE CONGRESS OF THE U.S. TO CAPT. JAMES BIDDLE. FOR HIS   AV   —   —
        GALLANTRY GOOD CONDUCT AND SERVICES *   *Rev.* Two ships in a naval engagement;   AR   1200   2200
        beyond, an island rock. CAPTURE OF THE BRITISH SHIP PENGUIN   *Ex.* OFF TRISTAN D'ACUNHA   AE   100   180
        MARCH XXIII MDCCCXV BY THE U.S. SHIP HORNET   *D.* 65 mm. By M. Fürst. *Julian* NA–5; *MH*   WM   50   85
        1928, 615; *Loubat* 48
        James Biddle (1783–1848), American naval officer. *See* No. 1027.

1066*   **English Army in The Netherlands 1815**
        Obv. River god reclining, r., before a galley. *Ex.* THE ENGLISH ARMY UPON THE SCHELD. *Rev.*   AR   30   55
        Bull standing, r., before a British standard inscribed G R; buildings beyond. *Ex.* MDCCCXV.   AE   9   15
        D. 41 mm. By A.J. Depaulis/Lefevre. *BHM* 867; *Bramsen* 1607; *Mudie* 33. *See* **Plate 29**   WM   3   7
        Struck in 1820, from Mudie's series commemorating British victories. *See* No. 1136.

1067*   **Waterloo Medal 1815**
        Obv. Busts l., conjoined, laureate and draped, of the Prince Regent, Francis II (Austria),   —   200
        Alexander I (Russia) and Frederick William III (Prussia). Above, Apollo driving a
        quadriga; around, border of allegorical and mythological allusions. *Rev.* Victory advancing,
        l., guides the equestrian figures of Wellington and Blücher, each in Roman dress. Above,
        Jupiter driving a quadriga; around, a border with a running depiction of the battle of giants.
        D. 133 mm. [By B. Pistrucci] *BHM* 870; *Hocking* 207–210. *See* **Plate 29**
        This was originally intended as a struck medal but the difficulties presented by its size limited the finished product to
        electrotype or gutta percha (a tough greyish substance with a resinous texture) examples made in two halves. Even in this
        form the medal was only ready c.1850 after more than thirty years of work by Pistrucci. In 1966 Messrs J. Pinches
        produced a struck 64 mm. version in gold and silver. Gebhard Leberecht von Blücher (1742–1819), Prussian field marshal
        who assisted Wellington at Waterloo. More than twenty medals commemorate the battle.

1068   **Battle of Waterloo 1815**
        Obv. As No. 988. *Rev.* Two clasped hands above an inscription JUNE XVIII. MDCCCXV. A   AR   30   55
        wreath around, entwined with a ribbon inscribed SALAMANCA VITTORIA PAMPELUNA ORTHES   AE   9   15
        TOULOUSE VIMIERA OPORTO TALAVERA BUSACO AND F^{TES} DE ONOR   *D.* 41 mm. By N.G.A.   WM   3   7
        Brenet. *BHM* 871; *Bramsen* 1645; *Mudie* 35
        Struck in 1820, from Mudie's series commemorating British victories. *See* No. 1136.

1069
        Obv. Bust r. HENRY WILLIAM MARQUIS OF ANGLESEY   *Rev.* Equestrian figure of Anglesey, l.,   AR   45   85
        leading a cavalry charge. CHARGE OF THE BRITISH AT WATERLOO   *Ex.* JUNE XVIII. MDCCCXV.   AE   14   25
        D. 41 mm. By G. Mills/A.J. Depaulis, *obv.* after F. Chantrey. *BHM* 859; *Bramsen* 1647;   WM   7   15
        Mudie 34
        Sir Henry William Paget, 1st Marquis of Anglesey (1768–1854), led the charge of the second brigade. Struck in 1820, from
        Mudie's series commemorating British victories. *See* No. 1136.

1070
        Obv. Bust facing, draped, head l., laureate. GEORGE P. REGENT   *Rev.* Victory seated, l., upon   AR   80   150
        a podium inscribed WATERLOO, holding palm and olive-branch. WELLINGTON   *Ex.* JUNE 18.
        1815   *D.* 41 mm. By T. Wyon Jr. [*obv.* after T. Lawrence] *BHM* 880; *Tancred* 78–9
        Intended as a presentation to officers, although never officially issued due to its size. Examples occur with impressed
        lettering on the edge, named to dignitaries.

1071
        Obv. Bust r. DUKE OF WELLINGTON   *Rev.* WATERLOO JUNE 1815 above laurel branch. *D.*   AV   —   45
        8 mm. By T. Wyon. *BHM* 893   AR   —   25
        One of a group of miniature medals commemorating Waterloo. It is unclear whether they are by T. Wyon Sr. or Jr.

1072   **Blücher and Wellington 1815**
        Obv. An angel supports an oval frame containing a uniformed bust of Wellington: above, a   AR   180   340
        radiate crown; below, a mantle inscribed SUCH WELLINGTON ART THOU. TRIUMPHANT FAME   AE   70   120

SHALL THRO THE WORLD IMMORTALIZE THY NAME. *Rev.* Equestrian figure of BLÜCHER, l., tramples upon a body. STRUCK BY J. PARISH. IN HONOUR OF HIS OLD FRIEND BLUCHER Below, on a ribbon THE FALL OF HAMBURGH'S TYRANT, DAVOUST ELBA'S EMPEROR Beyond, figures and a castle in the landscape. *D.* 74 mm. By T. Halliday. *BHM* 902; *Bramsen* 1736   WM 30 55

Louis Nicolas Davout (1770–1823), French marshal.

1073* ——

Obv. Heads of BLÜCHER and WELLINGTON face to face, within a wreath. *Rev.* DER   AV 350 550
SIEGGEWOHNTEN HELDEN HERRLICHSTER SIEG VON GOTT GEGEBEN ZUM UNVERWELKLICHEN AR 28 40
LORBEERKRANZ/VERNICHTUNG DES MEINEIDIGEN FEINDES NACH VIERTÆGIGER SCHLACHT BEI LA AE 12 25
BELLE ALLIANCE D. 18 JUNI 1815 *D.* 36 mm. By D.F. Loos. *Bramsen* 1641. *See* **Plate 30**

Another reverse has an angel and a wreath. D.F. Loos struck various medals of Blücher and Wellington, together and as single portraits.

1074 **British Victories of the Peninsular War 1815**

Obv. Bust l., uniformed. ENGLANDS GREAT CAPTAIN ARTHUR DUKE OF WELLINGTON. *Rev.* — 220
Victory seated, l., beneath a tree, inscribes a tablet RECORD OF BRITISH VALOUR *Ex.* PICTURE
MEDAL *D.* 75 mm. By J. Porter. *BHM* 866

A bronze box medal containing thirteen coloured 67 mm. discs engraved by Edward Orme *c.*1820, depicting actions at: Albuera, Badajoz, Bussaco, Ciudad Rodrigo, Duoro, Pamplona, Salamanca, San Sebastian, Talavera, Toulouse, Vimiera, Vitoria and Waterloo; each with a narrative inscription on the reverse. The box occurs in a gilt-tooled maroon leather case, inscribed RECORDS OF BRITISH VALOUR. A 78 mm. copy was made by Toye, Kenning and Spencer, dated 1975 and contained within a silver hallmarked box.

1075 ——

Obv. Bust l., uniformed. DUKE OF WELLINGTON. *Rev.* BY HIS CONSUMMATE SKILL AS A *a* — 50
GENERAL, HE HAS RAISED THE BRITISH ARMY TO THE HIGHEST EXCELLENCE, & HIMSELF THE MOST
NOBLE, & EXALTED HERO, IN THE ANNALS OF HISTORY. within a wreath. *D. a* 47 mm.; *b* 45 mm. *b* AE 25 45
(By?) *BHM* 885–6

Type *a* is a bronze box medal containing fourteen engraved monochrome discs with the names and dates of campaigns: Almarez; Roliea & Vimiera; Corunna/Oporto; Barrosa/Talavera; Almeida/Fuente De Honor; Buzaco/Coimbra; Albuera/Ciudad Rodrigo; Arroyo Del Molino/Badajoz; Madrid/Salamanca; Castalla/St. Sebastian; Biddassoa/Pampeluna; Pyrenees/Vitoria; Neive/Toulouse; Orthes/Waterloo. Type *b* is merely a struck version of the obverse and reverse.

1076 ——

Obv. Bust of Wellington, l. *Rev.* FIRST BATTLE PORTUGAL AUG. 17. 1808 LAST BATTLE FRANCE — 45
S.P. 10. 1814. *D.* 18 mm. By E. Thomason. *BHM* 888

A brass tube, inscribed BRITISH VICTORIES on its side, containing twenty-six 15 mm. medals with a uniform obverse, Victory flying, l. BY THE MERCY OF GOD. The reverses are inscribed with a military action (and the date): Albuhera; Almaraz; Almeida; Arroyo del Molino; Barrosa; Badajos; Biddassoa; Buzaco; Castalla; Ciudad Rodrigo; Coimbra; Corunna; Fuente De Onoro; Madrid; Neive; Oporto; Orthes; Pampeluna; Pyrenees; Roliera & Vimiera; St. Sebastian; Salamanca; Talavera; Toulouse; Vitoria; Waterloo. This series was struck from more than one die.

1077 **English Army Enters Paris 1815**

Obv. As No. 988. *Rev.* Frontal elevation of the COLONADE OF THE LOUVRE *Ex.* THE ENGLISH AR 30 55
ARMY ENTERS PARIS THE VII. OF JULY MDCCCXV. *D.* 41 mm. By N.G.A. Brenet. *BHM* 889; AE 9 15
Bramsen 1674; *Mudie* 36 WM 3 7

Struck in 1820, from Mudie's series commemorating British victories. *See* No. 1136.

1078* **Surrender of Napoleon 1815**

Obv. Bust r., uniformed. NAPOLEON BONAPARTE *Rev.* Fully-rigged British ship. AR 50 95
SURRENDERED TO H.B.M.S. BELLEROPHON CAP.ᵀ MAITLAND. *Ex.* XV JULY. MDCCCXV. *D.* 41 mm. AE 20 35
By T. Webb/N.G.A. Brenet. *BHM* 884; *Bramsen* 1691; *MH* 1919, 571; *Mudie* 37. *See* WM 8 15
Plate 30

Sir Frederick Lewis Maitland (1777–1839), rear-admiral. Struck in 1820, from Mudie's series commemorating British victories. *See* No. 1136.

1079 **Napoleon on St. Helena 1815**

Obv. As No. 1078. *Rev.* Napoleon seated pensively, upon a rock before a figure of History; AR 35 65
above, Fame. *Ex.* NAPOLEON AT Sᵀ HELENA *D.* 41 mm. By T. Webb/G. Mills. *BHM* 891; AE 14 22
Bramsen 1710; *Mudie* 38 WM 6 10

Struck in 1820, from Mudie's series commemorating British victories. *See* No. 1136.

1080 **Treaties of Paris 1814–1815**

Obv. As No. 1047. *Rev.* Victory standing upon a podium, inscribed TREATIES OF PARIS, AR 30 55
amidst arms and trophies. ARMIS ET CONSILIIS. *Ex.* XXX. MAY MDCCCXIV XX. NOVEMBER AE 9 15
MDCCCXV *D.* 41 mm. By G. Mills/N.G.A. Brenet. *BHM* 892; *Bramsen* 1784; *Mudie* 29 WM 3 7

Struck in 1820, from Mudie's series commemorating British victories. *See* No. 1136.

				£	£

1081   Scottish Regiments, Victory Honours 1815
Obv. Bust three-quarters l., of a soldier in Highland dress. NEMO ME IMPUNE LACESSIT. *Rev.*   AR   30   55
MDCCCI. EGYPT. PORTUGAL. SPAIN. FRANCE. BELGIUM MDCCCXV. within a wreath. *D.* 41 mm.   AE   9   15
By E.J. Dubois. *BHM* 868; *Bramsen* 1702; *Mudie* 10   WM   3   7
Struck in 1820, from Mudie's series commemorating British victories. *See* No. 1136.

1082   Marriage of Princess Charlotte and Leopold 1816
Obv. Busts r., conjoined and draped. CARLOTT. AUG. WALL. PR. ET. LEOP. G.F. COBOURG. SAX.   AR   65   110
AD. SAL. P P. *Rev.* Hymen standing, almost facing, with torch and garland. TÆDIS   AE   15   30
FELICIBUS *Ex.* MAY 2. 1816   *D.* 54 mm. By T. Halliday. *BHM* 907   WM   7   15
Prince George Chrétien Frédéric Leopold, Prince of Saxe-Coburg (1790–1865), Leopold I of Belgium 1831–65.

1083   Bombardment of Algiers 1816
Obv. Head r. ED. PELLEW EQUES VICE COMES EXMOUTH   *Rev.* SOCIETAS AD. PIRATAS. DELENDOS   AR   80   150
A. MDCCCXIV. INSTITVTA OB. LIBERATOS A. BARBARORVM. VINCVLIS. EVROPAEOS ALGERIA.   AE   30   55
A. MDCCCXVI. OPPVGNATA SOCIO. VICECOMITI. EXMOVTH VICTORI. ET. BENEMERITO DECREVIT
D. 55 mm. By A.D (?) *BHM* 922; *MH* 1919, 574
Edward Pellew, 1st Viscount Exmouth (1757–1833), admiral; received this medal by the Society for the Suppression of Piracy, for the liberation of Europeans from captivity. The signature could be that of A.J. Depaulis, A. Desboeufs, or A. Durand.

1084*   ——
Obv. Bust l., laureate, armoured and draped. TO TAME THE PROUD THE FETTER'D SLAVE TO FREE   AV   —   —
THESE ARE IMPERIAL ARTS AND WORTHY THEE   Below, GEORGE PRINCE REGENT   *Rev.* A naval   AR   100   190
engagement. *Ex.* ALGIERS BOMBARDED ITS FLEET DESTROYED & CHRISTIAN SLAVERY   AE   40   70
EXTINGUISHED AUG. 27 1816 EXMOUTH   *D.* 50 mm. By T. Wyon Jr./T. Wyon Sr. *BHM* 923;
MH 1919, 575. *See* **Plate 30**

1085*   ——
Obv. Bust r., uniformed. ADMIRAL LORD EXMOUTH   *Rev.* Neptune subduing a sea-horse   AR   30   55
with his trident. *Ex.* ALGIERS AUGUST 18 1816. *D.* 41 mm. By L. Brenet/Gérard. *BHM* 921;   AE   9   15
MH 1919, 572; *Mudie* 39. *See* **Plate 30**   WM   3   7
Struck in 1820, from Mudie's series commemorating British victories. *See* No. 1136.

1086*   British Naval Victories 1782–1816
Obv. Similar to No. 957, but with an added border of a garter, inscribed ENGLAND'S ADMIRAL
NELSON DUKE OF BRONTE   *Rev.* Similar to No. 957, but with an added border of a garter,   —   320
inscribed RECORD OF NAVAL VALOUR. EVERY MAN HAS DONE HIS DUTY   *D.* 75 mm. [By J.
Porter, after T. Webb/J. Flaxman] *BHM* 1056; *MH* 1919, 508. *See* **Plate 30**
A bronze box medal, produced *c*.1820, containing twelve coloured 67 mm. card discs engraved by Edward Orme, each with a naval action, and a narrative inscription on the reverse: Ld Rodney's Victory; Ld Howe's Victory; Ld Nelson boarding St Joseph; Ld Duncan's Victory; Battle of the Nile; Victory at Copenhagen; Ld Nelson Trafalgar; Sr R. Strachan's Victory; Boarding the Chesapeake; Bonaparte on the Northumberland; Storming of Algiers; Slaves deliv.^d Algiers. A monochrome endpaper on each inside lid is engraved with compass points upon an anchor. It sometimes occurs in a maroon leather case.

1087   Grand Sunderland Bridge 1816
Obv. Bridge spanning waterway; ship beneath. GRAND SUNDERLAND BRIDGE   *Ex.* BUILT A.D.   WM   8   18
1796   *Rev.* TO COMMEMORATE THE GRAND SUNDERLAND BRIDGE LOTTERY, & THE VERY
ADVANTAGEOUS PRICES AT WHICH IT WAS SOLD TO THE PUBLIC BY I. SIVEWRIGHT. CONTRACTOR.
1816, in the centre. PRESENTED TO ALL THOSE INTERESTED IN THIS LOTTERY. *D.* 46 mm. By
T. Halliday. *BHM* 930
A variety occurs without an inscription on the obverse.

1088*   Joseph Banks 1816
Obv. Bust r. R.^T HON.^{BLE} S.^R J. BANKS BAR.^T K.G. C.B. P.R.S. & c. 1816. *Rev.* An open book decorated   AR   45   70
with a garland and wheatsheaf; below, a forget-me-not. IN GENIUS. AND SUBSTANTIAL   AE   20   35
LEARNING. HIGH: *D.* 41 mm. By W. Wyon, *obv.* after T. Wyon Jr. *BHM* 911; *EPM* 1887,
262/1. *See* **Plate 30**
This medal may have been sponsored by the Royal Society as a tribute to Banks, who had been President since 1778.

1089   George III and the Royal Family 1816
Obv. IN RECORD OF THE REIGN OF GEORGE III AND CENTENARY OF THE HOUSE OF BRUNSWICK   —   270
within the Garter. *Rev.* THE FATHER AND FAMILY OF THE PEOPLE within the Star of the Garter.
D. 78 mm. By J. Porter. *BHM* 903
A bronze box medal containing seventeen monochrome 70 mm. discs, engraved by Edward Orme *c*.1820, with portraits of the Royal Family, and a biographical narrative on the reverse: George III; Charlotte; George, Prince Regent; Frederick, Duke of York; William, Duke of Clarence; Edward, Duke of Kent; Ernest, Duke of Cumberland; Augustus, Duke of Sussex; Adolphus, Duke of Cambridge; Prince Octavius; Prince Alfred; Princess Charlotte Augusta; Princess Augusta Sophia; Princess Elizabeth; Princess Mary; Princess Sophia; Princess Amelia. It sometimes occurs in a maroon leather case.

			£	£

1090 **Francis Horner, Memorial 1817**
Obv. Bust r., draped, of Horner. *Rev.* FUNGAR INANI MUNERE in the centre. FRANCIS HORNER   *AR*   50   90
NAT: 1778 OB: 1817   *D*. 45 mm. By W. Bain. *BHM* 954; *CP* 125/78   *AE*   25   40
<small>Francis Horner (1778–1817), Scottish politician and essayist.</small>

1091 **Waterloo Bridge Opened 1817**
Obv. Bust l., laureate. GEORGIUS. W.P. VICEM REGIS BRITANNIARUM GERENS. *Rev.* Royal   *AR*   10   18
Standard. WELLINGTON   *Ex.* WATERLOO DIE IUN. 18. 1815   *Edge.* PONTE WATERLOOENSI
DEDICATO. IUN: 18. 1817: (incuse). *D*. 27 mm. By W (T. Wyon Sr. or Jr.?) *BHM* 961; *Hocking*
248/19–21
<small>Examples occur without the edge inscription.</small>

1092* ——
Obv. Bust l., laureate. GEORGE P. REGENT   *Rev.* Elevation of the bridge. WATERLOO   *AR*   20   35
BRIDGE   *Ex.* JUNE 18. 1817   *D*. 20 mm. (By W. Wyon?) *BHM* 962; *Taylor* 67a. *See* **Plate 30**

1093 **The Florida Expedition 1817**
Obv. A cross within a wreath. DUCE MAC GREGORIO LIBERTAS FLORIDARUM   *Rev.* 29 JUNII 1817   *AE*   170   320
within a wreath. AMALIA VENI VIDI VICI   *D*. 33 mm. (By?) *BHM* 957; *MH* 1919, 806a
<small>Sir Gregor Macgregor (fl.1817), Scottish adventurer who attempted to liberate Florida; he took possession of Amelia Island for six months.</small>

1094 **Constitution given to the Ionian Islands 1817**
Obv. Britannia seated, l., holds the tablets of Constitution; beyond, statue of Neptune.   *AR*   80   150
MDCCCXVII   *Ex.* ENGLAND GIVES A CONSTITUTION TO   *Rev.* Seven females, each represent-   *AE*   25   45
ing one of the islands, gather around the British flag, their hands linked. *Ex.* THE IONIENNE   *WM*   12   22
ISLANDS   *D*. 41 mm. By A. J. Depaulis. *BHM* 958; *Mudie* 40
<small>Struck in 1820, from Mudie's series commemorating British victories. *See* No. 1136.</small>

1095 **Death of Admiral Duckworth 1817**
Obv. Bust l. ADMIRAL SIR J.T. DUCKWORTH BART G.C.B. *Rev.* DEDICATED BY HIS FOLLOWERS TO   *AR*   50   85
THE MEMORY OF THEIR ILLUSTRIOUS COMMANDER MDCCCXVII within a wreath. *D*. 46 mm. By   *AE*   15   30
G. Mills. *BHM* 951; *MH* 1919, 576
<small>John Thomas Duckworth (1748–1817), admiral.</small>

1096 **Death of Princess Charlotte 1817**
Obv. As No. 1041. *Rev.* Sarcophagus on a plinth, inscribed SACRED TO THE MEMORY OF   *AR*   45   85
CHARLOTTE AUGUSTA. *Ex.* BORN JAN. 7. 1796. MAR. TO LEO. OF SAXE COBOURG MAY 2. 1816. DIED   *AE*   15   30
NOV. 6. 1817   *D*. 54 mm. By T. Webb/J. Marrian. *BHM* 941   *WM*   8   15

1097 ——
Obv. Bust almost facing, draped, hair decorated with roses. H.R.H. PRINCESS CHARLOTTE   *AR*   45   85
AUGUSTA. *Ex.* BORN JAN 7 1796. MARRIED MAY 2. 1816. *Rev.* Britannia seated mournfully, l.,   *AE*   12   22
beside a funerary urn. DIED NOV. VI MDCCCXVII   *Ex.* WEEP BRITAIN THOU HAST LOST THE
EXPECTANCY AND ROSE OF THE FAIR STATE   *D*. 50 mm. By T. Webb/G. Mills. *BHM* 940

1098 **Charles Giesecke 1817**
Obv. Bust r. C.L. GIESECKE. EQV. AVRAT. MIN. PROF. S. HON. S.D.A. HIB. R.S. & c. *Rev.* Polar bear   *AR*   70   110
on an ice floe; beyond, a sea with icebergs. HYEMES. VII. SUB. ARCTO. TOLERAVIT. INGENTI.   *AE*   30   55
NATURÆ. PERCULSUS. AMORE. *Ex.* MDCCCXVII   *D*. 44 mm. By W. S. Mossop. *BHM* 953;
Frazer 1887/463; *Went* 1973, 31
<small>Sir Charles Lewis Metzler von Giesecke (1761–1833), German actor, musician, explorer and geologist. Whilst returning to England from Greenland his ship was captured and the mineral specimens which he had gathered were sold off. The medal was struck by the Royal Dublin Society where he was Professor of Mineralogy and Director of its museum.</small>

1099 **Matthew Wood, Lord Mayor of London 1817**
Obv. Bust r., draped. THE RT HONBLE M. WOOD TWICE LD MAYOR OF LONDON MDCCCXVI AND   *AE*   15   25
XVII   *Rev.* Londinia, brandishing a sword, banishes Conspiracy and protects Innocence.   *WM*   6   14
INDIGENCE RELIEVED. INNOCENCE PROTECTED. CONSPIRACY DEFEATED. *Ex.* THE CAUSE WHICH
HE KNEW NOT, HE SEARCHED OUT. JOB. *D*. 54 mm. By T. Halliday. *BHM* 956; *Thomason*
150–1
<small>Sir Matthew Wood (1768–1843), political reformer. This medal, struck at the expense of Edward Thomason, commemorates Wood's exertions in saving the lives of three Irishmen who were condemned to be hanged.</small>

1100 **William Dudley 1817**
Obv. Bust r., draped. RT HONBLE WILLM VISCT DUDLEY AND WARD BARON OF BIRMINGHAM & C.   *AR*   45   80
Rev. THE RICH MANS MODEL AND THE POOR MANS FRIEND MDCCCXVII. within a wreath.   *AE*   12   25
D. 54 mm. (By T. Halliday?) *BHM* 952   *WM*   5   10
<small>William Dudley, 3rd Viscount Dudley and Ward (1750–1823), politician; public benefactor.</small>

1817–18

				£	£

1101 George III 1817
Obv. Bust r., laureate. GEORGIUS III DEI GRATIA *Rev.* Star, radiate, above open landscape.
PROPRIO SPLENDORE REFULGET *Ex.* XXV. OCT. MDCCCXVII ANNO. REGNI LVIII *D.* 25 mm. By
W. Wyon. *BHM* 932

	AV	150	280
	AR	60	110
	AE	25	45

This medal celebrates the King's entry into his 58th year of reign, thereby exceeding that of any previous monarch. Examples of this medal occur with various coatings and combinations of metal. This display of mechanical ingenuity is probably the medallist's form of a tribute.

1102 ——
Obv. Bust r., laureate, of George III. HOC AVSPICE ORBIS SALVS. MDCCCXVII. *Rev.* Religion, standing, gives fortitude to Faith, seated. RELIGIONE FIDE ET CONSTANTIA *Ex.* MDCCCXVII. *D.* 41 mm. By T. Webb/A. J. Depaulis. *BHM* 933; *Mudie* 1

	AR	30	55
	AE	9	15
	WM	3	7

Struck in 1820; Mudie's dedication medal for his series commemorating British victories. *See* No. 1136.

1103* Annals of the Regency 1817
Obv. A cherub seated astride a lion. REGENCY *Rev.* Similar to No. 1089, but the Garter forming a separate piece, pinned on to the centre. *D.* 78 mm. By J. Porter. *BHM* 960. *See* **Plate 30**

		—	350

A bronze box medal containing twelve coloured 70 mm. engraved card discs by Edward Orme *c.*1820; each with a London view, and narrative description on the reverse: Covent Garden Theatre; Custom House; Drury Lane; Highgate Archway; Mary le Bone church; New Docks; Opera House; Regency Park; Waterloo Bridge; Waterloo Place; Westminster Abbey; Whitehall Chapel. The medal sometimes occurs in a maroon leather case inscribed with its title in gilt lettering.

1104 Tercentenary of Corpus Christi College, Oxford 1817
Obv. Bust almost facing, clerically robed. MVNIFICENTIAE RICARDI FOX ALVMNI C.C.C. OXON *Rev.* A plinth, inscribed COMMEMORATIO SAECVLARIS. DIE XVIII. MENS. IVNII ANNO. SALVTIS CHRISTIANAE M.D.CCC.XVII OB. ANNVM. EXPLETVM. A. COLLEGIO. FVNDATO TRECENTESIMVM IOANNE. COOKE S.T.P. PRAESIDENTE. FELICITER, within a wreath. *D.* 70 mm. By E. Avern, *obv.* after G. F. Pidgeon. *BHM* 959

	AR	40	70
	AE	15	25

Richard Foxe (1448?–1528), bishop of Winchester; founder of Corpus Christi College, Oxford.

1105 Giovanni Belzoni 1818
Obv. Bust l. GIOVANNI BELZONI *Rev.* View of a pyramid. OPENED BY G. BELZONI MARCH 2ND 1818 *D.* 54 mm. By T. I Wells [*obv.* after W. Brockedon] *BHM* 969; *EPM* 1888, 60

	AR	70	120
	AE	25	40

Struck *c.*1822. Giovanni Baptista Belzoni (1778–1823), Italian explorer, actor and engineer; opened the second pyramid of Gizeh and, within, the sarcophagus of its builder, King Chephren. In honour of this and other discoveries his native city of Padua struck a gold medal in 1819 depicting the two statues of the goddess Sekhmet which he had donated to the city.

1106 Candidature of Henry Brougham 1818
Obv. Head r. HENRY BROUGHAM *Rev.* TO THE PATRIOTIC INCORRUPTIBLE AND UNBOUGHT FREEHOLDERS OF THE COUNTY OF WESTMORELAND IV JULY MDCCCXVIII, within a wreath. *D.* 36 mm. By G. Mills. *BHM* 970; *EPM* 1888, 249

	AR	12	25

Occurs with a suspension loop. Henry Peter Brougham, Baron Brougham and Vaux (1778–1868), Lord Chancellor; politician.

1107 Death of Samuel Romilly 1818
Obv. Bust l. SIR SAMUEL ROMILLY M.P. *Rev.* THE DISTINGUISHED ADVOCATE, OF CIVIL & RELIGIOUS LIBERTY. DIED NOVR 2 AGED 60., in the centre. SIR, S, ROMILLY. ELECTED A MEMBER FOR WESTMINSTER, JULY 4. MDCCCXVIII. *D.* 52 mm. By E. Avern. *BHM* 973

	AR	35	65
	AE	10	18

Sir Samuel Romilly (1757–1818), law reformer.

1108 British Victories in India 1818
Obv. Bust l. MARQUIS OF HASTINGS K: G: GOVR GENL OF INDIA. *Rev.* Victory advancing, r., in a biga drawn by winged lions. PINDAREE & MAHRATTA CONFEDERACY DEFEATED 1818. *Ex.* Military trophy. *D.* 41 mm. By W. Wyon, after P. Rouw/[H. Howard] *BHM* 974; *EPM* 1892, 231

	AR	38	70
	AE	12	22
	WM	7	12

Francis Rawdon Hastings, 1st Earl of Hastings (1754–1826), served in the American War of Independence; Governor-General of Bengal.

1109 Saddleworth Pitt Club 1818
Obv. As No. 912. *Rev.* SADDLEWORTH PITT-CLUB 1818. within a wreath. THE RIGHT HONBLE WILLIAM PITT BORN MAY 28. 1759. DIED JAN. 23. 1806. AGED 47 YEARS. *D.* 53 mm. By J. G. Hancock.

	AR	35	60

See No. 1039.

1110 Charing Cross Hospital Medical School 1818
Obv. Façade of hospital building. CHARING CROSS HOSPITAL LONDON *Ex.* FOUNDED 1818 below the staff of Aesculapius. *Rev.* A wreath (space within, for recipient's name). SCHOLA MEDICINAE PALMAM PRAECLARIOR AUFERT *D.* 58 mm. By B. Wyon. *Storer* 5920; *Taylor* 109*a*

	AR	20	30
	AE	8	15

Struck and awarded from *c.*1843 in silver and bronze for over seventy years. Later examples have indistinct lettering through heavy use of the dies.

			£	£

1111   **Sir Charles Cockerell, Election Validated 1819**
Obv. View of a tower, and town seen through an archway; in foreground, a scroll LIBER AB   *AR*   45   70
HENRICO and a tablet with the town arms. THE RIGHT OF ELECTION IS IN THE MAYOR,   *AE*   12   25
ALDERMEN, CAPITAL AND OTHER BURGESSES, MEMBERS OF THE CORPORATION. *Rev.* PARVA   *WM*   6   12
CONCORDIA CRESCUNT. THIS MEDAL IS PRESENTED BY SIR CHARLES COCKERELL, BARONET TO THE
BURGESSES OF EVESHAM, MEMBERS OF THE CORPORATION, IN COMMEMORATION OF THE TRIUMPH
OF JUSTICE AND INDEPENDENCE OBTAINED BY HIS EXERTIONS, IN SUPPORT OF THEIR PETITION
BEFORE THE HONORABLE THE HOUSE OF COMMONS ON THE 23ᴰ OF FEBRUARY, 1819. *D.* 53 mm. By
J. P. Suffield. *BHM* 979; *EPM* 1890, 63
Sir Charles Cockerell (1755–1837), M.P.

1112*   **The Manchester Riots, 'Peterloo' 1819**
Obv. Troop of cavalry cutting down men, women and children. *Ex.* MANCHESTER AUGUST 16   *WM*   90   —
1819   *Rev.* THE WICKED HAVE DRAWN OUT THE SWORD THEY HAVE CUT DOWN THE POOR AND
NEEDY AND SUCH AS BE OF UPRIGHT CONVERSATION PSALM XXXVII XIV   *D.* 63 mm. (By?) *BHM*
989. *See* **Plate 31**
The riots followed speeches and a demonstration against working conditions of the labouring classes at St. Peter's Fields
near Manchester. The metal consistency of these medals varies markedly and they have a somewhat home-made
appearance; examples sometimes occur with a crude suspension loop and some appear to be cast.

1113   **Earl Fitzwilliam 1819**
Obv. Bust l., draped. THE Rᵀ HON. EARL FITZWILLIAM. *Rev.* HEIR TO THE VIRTUES AS WELL AS TO   *AR*   45   75
THE ESTATES OF HIS UNCLE CHARLES, MARQUIS OF ROCKINGHAM, AND NOT MORE NEARLY ALLIED   *AE*   15   25
TO HIM BY PROXIMITY OF BLOOD THAN BY SIMILARITY OF MANNERS./HE GOVERNED IRELAND IN   *WM*   7   12
PEACE, A.D. 1795, AND WAS LORD LIEUTENANT OF THE WEST-RIDING OF YORKSHIRE FROM 1798 TO
1819. *D.* 55 mm. By J. Wilson. *BHM* 988; *EPM* 1891, 91
Struck c.1824. William Wentworth Fitzwilliam, 2nd Earl Fitzwilliam (1748–1833), statesman.

1114   **Matthew Boulton, Tenth Anniversary of Death 1819**
Obv. Bust r., draped. MATTHAEVS BOVLTON   *Rev.* INVENTAS AVT QVI VITAM EXCOLVERE PER   *AE*   40   70
ARTIS within a wreath. *Edge.* PATRIS AMICIS M.R.B. CIƆIƆCCCXVIIII (incuse). *D.* 63 mm. By
G. F. Pidgeon [*obv.* after C. H. Küchler] *BHM* 976; *Pollard* pp.316–8
A dedicatory medal struck by Boulton's son, Matthew Robinson; examples occur without the edge inscription.

1115   **Death of James Watt 1819**
Obv. Bust r., draped. JAMES WATT F.R.S. DIED MDCCCXIX   *Rev.* A steam engine. *Ex.* WATT'S   *AR*   40   70
STEAM ENGINE MDCCLXXXVII   *D.* 46 mm. By G. Mills. *BHM* 983; *Eidlitz* 1928, 18   *AE*   18   30
James Watt (1736–1819), mechanical engineer and inventor.

1116   **James Watt, Obsequies 1819**
Obv. Statue of Watt seated, l., holding a plan and dividers. JAMES WATT   *Ex.* BORN 19   *AR*   35   60
JANUARY 1736 DIED 25 AUGUST 1819   *Rev.* A ribbon, inscribed INGENIO. ET: LABORE., around   *AE*   15   25
a shield decorated with caduceus and club. HIS OBSEQUIES AT HANDSWORTH STAFFORDSHIRE.
SEPᴿ 2. 1819. *D.* 46 mm. (By?) *BHM* 984; *Eidlitz* 1928, 17

1117   **Dedication of Freemasons Hall, Bath 1819**
Obv. Bust facing, draped. H.R.H. FREDᴷ DUKE OF SUSSEX M.W.G.M. *Rev.* Façade of building.   *AR*   30   50
FREE MASON'S HALL. A.L. 5817   *Ex.* DEDICATED SEPᴿ 23 1819. *D.* 38 mm. (By T. Halliday?)   *AE*   15   25
BHM 990; *Taylor* 70a; *Shackles* 15   *WM*   7   12

1118*   **Duke of Wellington, Governor of Plymouth 1819**
Obv. Bust l. ARTHUR DUKE OF WELLINGTON. *Rev.* Thirty-five line biographical inscription   *AE*   18   30
BORN MAY 1 1769 ENT. AS ENSIGN IN THE 73 REG. 1787 APP. LIEUT. ... GENERALISSIMO OF THE   *WM*   8   15
ALLIED ARMIES 1815 & MASTER OF THE ORDNANCE GOV. OF PLYMOUTH OCT. 9 1819   *D.* 55 mm.
By T. Webb, *obv.* after P. Rouw. *BHM* 986; *Bramsen* 1824. *See* **Plate 31**

1119   **Sir Patrick Ross 1819**
Obv. In the centre: a small bust, r.; P. ROSS on the truncation. Around, a plan of the lagoon of   *AE*   200   380
Santa Maura; passage of a canal delineated. *Rev.* Greek inscription [= To Commandant
P. Ross, in recognition of his just administration and many services, and of the recent
excavation of the Isthmus – a token of good will presented by the Leucadians, AD 1819]
within a wreath. *D.* 82 mm. Italian? (By?) *Parkes Weber* 245n
Issued by the inhabitants of Santa Maura to honour Sir Patrick Ross G.C.M.G. (1778–1850), British resident at Zante in
1819; Governor of Antigua in 1825, and of St. Helena in 1846. This irrigation canal was constructed by the Anglo-Ionian
Government and connected Fort Santa Maura with the town of Amaxichi.

1120   **Hudson's Bay Company 1820**
Obv. Bust l., armoured and draped. GEORGIUS III. D:G. BRITANNIARUM REX. FID. DEF. &   *Rev.*   *AR*   500   900
Arms of the Hudson's Bay Company, with crest, supporters and motto PRO PELLE CUTEM on   *AE*   130   220
a ribbon below. *D.* 48 mm. By C. H. Küchler. *BHM* 1062; *Leroux* 490
See No. 897.

1121   **Death of George III 1820**
Obv. Similar to No. 927. *Rev.* NATVS iVNII. IV. CIƆIƆCCXXXVIII. IMPER^M ACCEPIT. OCT XXV.   AR   80   150
CIƆIƆCCLX. EXCESSIT. JAN. XXIX CIƆIƆCCCXX., within a wreath. PATER: PATRIÆ. *D.* 48 mm. By   AE   15   30
C. H. Küchler. *BHM* 991

See No. 897. More than ten medals record the King's death.

1122   ——
Obv. Bust r., armoured and draped. GEORGE III ASCENDED THE BRITISH THRONE OCT. 25. 1760.   AR   30   55
Rev. An assembly of biblical figures; above, Elijah ascending in his chariot to heaven. ENTER   AE   10   20
THOU INTO THE JOY OF THE LORD   *Ex.* DIED JAN. 29 1820 AGED 81 YEARS   *D.* 41 mm. By   WM   6   12
T. Wyon Sr. *BHM* 1001

GEORGE IV, 1820–30

1123   **Accession of George IV 1820**
Obv. Bust facing, armoured and draped, head l., laureate. GEORGIVS IV DEI GRATIA   *a* AR   180   350
BRITANNIARVM REX   *Rev.* ACCESSIT XXIX IAN. MDCCCXX within a wreath. Below, Hanoverian   AE   65   140
horse. *D.* 70 mm. By Rundell, Bridge and Rundell. *BHM* 1010   WM   15   35

The portrait is similar to No. 1055. Type *b* is gilt and set within a richly wreathed silver-gilt frame, surmounted by a crown
with a suspension loop. The King's accession is recorded on more than ten medals.   *b* AR   400   700

1124   ——
Obv. Bust l., laureate. GEORGE IV KING OF ENGLAND   *Rev.* IN REMEMBRANCE OF THE   AR   60   110
ACCESSION OF HIS R.H. GEORGE FREDERICK AUGUSTUS PRINCE REGENT ON THE THRONE OF   AE   20   35
ENGLAND THE 30TH JANUARY 1820   *D.* 54 mm. By Renkin. *BHM* 1012

1125   **Accession of Caroline 1820**
Obv. Bust r., diademed. QUEEN CAROLINE CONSORT OF GEORGE IV   *Rev.* CAROLINE AMELIA   AR   60   110
ELIZABETH SECOND DAUGHTER OF WILL. D. OF BRUNSWICK BORN 17 MAY 1768 MARRIED 8 APRIL   AE   15   30
1795 TO GEORGE PRINCE OF WALES BY WHOM SHE HAD JAN^Y 7 1796 CHARLOTTE AUGUSTA SINCE   WM   8   18
DECEASED BECAME QUEEN CONSORT JAN^Y 29 1820. *D.* 55 mm. By G. Mills, *obv.* after P. Rouw.
BHM 1019; *Forrer* IV/81

1126   **George III, Obsequies 1820**
Obv. Bust l., uniformed. GEORGE III DIED JAN. 29. 1820. IN THE 82 YEAR OF HIS AGE & 60 OF HIS   *a* AR   35   65
REIGN. *Rev.* Funerary urn upon a tomb. IN MEMORY OF HIS OBSEQUIES AT WINDSOR. *Ex.* FEB.   AE   10   20
16 1820   *D.* *a* 45 mm.; *b* 34 mm. (By?) *BHM* 1006   WM   5   12

The inscription on type *b* varies in minor details. Type *a* also occurs with another reverse depicting an angel seated upon
clouds.   *b* AR   25   40
   AE   8   15

1127   **Death of Benjamin West 1820**
Obv. Bust l., draped. BENJAMIN WEST PRESIDENT OF THE ROYAL ACADEMY MDCCCXV   *Rev.*   AR   25   45
INSCRIBED BY G. MILLS IN GRATEFUL REMEMBRANCE OF THE PATERNAL SOLICITUDE FRIENDLY   AE   10   20
ADMONITIONS AND THE GREAT AND EXCELLENT EXAMPLE OF HIS FIRST PATRON BENJAMIN WEST
P.R.A. WHO DIED MAR XI MDCCCXX AGED LXXXII   *D.* 41 mm. By G. Mills. *BHM* 1055

Benjamin West (1738–1820), American painter; succeeded Joshua Reynolds as President of the Royal Academy. This
obverse also occurs on four medals struck in 1815, each with dedicatory inscriptions. George Mills (1792?–1824),
medallist; also produced a few unofficial pattern coins. See *Forrer IV*, 79–82; *VIII*, 59–61.

1128   **Election of Richard Talbot 1820**
Obv. Bust r., draped. RICHARD WOGAN TALBOT ESQ^R THE PEOPLES CHOICE. *Rev.* THE   AR   40   70
INDEPENDENCE OF THE COUNTY OF DUBLIN PRESERVED 28TH OF MARCH 1820 in the centre. THE   AE   20   35
MEMBER INCORRUPTIBLE * THE CONSTITUENTS GRATEFUL *   *D.* 44 mm. By W. S. Mossop.
BHM 1052; *Frazer* 1887/463

Richard Wogan Talbot, Lord Talbot of Malahide (1766–1849), politician.

1129   **Death of Henry Grattan 1820**
Obv. Bust r., draped. HENRICUS GRATTAN. *Rev.* PRO PATRIA ET VIVERE ET MORI within a   AR   45   75
wreath. NATVS DVB: 1746. OB. LONDON. 1820. *D.* 41 mm. By W. S. Mossop. *BHM* 1044;   AE   20   35
Frazer 1887/463   WM   12   22

Henry Grattan (1746–1820), statesman.

1130   **Return of Caroline to England 1820**
Obv. Bust l., laureate and draped. CAROLINE D: G. BRITT: REGINA. *Rev.* Britannia standing on   AR   35   65
the sea-shore welcoming a ship. HAIL! BRITAIN'S QUEEN! THY VIRTUES WE ACKNOWLEDGE AND   AE   12   25
LAMENT THY WRONGS. *Ex.* RETURNED TO ENGLAND JUNE 5. 1820   *D.* 40 mm. By P. Kempson.   WM   5   12
BHM 1021

			£	£

1131   Trial of Caroline 1820
Obv. Bust l., wearing a bandeau and draped. CAROLINE QUEEN OF ENGLAND   *Rev.* Britannia,   *AE*   45   75
as Minerva, displays a tablet inscribed QUEEN'S TRIAL and dismisses Discord. *Ex.*
MDCCCXX   *D.* 82 mm. By A.D (*see* No. 1083). *BHM* 1026; *Parkes Weber* 67
Caroline secured the abandonment of a bill in the House of Lords divorcing her on the grounds of adultery with Count
Bergami. *See* Nos. 1132–4.

1132   Caroline and Count Bergami 1820
Obv. As No. 1130. *Rev.* Bust facing, head r. COUNT B. BERGAMI   *D.* 40 mm. By P. Kempson.   *AR*   55   90
BHM 1030; *EPM* 1888, 66/1   *AE*   20   35
Count Bartolomeo Bergami (1790?–1841), Italian equerry and courtier; favourite of Caroline. *See* No. 1131.

1133   Withdrawal of the Divorce Bill 1820
Obv. As No. 1130. *Rev.* Peace, holding a scroll inscribed NO BILL, raises the kneeling figure   *AR*   35   65
of Caroline. VIRTUE WHEN WOUNDED FLOURISHES   *Ex.* BILL WITHDRAWN NOV: 10. *D.* 40 mm.   *AE*   12   25
By P. Kempson. *BHM* 1032   *WM*   5   12
See No. 1131.

1134*   Queen Caroline 1820
Obv. Bust l., draped. CAROLINE DE BRUNSWICK   *Rev.* Serpent on ground-line; above, CR and   *AE*   10   20
an imperial crown. *D.* 32 mm. French? (By?) *BHM* 1068. *See* **Plate 31**
Caroline was a popular figure held in high public esteem; this medal may have been produced at the time of the trial.

1135*   Birth of Princess Elizabeth 1820
Obv. Busts l., conjoined. DUKE & DUTCHESS OF CLARENCE. *Rev.* A cradle. PRINCESS ELIZABETH   *AR*   20   35
10 DEC^R 1820   *D.* 20 mm. (By?) *BHM* 1040. *See* **Plate 31**   *WM*   8   15
Princess Elizabeth Georgina Adelaide (1820–21), daughter of William, Duke of Clarence and Adelaide, Duchess of
Clarence (1792–1849). Adelaide was the daughter of George, Duke of Saxe-Coburg Meiningen; she married William in
1818.

1136   British Military and Naval Victories

1 George III Dedication 1817 (No. 1102)	22 Battle of Vitoria 1813 (No. 1033)	*AR*	—	2800
2 Settlement of the British at Bombay 1602: East India Co.'s Victory over the French 1804 (No. 952)	23 Battle of the Pyrenees 1813 (No. 1034)	*AE*	—	550
3 Naval Victory of the First of June 1794 (No. 856)	24 Battle of San Sebastian 1813 (No. 1036)	*WM*	—	200
4 Battle of Cape St. Vincent 1797 (No. 882)	25 Surrender of Pamplona 1813 (No. 1037)			
5 Battle of Camperdown 1797 (No. 886)	26 Battle of Toulouse 1814 (No. 1042)			
6 Horatio Nelson Memorial 1805 (No. 962 or 963)	27 Peace in Europe 1814 (No. 1046)			
7 Defence of Acre 1799 (No. 906)	28 England Gives Peace to the World 1814 (No. 1047)			
8 Arrival of the English Army in Egypt 1801 (No. 929)	29 Treaties of Paris 1814, 1815 (No. 1080)			
9 Egypt Delivered 1801 (No. 934)	30 Visit of the Allied Sovereigns to England 1814 (No. 1050)			
10 Victory Honours of Scottish Regiments 1815 (No. 1081)	31 English Army Re-enters Hanover 1814 (No. 1058)			
11 Royal Military College, Presentation of Colours 1813 (No. 1035)	32 Flight of Napoleon from Elba; Declaration of the Congress of Vienna 1815 (No. 1064)			
12 English Army Arrives in the Peninsula 1808 (No. 988)	33 British Army in The Netherlands 1815 (No. 1066)			
13 Battle of Vimiera: English Army Enters Lisbon 1808 (No. 989)	34 Charge of the British at Waterloo 1815 (No. 1069)			
14 Death of Sir John Moore 1809 (No. 994)	35 Battle of Waterloo 1815 (No. 1068)			
15 Passage of the Duoro 1809 (No. 997)	36 English Army Enters Paris 1815 (No. 1077)			
16 Battle of Talavera 1809 (No. 999)	37 Surrender of Napoleon 1815 (No. 1078)			
17 English Army on the Tagus 1810–1811 (No. 1016)	38 Napoleon on St. Helena 1815 (No. 1079)			
18 Battle of Albuera 1811 (No. 1017)	39 Admiral Lord Exmouth 1816 (No. 1085)			
19 Capture of Badajoz 1812 (No. 1021)	40 Constitution Given to the Ionian Islands 1817 (No. 1094)			
20 Battle of Almarez 1812 (No. 1024)				
21 Battle of Salamanca: British Army Enters Madrid 1812 (No. 1026)				

D. 41 mm. *BHM* 1057

£   £

The medals were published by James Mudie and struck at Edward Thomason's manufactory in Birmingham. They are found in a double layer gilt-tooled maroon case, with an accompanying list of subscribers. Individual medals were available on subscription in gold, silver and bronze, priced at fifteen guineas (£15.75p), one guinea (£1.05p) and half a guinea (52½p), respectively; complete sets at the pro rata price of £630, £42 and £21. No examples in gold have been seen. Examples in white metal were probably struck c.1830–1840 by G. R. Collis, the successor to Edward Thomason. A full account of the series is to be found in James Mudie's catalogue issued in 1820.

1137   **Astronomical Society of London, Newton Medal 1820**
Obv. Bust of Isaac Newton, r. THE ASTRONOMICAL SOCIETY OF LONDON INSTITUTED MDCCCXX   *AV*   550   650
NUBEM PELLENTE MATHESI   *Rev.* Herschel's telescope mounted in a frame. QUICQUID NITET   *AR*   60   110
NOTANDUM   *Ex.* Blank (for recipient's name). *D.* 48 mm. By G. Mills. *BHM* 1058; *MI ii*, 472/88

Awarded from 1822 in gold and silver. A similar version by W. Wyon, but with the bust of Newton, l., was struck in 1831 when the Society received its Royal Charter, and was used subsequently.

1138   **Horticultural Society of London, Banksian Medal 1820**
Obv. Bust r. SIR JOSEPH BANKS Bᵀ P:R:S BORN 1743 DIED 1820. *Rev.* Plain centre (for recipient's   *AV*   —   —
name). THE HORTICULTURAL SOCIETY OF LONDON   *D.* 38 mm. By W. Wyon. *BHM* 1041;   *AR*   10   18
EPM 1887, 262/2   *AE*   4   7

Awarded in silver, and latterly bronze. An example in gold was presented to Lady Banks. A new die was subsequently prepared, based on this medal. *See* No. 955.

1139*   **Map of the World c.1820**
Obv. Detailed map of the EASTERN HEMISPHERE; continents of AFRICA ASIA EUROPE and NEW   *a AR*   130   250
HOLLAND identified, together with countries and islands. *Rev.* Detailed map of the WESTERN   *AE*   70   120
HEMISPHERE; continents of NORTH AMERICA and SOUTH AMERICA identified, together with   *WM*   35   65
countries and islands. *D. a* 74 mm.; *b* 51 mm. (By T. Halliday?). *See* **Plate 31**

There are minor differences between the two sizes. These pieces may have been struck by E. Thomason.   *b AR*   80   150
   AE   40   70
   WM   20   35

1140   **The Elgin Marbles c.1820**
Obv. Royal Arms. THE ELGIN MEDALS DEDICATED BY PERMISSION TO HIS MAJESTY GEORGE IV.   *a AE*   8   15
Rev. A fragment from the Parthenon frieze. *D.* 48 mm. (By?) *BHM* 1061   *WM*   2   6

Struck by E. Thomason. Type *a* is a single medal illustrating a fragment from the frieze on the reverse. Type *b* is the set of forty-eight medals, each depicting a different fragment, contained within four folio-sized leather bound books. Both types   *b AE*   —   500
share the one standard dedicatory obverse. Thomas Bruce, 7th Earl Elgin (1766–1841), British diplomat; arranged   *WM*   —   200
conveyance of the 'Elgin Marbles' from the Acropolis in Athens to the British Museum 1803–12.

1141   **Coronation of George IV 1821**
Obv. As No. 1123. *Rev.* CROWNED JULY XIX MDCCCXXI crowned, within a wreath. GOD SAVE   *AR*   180   350
THE KING   Hanoverian horse, below. *D.* 70 mm. By Rundell, Bridge and Rundell. *BHM*   *AE*   65   140
1088; *Jamieson* 27   *WM*   15   35

Examples which occur gilt and with a suspension loop on the edge may have been presented to North American Indian chiefs. More than forty medals commemorate the coronation.

1142   ——
Obv. Bust r. GEORGIUS IV BRITANNIARUM REX   *Rev.* The equestrian figure, l., armoured and   *AR*   60   110
plumed, of the King's champion. PRO REGE DIMICO   *Ex.* CORONAT JULII XIX MDCCCXXI   *AE*   25   45
D. 55 mm. By G. Mills. *BHM* 1087

Henry Dymoke (1801–65). The ceremony of King's champion is one which has been performed at coronations by members of the Dymoke family since the 14th century.

1143   ——
Obv. Bust l., laureate and draped. GEORGIVS IV DEI GRATIA BRITANNIAR REX F: D: Border of   *AR*   70   120
roses, thistles and shamrocks. *Rev.* The King enthroned, facing, crowned by Britannia,   *AE*   20   35
Hibernia and Scotia. ANTE PROBATA MINISTRAT. *Ex.* CORON: XIX JUL: A: D: MDCCCXXI.
D. 54 mm. By Thomason & Jones. *BHM* 1091

According to Carlisle (p.196) the engraver of this medal was W. Wyon, who left it unsigned as he was dissatisfied with the result.

1144   ——
Obv. Bust r., laureate and draped. GEORGIUS IV D: G: BRITANNIARUM REX F: D: *Rev.*   *AR*   70   120
Britannia seated, r., beside a lion and shield, inscribes CORON: XIX JUL: MDCCCXXI upon a   *AE*   20   40
tablet. MAGNUS SÆCLORUM NASCITUR ORDO   *Ex.* Spray of rose, thistle and shamrock.
D. 51 mm. By T. Wyon Jr./B. Wyon. *BHM* 1101; *Hocking* 249/27

The portrait must have been prepared prior to 1817 (when T. Wyon Jr. died).

			£	£
1145	*Obv.* Bust l., laureate and draped. GEORGE IV KING OF GREAT BRITAIN AND IRELAND ASC.ᴰ THE THRONE JANʸ 29 1820. *Rev.* GR IV crowned, within a spray of rose, thistle and shamrock. CORONATION AT WESTMINSTER JULY 19 1821 *D.* 46 mm. (By?) *BHM* 1076	*AR* *AE* *WM*	45 10 5	75 18 10
1146*	*Obv.* Bust l., laureate. GEORGIUS IIII D.G. BRITANNIARUM REX F.D. *Rev.* George IV enthroned, l., crowned by Victory, behind; before him stand Britannia, Hibernia and Scotia. PROPRIO JAM JURE ANIMO PATERNO. *Ex.* INAUGURATUS DIE. JULII. XIX ANNO. MDCCCXXI *D.* 35 mm. By B. Pistrucci. *BHM* 1070; *Wollaston* 24. See **Plate 31**	*a AV* *AR* *AE*	250 25 12	450 45 22
	The official Royal Mint issue. Type *b* is a close copy by E. Avern, and is sometimes signed E.A. on the truncation. Examples in silver were worn by the Buckinghamshire Yeomanry Coronation Horse, who formed the Royal Escort at the ceremony, and occur with the edge inscribed B.Y.C.H. (*Payne* 214).	*b AR* *AE*	35 15	65 30
1147*	**George IV, Coronation and Visit to Hanover 1821** *Obv.* Bust r., laureate and draped. GEORGIVS IV D. G. BRITAN. ET HANNOV. REX FID. DEF. *Rev.* Equestrian figure of George IV, r., preceded by Hanover. FELICEM AVGVSTI ADVENTVM *Ex.* REGNVM HANNOVERAN CELEBRAT MDCCCXXI *D.* 40 mm. By C. Voigt. *Parkes Weber* 215. See **Plate 31**	*AR* *AE*	50 20	90 35
	Some examples have a lettered edge: EX OFFICINA MONETARIA D. LOOS FIL. BEROLINI.			
1148	**Death of Caroline 1821** *Obv.* As No. 1130. *Rev.* A funerary urn on a plinth, inscribed CR, beneath a weeping willow tree. HERE CALUMNY AND SLANDER CEASE TO WOUND *Ex.* DIED AUG. 7. 1821. ÆT 53ʸᴿˢ *D.* 40 mm. By P. Kempson. *BHM* 1138	*AR* *AE* *WM*	35 15 7	60 30 15
1149	**Visit of George IV to Ireland 1821** *Obv.* Bust l., laureate. GEORGE IV ASCENDED THE BRITISH THRONE JAN 29 1820 IN THE 58 YEAR OF HIS AGE *Rev.* Irish harp, crowned, within a spray of rose, thistle and shamrock. IRELAND HAILS WITH JOY THE VISIT OF HER SOVEREIGN. AUGUST 1821. *D. a* 46 mm.; *b* 34 mm. (By?) *BHM* 1117	*a AR* *AE* *WM*	35 15 8	65 30 15
		b AR *AE*	25 10	40 20
1150	*Obv.* Bust l., laureate. GEORGIVS IV D.G. BRIT. ET HIBERNIÆ REX F.D: *Rev.* Hibernia standing before an altar looking at a trophy of arms. ADVENIT REX CONCORDAT CIVITAS *Ex.* MDCCCXXI *D.* 43 mm. By W. S. Mossop. *BHM* 1127; *Frazer* 1887/464	*AR* *AE* *WM*	50 20 10	85 35 20
	Two additional reverses have narrative inscriptions, recording copper mines at Tygrony, Co. Wicklow 1821, and Cappagh, Co. Cork 1822.			
1151	**Installation of the Knights of the Order of St. Patrick 1821** *Obv.* Bust l., laureate, within collar chain and badge of the Order. GEORGIUS IIII. D: G: BRITANNARIUM REX. F: D: *Rev.* Exterior view of St. Patrick's Cathedral. *Ex.* ROYAL INSTALLATION AT Sᵀ PATRICKˢ DUBLIN AUGUST XXVIII MDCCCXXI *D.* 46 mm. By I. Parkes. *BHM* 1173; *Frazer* 1893/9	*AR* *AE* *WM*	60 25 12	110 45 22
1152	**Death of John Rennie 1821** *Obv.* Bust l., draped. IOHN RENNIE BORN IVNE VII MDCCLXI DIED OCT. IV MDCCCXXI *Rev.* CRINAN & LANCASTER CANALS LONDON LEITH & SHEERNESS DOCKS WATERLOO & SOUTHWARK BRIDGES PLYMOVTH HOWTH & DVNLEARY HARBOVRS &ᶜ &ᶜ &ᶜ within a wreath. *D.* 64 mm. By W. Bain. *BHM* 1164; *CP* 120/61	*AR* *AE* *WM*	80 40 15	150 70 28
	John Rennie (1761–1821), civil engineer and bridge-builder. The obverse and reverse sometimes occur 'muled' with those of No. 1166.			
1153	**St. Peter's Church, Ashton-under-Lyne 1821** *Obv.* Façade of church. Sᵀ PETER'S CHURCH ASHTON UNDER LYNE GLORY TO GOD IN THE HIGHEST *Rev.* Twenty-four line narrative inscription, THE CEREMONIAL STONE OF THIS CHURCH, DEDICATED TO ST PETER, WAS LAID ... FRANCIS. GOODWIN. ARCHITECT. LONDON. – WILLIAM & GEORGE BROADHEAD, MASONS. SAMUEL MOSS, CARPENTER. ASHTON UNDER LYNE *D.* 64 mm. (By?) *Taylor* 80a; *Eidlitz* 1927, 465	*AR* *AE*	35 15	65 25
	Uniform medals commemorate stone-layings at Christ Church, West Bromwich 1821; St. George's, Southwark 1822; Holy Trinity, Bordesley 1823; St. George's, Leicester 1823; St. George's, Kidderminster 1824; St. Peter's, Birmingham 1827; St. George's, Wolverhampton 1828. Francis Goodwin (1784–1835), specialised in ecclesiastical architecture, restoring old churches and building many new ones.			
1154	**Duke of Wellington 1821** *Obv.* Head r. FIELD MARSHAL ARTHUR DUKE OF WELLINGTON. K.G. 1815 *Rev.* Mars receives a dagger from Minerva. AUSPICIIS MINERVÆ TRIUMPHUM EGIT MARS *Ex.* 1821 *D.* 51 mm. By T. Wyon Jr./B. Wyon. *BHM* 1167; *Bramsen* 2313	*AR* *AE*	80 35	130 60
	The precise occasion commemorated is unclear. The date on the obverse is probably when the portrait was prepared.			

PLATE 31

1112

1118

1135

1134

1139

1146

1147

1157

PLATE 32

1158

1159

1161

1166

1178

1183

1171

1187

1155 **Lord Combermere's Peninsular Victories 1821**
Obv. Bust l. LIEUT. GENERAL LORD COMBERMERE G.C.B. K.T.S. K.S.F. *Rev.* Victory advancing, l., with a scroll inscribed TALAVERA TORRES VEDRAS FUENTES D'ONOR LLERENA SALAMANCA ORTHES TOULOUSE *Ex.* 1821 *D.* 41 mm. By B. R. Faulkner. *BHM* 1157; *EPM* 1890, 70
Sir Stapleton Cotton, Viscount Combermere (1773–1865), Field-marshal.

	£	£
AR	35	60
AE	15	25
WM	7	12

1156 **Sir Robert Wilson 1821**
Obv. Bust l., uniformed. Sᴿ ROBᵀ WILSON KNGᵀ M.P. K.M.T. Sᵀ G.Rᴰ E. Sᵀ A.T. & S. C. & C. 1821 *Rev.* CIVIBUS SERVATIS within a wreath. *D.* 41 mm. By J. Westwood Jr. *BHM* 1168
General Sir Robert Wilson (1777–1849), Governor of Gibraltar. This medal may refer to an incident at Queen Caroline's funeral when an encounter took place between the household cavalry and a mob; shots were fired and Wilson interposed, preventing bloodshed.

AR	50	90
AE	20	35

1157* **Charles Hutton 1821**
Obv. Bust l., draped. CAROLUS HUTTON, LL.D. R.S.S. ÆT. LXXXV 1821 *Rev.* A rule, from one end of which hangs a ball; from the other, a globe; below, a cannon suspended from a quadrant. FULMINA BELLI PONDUSQ. TERRÆ ÆSTIMATA *D.* 44 mm. By B. Wyon. *BHM* 1158; *EPM* 1892, 323. *See* **Plate 31**
Charles Hutton (1737–1823), mathematician; computed the earth's mean density.

AR	40	70
AE	12	25

1158* **William Shakespeare Memorial 1821**
Obv. Bust almost facing, draped; 1821 on truncation. WILLIAM SHAKESPEARE. BORN APRIL 23 1564. DIED APRIL 23 1616. *Rev.* A man seated beneath a tree watches a stag drinking from a stream. TO THE WHICH PLACE A POOR SEQUESTERED STAG THAT FROM THE HUNTERS AIM HAD TA'EN A HURT DID COME TO LANGUISH *D.* 45 mm. By J. Westwood Jr. *BHM* 1166; *Ogden* 47. *See* **Plate 32**
The scene and quotation on the reverse are from *As You Like It*.

AR	35	65
AE	18	30

1159* **Suffolk Pitt Club 1821**
Obv. Bust of Pitt l., similar to No. 1039. NON SIBI SED PATRIAE. *Rev.* SUFFOLK PITT CLUB MDCCCXXI within a wreath. *D.* 35 mm. (By?) *BHM* 1171; *Guest* 1129. *See* **Plate 32**
See No. 1039.

AR	30	55

1160 **Thomason's Metallic Vase 1821**
Obv. Decorative vase upon a pedestal. THE THOMASON METALLIC VASE 21 FEET IN CIRCUMFERENCE & 5 FEET 10 IN. IN HEIGHT. *Rev.* A view of the base from another angle. BEGUN IN THE 54ᵀᴴ YEAR OF KING GEORGE III AND COMPLETED IN THE FIRST YEAR OF KING GEORGE THE IV. *D.* 54 mm. (By?) *BHM* 1176.
Sir Edward Thomason (1769–1849), inventor; manufacturer of medals, buttons and plate in Birmingham. A similar medal dated 1829 states that the vase had received a peroxide coating.

AE	8	15

1161* **Popularity of Sport 1821**
Obv. Two pugilists, standing, face to face. THE GOOD OLD ENGLISH CUSTOM OF DECIDING A QUARREL *Ex.* NEAT & GAS *Rev.* A square, a lion within; its edges with depictions of hunting, baiting, dog-fighting and cock-fighting. THE SPORTSMAN'S DELIGHT: BLOOD. BONE. ACTION AND GAME: *D.* 41 mm. By W(?) *BHM* 1159. *See* **Plate 32**
Thomas Hickman, known as the 'gas-light man' (1785–1822) was beaten by his fellow pugilist William Neat (1791–1858), on 11 December 1821.

AE	30	55
WM	15	28

1162 **Visit of George IV to Scotland 1822**
Obv. Bust l., laureate. GEORGIUS IIII D: G: BRITANNIARUM REX F: D: *Rev.* Scotia, kneeling, presents a crown to the King; beyond, Edinburgh Castle. *Ex.* REGIS SCOTIANI SCOTICIQUE ARCEM REGNI VISENTIS MONUMENTUM MENSI AUG MDCCCXXII. *D.* 45 mm. By W. Bain. *BHM* 1178; *CP* 32/1
An additional reverse records the erection of the Scottish national monument. More than twenty medals record the King's visit.

AR	28	50
AE	12	22
WM	5	12

1163 **George Canning 1822**
Obv. Bust of Canning, l. *Rev.* INDIÆ IMPERIO DESTINATUM. VOTA BRITANNORUM RETINENT. SEPT. MDCCCXXII. *D.* 50 mm. By W. Bain, [*obv.* after F. Chantrey] *BHM* 1198; *EPM* 1888, 268
George Canning (1770–1827), statesman; his appointment as Governor-General of India was abandoned due to the death of the Foreign Secretary, Lord Castlereagh, whose post he received. Other uniform portrait medals by Bain include: Francis Chantrey, 1825; George Granville, Duke of Sutherland, 1833; George Clint, 1833; Harriet, Duchess of Sutherland, 1837; and Mary Somerville, 1839.

AR	35	65
AE	10	20
WM	6	15

1164 **Congress of Verona 1822**
Obv. Bust r., uniformed. ARTHUR DUKE OF WELLINGTON *Rev.* CONGRESS OF VERONA M.DCCC.XXII. *D.* 41 mm. By W. Binfield. *BHM* 1199; *Bramsen* 1859

AE	30	55

			£	£

1165 **Royal Academy of Music 1822**
Obv. Bust of Apollo, facing, head r.; a lyre beneath left shoulder. *Rev.* A wreath (space within, for recipient's name). ROYAL ACADEMY OF MUSIC INSTITUTED 1822 *D.* 42 mm. By B. Wyon. *D & W* 146/352

	AR	9	12
	AE	3	5

Occurs with a suspension loop; awarded in silver and bronze and used as a prize for many years, with lettering becoming progressively weaker through heavy use of the dies. New ones were subsequently prepared by Messrs J. Pinches and signed accordingly.

1166* **Sheerness Docks and Basin Opened 1823**
Obv. Bust l. JOHN RENNIE   *Rev.* Plan of the docks and basin; below, cross-sectional view of a ship in dry dock. BASIN AND DOCKS AT SHEERNESS BEGUN JANUARY XIX MDCCCXIV OPENED SEPTEMBER. V MDCCCXXIII. *D.* 64 mm. By W. Bain. *BHM* 1220; *CP* 120/60. See **Plate 32**
See No. 1152.

	AR	120	200
	AE	65	110
	WM	25	45

1167 **William Wellesley-Pole 1823**
Obv. Bust of Pole, r. *Rev.* Nineteen line dedicatory inscription IN. HONOREM VIRI. PRÆNOR. G.V. POLE BARON MARYBOROUGH . . . CVDI. FECERVNT. MONETARII IN. OFFICINA. REGIA. LOND. A.S. MDCCCXXIII   *D.* 50 mm. By B. Pistrucci. *BHM* 1211; *Hocking* 236/16

	AR	60	110
	AE	25	45

William Wellesley-Pole, Lord Maryborough (1763–1845), Master of the Mint 1814–23; brother of Arthur, Duke of Wellington and Richard, Marquis Wellesley.

1168 **Brighton Royal Pier 1823**
Obv. Bust r., laureate. GEORGIUS IIII D: G: BRITANNIAR: REX F: D: *Rev.* View of the chain pier. BRIGHTHELMSTONE ROYAL PIER   *Ex.* DESIGNED & ERECTED BY SAMUEL BROWN ESQ: COMMANDER IN HIS MAJESTY'S NAVY 1823   *D.* 52 mm. By B. Wyon. *BHM* 1215; *Taylor* 79a

	AR	70	120
	AE	35	65

Sir Samuel Brown (1776–1852), engineer; invented an improved method of manufacturing links for chain cables.

1169 **Visit of George IV to Southampton 1823**
Obv. Bust l., laureate. GEORGIUS IV D: G: BRITANNIARUM REX   *Rev.* A naval crown within a wreath. PORTUM SUTHAMPTONIÆ INTRAVIT   *Ex.* VOTIS COMMUNITATIS: 1823   *D.* 54 mm. By W. Wyon. *BHM* 1205; *Hocking* 250/30
The visit did not in fact take place.

	AR	70	120
	AE	30	55

1170 **Royal Mechanics Institution, Manchester 1823**
Obv. Bust r., draped. B.A. HEYWOOD   *Rev.* Façade of the institution. INSTITVTVM REGIVM MANCVNIENSE   *Ex.* MDCCCXXIII. *D.* 50 mm. By W. Wyon. *BHM* 1209; *Taylor* 111a

	AR	40	70
	AE	20	35

Benjamin Arthur Heywood (died 1828), benefactor; he presented £500 to the Institution, which established a prize fund.

1171* **George IV 1824**
Obv. Bust l., hair bound with a ribbon, of George IV. ΓΕΩΡΓΙΟΣ Δ ΜΕΓ. ΒΡΕΤ. ΒΑΣΙΛΕΥΣ   *Rev.* An ornamental upright trident, flanked by two dolphins, dividing the date ᴬΩΚΔ (1824). *D.* 60 mm. By B. Pistrucci. *BHM* 1221; *Parkes Weber* 191. See **Plate 32**
The occasion commemorated by this medal is unclear.

	AV	—	—
	AR	250	400
	AE	80	150

1172 **Death of Lord Byron 1824**
Obv. Head l.; ΒΥΡΩΝ behind. *Rev.* A bay-tree remains uninjured by lightning. ΑΦΘΙΤΟΝ ΑΙΕΙ (Imperishable forever). *Edge.* F. ΠΙΚΕΡΙΝ. ΚΑΙ. F. ΦΟΡΘΙΝ ΤΩΝΤΙΔΣ. ΚΑΘΙΕΡΩΣΙΣ. Α. Ι. ΣΤΟΘΑΡ. Επ, aw δ (Dedication of W. Pickering and W. Worthington. A. J. Stothard 1824)   *D.* 64 mm. By A. J. Stothard. *BHM* 1231; *Forrer* V/695
George Gordon Byron, 6th Lord Byron (1788–1824), poet; joined Greek insurgents in their struggle for independence. At least ten medals commemorate Byron.

	AR	120	220
	AE	45	80

1173
Obv. Bust l., draped. GEORGE GORDON LORD BYRON. *Rev.* Byron, as Apollo, standing upon a mountain playing a lyre; lightning flashes from clouds. *D.* 51 mm. By B. R. Faulkner. *BHM* 1225; *EPM* 1888, 259/3

	AR	80	130
	AE	30	55

1174 **Royal National [Life-boat] Institution 1824**
Obv. Bust l. GEORGE THE FOURTH PATRON. ROYAL NATIONAL INSTITUTION FOR THE PRESERVATION OF LIFE FROM SHIPWRECK. 1824. *Rev.* Three men in a boat, one pulling a survivor out of the water. LET NOT THE DEEP SWALLOW ME UP   *D.* 35 mm. By W. Wyon [after H. Howard] *BHM* 1246; *MH* 1919, 835

	AV	700	1000
	AR	150	230
	AE	15	25
	WM	8	15

This medal was awarded in gold and silver to those who displayed exceptional bravery in saving, or attempting to save, life in shipwrecks on the coasts of the United Kingdom. It occurs with an elaborate suspension clasp which varies in form. *See* W. P. Dawson, 'Royal National Life-boat Institution's Medals', *OMRS* 1968, 78–84. The medallist, W. Wyon, has portrayed himself on the reverse, as the figure pulling the survivor out of the water.

1175 **Plymouth Dockyard Renamed Devonport 1824**
Obv. Fame, unfurling a ribbon inscribed DEVONPORT, heralds the arrival of Neptune, standing in a marine car, who points towards the dockyard. PORTUS ET ARA TUIS   *Rev.* IN GRATEFUL COMMEMORATION OF THE CONDESCENSION OF HIS MOST GRACIOUS MAJESTY GEORGE

	AR	35	60
	AE	12	25
	WM	8	15

IV, WHO CONFERED UPON THE TOWN FORMERLY KNOWN AS PLYMOUTH DOCK THE NAME OF DEVONPORT. ANN. DOM. MDCCCXXIV   *D.* 54 mm. By T. Halliday, *obv.* after R. Ellis. *BHM* 1244

£   £

1176   Isaac Walton 1824
Obv. Half-length bust, almost facing, draped. IZAAK WALTON. *Ex.* MDCCCXXIV   *Rev.* An angler leans mournfully against a tomb, inscribed IZAAK WALTON BORN 1593 DIED 1683. PISCATORIBUS SACRUM. *Ex.* T. GOSDEN. *D.* 36 mm. By E. Avern. *MI* i, 591/271; *BHM* 1239

AR	30	55
AE	15	25

In 1824 an edition of *The Complete Angler of Izaak Walton and Charles Cotton* was published by Thomas Gosden, bookseller, who may have issued this medal. Isaac Walton (1593–1683), biographer and author; Charles Cotton (1630–87), poet.

1177   Edinburgh Academy, Homer Medal 1824
Obv. Bust of Homer, l. ACADEMIA EDINENSIS JUVENTUTIS STUDIIS SACRATA: MDCCCXXIV: *Rev.* A wreath (space within, for recipient's name). Η ΠΑΙΔΕΙΑ ΚΑΙ ΤΗΣ ΣΟΦΙΑΣ ΚΑΙ ΤΗΣ ΑΡΕΤΗΣ ΜΗΤΗΡ   *D.* 51 mm. By W. Wyon. *CP* 138/14; *D & W* 224/172

AR   12   20

Awarded in silver and occurs with a suspension loop. A 39 mm. medal with the head of Virgil was also used by the Academy as a prize. Homer(?) Greek poet.

1178*   East Indiaman *Kent* Medal 1825
Obv. A burning ship from which departs a rowing boat carrying survivors towards another ship. *Ex.* 1. MARCH, 1825. *Rev.* TO COMMEMORATE THE DESTRUCTION OF THE KENT EAST INDIAMAN BY FIRE, IN THE BAY OF BISCAY; AND THE RECEPTION ON BOARD THE BRIG CAMBRIA, WILLIAM COOK, MASTER, OF 547 PERSONS, THUS PROVIDENTIALLY DELIVERED FROM DEATH., in the centre. FROM FALMOUTH, TRURO, HELSTON, PENRYN, AND Sᵀ IVES. *D.* 48 mm. By T. Halliday. *BHM* 1250; *MH* 1919, 578. *See* **Plate 32**

AR	70	120
AE	25	45
WM	12	25

Examples in silver sometimes occur with the edge inscribed with the name of a participant in the rescue.

1179   London Bridge, Stone-laying 1825
Obv. As No. 1166. *Rev.* THE FIRST STONE OF THIS WORK WAS LAID BY THE RIGHT HON. JOHN GARRATT LORD MAYOR OF LONDON ON THE XV DAY OF JUNE MDCCCXXV AND IN THE SIXTH YEAR OF THE REIGN OF HIS MAJESTY GEORGE IV   Above, view of the bridge; below, foundation stone, trowel and mallet. JOHN RENNIE ESQ. F.R.S. ENGINEER. JOLIFFE AND BANKS CONTRACTORS. *D.* 64 mm. By W. Bain. *BHM* 1253

AR	90	150
AE	50	80

1180   ——
Obv. Busts r., conjoined, she wearing a bandeau. THE R: HON: THE LORD MAYOR & LADY MAYORESS. *Rev.* TO COMMEMORATE THE LAYING OF THE FIRST STONE OF LONDON BRIDGE BY THE Rᵀ HON JOHN GARRATT LORD MAYOR ON THE 15ᵀᴴ OF JUNE 1825 IN THE PRESENCE OF H:R:H THE DUKE OF YORK. VARIOUS BRANCHES OF THE NOBILITY & THE CORPORATION OF THE CITY. AND IN TESTIMONY OF HIS LORDSHIPS PUBLIC WORTH AND PRIVATE VIRTUES. THIS MEDAL WAS DESIGNED AT THE REQUEST OF HIS FELLOW CITIZENS BY JOSEPH YORK HATTON   *D.* 47 mm. By W. Wyon, *obv.* after P. Rouw. *Carlisle* 198

AE   25   45

1181   Ross Horticultural Society, Kyrle Medal 1825
Obv. Bust l., draped, of Kyrle. THE MAN OF ROSS. A wreath around; gardening implements below. *Rev.* Two female figures, standing, hold a festoon of flowers in an arc over their heads. ROSS HORTICULTURAL SOCIETY ESTABLISHED MDCCCXXV   *D.* 49 mm. By S. W(?) *D & W* 178/594

AR	30	50
WM	8	15

Awarded in silver. John Kyrle, the Man of Ross (1637–1724), landscape and town planner; developer of Ross-on-Wye.

1182   University of London 1826
Obv. Façade of buildings: central portico, dome, and wings; W. WILKINS M.A. ARCᵀ below. DESIGN ADOPTED BY THE COUNCIL FOR THE UNIVERSITY OF LONDON 1826   *Rev.* Twenty-four line inscription of council members, COUNCIL HON. JAMES ABERCROMBIE M.P. .... THOMAS WILSON, in the centre. HISTORY. POLITICAL ECONOMY. MEDICAL SCIENCES. LANGUAGE. MATHEMATICS. PHYSICS. MENTAL SCIENCE. MORAL SCIENCES. *D.* 81 mm. (By?) *BHM* 1270; *Taylor* 97a

AR	70	120
AE	35	60

William Wilkins (1778–1839), architect; worked on Freemasons Hall, Bath (No. 1117) and The National Gallery, London.

1183*   Surrender of Bhartpur 1826
Obv. As No. 1155. *Rev.* Plan of BHURTPOOR and surrounding military positions. SURRENDER OF BHURTPOOR JANUARY 18 1826. *D.* 41 mm. By B. R. Faulkner. *BHM* 1263; *EPM* 1890, 71/2. *See* **Plate 32**

AR	45	85
AE	20	35
WM	8	15

1184   Death of Taylor Combe 1826
Obv. Bust of Combe, l. *Rev.* TAYLOR COMBE M.A. SEC. ROY. SOC. DIRECT. SOC. ANT. KEEPER OF COINS & ANTIQUITIES BRITISH MUSEUM DIED 1826 AGED 52, within a wreath. *D.* 45 mm. By W. J. Taylor, *obv.* after B. Pistrucci. *BHM* 1258; *EPM* 1890, 69.

AR	60	110
AE	25	45
WM	10	20

Taylor Combe (1774–1826), numismatist and archaeologist.

			£	£

1185   **Death of John Flaxman 1826**
Obv. Head l.; FLAXMAN behind. *Rev.* Female leaning on a short column upon which is a ribbon, inscribed TO GREAT MEN   *Ex.* MDCCCXXVI   D. 62 mm. By A. J. Stothard, *obv.* after E. H. Baily. *BHM* 1259; *EPM* 1891, 92   *AE*   20   35

John Flaxman (1755–1826), sculptor and draughtsman. From a series of 'Great Men' published by S. Parker; other portraits with this reverse include those of George Canning, Walter Scott, James Watt, and Frederick Duke of York.

1186   **The Royal Society, King's Medal 1826**
Obv. Bust r. GEORGIVS IIII REX SOC. REG. LOND. PATRONVS. 1826   *Rev.* Statue of NEWTON, between drawings of his theories: planetary solar system, l.; 66th proposition of the *Principia*, r. REGIS MVNIFICENTIA ARBITRIO SOCIETATIS   D. 72 mm. By W. Wyon [*obv.* after F. Chantrey] *BHM* 1271; *Hocking* 250/30A   *AV*   —   —   *AR*   250   450

Two gold medals were awarded annually from 1833 for the most important contributions to the advancement of natural knowledge, each in a triennial cycle of subjects: 1. astronomy; physiology. 2. physics; geology or mineralogy. 3. mathematics; chemistry. Until 1939 recipients also received a replica of their medal in silver, sometimes found frosted and set within a watch-style glass bound by a silver frame. The statue of Isaac Newton, by F. L. Roubiliac, is in Trinity College, Cambridge. The establishment of the Royal Medal was due largely to the endeavours of Sir Robert Peel; *see* R. M. Macleod, 'Of Medals and Men; A Reward System in Victorian Science 1826–1914', *Notes and Records of the Royal Society, Vol. 26*, No. 1, June, pp.81–105. *See also* No. 540.

1187*   **Zoological Society of London 1826**
Obv. A group of twelve different birds. *Ex.* ZOOLOGICAL SOCIETY OF LONDON 1826   *Rev.* A group of seven animals. D. 77 mm. By B. Wyon, after T. Landseer. *BHM* 1272. *See* **Plate 32**   *AV* — —   *AR* 200 350   *AE* 100 170

The design was approved by the Society's Council in 1837; the first medal was awarded, in silver, in 1847 for the introduction of European Bison. The last published list of recipients in 1957 (List of Fellows of the Z.S.L.) records the number of medals which have been awarded: five in gold (for special services); fifty-nine in silver; twenty-two in bronze (for keepers). *See* P. Chalmers Mitchell, *Centenary History of the Zoological Society of London*, London, 1919.

1188   **H.M. Ships *Adventure* and *Beagle* 1826**
Obv. GEORGE IV., in the centre. H.B.M.S. ADVENTURE AND BEAGLE. 1826   *Rev.* Britannia holding an olive-branch, seated, l., beneath a crown; wreath border. D. 26 mm. (By?) *BHM* 1262; *MH* 1919, 579   *AE*   15   28

Examples are also dated 1827 and 1828. The two ships were used in surveying the Straits of Magellan between 1826–8. These pieces appear to serve some function other than the purely commemorative.

1189   **Death of the Duke of York 1827**
Obv. Bust r. FREDERICK DUKE OF YORK AND ALBANY   *Rev.* Twenty-three line laudatory inscription ADMIRABLE AND EXEMPLARY AS A SON BROTHER & SUBJECT ... BORN 16 AUG. 1763 DIED 5 JAN. 1827   D. 60 mm. By B. Pistrucci. *BHM* 1283; *Parkes Weber* 187   *AV* — —   *AR* 70 120   *AE* 25 45

Frederick was much lamented; more than twenty medals commemorate his death and obsequies.

1190   ———
Obv. As No. 1035. *Rev.* A soldier standing, mournfully, beside a large funerary urn. DIED JAN. 5 1827. BELOVED BY HIS COUNTRY   D. 41 mm. By T. Webb. *BHM* 1286; *Bramsen* 1886   *AR* 35 60   *AE* 15 25   *WM* 5 12

1191*   **Duke of Wellington, Commander-in-Chief 1827**
Obv. Bust r.; WELLINGTON behind. *Rev.* Equestrian figure of Wellington, r., leading his troops. *Ex.* MDCCCXXVII   D. 63 mm. By J. Henning Sr./J. Henning Jr. *BHM* 1313; *Bramsen* 1644. *See* **Plate 33**   *AR* 110 180   *AE* 50 90

1192   **Duke of Clarence, Lord High Admiral 1827**
Obv. Bust of the Duke of Clarence, r. H.R.H. WILLIAM HENRY DUKE OF CLARENCE LORD HIGH ADMIRAL OF GREAT BRITAIN AND IRELAND. GEOR: IV: REX: MDCCCXXVII   *Rev.* Britannia advancing, r., across the sea; beyond, two ships. HER MARCH IS O'ER THE MOUNTAIN WAVE HER HOME IS ON THE DEEP. D. 65 mm. By J. Henning Sr. [*rev.* after A. R. Freebairn] *BHM* 1296; *MH* 1919, 583   *AR* 55 90   *AE* 20 35

Silver examples are usually gilt.

1193   **Plymouth Royal Regatta 1827**
Obv. Neptune advancing in his marine car, heralded by two mermen. *Rev.* View of the regatta. PORT OF PLYMOUTH ROYAL CLARENCE REGATTA   D. 51 mm. By T. W. Ingram. *BHM* 1315   *AR* 35 60   *AE* 15 25

A number of regattas during the nineteenth century are commemorated on medals.

1194   **Completion of the Gloucester and Berkeley Canal 1827**
Obv. A partially-rigged ship on water. GLOUCESTER & BERKELEY CANAL   *Ex.* COMMENCED 1793   *Rev.* RESUMED UNDER THE AUSPICES OF HIS ROYAL HIGHNESS THE DUKE OF GLOUCESTER 15 JULY, A.D. 1818; AND COMPLETED 26 APRIL 1827   D. 44 mm. By T. Halliday. *BHM* 1316   *AE* 45 75   *WM* 20 35

1195   **Death of George Canning 1827**
Obv. Bust l., draped. Rᵀ HON^{BLE} GEORGE CANNING BORN 1771   *Rev.* DIED AT CHISWICK THE
SEAT OF THE DUKE OF DEVONSHIRE AUGUST THE 8ᵀᴴ 1827   *D.* 46 mm. (By?) *BHM* 1304; *EPM*
1888, 270/6

	£	£
AR	25	40
AE	8	15
WM	5	12

More than ten medals commemorate Canning's death.

1196   **Battle of Navarino 1827**
Obv. Head of Pallas, r., helmeted. LA FLOTTE ANGLO FRANCO RUSSE VAINQUIT LES TURCS A
NAVARIN LE 20 OCTO: 1827   *Rev.* Crowns of France, England and Russia in a triangle;
between each, a radiate cross piercing a crescent. DE RIGNY CODRINGTON HEIDEN. *D.* 35 mm.
By Boyard. *MH* 1919, 581; *EPM* 1890, 65

AR	30	50
AE	15	25

Sir Edward Codrington (1770–1851), admiral; served under Howe at the First of June, Trafalgar, and in North America.
The medal was struck from three dies; it has also been restruck.

1197   **Earl of Eldon, Lord Chancellor 1827**
Obv. Bust l., wigged and robed. JOHN EARL OF ELDON LORD HIGH CHANCELLOR OF GREAT
BRITAIN 1827   *Rev.* Twelve-line biographical inscription BORN 4 JUNE 1751 CALLED TO THE
BAR 1776 ... CREATED VISC. ENCOMBE EARL OF ELDON 1821   *D.* 48 mm. By C. Voigt. *BHM*
1308; *Parkes Weber* 213.

AR	25	40
AE	8	15

John Scott, 1st Earl of Eldon (1751–1838), politician and attorney-general.

1198   **University of London, Fellowes Medal 1827**
Obv. Bust l. ROBERTVS FELLOWES. L.L.D. MERENTI PROPOSVIT.   *Rev.* Minerva seated, l.,
holding scroll and wreath. CUNCTI ADSINT MERITAEQUE EXPECTENT PRAEMIA PALMAE   *Ex.*
MDCCCXXVII   *D.* 38 mm. By W. Wyon. *Hocking* 297/39

AV	280	350
AR	12	20

Robert Fellowes (1771–1847), philanthropist; promoter of the University. The 'Fellowes' medals, of which there are two
others also sharing this obverse, were used as prizes well into the nineteenth century. The University of London changed
its name to University College in 1836.

1199   **Repeal of the Sacramental Test 1828**
Obv. Religion looks on as Liberty hands a scroll to Britannia, seated. SACRAMENTAL TEST
ABOLISHED. *Ex.* MAY 9ᴴ 1828   *Rev.* TRUTH FREEDOM PEACE CHARITY within a wreath. *D.*
61 mm. By S. Clint. *BHM* 1332

AE	12	22

The Test Act of 1673 required members of both Houses of Parliament to take the sacrament as a guard against the
introduction of Roman Catholics.

1200   **Daniel O'Connell 1828**
Obv. Bust l., draped. DAN O'CONNELL. M.P.   *Rev.* ELECTED FOR THE Cᴼ CLARE JULY 1828
within a wreath. THE MAN OF THE PEOPLE   *D.* 26 mm. By W. Woodhouse. *BHM* 1326;
Frazer 1887/613

AE	6	12

Daniel O'Connell (1775–1847), Irish national leader.

1201   **Royal Mint, Visit of Prince George of Cumberland 1828**
Obv. Head of George IV, l. GEORGIUS IV DEI GRATIA 1825   *Rev.* PRINCE GEORGE OF
CUMBERLAND VISITED THE MINT THE XVII DAY OF MAY MDCCCXXVIII   *D.* 38 mm. By W. Wyon.
BHM 1320; *Hocking* 240/51

AR	—	600

The portrait is that from the coinage die for a crown (*Seaby* 3806 sim). Prince George (1819–66), George V of Hanover
1851–66; son of Ernest Augustus, Duke of Cumberland.

1202   **Restoration of Windsor Castle 1828**
Obv. Bust r. GEORGIVS IV DEI GRATIA BRITANNIARVM REX   *Rev.* Façade of Windsor Castle.
WINDSOR CASTLE FOUNDED BY WILLIAM THE CONQUEROR. *Ex.* A phoenix: RESTORED BY GEORGE
IV 1828   *D.* 72 mm. By A. J. Stothard. *BHM* 1337; *Taylor* 131*a*

AR	130	250
AE	80	150

Uniface strikings of the obverse and reverse are sometimes found set into the lids of wooden boxes made from the old castle
beams.

1203   **Geological Society of London, Wollaston Medal 1828**
Obv. Bust l., draped; WOLLASTON behind.   *Rev.* THE GEOLOGICAL SOCIETY OF LONDON within a
wreath. *D.* 45 mm. By W. Wyon. *BHM* 1543; *Woodward* 89–91

Pd.	400	550
AV	400	550
AR	35	60
AE	15	30

First struck and awarded in 1831. William Hyde Wollaston (1766–1828), physiologist, chemist and physicist; discoverer of
the metal palladium. He was a benefactor of the Geological Society and endowed this medal, awarded annually in gold (and
in palladium from 1846 to 60) for research in the mineral structure of the earth.

1204   **Improvement in the Art of Coining 1828**
Obv. Head l. GEORGIUS IIII D.G. BRITANNIARUM REX F.D.   *Rev.* A SPECIMEN OF IMPROVEMENT IN
THE ART OF COINING within a wreath. *Edge.* TO FACILITATE LEGAL COINING AND DETER FROM
FORGERY, 1828   *D.* 42 mm. By T. Halliday. *BHM* 1334

AR	35	65
AE	12	25

Another reverse proclaims George IV as Patron of the Arts.

1205   **Richard Duppa 1828**
Obv. Bust l. RICARDVS DVPPA LL.B.   *Rev.* Rose, mitre and crozier on scrolls, inscribed M.
ANGET RAFF SVB[VER]TION OF [T]HE [PA]PAL [GOVER]NMENT, within a wreath. MDCCCXXVIII   *D.*

AR	45	70
AE	18	35

			VF	EF
			£	£

35 mm. By W. Wyon. *BHM* 1322; *EPM* 1891, 68

Richard Duppa (1770–1831), artist and author; the Papal symbols allude to his work 'A Journal . . . upon the Subversion of the Ecclesiastical Government in 1798'.

1206   Institution of Civil Engineers, Telford Medal 1828
Obv. Bust l.; TELFORD behind. *Rev.* View of the Menai suspension bridge; shipping below.
Ex. INSTIT: CIV: ENGINEERS. INCORP. 1828. *D.* 58 mm. By W. Wyon. *BHM* 1328; *Hocking*
296/26

	AV	—	—
	AR	60	110
	AE	30	50

Thomas Telford (1757–1834), civil engineer; the Menai Bridge was one of the first to adopt the suspension principle, using Samuel Brown's improved method of links (*see* No. 1168). Telford's bequest to the Institution made provision for the award of various annual premiums. It provided the funds for this medal, awarded from 1837 in gold, silver and bronze; since 1902 it has, with exceptions, only been presented in gold. Silver examples sometimes occur frosted and set within a watch-style glass bound with a silver frame. New dies, based on this medal, were prepared by J. S. & A. B. Wyon, *c.*1870. *See A Brief History of the Institution of Civil Engineers*, *The Medals 46–8*, London, 1928.

1207*   Institution of Civil Engineers, Watt Medal 1828
Obv. Bust r., draped; JAMES WATT 1736–1819 behind. *Rev.* A steam engine. *Ex.* INST. OF CIVIL
ENGINEERS INCORPORATED 1828   *D.* 48 mm. By J. S. Wyon. *BHM* 1329; *Eidlitz* 1928, 34.
See **Plate 33**

	AV	500	600
	AR	35	60
	AE	15	25

Struck in 1858 and awarded annually thereafter, usually in gold. *See* No. 1206.

1208   York Minster, Choir Destroyed by Fire 1829
Obv. Façade of the Minster. *Ex.* YORK MINSTER 1825   *Rev.* Interior of the cathedral. *Ex.* THE
CHOIR OF YORK MINSTER DESTROYED BY FIRE FEB^RY 2ND 1829. *D.* 45 mm. By Messrs. Barber,
Cattle and North. *BHM* 1361; *Taylor* 13*b*

	AE	12	20
	WM	5	12

A number of various medals commemorate events in the Minster's history.

1209   Death of Earl of Bridgewater 1829
Obv. Bust r., of Bridgewater. *Rev.* FRANCIS HENRY EGERTON, EARL OF BRIDGEWATER   *D.*
42 mm. By Donadio. *BHM* 1340; *Storer* 942

	AR	20	35
	AE	8	15

Francis Henry Egerton, 8th Earl of Bridgewater (1756–1829), author and literary scholar.

1210   Roman Catholic Emancipation 1829
Obv. As No. 1118. *Rev.* CATHOLIC DISABILITIES REMOVED APRIL 13TH 1829. IRELAND PACIFIED,
in the centre. GEORGE IV KING. ARTHUR DUKE OF WELLINGTON PRIME MINISTER. *D.* 55 mm. By
T. Webb, *obv.* after P. Rouw. *BHM* 1345

	AE	35	65

1211   ——
Obv. Bust r., draped. *D.* O'CONNELL ESQ^R MP THE UNDAUNTED ASSERTOR OF IRELAND'S RIGHTS.
Rev. Hibernia seated on the sea-shore, upon the British lion, displaying an olive-branch;
beyond, a ship sailing tranquilly. EMANCIPATION. OBTAINED. APRIL. 13. 1829. *D.* 49 mm. By
J. Jones. *BHM* 1344; *Frazer* 1887/320

	AE	35	65
	WM	15	28

Another reverse commemorates the Repeal of the Legislative Union.

1212*   Opening of Bure Bridge, Great Yarmouth 1829
Obv. View of the chain suspension bridge spanning the river. R^TO CORY R. FILIO
CONCIVES   *Ex.* J.J. SCOLES ARCH. M. IERN. M.DCCC.XXIX   *Rev.* OB PONT. FL. GARIENI D.S.P.
IMPOSIT. within a wreath. *D.* 49 mm. By B. Wyon. *BHM* 1354. *See* **Plate 33**

	AR	70	110
	AE	35	65

Joseph John Scoles (1798–1863), architect and archaeologist.

1213   Sir Frederick Hankey 1829
Obv. Hellas seated, l., feeds a serpent from a patera. ΑΤΕΡΜΑΝΤΟΥΣ ΧΑΡΙΤΑΣ ΤΗ ΠΡΟΣΤΑΤΙΔΙ.
Ex. IONIA   *Rev.* Greek dedicatory inscription [= To Sir Frederick Hankey, on behalf of his
Public Services, from the Legislative Union with gratitude] within a wreath; a phoenix
above. *D.* 56 mm. By Rundell, Bridge and Rundell.

	AR	180	280
	AE	80	140

Sir Frederick Hankey (1774–1855), colonel; administrator in the Ionian Islands.

1214   The Royal Society, Davy Medal 1829
Obv. Bust of Davy, r., draped. *Rev.* THE ROYAL SOCIETY TO (space, for recipient's name) IN
ACCORDANCE WITH THE WILL OF HUMPHREY DAVY WHO DEVOTED THE TESTIMONIAL PRESENTED
TO HIM BY THE COAL OWNERS OF THE TYNE AND WEAR TO THE ENCOURAGEMENT OF CHEMICAL
RESEARCH (space, for date). *D.* 75 mm. By N. Macphail, *obv.* after A. Bruce-Joy. *BHM* 3043;
Storer 804.

	AV	—	—
	AR	45	70
	AE	15	28

Sir Humphrey Davy (1778–1829), natural philosopher and chemist. Struck in 1877, and awarded annually in gold (in bronze from 1935) for important discoveries in chemistry.

1215   Death of Sir Thomas Lawrence 1830
Obv. Bust r., 1830 (incuse) on truncation; LAWRENCE behind. *Rev.* SIR THO^S LAWRENCE. BORN
VI MAY MDCCLXIX. ELECTED PRESIDENT OF THE ROYAL ACADEMY XXX MARCH MDCCCXX DIED VII
JAN: MDCCCXXX   *D.* 42 mm. By S. Clint. *BHM* 1449

	AE	15	25

Thomas Lawrence (1769–1830), royal portrait painter. Another reverse has a different view of Lawrence, bust l., after E. H. Baily.

1216 Death of George IV 1830

			£	£
Obv. Bust r.; GEORGE IIII behind. *Rev.* HIS REIGN BROUGHT VICTORY, PEACE, AND CONCORD., within a beaded circle. GEORGE. IV. BY. THE. GRACE. OF. GOD. KING. OF. GREAT. BRITAIN & IRELAND. DEFENDER. OF. THE. FAITH. KING. OF. HANOVER & BRUNSWICK. &c BORN. XII. AUGUST. MDCCLXII. ASCENDED. THE. THRONE. XXIX. JANUARY. MDCCCXX DIED. XXVI. JUNE. MDCCCXXX. *D.* 114 mm. By A. J. Stothard, *obv.* after F. Chantrey. *BHM* 1364		*a AE*	140	240
		b AE	45	80

Type *a* is a complete struck medal (and one of the largest in the entire British series). Type *b* is made in two halves and joined by a rim; the obverse is sometimes found on its own mounted in a frame. More than forty medals record the King's death.

1217 ——

Obv. Bust r., laureate and draped. GEORGIUS IIII DEI GRATIA REX *Rev.* Similar to No. 1216. *D.* 62 mm. By A. J. Stothard. *BHM* 1363	*AE*	18	35

1218 ——

Obv. Bust facing, draped. KING GEO. IV *Rev.* Death, upon a flight of steps, reaches for crown, cushion and book upon a plinth; below, Prince's plumes and coronet. GEO. IIII *Ex.* DIED JUNE 26 1830 *D.* 51 mm. By E. Avern. *BHM* 1365	*AR*	60	110
	AE	25	40

1219*

Obv. Bust l. HIS MOST GRACIOUS MAJESTY GEORGE IV *Rev.* Façade of Windsor Castle. *Ex.* DIED AT WINDSOR CASTLE JUNE 26 1830. AGED 67. *D.* 51 mm. (By B. R. Faulkner?) *BHM* 1391; *Taylor* 131*b. See* **Plate 33**	*AR*	60	110
	AE	15	30
	WM	8	15

WILLIAM IV, 1830–37

1220 Accession of William IV 1830

Obv. Bust r. GUILELMO IIII D: G: BRITANNIAR: REGI F: D: *Rev.* ADELAIDE REGINA CUDI JUSSIT MDCCCXXX, trident below; within a wreath. *D.* 68 mm. By W. Wyon, *obv.* after F. Chantrey. *BHM* 1414; *Hocking* 250/31	*AR*	180	350
	AE	60	110

Another reverse has a crown added above the inscription. More than twenty medals celebrate the King's accession.

1221 ——

Obv. Bust r. HIS MOST GRACIOUS MAJESTY WILLIAM IV 1830 *Rev.* Bust r., draped. HER MOST GRACIOUS MAJESTY QUEEN ADELAIDE 1830 *D.* 55 mm. By E. Thomason. *BHM* 1423	*AR*	70	130
	AE	18	35
	WM	10	18

1222 Princess Victoria, Visit to the Soho Mint 1830

Obv. VICTORIA MAGNÆ SPES ALTERA BRITANNIÆ. SOHO. 6. AUG. 1830 *Rev.* Britannia seated upon a rock, l., holding olive-branch and trident. BRITANNIA *D.* 34 mm. By C. H. Küchler. *BHM* 1435	*AR*	—	120
	AE	—	45

Alexandrina Victoria (1819–1901), Queen Victoria 1837–1901; grand-daughter of George III and only child of Edward, Duke of Kent and Mary Louisa Victoria of Saxe-Coburg and Saalfeld. The reverse die is that from the 1806–7 currency penny (*Seaby* 3780). Another obverse records the visit of the Duchess of Kent, Victoria's mother, on the same day.

1223 Liverpool and Manchester Railway Opened 1830

Obv. Train crossing viaduct in an open landscape; canal below. VIADUCT OVER THE SANKEY CANAL & VALLEY *Ex.* TO COMMEMORATE THE OPENING OF THE LIVERPOOL AND MANCHESTER RAILROAD. SEP. 15. 1830 *Rev.* Twin tunnel entrances seen through an archway beneath which locomotives pass along a cutting. ENTRANCE TO THE LIVERPOOL STATION & TUNNELS *D.* 49 mm. By T. Halliday. *BHM* 1458; *Moyaux* 4	*AR*	80	150
	AE	35	65
	WM	15	30

1224*

Obv. Bust l. GEO. STEPHENSON ESQ. ENGINEER *Rev.* Train crossing viaduct in a landscape. BRIDGE AT NEWTON *Ex.* LIVERPOOL & MANCHESTER RAILWAY OPENED SEPT. 15 1830. *D.* 46 mm. (By?) *BHM* 1459; *Moyaux* 3. See **Plate 33**	*AR*	80	150
	AE	35	65
	WM	18	35

George Stephenson (1781–1848), inventor and civil engineer.

1225 William Huskisson, Memorial 1830

Obv. Bust l.; HUSKISSON behind. *Rev.* THE SUCCESSFUL VINDICATOR OF HIS OWN ENLIGHTENED SYSTEM OF COMMERCIAL POLICY, HE LIVED TO TRIUMPH OVER PREJUDICE AND TO FOUND A LASTING FAME. MDCCCXXX. *D.* 62 mm. (By?) *BHM* 1447; *EPM* 1892, 319	*AE*	15	28

William Huskisson (1770–1830), statesman; present at the opening of the Liverpool–Manchester Railway in 1830 and accredited as the first railway fatality on that occasion.

1226 Earl Grey Appointed Prime Minister 1830

Obv. Head l. .EARL GREY. BRITONS BE TRVE TO YOUR KING *Rev.* Equestrian figure, l., attacked by two lions; reins loose and broken. BY TRAMPLING ON LIBERTY I LOST THE REINS.	*AE*	2	3

1830. *D.* 22 mm. (By?) *BHM* 1442; *EPM* 1891, 399   £   £

This refers to Wellington's unpopularity as Prime Minister in refusing parliamentary reform, and his subsequent resignation. Charles Grey, 2nd Earl Grey (1764–1845), statesman.

1227*	**Middlesbrough Branch Railway Opened 1830**		
	Obv. End view approach to the bridge. SUSPENSION BRIDGE NEAR STOCKTON *Ex.*	*AR*	65	120
	MIDDLESBRO' BRANCH RAILWAY OPENED DEC^R 27. 1830. *Rev.* Ships and barges moored at a	*AE*	45	75
	wharf. STOCKTON & DARLINGTON RAILWAY CO^S COAL STAITHS. AT MIDDLESBRO' *D.* 45 mm.	*WM*	20	35
	By T. W. Ingram. *BHM* 1464; *Moyaux* 7. See **Plate 33**			

1227*   **Middlesbrough Branch Railway Opened 1830**
Obv. End view approach to the bridge. SUSPENSION BRIDGE NEAR STOCKTON *Ex.*   *AR*   65   120
MIDDLESBRO' BRANCH RAILWAY OPENED DEC^R 27. 1830. *Rev.* Ships and barges moored at a   *AE*   45   75
wharf. STOCKTON & DARLINGTON RAILWAY CO^S COAL STAITHS. AT MIDDLESBRO'   *D.* 45 mm.   *WM*   20   35
By T. W. Ingram. *BHM* 1464; *Moyaux* 7. See **Plate 33**

1228A   **Royal Academy of Arts 1830**
Obv. Bust r. GVLIELMVS IIII D: G: BRITANNIARVM REX MDCCCXXX PATRONVS. *Rev.* Represen-   *AR*   70   130
tation of the Torso Belvedere. ROYAL ACADEMY INSTITUTED MDCCLXVIII   Below STVDY   *D.*   *AE*   20   35
55 mm. By W. Wyon, [*obv.* after F. Chantrey] *BHM* 1466; *Hocking* 250/33

Awarded in silver. *See* No. 724.

1228B   *Obv.* As *A. Rev.* The three Graces, personifying Architecture, Painting and Sculpture.   *AV*   700   1000
AEMULA QUAEQUE SORORIS   *Ex.* ROYAL ACADEMY OF ARTS LONDON. INSTITUTED   *AR*   70   120
MDCCLXVIII   *D.* 55 mm. By W. Wyon [after F. Chantrey/T. Stothard] *BHM* 1465

Awarded biennially in gold, in the three disciplines represented, until 1936. *See* Nos. 723–4.

1229   **Royal Geographical Society, Founder's Medal 1830**
Obv. Bust r. GVLIELMVS IIII D: G: BRITANNIARVM REX MDCCCXXX. FVNDATOR. *Rev.* Britannia   *AV*   600   800
standing, l., beside sextant and globe, holding wreath and scroll. OB TERRAS RECLUSAS.   *Ex.*   *AR*   80   130
ROYAL GEOGRAPHICAL SOCIETY OF LONDON.   *D.* 55 mm. By W. Wyon. *BHM* 1467; *Hocking*   *AE*   30   45
294/10; *Poulsom* 88

Awarded annually since 1839 in gold, and from 1975 in silver gilt; given for the encouragement and promotion of geographical science and discovery; the reverse is shared by other prize medals of the Society, including the Patron's Medal which carries an effigy of the reigning monarch.

1230   **Royal College of Surgeons, Blane Medal 1830**
Obv. Bust l. GILBERT BLANE BARONETTVS ARCHIATRVS AET: LXXXI. *Rev.* A sailor, supporting a   *AV*   270   400
lifeless body, regards Britannia, standing beside a pedestal with medicinal plants. MENTE   *AR*   80   150
MANVQVE   *Ex.* FOUNDED MDCCCXXX. *D.* 38 mm. By B. Pistrucci. *BHM* 1439; *Storer* 393;   *AE*   20   35
Payne 302; *MH* 1919, 585

Sir Gilbert Blane (1749–1834), physician; introduced the use of lime juice in the Navy to prevent scurvy. Awarded in gold, and occasionally gilt silver, to naval medical officers for the advancement of medical science in the Royal Navy. *See* R. P. Phillips, 'The Gilbert Blane Medal', *OMRS* 1975, 146–8.

1231   **Liverpool Agricultural Society 1830**
Obv. Farming landscape, with animals and harvesting. *Rev.* A wreath (space within, for   *AR*   25   38
recipient's name); above, a liver bird. LIVERPOOL AGRICULTURAL SOCIETY INSTITUTED
1830   *D.* 47 mm. By B. R. Faulkner.

Examples occur frosted and set within a watch-style glass bound with a silver frame.

1232   **Masonic Charity Jewel 1830**
Obv. HONORABLE TESTIMONIAL OF MASONIC CHARITY & BENEVOLENCE INSTITUTED BY H: R: H: *AR*   10   18
AUG FRED: DUKE OF SUSSEX M.W. GRAND MASTER   Below, square and compasses. *Rev.* Female   *AE*   2   5
figure of Charity, her arms around a boy and girl; above, Eye of Providence. *Ex.*
MDCCCXXX   *D.* 36 mm. (By?) *BHM* 1463; *Shackles* 16

Examples of this medal have been struck for many years; they frequently occur gilt and set within a watch-style glass.

1233   **Society of Apothecaries, Linnaeus Medal 1830**
Obv. Bust r., draped. CAROLUS LINNAEUS   *Rev.* Hygeia, seated, instructs a youth in the   *AR*   35   65
science of Botany, and points to a tablet, inscribed RAY, LINNAEUS, JUSSIEU, SLOANE   To r.,   *AE*   15   25
vase with medicinal plants. OB SOLERTIAM IN STUDIIS BOTANICIS LAUDATAM SOC. PHARM.
LOND. VOLUIT A.D. 1830   *Ex.* Caduceus decorated with the Society's badge. *D.* 47 mm. By
W. Wyon. *Storer* 6530; *Hyckert I*, 258/18

Awarded in silver. Charles Linnaeus, real name Carl von Linné (1707–1778), Swedish botanist.

1234*   **Charles Linnaeus, Plant Classification** *c.*1830
Obv. THE 24 CLASSES OF PLANTS BY LINNÆUS, within a small central circle. Around, thirteen   *WM*   8   18
classes of plants, numbered 1 to 13 and identified. *Rev.* Bust l., draped. C. LINNÆUS BORN
1707, within a small central circle. Around, eleven classes of plants, numbered 14 to 24 and
identified. *D.* 49 mm. (By?) *Storer* 2198; *Hyckert I*, 253/8. See **Plate 33**

1235   **Liverpool Botanic Garden** *c.*1830
Obv. Bust l., draped. CAROLUS LINNÆUS   *Rev.* A liver bird between two bountiful   *AR*   30   48
cornucopiae. LIVERPOOL BOTANIC GARDEN   *D.* 50 mm. By Sheriff. *Storer* 2177; *Hyckert I*,   *AE*   15   25
258/17

PLATE 33

1191

1207

1212

1219

1224

1227

1234

1237.13

1242

PLATE 34

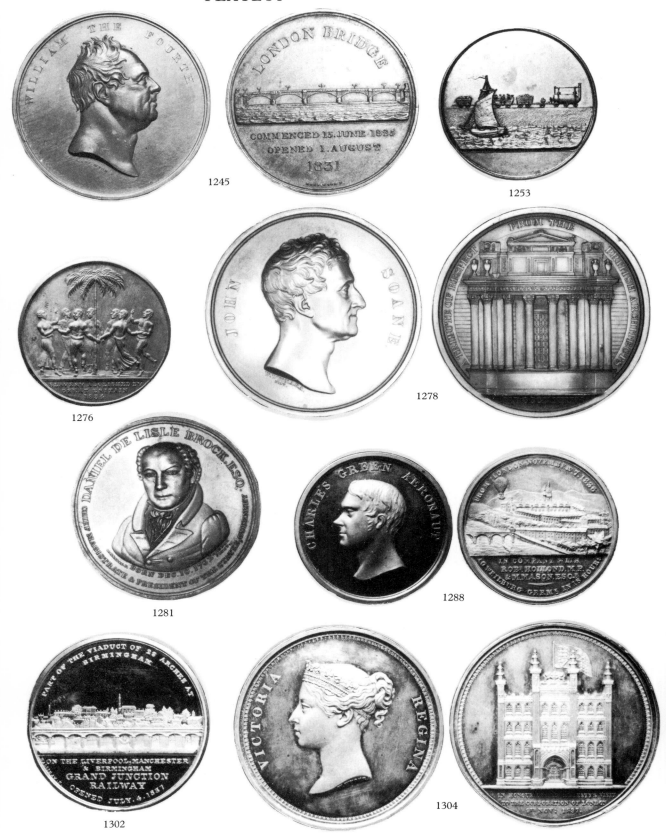

1245

1253

1276

1278

1281

1288

1302

1304

The period *c.*1824–50 saw the establishment of botanic gardens and societies throughout B. Isles. Several issued prize medals with the effigy of Linnaeus, including those of Birmingham; Dereham; Diss; Durham, Northumberland and Newcastle; Handsworth; Holt; Jersey; Sheffield; South London; Wellington.

                                                                         £   £

1236   **Kings and Queens of England** *c.*1830

Obv. Portrait of a British sovereign. *Rev.* Biographical inscription. *D.* 40 mm. By E. Thomason [after J. Dassier] and J. Marrian. *BHM* 1437

           a AE   —   220
           WM   —   140

Type *a* consists of thirty-six medals of British sovereigns, William I to George IV; their portraits after Dassier's series (No. 526), except those of George III (bust l.) and George IV (bust r.), which are both by J. Marrian. Each medal has a biographical inscription on the reverse. The set sometimes occurs on trays or in book form. Type *b* consists of the thirty-four medals as contained in No. 526*a*, but later strikings (some are struck from reworked dies), with the addition of medals of George III (bust l./Britannia mourning) and George IV (bust r./biographical inscription, as in No. 1236*a*) by J. Marrian. These thirty-six medals sometimes occur on wooden trays.

           b AE   —   220

1237*   **Scientific and Philosophical Medals** *c.*1830

1 Astronomy	7 Mechanics	12 Optics
2 Chemistry	8 Metallurgy	13 Phrenology
3 Crystallography	9 Mineralogy	14 Trevithick's/Savery &
4 Electricity	10 Mountains	Worcester's Engine
5 Geology	11 Newcomen & Broughton's/	15 Watt's single engine
6 Hydraulics/Hydrostatics	Perkin's Engine	16 Watt's double engine

           a   25   45
           b   —   280

Each with an illustration or a narrative inscription. *D.* 73 mm. By E. Thomason. *BHM* 1336. *See* **Plate 33**

The value stated for single pieces is for those with a documentary illustration. Type *b* comprises the sixteen medals contained in a leather-bound case with a magnifying glass. Thomas Newcomen (1663–1729), inventor of the atmospheric steam engine. Angier March Perkins (1799?–1881), American engineer and inventor. Thomas Savery (1650?–1715), engineer. Edward Somerset, 6th Earl of Worcester (1601–67), claimed to have invented a steam engine. Richard Trevithick (1771–1833), 'father' of the locomotive engine.

1238   **Medallic Bible** *c.*1830

Obv. Enactment of a biblical episode. *Rev.* Narrative inscription and date of the depiction. *D.* 73 mm. By E. Thomason. *BHM* 1468

           a AR   —   —
           WM   4   8
           b AR   —   —
           WM   —   250

Type *b* comprises the entire series of sixty medals, which occur in five leather-bound volumes. In 1969 a set in silver, of reduced diameter, was produced in the United States.

1239   **Brokers' Pass** *c.*1830

Obv. Royal arms; below, spray of rose, thistle and shamrock, and motto DIEU ET MON DROIT *Rev.* Arms and motto of the City of London. *Ex.* Plain (for holder's name). *D.* 40 mm. By B. Wyon. *Caldecott* 4; *Guest* 1336

           AR   28   40
           AE   12   20

Examples in bronze are specimen strikings. *See* No. 426.

1240   **Winchester College, King's Medal** *c.*1830

Obv. Head r., of William IV. HONOREM PRINCEPS PROPONIT Below, W. IV. R. *Rev.* Tomb of William of Wykeham at Winchester. ETIAM SEPULTI VIVIT FAMA WYKEHAMI *Ex.* OBIT XXVII. SEPT. A.D. MCCCCIV *D.* 49 mm. By S. Clint. *MI i*, 11/5; *BHM* 1560

           AR   40   60
           AE   10   18

Awarded in silver. The college has awarded medals with portraits of subsequent sovereigns, each with this reverse.

1241   **Joseph Hume** *c.*1830

Obv. Bust almost facing, draped. JOS. HUME ESQ M.P. F.R.S. *Rev.* OF CIVIL AND RELIGIOUS LIBERTY, THE VIRTUOUS AND ENLIGHTENED FRIEND: OF JUSTICE AND NATIONAL INTEGRITY, THE IMPARTIAL & UNDAUNTED DEFENDER. Laurel wreath, above. *D.* 38 mm. By T. Halliday. *BHM* 1531; *CP* 124/76; *Storer* 1711

           AE   15   28
           WM   6   10

Joseph Hume (1777–1855), radical politician; surgeon to the East India Company.

1242*   **New Channel to Newport Opened** 1831

Obv. Shipping on the channel; hills beyond. IN COMMEMORATION OF THE OPENING OF THE NEW CHANNEL TO NEWPORT ON THE 10 FEBY 1831 *Ex.* AND OTHER IMPROVEMENTS FOR DEEPENING & STRAIGHTENING THE REST OF THE CHANNEL OF THE RIVER BETWEEN STOCKTON & THE SEA *Rev.* A fully-rigged ship. TEES NAVIGATION COMPY INCORPORATED BY ACT OF PARLT 1808 NEW CHANNEL OPENED 27 SEPR 1810 MELIORA SPERAMUS *D.* 51 mm. By Ottley, *obv.* after W. A. Brooks. *BHM* 1549. *See* **Plate 33**

           AE   35   65
           WM   20   35

1243   **Duke of Cambridge, Viceroy of Hanover** 1831

Obv. Bust l., draped. ADOLPH FRIEDRICH HERZOG V. CAMBRIDGE *Rev.* DEM ALLGELIEBTEN VICEKOENIGE HANNOVER 22 FEBRUAR 1831 within a wreath. *D.* 40 mm. By M. Fürst. *BHM* 1526

           AE   18   30

1244   **Presentation of the Reform Bill** 1831

Obv. Four portrait medallions of H.M.G. MAJESTY WILLIAM IIII/EARL GREY/LD. CHANCEL BROUGHAM/LD. JOHN RUSSELL; below, an anchor on a scroll inscribed THE CONFIDENCE OF THE PEOPLE *Rev.* THE DESIRE OF THE PEOPLE THE REFORM BILL, spray of rose, thistle and

           AE   15   28
           WM   7   12

		£	£

shamrock. NO UNMERITED PENSIONS NO TITHES NO CORN LAWS NO GAME LAWS NO STAMP TAXES NO EAST INDIA MONOPOLY NO COLONIAL SLAVERY   *D.* 46 mm. By T. Halliday. *BHM* 1535; *EPM* 1891, 403/6.

Lord John Russell, 1st Earl Russell (1792–1878), statesman. More than sixty medals commemorate the various stages of the Reform Bill.

1245*   **London Bridge Opened 1831**
Obv. Bust r. WILLIAM THE FOURTH   *Rev.* Five-arched bridge spanning river. LONDON BRIDGE   *Ex.* COMMENCED 15 JUNE 1825 OPENED 1. AUGUST 1831   *D.* 51 mm. By B. Wyon. *BHM* 1544; *Taylor* 102a; *Welch* 1. See **Plate 34**   *AE*   18   35

The first of twenty-eight medals issued by the Corporation of the City of London. They celebrate occasions such as the opening of buildings and the reception of British and foreign royalty in the City; *see* Index. All except the first five and No. 1658 were issued in fitted cases, with a narrative inscription of the ceremony in gilt lettering on the lid; some were issued in cases holding two examples of the medal.

1246   ——
Obv. NEW LONDON BRIDGE THE FIRST STONE WAS LAID BY THE Rᵀ HON THE LORD MAYOR JOHN GARRATT ESQᴿ ON THE 15 JUNE 1825 AND THE BRIDGE OPEN'D BY THEIR MAJESTIES THE 1ˢᵀ AUGˢᵀ 1831 COST 506,000 POUNDS   *Rev.* Five-arched bridge spanning river with ships. LENGTH 928 Fᵀ WIDTH 56 Fᵀ CARRIAGE WAY 36 Fᵀ   *Ex.* WATER WAY 692 FEET CENTRE ARCH 152 SIDE ARCHES 140 EXTREME 130 HEIGHT 55   *D.* 29 mm. (By?) *BHM* 1548; *Taylor* 102b   *Br.*   3   5   *WM*   2   4

1247   ——
Obv. City of London shield, crest and motto. *Rev.* LONDON BRIDGE COMMENCED 15. JUNE 1825 OPENED 1. AUGUST 1831. Above, badge of the Bridge-House Estates. *D.* 27 mm. [By B. Wyon] *BHM* 1545; *Welch* 2   *AR*   45   75   *AE*   17   32   *WM*   12   22

Issued by the Corporation of London. See No. 1245.

1248   **Coronation of William IV 1831**
Obv. Bust r., similar to No. 1220. GULIELMUS IIII D: G: BRITANNIAR: REX F: D: *Rev.* CROWNED SEP VIII MDCCCXXXI   Above, trident and oak branch within a naval crown. Beyond, clouds above an open sea. COLLECTASQUE FUGAT NUBES SOLEMQUE REDUCIT   *D.* 68 mm. By W. Wyon, [*obv.* after F. Chantrey] *BHM* 1476   *AR*   180   350   *AE*   60   110

More than fifty medals commemorate the coronation.

1249   ——
Obv. Busts r., conjoined, she diademed. HIS MOST GRACIOUS MAJESTY WILLIAM IV AND QUEEN ADELAIDE   *Rev.* Britannia and lion stand on the shore awaiting an approaching ship. CROWN'D AT WESTMINSTER ABBEY SEPTᴿ 8. 1831   *Ex.* KING WILLIAM IV AND QUEEN ADELAIDE   *D. a* 47 mm.; *b* 35 mm. (By?) *BHM* 1497   *a AR*   40   70   *AE*   20   30   *WM*   4   10

     b AR   25   40   *AE*   2   6

1250   ——
Obv. Busts r., conjoined and draped. THEIR MOST GRACIOUS MAJESTIES WILLIAM IV & ADELAIDE. *Rev.* Britannia, Hibernia and Scotia stand before the King and Queen, enthroned, and observe the ceremony, heralded by Fame, above. KING WILLIAM IV. BORN AUGᵀ 21ˢᵀ 1765. QUEEN ADELAIDE BORN AUGᵀ 13ᵀᴴ 1792. *Ex.* CROWNED SEPᴿ 8ᵀᴴ 1831. *D.* 42 mm. By T. W. Ingram. *BHM* 1485.   *AR*   40   70   *AE*   15   28   *WM*   6   10

1251   ——
Obv. Bust r. WILLIAM THE FOURTH CROWNED SEP: 8 1831   *Rev.* Bust r., diademed. ADELAIDE QUEEN CONSORT. CROWNED SEP: 8 1831. *D.* 33 mm. By W. Wyon, *obv.* after F. Chantrey. *BHM* 1475; *Wollaston* 25   *AV*   280   420   *AR*   25   55   *AE*   12   25

The official Royal Mint issue.

1252   **Sunday Schools, 50th Anniversary 1831**
Obv. Bust l., draped. ROBERT RAIKES ESQᴿ FOUNDER OF SUNDAY SCHOOLS. SUNDAY SCHOOL JUBILEE SEPᴿ 14ᵀᴴ 1831. BIRMᴹ SUNDAY SCHOOL UNION. *Rev.* FROM A CHILD THOU HAST KNOWN THE SCRIPTURES WHICH ARE ABLE TO MAKE THE WISE UNTO SALVATION in the centre. Above, Eye of Providence; below, palm and laurel. REMEMBER THE SABBATH DAY TO KEEP IT HOLY. SEARCH THE SCRIPTURES. *D.* 38 mm. By T. W. Ingram. *BHM* 1551   *AR*   25   35   *AE*   6   10   *WM*   2   5

Robert Raikes (1735–1811), founder of Sunday Schools; publisher.

1253*   **Gloucester and Cheltenham Railway c.1831**
Obv. Locomotive pulling passengers and freight in three open wagons; in foreground, barge on canal. *Rev.* ROYAL WILLIAM LOCOMOTIVE ENGINE CLASS Nº 1, in the centre. GLOUCESTER AND CHELTENHAM RAILWAY   *D.* 43 mm. (By T. Halliday?) *Moyaux* 2; *D & W* 326/20–1. See **Plate 34**   *AE*   25   45   *WM*   15   30

The line was originally a tram-road built in 1811 by the Gloucester and Cheltenham Railway Co. for the two-way traffic of rocks and coal from Leckhampton Quarry to Gloucester Docks, where it met the Gloucester & Berkeley Canal. The Company held unsuccessful trials on the line for a passenger service. These medals appear to have served as a ticket or pass; a similar piece is inscribed Class Nº 2.

		£	£

1254　The Reform Bill 1832

Obv. REFORM IN THE REPRESENTATION OF THE PEOPLE IN THE COMMONS HOUSE OF PARLIAMENT 1832, crown above; within a wreath decorated by the City of London shield. *Rev.* Liberty, kneeling, presents a bill of REFORM to Britannia who stands before a plaque, inscribed GREY BROUGHAM ALTHORP RUSSELL, on which rests a medallion of WILLIAM THE [F]OURTH *Ex.* 2ND & 3RD WILLIAM IV　D. 51 mm. By B. Wyon. *BHM* 1603; *Welch* 3

		VF	*EF*
	AR	30	65
	AE	15	32
	WM	10	18

Issued by the Corporation of London (*see* No. 1245). John Charles Spencer, Viscount Althorp and 3rd Earl Spencer (1782–1845), statesman.

1255　——

Obv. The King, enthroned, attended by Britannia displaying a banner, inscribed UNION, and four figures. OUR CAUSE HATH TRIUMPHED GLORIOUSLY THE HORSE & HIS RIDER HATH HE THROWN INTO THE SEA　*Ex.* EXODUS CHAP.15.V.21　*Rev.* A rectangular table in the centre enumerating the Bill's various stages: times, dates, readings and votes. Around sides: MINISTERIAL BILL OF REFORM INTRODUCED BY L.J. RUSSEL MAR. 1. 1831 ROYAL ASSENT JUNE 7. 1832/PARLIAMENT BY THE KING IN PERSON DISSOL. APRIL 22 OPEND. JUNE 21 PROROG OCT. 20 REASSEM DEC. 6 1831/INTRODUCED COMM. MAR. 1 1831 TIME (1) JUNE 24 (2) DEC. 12 (3) LORDS SEP. 22 1831 MAR. 26 1832/EARL GREY AND HIS MINISTERS RESIGNED MAY 8. 1832 REAPPOINTED MAY 15. 1832　D. 51 mm. By J. Davis. *BHM* 1578

		VF	*EF*
	AR	28	55
	AE	15	25
	WM	8	15

1256　——

Obv. Portrait medallion of WILLIAM IV. KING OF GREAT BRITAIN, r., within a central circle. Around, three segments inscribed THE REFORM BILL PASSED THE COMMONS MARCH 23 THE LORDS JUNE 4 RECᴰ THE ROYAL ASSENT JUNE 7. 1832/56 BOROUGHS DISFRANCHISED 30 OLD BOR. TO RETURN 1 MEMBER EA. 22 NEW BOR. TO RET. 2 MEM. EA. 21 NEW BOR. 1 MEM. EA./THE ELECTIVE FRANCHISE VESTED IN FREEHOLDERS COPYHOLDERS OF £10 P. AN. LEASEHOLDERS £50 P. AN. HOUSEHOLDS £10 P. AN.　*Rev.* Justice and Mercury observe Britannia, brandishing a sword, who drives Corruption, holding money-bag, into the sea; radiate triangle, inscribed KING LORDS COMMONS, above. BRITANNIA SUPPORTED BY JUSTICE DRIVES CORRUPTION FROM THE CONSTITUTION　*Ex.* MDCCCXXXII　D. 51 mm. By T. Halliday. *BHM* 1587; *EPM* 1891, 404/10 (sim.)

		VF	*EF*
	AE	12	25
	WM	6	10

The reverse occurs with different obverses.

1257　——

Obv. Bust l. RᵀHONᴮᴸᴱ EARL GREY REAPPOINTED TO OFFICE THROUGH THE UNANIMOUS VOICE OF THE PEOPLE MAY 15. 1832. *Rev.* Lion reclining amidst REFORM BILLS, cornucopiae, fasces and staff of liberty. MAJORITY 84/ENGLISH REFORM BILL FINALLY　*Ex.* PASSED THE HOUSE OF LORDS JUNE 4. 1832. D. 43 mm. By J. Davis. *BHM* 1579; *EPM* 1891, 405/11

		VF	*EF*
	AR	25	45
	AE	12	20
	WM	4	8

1258　Thomas Attwood, Parliamentary Reform 1832

Obv. Bust l., draped. THOMAS ATTWOOD ESQ FOUNDER OF POLITICAL UNIONS　*Rev.* Lion l., upon sea-shore near rocks. OUR WEAPONS ARE PEACE LAW ORDER LOYALTY & UNION　D. 41 mm. [By J. Davis] *BHM* 1564; *EPM* 1887, 258/3

		VF	*EF*
	AE	15	25
	WM	6	10

Thomas Attwood (1783–1856), politician and banker. Several medals record political unions including those of Birmingham 1830, Chard 1831, and Renfrewshire 1832.

1259　Joshua Scholefield, M.P. for Birmingham 1832

Obv. Bust l., draped. JOSHUA SCHOLEFIELD. M.P. BORN MAY 23. 1775　*Rev.* THE ENLIGHTENED ADVOCATE OF PARLIAMENTARY REFORM, THE ARDENT FRIEND OF COMMERCIAL, CIVIL & RELIGIOUS FREEDOM, THE CHOICE OF A FEARLESS AND INDEPENDENT PEOPLE TO REPRESENT THEM IN THE FIRST REFORMED PARLIAMENT DEC. 12. 1832.; above, Mercury with the Union flag. D. 41 mm. By T. Halliday. *BHM* 1577

		VF	*EF*
	AE	15	25
	WM	6	10

Joshua Scholefield (1775–1844), politician, banker and manufacturer.

1260　Robert Owen 1832

Obv. Bust r.; below, TRUTH, and a panoramic view of a factory within a rectangular plaque. ROBᵀ OWEN　*Ex.* 1832　*Rev.* THE KNOWLEDGE THAT THE CHARACTER OF MAN IS FORMED FOR AND NOT BY HIM CAN ALONE PRODUCE UNIVERSAL CHARITY AND LOVE. D. 33 mm. By W. Bain. *BHM* 1575

		VF	*EF*
	AR	25	40
	AE	15	25
	WM	8	15

Robert Owen (1771–1858), socialist; pioneer of industrial co-operation.

1261　George Clint 1832

Obv. Bust l., draped, of Clint. *Rev.* GEO CLINT A.R.A. 1832 (in running script). D. 52 mm. By S. Clint, *obv.* after H. Burlowe. *BHM* 1570; *EPM* 1890, 59

		VF	*EF*
	AE	12	22

George Clint (1770–1854), portrait painter and engraver. He is the medallist's father.

				£	£

1262   **Death of Sir Walter Scott 1832**
Obv. Bust l. SIR WALTER SCOTT. BART: *Rev.* A scene from *Lady of the Lake.* *Ex.* LADY OF THE LAKE CANTO 1 ST XVII   *D.* 49 mm. By W. Bain/B. R. Faulkner. *BHM* 1576; *CP* 121/67
Walter Scott (1771–1832), poet, novelist and historian.

		AR	25	45
		AE	12	20
		WM	5	10

1263   **Death of Jeremy Bentham 1832**
Obv. Head r. JEREMY BENTHAM ESQ. M.A.   *Rev.* DIED JUNE 6 1832 AGED 85 within palms. *D.* 33 mm. By T. Halliday. *BHM* 1568; *EPM* 1888, 63
Jeremy Bentham (1748–1832), political and social reformer; one of the promoters of University College, London.

		AR	40	70
		AE	25	45
		WM	12	22

1264   **Brighton Pavilion 1832**
Obv. View of gardens before the domed pavilions. THE ROYAL PAVILION BRIGHTON   *Ex.* Royal arms, radiate. *Rev.* View of the ornate entrance; above, W.R. IIII A.D. MDCCCXXXII across the arch. THE PRINCIPAL ENTRANCE TO THE ROYAL PAVILION   *D.* 57 mm. By J. Langridge. *BHM* 1643
The reverse occurs coupled with an obverse of Queen Victoria.

| | | AE | 50 | 90 |
| | | WM | 22 | 40 |

1265   **William IV and Adelaide 1832**
Obv. Busts r., conjoined; he laureate and she diademed. WILLIAM IIII. ADELAIDE   *Rev.* W A cypher, crowned. WHOM GOD PRESERVE 1832   *D.* 11 mm. By J. B. Merlen. *BHM* 1561; *Hocking* 244/100
This may allude to an incident at Ascot in June when someone threw a stone at the King, without injuring him.

| | | AV | — | 35 |
| | | AR | — | 15 |

1266   **Robert Cutlar Fergusson 1832**
Obv. Head l., of Fergusson. NEC DEERUNT QUI MEMINERINT MEI   *Rev.* ROBERTO CUTLAR FERGUSSON CANDIDO AC TENACI JURIS GENTIUM PROPUGNATORI VI OPPRESSA GENIO SUPERSTES POLONIA DICAVIT. M.D.CCC.XXXII., within a wreath decorated with the Polish shield. *D.* 50 mm. By W. Oleszczinski. *BHM* 1572; *CP* 122/70
Robert Cutlar Fergusson (1768–1838), M.P. and Judge-Advocate-General; advocate on behalf of Poland, whose exiles caused this medal to be struck.

| | | AE | 15 | 25 |

1267   **Polish Associations of Great Britain 1833**
Obv. THE POLISH ASSOCIATIONS OF GREAT BRITAIN TO UNHAPPY HEROIC POLAND 1833 within a wreath. *Rev.* Standing female figure of Polonia being comforted by that of Britannia. POLAND THOU ART NOT LOST   *D.* 41 mm. By T. Halliday. *BHM* 1654

| | | AE | 12 | 22 |
| | | WM | 4 | 9 |

1268   **Sir Ronald Crauford Ferguson 1833**
Obv. Head of Ferguson, r. *Rev.* TO GENERAL SIR R.C. FERGUSON K.C.B. M.P. MDCCCXXXIII W. BAIN., within a wreath. LET GRATEFUL ART RECORD THE PATRIOT'S NAME. *D.* 49 mm. By W. Bain. *BHM* 1649; *CP* 122/71
Sir Ronald Crauford Ferguson (1773–1841), Scottish officer in the Peninsular War. A dedicatory medal from the artist.

| | | AR | 30 | 55 |
| | | AE | 12 | 22 |

1269   **Walgherton Female Friendly Society 1833**
Obv. INSTITUTED JULY 23ᴿᴰ 1833 in the centre. WALGHERTON FEMALE FRIENDLY DIVIDEND SOCIETY. *Rev.* Shield, crest and motto. JOHN TWEMLOW ESQ. OF HATHERTON PATRON   *D.* 36 mm. by 44 mm. Oval. (By?) *D & W* 195/749
The establishment of several friendly societies is recorded on medals, such as Hafod, 1798; Handsworth, 1830; and Wiltshire, 1828.

| | | AE | 12 | 18 |

1270   **British and Foreign Temperance Society 1833**
Obv. Female seated, her hand resting on the HOLY BIBLE, the other holding a shield, inscribed TOTAL ABSTINENCE FROM ALL INTOXICATING LIQUORS; a scroll, inscribed MODERATION, by her foot. TEMPERANCE SOCIETY   *Ex.* ESTABLISHED 1833   *Rev.* UNION IS STRENGTH; above, clasped hands and the Eye of Providence. All within a wreath interlaced with a ribbon inscribed RELIGION HEALTH PEACE VIRTUE   *D.* 44 mm. By W.S (?) *BHM* 1656

| | | AR | 25 | 40 |
| | | WM | 8 | 15 |

1271   **The Royal Society, King's Medal 1833**
Obv. Bust r. GVLIELMVS IIII REX SOC: REG: LOND: PATRONVS. 1833   *Rev.* As No. 1186. *D.* 72 mm. By W. Wyon. *BHM* 1655
See No. 1186.

| | | AV | — | — |
| | | AR | 250 | 450 |

1272   **Royal Cornwall Polytechnic Society 1833**
Obv. Bust l., draped. JAMES WATT   *Rev.* ROYAL CORNWALL POLYTECHNIC SOCIETY INSTITUTED 1833/FIRST CLASS within a wreath. *D.* 45 mm. By W. Wyon. *Eidlitz* 1928, 23; *CP* 118/56
Awarded as a prize, usually in silver, for many years; it was also given in other classes. Several scientific societies and technical schools used a portrait of Watt on their prize medals.

| | | AR | 15 | 25 |
| | | AE | 6 | 10 |

1273   **Duke of Wellington, Chancellor of Oxford University 1834**
Obv. As No. 1118. *Rev.* IN ACADEMIAE CANCELLARIATVM COMMVNI. OMNIVM. PLAVSV COOPTATVS ARTHVRVS. DVX. DE. WELLINGTON DEDVCENTIBVS. EVM. PRAELATIS PROCERIBVS.

| | | AE | 18 | 30 |

		VF £	EF £

PRINCIPIBVS OXONIAM. INVISIT MENSE. IVNIO ANNO. SACRO CIƆ IƆ CCC XXXIIII *D.* 55 mm. By T. Webb, *obv.* after P. Rouw. *BHM* 1664; *Bramsen* 1929

On some examples the signature is indistinct.

1274 ——

Obv. Bust r., draped, of Wellington. *Rev.* HIS GRACE THE DUKE OF WELLINGTON CHANCELLOR OF THE UNIVERSITY OF OXFORD INSTALLED JUNE 10TH 1834 *D.* 38 mm. (By?) *BHM* 1663; *D & W* 268/487

		AR	28	45
		AE	12	20
		WM	4	9

1275 Abolition of Slavery 1834

Obv. A negro standing, facing, in an open landscape, his arms raised. ENGLAND I REVERE. GOD I ADORE. NOW I AM FREE. *Ex.* MDCCCXXXIV *Rev.* COLONIAL SLAVERY ABOLISHED THROUGHOUT THE BRITISH DOMINIONS AUGUST 1. 1834. IN THE REIGN OF WILLIAM IV. crowned, within a wreath. *D.* 51 mm. By J. Davis. *BHM* 1668

AR	90	160
AE	35	60
WM	15	30

More than ten medals celebrate the abolition of colonial slavery.

1276* ——

Obv. William IV seated beneath a canopy, facing, attended by advisors. *Ex.* I ADVOCATE THIS BILL AS A MEASURE OF HUMANITY *Rev.* Seven negroes, their hands linked, dance joyously around a palm tree. *Ex.* SLAVERY ABOLISHED BY GREAT BRITAIN 1834 *D.* 41 mm. (By T. Halliday?) *BHM* 1673. *See* **Plate 34**

AR	70	120
AE	30	50
WM	12	25

1277 Completion of Birmingham Town Hall 1834

Obv. Façade of building. BIRMINGHAM TOWN HALL 1834 *Ex.* HANSOM & WELCH ARCHTS *Rev.* Twenty-two line inscription detailing the building's dimensions and advisory committee THE COMMITTEE APPOINTED TO SUPERINTEND THE ERECTING OF THE BUILDING ... THE ORGAN IS THE MOST POWERFUL ONE IN EUROPE, AND IS 40 FEET WIDE AND 45 FEET HIGH. *D.* 73 mm. (By?) *BHM* 1678; *Taylor* 108d

AR	40	70
AE	15	30
WM	8	15

Several medals record the erection of Birmingham Town Hall. Joseph Aloysius Hansom (1803–82), architect and designer. He was instrumental in founding the journal, *The Builder*, and also registered a design for the carriage to which he gave his name. Edward Welch (?), architect.

1278* Sir John Soane 1834

Obv. Bust r. JOHN SOANE. *Rev.* Façade of the Bank of England. A TRIBUTE OF RESPECT FROM THE BRITISH ARCHITECTS *Ex.* MDCCCXXXIV *D.* 57 mm. By W. Wyon [*obv.* after F. Chantrey] *BHM* 1662; *Taylor* 106a. *See* **Plate 34**

AV	—	—
AR	45	80
AE	20	35

Sir John Soane (1753–1837), architect; his house in Lincoln's Inn Fields, central London, survives today as a delightful museum. An example of this medal in gold was subscribed to and presented as a testimonial to Soane.

1279 City of London School Founded 1834

Obv. Façade of the school building. CITY OF LONDON SCHOOL *Ex.* FOUNDED BY THE CORPORATION 1834 I.B. BUNNING ARCH. *Rev.* Knowledge seated, r., instructs a youth who leans upon a tablet, inscribed IOHN CARPENTER 1447, and decorated with the City arms. FOR THE RELIGIOUS & VIRTUOUS EDUCATION OF BOYS & THEIR INSTRUCTION IN LITERATURE & USEFUL KNOWLEDGE. *D.* 58 mm. By B. Wyon. *BHM* 1680; *Taylor* 120a; *Welch* 4

| AR | 30 | 45 |
| AE | 15 | 25 |

Issued by the Corporation of London (*see* No. 1245). The school opened in 1837; this medal, and designs based on it, were used as prizes, in silver, for various subjects during the nineteenth century. James Bunstone Bunning (1802–63), City architect whose work includes the Coal Exchange and Holborn Valley Viaduct. John Carpenter (1370?–144?), town clerk of London; his bequest endowed the foundation of a new school.

1280 Institute of British Architects, Honorary Medal 1834

Obv. Façade of the temple of Theseus, decorated with the Institute's badge. VSVI CIVIVM DECORI VRBIVM *Ex.* MDCCCXXXIV *Rev.* INSTITVTE OF BRITISH ARCHITECTS within a wreath. *D.* 57 mm. By B. Wyon, *obv.* after T. L. Donaldson. *Taylor* 24a

| AR | 28 | 45 |
| AE | 12 | 20 |

Awarded annually, usually in silver, for an essay or a set of measured drawings. *See The Royal Institute of British Architects, Studentships and Prizes 1896–97.* Thomas Leverton Donaldson (1795–1885), architect; designed the Institute's motto and badge. Author of *Architectura Numismatica*, 1859. *See* No. 1582.

1281* Daniel de Lisle Brock 1835

Obv. Bust facing, draped. DANIEL DE LISLE BROCK, ESQ. BORN DEC. 10. 1762 CHIEF MAGISTRATE & PRESIDENT OF THE STATES, GUERNSEY *Rev.* WHOSE DEVOTION TO HIS COUNTRY'S WEAL HAS OBTAINED HIM A NAME MORE LASTING AND IMPERISHABLE THAN ALL THE HONOURS WHICH RANK AND TITLES COULD BESTOW. 1835 within a wreath. Above, arms of Guernsey. *D.* 51 mm. By T. Halliday, after E. Le Bas. *BHM* 1684; *EPM* 1888, 89. *See* **Plate 34**

AR	50	90
AE	28	45
WM	15	25

Daniel de Lisle Brock (1762–1842), Bailiff of Guernsey.

1282 Marquis of Camden, Chancellor of Cambridge University 1835

Obv. Bust l., draped. JOAN: JEFFREYS MARCH: CAMDEN: NOBILISS: ACAD: CANTAB: CANCELL: 1835 *Rev.* Interior view of Senate House. *Ex.* DEUM TIMETO: REGEM HONORATO: VIRTUTEM

| AR | 20 | 35 |
| AE | 5 | 9 |

COLITO: DISCIPLINIS BONIS OPERAM DATO. *D.* 44 mm. [By J. Peters] *BHM* 1685; *Taylor* 45a	*WM*	2 4

Sir John Jeffreys Pratt, 1st Marquis of Camden (1759–1840), politician. Another reverse has an exterior view of the Senate House. Uniform medals of Cambridge chancellors were published by J. Peters and include those of Prince Albert 1847, and the Duke of Devonshire 1862 (No. 1559).

1283   **First English Bible, Tercentenary 1835**

Obv. Bust almost facing, draped. MYLES COVERDALE BISHOP OF EXETER *Rev.* TO COMMEMORATE THAT GLORIOUS EVENT THE PUBLICATION OF THE FIRST ENGLISH BIBLE BY MYLES COVERDALE OCT^R 4TH 1535 AND OF THE THIRD CENTENARY OF THE PROTESTANT REFORMATION CELEBRATED OCT^R 4TH 1835   *D.* 44 mm. By J. Davis. *MI* i, 37/25; *BHM* 1691

	AR	22 38
	AE	6 10
	WM	3 5

Miles Coverdale (1488–1568), translator of the Bible.

1284   **General Agricultural Association of Ayrshire 1835**

Obv. Farm animals in a landscape. *Rev.* A wreath (space within, for recipient's name). GENERAL AGRICULTURAL ASSOCIATION OF AYRSHIRE INST. MDCCCXXXV   *D.* 46 mm. (By?) *CP* 180/13; *D & W* 104/25   *AR*   20   30

Other Scottish agricultural societies which issued prize medals include Dumfries 1776, Renfrewshire 1819, and Dumbartonshire 1896.

1285   **Christ Church, Newark 1836**

Obv. Façade of the church. JULY 1836 *Ex.* CHRIST CHURCH NEWARK *Rev.* ERECTED BY VOLUNTARY CONTRIBUTION UNDER 1 & 2 W.IV.C.38 – JAMES THORPE ESQ^RE MAYOR Scroll inscribed 2 CHRONICLES C.VI.40. 41.42 *D.* 50 mm. By Ottley. *Taylor* 114a   *WM*   8   15

Churches throughout Britain are commemorated on numerous medals during the nineteenth century, including Argyle Chapel, Bath; St. Philips, Birmingham; St. Peter's, Brighton; St. Thomas's, Dudley; St. Mary's, Nantwich; St. Peter and St. Paul, Shepton Mallet; St Mary's, Stockport; St. Mary and St. Nicholas, Wiltshire. *See* Nos. 1153, 1403 and 1504.

1286   **Wesleyan Methodist Conference, Birmingham 1836**

Obv. Half-length bust, l., at a pulpit. REV^D JOHN WESLEY. A.M. NAT. 1703 OB 1791. WHAT HATH GOD WROUGHT *Rev.* THE NINETY-THIRD CONFERENCE OF THE WESLEYAN METHODISTS. (THE FIRST HELD IN BIRMINGHAM) BEGUN JULY 27 1836. THE REV^D DR BUNTING – PRESIDENT – THE REV^D R NEWTON SECRETARY THE REV^D DR FISK REPRESENTATIVE FROM AMERICA. THE REV^D MESS^RS STEWART & WAUGH FROM IRELAND   *D.* 46 mm. By Ottley. *BHM* 1714

	AR	48 75
	AE	22 38
	WM	10 20

A similar medal commemorates a conference held at Bristol in 1838.

1287   **Death of Nathan Mayer Rothschild 1836**

Obv. Bust r. NATHAN. MAYER. ROTHSCHILD. *Rev.* NUMMIS MAXIMUS REPERITUR. OB. JUL: XXVIII MDCCCXXXVI   *D.* 61 mm. [By J. Barber] *BHM* 1706; *JMC* 1185   *AE*   80   140

Nathan Mayer Rothschild (1777–1836), merchant banker; founder of the English branch of the Rothschild family. Both this medal and No. 1370 were published by Hyam Hyams.

1288*   **Charles Green, Aerial Voyage to Weilburg 1836**

Obv. Bust l. CHARLES GREEN AERONAUT *Rev.* Balloon floating over town and landscape. FROM LONDON NOVEMBER 7. 1836 *Ex.* IN COMPANY WITH ROB^T HOLLOND, M.P. & M. MASON, ESQ^R TO WEILBURG GERM^Y IN 18 HOURS   *D.* 42 mm. By W. J. Taylor. *BHM* 1704; *EPM* 1891, 396. *See* **Plate 34**

	AR	100 180
	AE	70 120
	WM	28 50

Charles Green (1785–1870), aeronaut.

1289   **Captain John Ross 1836**

Obv. Bust l., draped. CAPT. SIR JOHN ROSS C.B. & c. 1836   Without reverse. *D.* 179 mm. Cast. By D. d'Angers. *Parkes Weber* 50   *AE*   —   150

Sir John Ross (1777–1856), Arctic explorer who made an unsuccessful search for John Franklin. David d'Angers executed a gallery of cast portrait medals of European celebrities, generally from 90 mm. to 180 mm. in diameter. Those relating to Britain include Marc Isambard Brunel, Lord Byron, George Canning, John Franklin, Arthur O'Connor, and Amelia Opie.

1290   **Horticultural Society of London, Knightian Medal 1836**

Obv. Bust l., draped. THOMAS ANDREW KNIGHT PRESIDENT. MDCCCXXXVI. *Rev.* THE ROYAL HORTICULTURAL SOCIETY within a wreath. *D.* 44 mm. By W. Wyon. *BHM* 1705; *Hocking* 217/32–3

	AV	gold value
	AR	15 25

Awarded in gold and silver for specimens of edible fruits and greenhouse plants; medals with this particular reverse were struck after 1861, when the Society was designated 'Royal'. Thomas Andrew Knight (1759–1838), vegetable physiologist and horticulturalist. W. Wyon engraved the Society's Flora Medal in the same year. *See* No. 955.

1291   **Robert Peel, Rector of Glasgow University 1837**

Obv. Bust almost facing, draped. THE R^T HON^BLE SIR ROBERT PEEL, BAR^T M.P. INSTALLED LORD RECTOR OF THE UNIVERSITY OF GLASGOW JAN^Y 11 1837 *Rev.* University's arms and insignia within a wreath. ENTERTAINED AT A PUBLIC DINNER IN GLASGOW BY UPWARDS OF 3000 CITIZENS. *D.* 46 mm. By Ottley. *BHM* 1749; *CP* 157/22

	AR	25 45
	AE	8 15
	WM	5 10

Sir Robert Peel, 2nd Baronet (1788–1850), politician.

1292   **Majority of Princess Victoria 1837**

				£	£
Obv, Bust l., draped, head almost facing. PRINCESS ALEXANDRINA VICTORIA *Rev*. BORN 24		*a AE*		20	35
MAY 1819 DAUGHTER OF HIS LATE ROYAL HIGHNESS EDWARD DUKE OF KENT within a wreath. TO		*WM*		5	12
COMMEMORATE HER ROYAL HIGHNESS ATTAINING HER LEGAL MAJORITY 24 MAY 1837 *D. a*					
51 mm.; *b* 34 mm. By Ottley. *BHM* 1743		*b AE*		12	20
More than ten medals celebrate Victoria's majority.		*WM*		3	7

1293   ——

		£	£
Obv. Bust three-quarters r., draped. H.R.H. PRINCESS ALEX: VICTORIA BORN MAY 24.	*AR*	40	70
1819 *Rev*. Victoria seated, facing, upon an island rock; around, figures of Britannia,	*AE*	15	30
Hibernia and Scotia. THE BIRTH DAY OF THE HEIRESS PRESUMPTIVE TO THE BRITISH	*WM*	4	9
THRONE *Ex*. MAY 24. 1837 *D*. 45 mm. By T. Halliday. *BHM* 1737			

1294   ——

		£	£
Obv. Bust l., of Victoria, wreath of roses in her hair; 1837 below. *Rev*. HER ROYAL HIGHNESS	*AR*	45	80
THE PRINCESS VICTORIA BORN XXIV MAY MDCCCXIX. within a wreath. *D*. 36 mm. By W. Wyon.	*AE*	25	45
Hocking 250/34			

1295   **Death of William IV 1837**

		£	£
Obv. Bust of William IV, r. *Rev*. WILLIAM IIII OBIT. JUNE. XX 1837, above a spray of rose,	*AR*	35	65
thistle and shamrock; all within a wreath. *D*. 58 mm. By J. Barber. *BHM* 1717	*AE*	12	22
	WM	5	10

VICTORIA, 1837–1901

1296   **Accession of Victoria 1837**

		£	£
Obv. Bust l., crowned. VICTORIA DEI GRATIA REGINA. *Rev*. BORN 24. MAY. 1819 ASCENDED THE	*AR*	55	100
THRONE JUNE. 20. 1837., within a wreath; above, radiate crown upon a cushion. *D*. 61 mm. By	*AE*	18	35
J. Barber. *BHM* 1756	*WM*	5	12
More than fifteen medals commemorate Victoria's accession.			

1297   —

		£	£
Obv. Bust of Victoria, l., hair in a fillet. *Rev*. VICTORIA BRITANNIARUM REGINA XX IVN:	*AR*	65	110
MDCCCXXXVII within a wreath. *D*. 36 mm. By W. Wyon. *BHM* 1764; *Hocking* 250/35	*AE*	35	65

1298   **William IV, Obsequies 1837**

		£	£
Obv. Bust r. WILLIAM IIII ASCENDED THE BRITISH THRONE JUNE 26 1830 IN THE 65 YEAR OF HIS	*AE*	10	18
AGE *Rev*. Funerary urn on a plinth, inscribed DIED 20 JUNE 1837 AGED 71 YEARS within a	*WM*	5	10
wreath. IN MEMORY OF HIS OBSEQUIES AT WINDSOR JULY 8 1837 *D*. 45 mm. By W. Bain. *BHM*			
1732			

1299   **Earl of Mulgrave 1837**

		£	£
Obv. Head of Mulgrave, l. PACIFICATOR HIBERNIÆ MDCCCXXXVII *Rev*. THE TRIBUTE OF A	*AE*	20	35
GRATEFUL PEOPLE TO CONSTANTINE HENRY EARL OF MULGRAVE LORD LIEU.^T GEN.^L & GEN.^L GOV.^R OF			
IRELAND 1837. within a wreath, crowned. *D*. 52 mm. By G. Brown, *obv*. after B. Mulrenin.			
BHM 1750			

Sir Constantine Henry Phipps, 2nd Earl of Mulgrave (1798–1863), politician; this medal was struck as a tribute to his efforts as a peacemaker during the Whiteboys disturbances. He distributed a medal of merit (*Frazer* 1887/616) to local gentry and constabulary in gratitude for their help in suppressing these ruffian outrages.

1300   **Reverend William Knibb 1837**

		£	£
Obv. Bust r., draped. REV.^D WILLIAM KNIBB, JAMAICA. *Rev*. Façade of chapel. KING S.^T CHAPEL,	*AR*	90	150
FALMOUTH JAMAICA *Ex*. ERECTED BY THE REV.^D W. KNIBB BAPTIST MISSIONARY 1837	*AE*	50	80
DIMENSIONS 80 FEET BY 60/SEATS FOR 2000 PERSONS & 600 SCHOOL CHILDREN COST NEARLY £6000	*WM*	25	45
ST. *D*. 41 mm. By J. Davis. *BHM* 1755			

William Knibb (1803–45), missionary; slavery abolitionist.

1301   **Isaac Pitman 1837**

		£	£
Obv. Bust three-quarters, r., draped, IZAC PITMAN *Rev*. Three line inscription, in	*AE*	20	35
shorthand [In commemoration of an invention of phone by Isaac Pitman], above, a quill;	*WM*	10	18
below, 1837. All within a wreath. *D*. 44 mm. By Allen & Moore.			

Sir Isaac Pitman (1813–97), published his invention of Phonography, or shorthand, entitled *Stenographic Sound Hand*, in 1837; this medal may have been issued to coincide with publication. Prize medals, by A. Wyon, were awarded by Pitman's schools in the 1890s.

1302*   **Grand Junction Railway Opened 1837**

		£	£
Obv. Entrance to railway station. NEW GRAND ENTRANCE. *Ex*. OF THE RAILWAY STATION AT	*AR*	70	120
LIVERPOOL *Rev*. Viaduct spanning landscape; town beyond. PART OF THE VIADUCT OF 28	*AE*	35	65

ARCHES AT BIRMINGHAM   *Ex.* ON THE LIVERPOOL, MANCHESTER & BIRMINGHAM GRAND   WM   15   30
JUNCTION RAILWAY OPENED JULY. 4. 1837   *D.* 49 mm. By T. Halliday. *BHM* 1789; *Moyaux*
11, p. 253; *Taylor* 113a. *See* **Plate 34**
One of four medals of the Grand Junction railway.

1303   **Victoria, Visit to the City of London 1837**
      Obv. As No. 1296. *Rev.* Victoria standing beneath a canopy, attended by Britannia, is   AR   55   100
      welcomed by the Lord Mayor; City arms above. WELCOME   *Ex.* IN COMMEMORATION. OF.   AE   18   35
      HER MAJESTYS. VISIT. TO. THE. CITY OF. LONDON. NOV^R 9TH 1837 THE. RIGHT. HONOR^LE JOHN.   WM   5   12
      COWAN. LORD. MAYOR   *D.* 61 mm. By J. Barber. *BHM* 1772
      More than ten medals record the Queen's visit.

1304*   ——
      Obv. Bust l., diademed. VICTORIA REGINA   *Rev.* Façade of the Guildhall. *Ex.* IN HONOUR OF   AR   100   180
      HER MAJESTY'S VISIT TO THE CORPORATION OF LONDON 9TH NOV: 1837 *D.* 55 mm. By W. Wyon.   AE   45   80
      BHM 1775; *Taylor* 53b; *Welch* 5. *See* **Plate 34**
      Issued by the Corporation of London (*see* No. 1245). Wyon's portrait was subsequently used on the first postage stamp, the
      'Penny Black', in 1840.

1305   ——
      Obv. Bust l.; VICTORIA behind. *Rev.* Façade of the Guildhall. *Ex.* THE QUEEN VISITS THE CITY   AV   —   —
      OF LONDON NOV. 9 1837   *D.* 22 mm. By W. Wyon. *BHM* 1777; *Taylor* 53a   AR   28   50
         AE   12   22

1306   **Royal Academy of Arts 1837**
      Obv. Bust similar to No. 1304. VICTORIA D: G: BRITANNIARUM REGINA MDCCCXXXVII.   AR   35   60
      PATRONA. *Rev.* As No. 1228a. *D.* 55 mm. By W. Wyon. *BHM* 1794; *Hocking* 251/41   AE   12   20
      Awarded in silver; some examples have indistinct lettering through heavy use of the dies. *See* No. 724.

1307   **Destruction of the Royal Exchange 1838**
      Obv. Façade of the building. ROYAL EXCHANGE   *Ex.* BUILT. BY. S^R.THO. GRESHAM. 1566   AR   55   100
      DESTROYED. BY. THE. FIRE. OF. LONDON REBUILT. 1669. AGAIN. BURNT. JAN^RY. 10. 1838   *Rev.*   AE   18   35
      Elizabeth I, standing, in decorative dress, surrounded by courtiers. *Ex.* QUEEN. ELIZABETH.   WM   6   15
      PROCLAIMING. THE. BURSE. TO. BE. CALLED THE. ROYAL. EXCHANGE. FOR. EVER. 1570   *D.* 61 mm.
      By J. Barber. *BHM* 2071; *Taylor* 36a
      Sir Thomas Gresham (1519?–79), financier; founder of the Royal Exchange, London. The reverse occurs coupled with an
      obverse of the new Royal Exchange. This commemorates the stone-laying in 1842.

1308   **Theobald Mathew 1838**
      Obv. Bust almost facing, draped. THE VERY REV^D T. MATHEW   *Rev.* HE REASONED OF   AR   40   70
      RIGHTEOUSNESS TEMPERANCE AND JUDGMENT TO COME ACTS CHAP 24 V.25., within a wreath   AE   22   38
      entwined with a ribbon, inscribed THE APOSTLE OF TEMPERANCE; above, radiate cross. *D.*   WM   8   15
      44 mm. By J. Davis. *BHM* 1867
      A variety has an added inscription beneath the bust. Theobald Mathew, or 'Father Mathew' (1790–1856), Irish priest and
      orator; a prime mover in the formation of the total-abstinence movement. More than twenty medals record the
      establishment of abstinence societies throughout Ireland in the period 1838–40, such as those at Baldoyle, Clones, Cork,
      Drogheda, Kilkenny, Kingstown, Lisburn, Meath and Myra.

1309   **Coronation of Queen Victoria 1838**
      Obv. Bust l., wearing a bandeau, lightly draped. ALEXANDRINA VICTORIA   *Rev.* DA FACILEM   AR   180   350
      CURSUM ATQUE ADNUE COEPTIS 1838   *D.* 87 mm. By B. Pistrucci. *BHM* 1802; *Forrer* IV/609   AE   70   130
      More than sixty medals commemorate Victoria's coronation.

1310   ——
      Obv. Bust l. VICTORIA D: G: BRITANNIARUM REGINA F: D: *Rev.* Victoria, enthroned, upon an   AR   80   150
      island rock, crowned by archbishop, and attended by Britannia, Hibernia and Scotia;   AE   32   60
      Neptune and Mercury seated at the base. *Ex.* ASCENDED THE THRONE JUNE 20. 1837. CROWNED   WM   10   24
      JUNE 28. 1838. *D.* 74 mm. By G. R. Collis. *BHM* 1805

1311   ——
      Obv. Bust almost facing, draped and holding a sceptre, head l., crowned. VICTORIA QUEEN OF   AR   60   110
      ENGLAND. *Rev.* The Queen, holding orb and sceptre, leads a procession beneath a canopy   AE   20   35
      supported by courtiers. *Ex.* CROWN'D JUNE 28 1838. *D.* 61 mm. By J. Barber. *BHM* 1803   WM   6   14

1312   ——
      Obv. Bust l. VICTORIA QUEEN OF GREAT BRITAIN BORN MAY 24. 1819   *Rev.* The Queen,   AR   60   110
      enthroned, crowned by Britannia, Hibernia, Scotia and Religion; above, Fame flying. LONG   AE   20   38
      LIVE THE QUEEN   *Ex.* CORONATION JUNE 28. 1838   *D.* 54 mm. By T. Halliday. *BHM* 1821   WM   5   12

			£	£

1313* ——

Obv. Bust l., diademed. VICTORIA ASCENDED THE BRITISH THRONE JUNE 20, 1837 IN THE 19.
YEAR OF HER AGE. *Rev.* Victoria enthroned, facing, attended by Britannia and Justice and
flanked by Commerce and Industry. CORONATION *Ex.* AT WESTMINSTER JUNE 28TH 1838. *D. a*
51 mm.; *b* 45 mm.; *c* 35 mm. (By J. Davis?) *BHM* 1842. *See* **Plate 35**

a,b AR	45	80
AE	15	25
WM	4	10
c AR	35	60
AE	12	20
WM	3	8

1314 ——

Obv. Bust r. VICTORIA *Rev.* Equestrian figure of a knight, r., having thrown down the
gauntlet. FOR THE QUEEN *Ex.* CORONATION 1838 *D.* 42 mm. By W. J. Taylor. *BHM* 1838

AR	40	70
AE	15	25
WM	5	12

1315 ——

Obv. Bust l., draped, and wearing a bandeau. VICTORIA D.G. BRITANNIARUM REGINA F.D. *Rev.*
Victoria enthroned, l., receives a crown from Britannia, Hibernia and Scotia. ERIMUS TIBI
NOBILE REGNUM *Ex.* INAUGURATA DIE JUNII XXVIII MDCCCXXXVIII *D.* 36 mm. By
B. Pistrucci. *BHM* 1801; *Wollaston* 26

The official Royal Mint issue.

Pt.	—	—
AV	250	480
AR	35	75
AE	15	35

1316 Richard Oastler 1838

Obv. Bust r. THE OASTLER NATIONAL TESTIMONIAL 1838 *Rev.* Cottage in wooded landscape,
church beyond. DWELL IN THE LAND & VERILY THOU SHALT BE FED *Ex.* LIVE AND LET LIVE; a
beehive, above. *D.* 39 mm. By T. Halliday. *BHM.* 1871

Richard Oastler (1789–1861), 'Factory King'; worked to improve factory legislation, and opposed the new Poor Laws.

AE	12	20
WM	4	10

1317* Abolition of Negro Apprenticeship 1838

Obv. TO COMMEMORATE THE ABOLITION OF NEGRO APPRENTICESHIP IN JAMAICA BARBADOS
GRENADA ST. VINCENTS ST. KITTS NEVIS MONTSERRAT & THE VIRGIN ISLANDS BY ACTS OF THE
RESPECTIVE LOCAL LEGISLATURES AUGUST 1ST 1838 *Rev.* A negro family seated beneath a palm
tree. LIBERTY PEACE AND INDUSTRY. *Ex.* MDCCCXXXVIII. *D. a* 51 mm.; *b* 38 mm. By J. Davis.
BHM 1876. *See* **Plate 35**

a AR	80	140
AE	40	70
WM	20	35
b AR	60	110
AE	30	50
WM	15	30

1318* ——

Obv. A white man and woman, standing in a palm landscape, shake hands with a negro
family. WE ARE MEN AND BRETHREN *Ex.* EMANCIPATION AUG. 1. 1838 *Rev.* PENN GRAN.
SHARP WILBERFORCE BENEZET CLARKSON BUXTON BROUGHAM STURGE SLIGO within a wreath.
THEIR NAMES SHALL BE SACRED IN THE MEMORY OF THE JUST *D.* 41 mm. By T. Halliday.
BHM 1880. *See* **Plate 35**

Anthony Benezet (1713–84), Quaker and philanthropist. Thomas Fowell Buxton (1786–1845), abolitionist and
philanthropist. Thomas Clarkson (1760–1846), abolitionist. Granville Sharp (1735–1813), founding member of the Anti-
Slavery Society. Marquis of Sligo (1788–1845), Governor of Jamaica. Joseph Sturge (1793–1859), abolitionist.

AR	60	110
AE	30	50
WM	15	30

1319 London and Birmingham Railway 1838

Obv. View of Euston Arch and station. LONDON AND BIRMINGHAM RAILWAY. *Ex.* ENTRANCE
FRONT OF THE LONDON STATION – HEIGHT TO THE TOP OF THE PEDIMENT 72FT. HEIGHT OF
ENTABLATURE 16FT. HEIGHT OF COLUMNS 44FT. LOWER DIAMR OF COLS 8FT. 6IN UPPER DIAMR OF COLS
6FT 4IN – PHILIP HARDWICK ESQR F.R.S. ARCHITECT *Rev.* Twenty-three line inscription listing
directors and builders THE DIRECTORS OF THE LONDON & BIRMINGHAM RAILWAY COMPANY –
1838 . . . ROBT STEVENSON ESQ. ENGINEER IN CHIEF *D.* 73 mm. By G. R. Collis. *BHM* 1874;
Taylor 125a; *Moyaux* 254/15

Philip Hardwick (1792–1870) architect. Robert Stephenson (1803–59), civil engineer; son of George.

AR	90	170
AE	35	65
WM	12	25

1320 Numismatic Society of London 1838

Obv. Bust r., draped, of John Lee. *Rev.* NUMISMATIC SOCIETY OF LONDON FOUNDED DECR XXII
MDCCCXXXVIII JOHN LEE L.L.D F.R.S: F.S.A: F.R.A.S PRESIDENT *D.* 45 mm. By A. J. Stothard.
BHM 1882

John Lee (1783–1866), antiquarian and scientist. First president of the Numismatic Society of London, which was actually
founded in 1836. In 1904 it became the Royal Numismatic Society, by Royal Charter.

AR	70	110
AE	25	40
WM	8	18

1321 London–Greenwich Railway 1838

Obv. Bust l. THOSE CONNECTED WITH THE GREENWICH RAILWAY THUS RECORD TO WHOM THE
SOUTH OF ENGLAND IS PRINCIPALLY INDEBTED. THE ZEAL AND PERSEVERANCE OF GEO. WALTER
ESQ. FOR THE INTRODUCTION OF RAILWAYS. *Ex.* LATE RESIDENT DIRECTOR CÆSARI. QUÆ.
CÆSARIS MDCCCXXXVIII *Rev.* Train crossing section of a viaduct, r. GREENWICH RAILWAY
VIRES ACQUIRIT EUNDO. *Ex.* ACT. OBTAINED. XVII. MAY. MDCCCXXXIII A.R. DOTTIN. ESQ. MP.
CHAIRMAN J.T WELLS. ESQ. DEP. CHAIRMAN WORKS. COMMENCED. APRIL. MDCCCXXXIV

AE	50	90
WM	20	35

                                                                               £   £

PROJECTOR. AND ENGINEER. CO.^L LANDMANN CONTRACTOR. HUGH M^CINTOSH. ESQ OPENED. TO. DEPTFORD. MDCCCXXXVI COMPLETED. MDCCCXXXVIII   *D.* 61 mm. By J. Barber. *BHM* 1875; *Moyaux* 14

George Walter (1790–1854); *see* R. H. D. Thomas, *London's First Railway*, London, 1972.

1322   The Royal Society, Queen's Medal 1838
Obv. Bust l., diademed. VICTORIA REGINA SOC: REG: LOND: PATRONA. MDCCCXXXVIII   *Rev.* Similar to No. 1186, but legend begins REGINAE in place of REGIS. *D.* 72 mm. By W. Wyon. *BHM* 1885; *D & W* 161/463

	VF	EF
AV	—	—
AR	100	180
AE	—	—

See No. 1186.

1323   Royal Scottish Academy 1838
Obv. Genius of Art kneeling, l., supports a chained platform upon which are Pegasus and the eternal flame. *Rev.* Laurel branch upon tripod. ROYAL SCOTTISH ACADEMY OF PAINTING SCVLPTVRE AND ARCHITECTVRE INSTI 1826 INCOR 1838   *D.* 68 mm. By B. Wyon, *obv.* after J. N. Paton. *BHM* 1884; *CP* 146/44

	VF	EF
AR	40	70
AE	15	25

Awarded in silver and bronze. Struck *c.*1850.

1324   Counties of the United Kingdom 1838
Obv. Royal arms and supporters within a central circle, inscribed MAP OF THE COUNTIES OF THE UNITED KINGDOM Around, three segments containing the counties of 1 SCOTLAND / 2 IRELAND / 3 ENGLAND & WALES   *Rev.* Map of the United Kingdom, divided into counties, numbered; coastal waters and islands identified. *D.* 64 mm. By J. Davis. *BHM* 1873

	VF	EF
AE	20	35
WM	8	15

Another obverse has a portrait of the Queen.

1325   St. Mary's College, New Oscott, Birmingham 1838
Obv. Exterior view of the college buildings. COLLEGIVM SANCTÆ MARI. L. DE. OSCOTT   *Ex.* OB. EXTRVCTVM. SEMINARIVM. ET. ECCLESIAM. DEDICATAM. ANNO. SALVTIS. M.CIↃ.CCC.XXX.VIII   *Rev.* Chapel interior. VIRGINI DEIPARÆ   *D.* 56 mm. By D & R (?) *Taylor* 124a

	VF	EF
AR	15	25

Catholic seminaries recorded on other medals include: Mount St. Mary's College, Spinkhill, Sheffield; St. Edmund's College, Herts.; Stonyhurst College, Lancs.; Ushaw College, Durham.

1326   Aylesbury Railway Completed 1839
Obv. Head r. GEORGE CARRINGTON ESQ. *Rev.* Thirteen line inscription detailing directors and engineers AYLESBURY RAILWAY COMPLETED JUNE 10. 1839. DIRECTORS G. CARRINGTON ESQ. .... R. STEPHENSON ESQ. ENGINEER. *D.* 50 mm. By A. J. Stothard. *BHM* 1890; *Moyaux* 16

	VF	EF
AR	60	110
AE	25	45
WM	15	25

1327   Royal Botanical Society 1839
Obv. A wreath (space within, for recipient's name), crowned. ROYAL BOTANICAL SOCIETY OF LONDON   *Rev.* A thick cluster of tropical plants. *Ex.* 1839   *D.* 51 mm. By B. Wyon. *Storer* 6552

	VF	EF
AR	30	55
AE	15	25

Awarded for more than fifty years.

1328   Duke of Wellington, Warden of the Cinque Ports 1839
Obv. Bust l. WELLINGTON   *Rev.* View of Dover Castle. *Ex.* IN COMMEMORATION OF THE CINQUE PORTS BANQUET TO THE DUKE OF WELLINGTON DOVER 1839, shield of Dover in the centre. *D.* 55 mm. By B. Wyon. *BHM* 1889; *Taylor* 25a

	VF	EF
AR	70	120
AE	20	35

Examples sometimes occur named on the edge.

1329   Centenary of Wesleyan Methodism 1839
Obv. Bust l., draped. JOHN WESLEY, M.A. BORN AT EPWORTH, JUNE 17TH 1703. DIED IN LONDON MARCH 2ND 1791   *Rev.* Façade of building. CENTENARY OF WESLEYAN METHODISM, 1839. "THE WORLD IS MY PARISH." *Ex.* CENTENARY HALL AND MISSION HOUSE LONDON. *D. a* 65 mm.; *b* 48 mm. By C. F. Carter. *BHM* 1895; Taylor 127*a, b*

	VF	EF
a AR	70	120
AE	35	60
WM	15	28
b AR	45	70
AE	20	35
WM	10	18

Type *b* has an abbreviated obverse inscription. Several medals commemorate the centenary; a few state John Wesley's date of birth as June 14th.

1330*   —
Obv. Bust l., draped. JOHN WESLEY, M.A. BORN 1703. DIED 1791. "THE WORLD IS MY PARISH"   *Rev.* Bust three-quarters l., draped. CHARLES WESLEY, M.A. BORN 1708. DIED 1788. CENTENARY OF WESLEYAN METHODISM 1839. *D.* 38 mm. By C. F. Carter. *BHM* 1899. See **Plate 35**

	VF	EF
AR	25	45
AE	15	25

Charles Wesley (1707–88), divine and hymn writer; John's youngest brother. This portrait of Charles also occurs on another medal with just an inscription on the reverse.

1331*   Anti-Slavery Society, Jamaica 1839
Obv. Bust r., draped. JOSEPH STURGE SLAVERY ABOLISHED AUG 1. 1838 ANTI SLAVERY SOCIETY FORMED AT S.^T ANN'S BAY DEC. 9. 1839   *Rev.* Negro family seated beneath a palm tree. TEMPERANCE INDUSTRY AND HAPPINESS. *Ex.* EMANCIPATION AUG. 1, 1838. *D.* 41 mm. [By J. Davis] *BHM* 1893. See **Plate 35**

	VF	EF
AR	80	140
AE	40	70
WM	20	35

1332   Mary Somerville 1839

Obv. Bust r., of Somerville. *Rev.* MARY SOMERVILLE. 1839. *D.* 49 mm. By W. Bain. *BHM*
1888

Mary Somerville (1780–1872), astronomer and musician; writer on scientific matters. Somerville College, Oxford is named after her.

		£	£
	AR	30	55
	AE	12	20
	WM	4	10

1333   Lloyd's Medal 1839

Obv. Leucothoë delivers her scarf to Ulysses, clinging to a floating spar in a tempestuous sea. LEUCOTHOE NAUFRAGO SUCCURRIT   *Ex.* 1839. *Rev.* OB CIVES SERVATOS within a wreath. PRESENTED BY LLOYD'S   *D.* 73 mm. By W. Wyon. *MH* 1919, 853; *Payne* 314/1

	AR	170	250
	AE	80	120

Awarded in silver and bronze for saving life at sea; examples sometimes occurs frosted and set within a watch-style glass bound with a silver frame. In 1896 this medal was superseded by a smaller medal of 36 mm. which could be worn by those to whom it had been presented. The Corporation of Lloyd's have subsequently awarded medals for saving life on land and in the air.

1334*   Marriage of Victoria and Albert 1840

Obv. Busts l., conjoined, she laureate. VICTORIA REGINA. ALBERTVS PRINCEPS   *Rev.* Hymen, head l., stands holding a torch. FELICIBVS AVSPICIIS   *Ex.* X FEB. MDCCCXL   *D.* 89 mm. By B. Wyon, after E. H. Baily. *BHM* 1919; *RWE* 16. *See* **Plate 35**

	AR	140	290
	AE	70	130

Prince Albert Francis Charles Augustus Emmanuel of Saxe-Coburg-Gotha (1819–61), younger son of Ernest I. The marriage is recorded on more than forty medals.

1335   ——

Obv. Busts l., conjoined. VICTORIA AND ALBERT DEDICATED WITH PERMISSION TO HER GRACE THE DUCHESS OF SUTHERLAND. *Rev.* Victoria and Albert stand before an archbishop performing the ceremony; to r., attendants. Above, an infant genius records the event. QUEEN VICTORIA BORN MAY 24. 1819. CROWNED JUNE 28. 1838 MARRIED TO PRINCE ALBERT FEB 10. 1840. *D.* 74 mm. By G. R. Collis. *BHM* 1908

	AR	80	150
	AE	32	60
	WM	8	20

1336   ——

Obv. Busts l., conjoined. ALBERT VICTORIA   *Rev.* Upright torch dividing shields of Britain and Saxe-Coburg-Gotha. EVER MAY LOVE SHED ROSY GARLANDS ROUND * FEBRUARY X. MDCCCXL. * *D.* 46 mm. By B. Wyon. *BHM* 1920; *RWE* 17

	AV	450	600
	AR	35	65
	AE	15	28

Examples in silver sometimes occur frosted and set within a watch-style glass bound with a silver frame.

1337*   ——

Obv. Busts l., conjoined. VICTORIA BRITAN. REGINA. ET ALBERT SAX COBURG GOTHA PRINCEPS. *Rev.* Scene of the marriage ceremony. DEO FAVENTE, VIVITE FELICIS   *Ex.* MARRIED FEB. 10 1840   *D.* 45 mm. By T. Halliday. *BHM* 1911; *RWE* 11. *See* **Plate 35**

	AR	45	80
	AE	14	28
	WM	4	10

Struck from more than one pair of dies.

1338   ——

Obv. Busts l., conjoined, she wearing a wreath of roses. VICTORIA. REGINA MAGNAE BRITANNIAE. ALBERTUS DUX SAXONIAE. *Rev.* Victoria and Albert seated in an ornate car, r., drawn by two angels. FELICES QUOS JUNGIT AMOR. DIE X. M. FEBRUARII MDCCCXL   *D.* 45 mm. By F. F. Helfricht. *Parkes Weber* 109

	AR	40	70
	AE	15	30

1339*   Newcastle-upon-Tyne to Carlisle Railway 1840

Obv. Mercury flying, l., over town and landscape between which a train crosses a viaduct. PLANUM PER ARDUA DUCO   *Ex.* NEWCASTLE UPON TYNE AND CARLISLE RAILWAY   *Rev.* Shields of Newcastle and Carlisle divided by a winged caduceus to which are tied two cornucopiae. BY ORDER OF THE SHAREHOLDERS MARCH XXIV MDCCCXL   An outer border (blank, for a director or shareholder's name). *D.* 50 mm. By W. Wyon. *BHM* 1983; *Moyaux* 17. *See* **Plate 35**

	AR	100	160
	AE	30	50

Silver examples occur frosted and set within a watch-style glass bound with a silver frame. Examples in bronze are probably specimen strikings.

1340   Royal Agricultural Society Medal 1840

Obv. Bust similar to No. 1304. HER MAJESTY QUEEN VICTORIA PATRONESS   *Rev.* PRACTICE WITH SCIENCE (the Society's motto) within a wreath. ROYAL AGRICULTURAL SOCIETY OF ENGLAND 1840 *D.* 55 mm. By W. Wyon. *BHM* 1985; *Hocking* 251/43

	AV	gold	value
	AR	35	55
	AE	10	18

Usually found awarded in silver.

1341   Death of James Morison 1840

Obv. Bust l. JAMES MORISON THE HYGEIST. BORN MDCCLXX. DIED MDCCCXL   *Rev.* JAMES MORISON THE HYGEIST PROCLAIMED FIRST THAT THE VITAL PRINCIPLE IS IN THE BLOOD SECOND THAT ALL DISEASES ARISE FROM IMPURITY OF THE BLOOD THIRD THAT SUCH IMPURITY CAN ONLY BE ERADICATED BY A PURGATIVE SUCH AS THE VEGETABLE UNIVERSAL MEDICINE OF THE BRITISH COLLEGE OF HEALTH LONDON FOURTH THAT THE DEADLY POISONS USED AS MEDICINES BY THE

	AR	75	120
	AE	35	60
	WM	15	28

DOCTORS ARE TOTALLY UNNECESSARY IN THE CURE OF DISEASES *Edge.* THE * GREAT * MEDICAL * REFORMER * (incuse). *D.* 67 mm. By T. R. Pinches. *BHM* 1964; *Storer* 2528

James Morison (1770–1840), medical reformer; vendor of vegetable universal medicines.

			£	£
1342*	**Anti-Slavery Convention, London 1840**			
	Obv. Bust r., draped. THOMAS CLARKSON *Rev.* Negro slave kneeling, r., his manacled hands raised. AM I NOT A MAN AND A BROTHER, below. BRITISH & FOREIGN ANTI-SLAVERY SOCIETY/ GENERAL ANTI-SLAVERY CONVENTION HELD IN LONDON 1840 PRESIDENT THOMAS CLARKSON AGED 81 *D.* 52 mm. By J. Davis, *obv.* after B. R. Haydon. *BHM* 1977; *EPM* 1890, 58; *Forrer* I/536. *See* **Plate 35**	*AR*	60	110
		AE	30	50
		WM	12	25

1343	**Augusta Sophia, Memorial 1840**			
	Obv. Head r., wearing a turban. AUGUSTA SOPHIA PRINCESSE D'ANGLETERRE. PROTECTRICE DE L'INSTITUTION DES D^{LLES} ORPHELINES ADULTES. *Rev.* SON IMAGE, EN NOUS RAPPELANT SES BIENFAITS, EST NOTRE PLUS DOUCE RÉCOMPENSE. PRIX DE FRANÇAISE DÉCERNÉ PAR J. B^{TE} GRÉGOIRE À MLLE *D.* 18 mm. By J. B. Merlen. *BHM* 1958	*AR*	12	20

Princess Augusta Sophia (1768–1840), 2nd daughter of George III.

1344	**Death of Henry Dawson 1840**			
	Obv. Bust l., draped. THE VERY REV^D HENRY RICHARD DAWSON D.S.P.D. *Rev.* Mother, infant and baby, together with Art and Time, grouped mournfully beside a tomb. *Ex.* OB. OCT. XXIV. M.DCCC.XL *D.* 43 mm. By W. Woodhouse, *rev.* after J. Barton. *BHM* 1961; *Frazer* 1887/611	*AR*	30	55
		AE	15	25

Struck in 1842, by the Royal Irish Art Union. Henry Richard Dawson (?–1840), Dean of St. Patrick's, Dublin; antiquary and numismatist.

1345	**Birth of Victoria, Princess Royal 1840**			
	Obv. Similar to No. 1337. *Rev.* Britannia seated before Cupid receives the Princess from Hymen. AMORIS MUTUI PIGNUS *Ex.* VICTORIA ADELAIDE LOUISA NATA NOV. 21 1840 *D. a* 45 mm.; *b* 39 mm. By T. Halliday. *BHM* 1949	*AR*	45	75
		AE	14	28
		WM	4	10

Princess Victoria Adelaide Mary Louise (1840–1901), eldest child of Victoria and Albert. More than ten medals celebrated her birth.

1346	──────			
	Obv. Heads l., conjoined. VICTORIA REGINA ET ALBERTVS PRINCEPS *Rev.* OB FILIAM NATAM NOV^S XXI° MDCCCXL within a wreath. *D.* 40 mm. By A. J. Stothard. *BHM* 1953	*AR*	35	60
		AE	12	25

1347*	**African and North American Indian Chiefs' Medal 1840**			
	Obv. Bust l., diademed. VICTORIA DEI GRATIA BRITANNIARUM REGINA F: D: *Rev.* Royal arms, supporters, motto and crest; 1840 below. *D. a* 75 mm.; *b* 60 mm.; *c* 38 mm. By W. Wyon. *BHM* 1975; *Jamieson* 29–31. *See* **Plate 35**	*a AR*	1200	—
		b AR	1000	—
		c AR	800	—
		AE	—	80

Usually occurs with a suspension loop. Type *c* has an abbreviated obverse inscription. Examples in bronze are specimen strikings. Apart from general distribution as a presentation to Indian chiefs, this medal was adapted for use during the visit of the Prince of Wales to Canada in 1860; the Prince's plumes and that date were engraved in the field on either side of the Queen's head, *Jamieson* 33–5. *See* No. 472.

1348	**Glasgow University, Newton Medal** *c.*1840			
	Obv. Bust r. ISAACUS NEWTONUS *Rev.* Façade of the old Hunterian Museum, Glasgow. *Ex.* EX ACADEMIÆ GLASGUENSIS DECRETO *D.* 51 mm. By W. Wyon. *BHM* 1471; *CP* 150/1	*AR*	25	45
		AE	10	18

Found awarded in silver.

1349	**Sir John Franklin** *c.*1840			
	Obv. Bust r., draped. SIR JOHN FRANKLIN. R.N. *Rev.* TO GREAT MEN within a wreath. ROYAL POLYTECHNIC INSTITUTION LONDON. *D.* 28 mm. By A. J. Stothard. *BHM* 2101	*WM*	10	18

Sir John Franklin (1786–1847), Arctic explorer. Medals of Prince Albert, Sir Charles Napier and the Duke of Wellington were also struck with this reverse.

1350	**Royal Scottish Society of Arts 1841**			
	Obv. Bust of Athena, r. *Rev.* A wreath (space within, for recipient's name). ROYAL SCOTTISH SOCIETY OF ARTS INSTIT. 1821. INCORP. 1841. *D.* 49 mm. By A. Kirkwood. *D & W* 182/626	*AR*	25	45

A similar prize medal was issued prior to the Society's Incorporation.

1351	**Sir Charles Napier 1841**			
	Obv. Bust l. SIR CHARLES NAPIER. *Rev.* Head of an upright trident decorated with two dolphins, within a wreath; 1841 below. *D.* 61 mm. By J. Barber. *BHM* 2006; *MH* 1919, 591	*AE*	80	140
		WM	35	60

Charles Napier (1786–1860), admiral. This may commemorate his return as M.P. for Marylebone, and subsequent receiving of the Freedom of the City of London.

PLATE 35

1313

1317

1318

1330

1331

1334 (× ⅔)

1337

1339

1342

1347

PLATE 36

1353 (× ⅔)

1367

1370

1372

1390

1375

THAMES TUNNEL 1842

1382

1394

1352   **Lord John Russell, M.P. for the City of London 1841**
Obv. Head l.; JUNE 29 1841 on truncation. Rᵀ HONᴮᴸᴱ LORD JOHN RUSSELL M.P.   *Rev.* FREE
TRADE within a wreath. PER MARE PER TERRAM   *D.* 44 mm. By A. J. Stothard. *BHM* 2010
A similar medal occurs with Russell's head r.

	VF	EF
	£	£
AR	25	45
AE	10	18

1353*   **Duke of Wellington 1841**
Obv. Bust l. FIELD MARSHAL ARTHUR DUKE OF WELLINGTON   *Rev.* Bellerephon helmet:
plumed ornate helmet decorated with Pegasus spearing the Chimaera; thunderbolt below.
NOVA CANTAMVS TROPÆA AVGVST. 1841   *D.* 61 mm. By B. Pistrucci. *BHM* 2011; *Parkes
Weber* 189; *Forrer* IV/610. See **Plate 36**
It is unclear precisely what this medal commemorates; however, in August 1841, on his party's return to power, the Duke
accepted a seat in the Cabinet, without office, although he took an active part in the business of the country. Examples of
this medal sometimes occur named on the edge, and inscribed VIS VIRTVS VERITAS.

| AR | 150 | 280 |
| AE | 50 | 110 |

1354   **Feargus O'Connor 1841**
Obv. Bust l. FEARGUS O'CONNOR UNIVERSAL SUFFRAGE AND NO SURRENDER   *Rev.* View of
gateway to castle. FEARGUS O'CONNOR WAS CONFINED FOR 16 MONTHS IN THE CASTLE OF YORK
BY THE WHIGS FOR LIBEL   *D.* 43 mm. (By?) *BHM* 2009
Feargus O'Connor (1794–1855), Chartist leader, reformer and activist.

| WM | 12 | 22 |

1355   **Daniel O'Connell, Lord Mayor of Dublin 1841**
Obv. Bust r., draped. DANIEL. O CONNELL ESQ. M.P.   *Rev.* Hibernia, Liberty and Plenty
beside an altar, inscribed VOX POPULI SUPREMA LEX. Cap of liberty upon flag in clouds. CIVIL
AND RELIGIOUS LIBERTY ALL OVER THE WORLD   *Ex.* ELECTED LORD MAYOR OF DUBLIN THE 1ˢᵀ
OF NOVᴿ 1841   *D.* 49 mm. By W. Woodhouse, *obv.* after P. Turnerelli. *BHM* 2007; *Frazer*
1887/612
The obverse also occurs with another reverse for his mayoralty of Dublin.

| AE | 25 | 40 |
| WM | 12 | 22 |

1356   **Birth of Albert Edward, Prince of Wales 1841**
Obv. Britannia, with attendants, holds the infant Prince. *Ex.* PRINCE OF WALES AND DUKE OF
CORNWALL BORN NOV: 9. 1841.   *Rev.* Two cherubs display a garland and mantle, inscribed
MAY HE BE GREAT IN THE SIGHT OF THE LORD, AND RULE HIS PEOPLE IN EQUITY; radiate crown,
above. PRINCE OF WALES AND DUKE OF CORNWALL BORN NOVᴿ 9. 1841   *D.* 48 mm. By J. Taylor.
BHM 1994
Albert Edward, Prince of Wales (1841–1910), King Edward VII 1901–10; eldest son of Victoria and Albert. His birth is
commemorated on more than eight medals.

| AE | 18 | 35 |
| WM | 8 | 15 |

1357   ——
Obv. Similar to No. 1337. *Rev.* Priest, with attendants, holds the infant Prince. H.R.H.
ALBERT EDWARD PRINCE OF WALES   *Ex.* BORN NOV. 9. 1841   *D.* 45 mm. By T. Halliday. *BHM*
1992

AR	45	80
AE	14	28
WM	4	10

1358   **Return of Conservative M.P.s for Shropshire 1841**
Obv. Sword, sceptre and crown upon a cushion, and a ribbon GOD SAVE THE QUEEN, within a
wreath inscribed CLIVE GORE D'ISRAELI BOTFIELD PIGOT GASKELL FORESTER WHITMORE ACKERS
TOMLINE DARLINGTON HILL on the leaves. FESTIVAL AT SHREWSBURY TO CELEBRATE THE
RETURN TO PARLIAMENT OF THE XII CONSERVATIVE MEMBERS FOR SHROPSHIRE NOVEMBER 12.
1841 EARL OF POWIS PRESIDENT. *Rev.* View of the Wrekin and surrounding landscape. ALL
FRIENDS ROUND THE WREKIN   *D.* 57 mm. By T. Halliday. *Fearon* 292/7

| AE | 14 | 25 |
| WM | 7 | 12 |

1359   **Sir Benjamin Brodie 1841**
Obv. Bust l.; BRODIE behind. *Rev.* Hygeia kneeling, l., lights an antique lamp upon a pillar
entwined with a serpent. E. TENEBRIS. TANTIS. TAM. CLARUM. EXTOLLERE. LUMEN. QUI.
POTUISTI. *Ex.* CONSOCII. ET. DISCIPULI GRATULANTES MDCCCXLI   *D.* 73 mm. By W. Wyon.
BHM 2003; *Storer* 483
Sir Benjamin Collins Brodie (1783–1862), surgeon.

AR	60	100
AE	25	45
WM	8	18

1360   **Society of Apothecaries, Galen Medal 1841**
Obv. Bust r.; GALEN behind. *Rev.* Hygeia indicates apparatus on a wall. OB STUDIA FELICITER
INSTITUTA   *Ex.* SOC: PHARM: LOND: DONAVIT. MDCCCXLI   *D.* 45 mm. By W. Wyon. *BHM*
2024; *Storer* 6532
Awarded in silver, and sometimes gold, for work in therapeutics.

AV	350	450
AR	40	65
AE	15	30

1361   **Baptist Missionary Society, Scriptures Translated 1841**
Obv. Bust three-quarters r., draped. WILLIAM CAREY   *Rev.* BAPTIST MISSION FORMED OCTᴿ
2ᴺᴰ 1792 COMMENCED IN E. INDIES 1793. W. INDIES 1813. W. AFRICA 1840. STATIONS 157.
MISSIONARIES 71. TEACHERS & NATIVE PREACHERS 127. MEMBERS UPWARDS OF 30,000. SCHOLARS
ABOUT 18,000. SCRIPTURES TRANSLATED INTO 40 LANGUAGES & DIALECTS. COPIES ISSUED IN THE

AR	35	55
AE	12	20
WM	3	8

| | | | | £ | £ |

YEAR 1841. 85,000. SLAVERY ABOLISHED AUG.^T 1ST 1838, in the centre. EXPECT GREAT THINGS FROM GOD. ATTEMPT GREAT THINGS FOR GOD   *D.* 44 mm. By J. Davis. *BHM* 2027
William Carey (1761–1834), missionary and orientalist.

1362   Royal Exchange, Stone-Laying 1842
Obv. Busts l., conjoined. VICTORIA BRITAN: REGINA, ET ALBERT SAX COBURG GOTHA PRINCEPS   *Rev.* Façade of the building. NEW ROYAL EXCHANGE   *Ex.* THE FOUNDATION STONE LAID BY H.R.H. PRINCE ALBERT JANUARY 17. 1842   *D.* 61 mm. By T. Halliday. *BHM* 2074; *Taylor* 146*b*

| | *AE* | 20 | 35 |
| | *WM* | 6 | 14 |

The stone-laying is commemorated on more than ten medals.

1363   Christening of the Prince of Wales 1842
Obv. Similar to No. 1362. *Rev.* Priest holding the infant Prince at a font, observed by people on either side. *Ex.* Prince's plumes and coronet. ALBERT PRINCE OF WALES BORN NOV: 9 1841 CHRISTENED JAN: 25 1842   *D.* 61 mm. By T. Halliday. *BHM* 2046

| | *AE* | 20 | 35 |
| | *WM* | 7 | 15 |

This event is commemorated on at least six medals.

1364   ——
Obv. Bust r. FREDERICUS GULIELMUS IV D.G. BORUSSIAE REX   *Rev.* Crowned shield of Prussia between those of Britain and Saxe-Coburg-Gotha; beyond, Prince's plumes, coronet and motto. SPONSOR ET HOSPES XXV JAN. MDCCCXLII   *D.* 46 mm. By B. Wyon. *BHM* 2051; *Wurzbach* 2977

| | *AR* | 35 | 65 |
| | *AE* | 15 | 35 |

Frederick William IV (1795–1861), emperor of Prussia 1840–61; godfather of the Prince of Wales. Examples in silver sometimes occur frosted and set within a watch-style glass.

1365   Opening of the Edinburgh–Glasgow Railway 1842
Obv. Train crossing viaduct spanning valley. GREAT VIADUCT OVER THE VALLEY OF THE ALMOND NEAR EDINBURGH   *Ex.* TO COMMEMORATE THE OPENING OF THE EDINBURGH AND GLASGOW RAILWAY FEBRUARY 18. 1842   *Rev.* View of a tunnel entrance through which pass trains on twin tracks. ENTRANCE TO THE GLASGOW RAILWAY STATION AND TUNNEL   *D.* 48 mm. By S. Woolfield. *BHM* 2068; *Moyaux* 18

	AR	70	120
	AE	30	55
	WM	12	25

1366   Dr. John Dalton 1842
Obv. Bust l. JOHN DALTON, D.C.L. F.R.S.   *Rev.* STRUCK IN COMMEMORATION OF THE MEETING OF THE BRITISH ASSOCIATION HELD IN MANCHESTER AND IN HONOUR OF DR JOHN DALTON BY THE PROPRIETORS OF BRADSHAW'S JOURNAL JUNE 1842, within a wreath. *D.* 45 mm. By C. F. Carter. *BHM* 2054; *Storer* 734

	AR	30	50
	AE	12	22
	WM	5	12

Dr. John Dalton (1766–1844), chemist; discovered the condition of colour-blindness.

1367*   Treaty of Nanking 1842
Obv. Bust l. VICTORIA D: G: BRITANNIAR: REGINA F: D: *Rev.* Fame heralds the signing and exchange of the treaty between the British and Chinese delegations. *Ex.* THE TRIUMPH OF THE BRITISH ARMS 1842   *D.* 64 mm. By J. Davis. *BHM* 2061. *See* **Plate 36**

	AR	70	120
	AE	35	55
	WM	15	28

This treaty ended a monopolistic system of maritime trade in China and opened up ports to foreign trade.

1368   Visit of Victoria to Scotland 1842
Obv. As No. 1334. *Rev.* ADVENTVI REG. SCOTIAE SEPT. I MDCCCXLII   *D.* 89 mm. By B. Wyon, *obv.* after E. H. Baily. *BHM* 2037

| | *AR* | 120 | 220 |
| | *AE* | 60 | 110 |

A large number of medals commemorate numerous visits which the Queen made throughout Britain, such as those to Tamworth, 1843; Channel Islands, 1846; Ireland, 1849; Newcastle, 1849; Liverpool, Manchester, 1851; Birmingham, Warwick, Leeds, 1858; Wolverhampton, 1866; Llangollen, 1889; Sheffield, 1897.

1369   Baptist Missionary Society, Jubilee 1842
Obv. Busts three-quarters r., draped. CAREY AND THOMAS THE FIRST MISSIONARIES   *Rev.* Façade of the mission house. JUBILEE OF BAPTIST MISSION. *Ex.* FORMED AT KETTERING OCT.^R 2ND 1792. *D.* 43 mm. By J. Taylor. *BHM* 2064; *Taylor* 40*b*

	AR	35	55
	AE	12	20
	WM	3	8

John Fryer Thomas (1797–1877), educationalist; promoter of the Baptist Missionary Society.

1370*   Solomon Hirschel 1842
Obv. Bust r., in rabbinic robes and cap. SOLOMON HIRSCHEL CHIEF RABBI. *Rev.* Scroll of the Law. Hebrew inscription around [= In commemoration of the passing away of the late Gaon Solomon, 27th Marheshavan 5603 (1842). For forty years he was shepherd of his holy flock of sheep here, and his days were eighty-one years.] *D.* 62 mm. [By J. Barber] *JMC* 1159; *EPM* 1892, 240. *See* **Plate 36**

| | *WM* | 80 | 150 |

Solomon Hirschel (1761–1842), Chief Rabbi of the Jewish Ashkenazi community in Britain. *See* No. 1287.

1371   Birmingham School of Design 1842
Obv. Bust of female, r., with turreted crown, within a quatrefoil. BIRMINGHAM SOCIETY OF ARTS FOUNDED MDCCCXXI   *Rev.* Shield between instruments of art and design; ribbon

| | *AR* | 20 | 35 |
| | *AE* | 8 | 15 |

		VF	*EF*

inscribed FORWARD All within a quatrefoil. BIRMINGHAM SCHOOL. OF. DESIGN. FOUNDED.   £   £
MDCCCXLII   *D.* 49 mm. By J. Moore. *D & W* 211/85

Struck *c.*1870; a prize medal awarded in silver.

1372*   **Thames Tunnel Completed 1842**
Obv. Head l. SIR ISAMBART MARC BRUNEL, F.R.S. & c. *Rev.* View of the tunnel's twin entrances;   AV   350   650
above, shipping on river. *Ex.* THAMES TUNNEL 1842   *D.* 42 mm. By W. J. Taylor. *BHM*   AR   50   85
2084; *Moyaux* 25; *Eidlitz* 1927, 143. *See* **Plate 36**   AE   15   25

Sir Marc Isambart Brunel (1769–1849), inventor, engineer and architect. More than thirty medals record the completion   WM   4   10
and opening of the tunnel.

1373   **Thames Tunnel Opened 1843**
Obv. Similar to No. 1372. *Rev.* Twin entrances to the tunnel. *Ex.* THAMES TUNNEL 1200 F^T L^{NG} AR   80   150
COMMENCED 1824 BROKE IN 1828 RECOMMENCED 1835 OPENED TO PEDESTRIANS 1843   *D.*   AE   35   65
62 mm. By J. Taylor. *BHM* 2134; *Moyaux* 20; *Eidlitz* 1927, 122   WM   10   25

Struck from several pairs of dies, with many varieties. A similar piece is dated 1842.

1374   **Death of the Duke of Sussex 1843**
Obv. Head r., in tasselled skull cap. H.R.H. AUG. FRED. DUKE OF SUSSEX. G.M.   *Rev.* Royal   AR   40   65
shield within the Garter; around, a masonic chain. NEAR TO THE THRONE BUT NEARER TO HIS   AE   15   28
FELLOW MAN BORN JAN. 27. 1773 DIED APRIL 21 1843   *D.* 42 mm. By W. J. Taylor, *obv.* after   WM   5   12
H. Weigall. *BHM* 2096; *Shackles* 14

1375*   **Launching of the *Great Britain* 1843**
Obv. Busts l., conjoined and draped, she diademed; above, symbols of the monarchy. A   AR   80   150
wreath border. QUEEN VICTORIA & PR: ALBERT   *Rev.* Broadside view of THE GREAT BRITAIN,   AE   30   55
fully rigged and under steam. LENGTH 322 F^T BREADTH 50 F^T 6^{IN} DEPTH 52 F^T 6^{IN} 26 STATE ROOMS   WM   12   25
WITH 1 BED E^H 113 WITH 2 BEDS E^H TOTAL W^{HT} OF IRON 1500 T^{NS}. 1000 HORSE POWER LAUNCHED
BY H.R.H. PRINCE ALBERT JULY 19. 1843   On exergual line BUILT BY THE GREAT WESTERN STEAM
SHIP COMP^Y *D.* 51 mm. By Allen & Moore. *BHM* 2114. *See* **Plate 36**

More than eight medals record the launching; another records an experimental voyage from Bristol to London in 1845.
The *Great Britain* was the first ocean screw steamship. It was built by Isambard Kingdom Brunel (1806–59), inventor and
engineer; son of Marc Isambard Brunel.

1376   **Hebrew National School, Birmingham 1843**
Obv. Façade of the building. STRUCK TO COMMEMORATE LAYING THE FOUNDATION STONE. OF   AR   130   180
THE HEBREW NATIONAL SCHOOL BIRMINGHAM BY SIR MOSES MONTEFIORE. F.R.S ASSISTED BY   AE   65   100
BARON DE ROTHSCHILD. A.A.GOLDSMID ESQ. I. COHEN ESQ. D. SALOMONS ESQ. AND OTHER   WM   45   70
DISTINGUISHED INDIVIDUALS. *Rev.* A biblical scene. JOSEPH INTRODUCING HIS FATHER JACOB
TO PHARAOH KING OF EGYPT   *D.* 73 mm. By G. R. Collis. *BHM* 2108; *Taylor* 139a

A similar 45 mm. medal was also struck. Sir Moses Montefiore (1784–1885), Jewish missionary; merchant and
philanthropist. Lionel Nathan Rothschild (1807–79), political emancipator and financier; funded purchase of Suez Canal
shares. Eldest son of Nathan Mayer. Sir David Salomons (1797–1873), founder of the joint-stock banking system; pioneer
of Jewish emancipation.

1377   **Nelson Memorial, Trafalgar Square 1843**
Obv. Bust l., uniformed, of Nelson. ENGLAND EXPECTS EVERY MAN WILL DO HIS DUTY. on a   AR   50   90
garter. *Rev.* Statue of Nelson upon a column; beyond, buildings along northern perimeter   AE   18   32
of Trafalgar Square. THE NELSON COLUMN LONDON, ERECTED 1843 *Ex.* W. RAILTON ESQ: WM   7   15
ARCH. *D.* 44 mm. By J. Davis. *BHM* 2124; *MH* 1919, 532; *Taylor* 143a

William Railton (d.1877), architect. The bas-reliefs adorning the four sides were completed in 1849. The statue of Nelson
is by E. H. Baily.

1378   **Shipwrecked Fishermen & Mariners' Benevolent Society 1843**
Obv. As No. 1377. *Rev.* CASES RELIEVED FROM 8TH MAY 1839 TO 30TH SEPTEMBER 1843 / WIDOWS   AE   15   30
424 ORPHANS 1,557 AGED PARENTS 280 SHIPWRECKED PERSONS 4,281 FISHERMEN DESTITUTE 475   WM   5   10
TOTAL 7,017 in the centre. SHIPWRECKED FISHERMEN & MARINERS BENEVOLENT SOCIETY
1839   *D.* 44 mm. By J. Davis. *BHM* 2110; *MH* 1919, 864

The Society was formed to alleviate every aspect of distress caused by shipwrecks. From 1850 it was designated 'Royal' and
medals, with a 35 mm. diameter, were struck in gold and silver and presented for exertions in saving life from drowning.
See W. P. Dawson, 'Shipwrecked Mariners' Society', *OMRS* 1969, 45–52.

1379   **Repeal of the Union 1843**
Obv. Bust l., draped, of Daniel O'Connell; LIBERATOR below. REPEAL OF THE UNION   *Rev.*   AE   15   25
Irish harp, surmounted by crown, between two shamrocks. "GREAT, GLORIOUS AND FREE,   WM   5   10
FIRST FLOWER OF THE EARTH, & FIRST GEM OF THE SEA"   *D.* 35 mm. (By?) *BHM* 2022

Various associations were formed for the Repeal, which is commemorated by several medals.

1380   ——
Obv. Bust l., draped. DANIEL O'CONNELL THE LIBERATOR OF IRELAND   *Rev.* Hibernia   AR   45   80
standing, facing, in a landscape; broken shackles at her feet. WHO WOULD BE FREE, HIMSELF   AE   25   40
MUST STRIKE THE BLOW   *Ex.* REPEAL YEAR 1843   *D.* 44 mm. By G. K. (?) *BHM* 2104   WM   8   15

                                                                        £   £

1381   **Francis Chantrey 1843**

Obv. Head r. CHANTREY SCULPTOR ET ARTIUM FAUTOR. *Rev.* Chantrey's monument of WATT   *AR*   60   130
(seated on a plinth). *Ex.* FRANCISCI CHANTREY OPUS   *Edge.* ART-UNION OF LONDON 1843   *AE*   15   30
(incuse). *D.* 55 mm. By W. Wyon. *BHM* 2227; *Beaulah* 1

Struck in 1846; the edges of some examples are unlettered. Sir Francis Legatt Chantrey (1781–1841), sculptor. The Art-Union of London was founded in 1837 to foster and encourage interest in the fine arts. Members paid an annual subscription of one guinea for which they received an engraving; the funds which accrued enabled the Union to become patrons and purchase art which they considered had merit. Between 1842–87 they sponsored the production of a group of medals with the portrait of eminent artists together with an illustration of their work: not only to revive interest in medallic art but as presentations, in silver, to artists and craftsmen whose goods gained the Council's approval. Bronze medals were given to members of the Union who would otherwise have chosen the engraving. At its peak in the 1870s membership stood at 20,000. The average number issued of each type is to be reckoned in the low hundreds (200?) for those in bronze, and about thirty of each in silver (see *Beaulah*). The movement was wound up in 1912. See *Annual Reports of The Council of the Art-Union of London* (1837–1911).

1382*   **Old Sarum 1217: Stonehenge 1843**

Obv. Equestrian figure before a wooded and hilly landscape. OLD SARUM   *Ex.* DESERTED IN   *AR*   70   110
THE YEAR 1217   *Rev.* View of Stonehenge; Y GWIR YN ERBYN Y BYD [= The truth against the   *AE*   35   60
world] on a ribbon. *Ex.* STONEHENGE ON SALISBURY PLAIN 1843   *D.* 50 mm. By T. Halliday.   *WM*   15   30
BHM 2130. *See* **Plate 36**

1383   **Royal Society for the Protection of Life from Fire 1843**

Obv. A man carries a woman from a burning building. ACTIONS ARE OUR'S RESULTS ARE   *AR*   60   100
GOD'S   *Rev.* Crown above a wreath (space within, for recipient's name). ROYAL SOCIETY FOR   *AE*   35   60
THE PROTECTION OF LIFE FROM FIRE 1843   *D.* 44 mm. By B. Wyon. *Payne* 318

Awarded in silver and bronze, and usually found with a suspension clasp and loop.

1384   **London Missionary Society, Missionary Ship,** *John Williams* **1844**

Obv. Broadside view of a fully-rigged ship. THE JOHN WILLIAMS MISSIONARY SHIP   *Ex.*   *AE*   25   40
LAUNCHED AT HARWICH MAR. 20 1844, 296 TONS; LENGTH 103 FEET, BREADTH 24 FEET 8 INCHES   *WM*   12   22
DEPTH IN HOLD 16 FEET: HAS 10 STATE ROOMS   *Rev.* THIS SHIP, THE PROPERTY OF THE LONDON
MISSIONARY SOCIETY, IS INTENDED TO CONVEY ITS MISSIONARIES TO THE ISLANDS OF THE SOUTH
PACIFIC, AND TO BE EMPLOYED IN VISITING THE DIFFERENT GROUPS OF ISLANDS IN THAT OCEAN,
IN PROMOTING THE GOSPEL AMONG THEM; SHE HAS BEEN PURCHASED FROM A FUND OF UPWARDS
OF £6200 RAISED BY THE JUVENILE FRIENDS OF THE SOCIETY. *D.* 41 mm. By J. Davis. *BHM*
2201

Struck from more than one pair of dies. John Williams (1796–1839), missionary in the Pacific Islands on behalf of the London Missionary Society.

1385   **Royal Zoological Society of Ireland 1844**

Obv. Busts l., conjoined; LINNÆUS and CUVIER either side. R. ZOOLOG. SOC. OF IRELAND.   *AE*   18   32
MDCCCXXXI. *Rev.* A giraffe. ADMIT BEARER TO THE GARDENS PHOE^x PARK ON SUNDAY AFTER 2   *WM*   8   15
O CLOCK / GIRAFFE BORN IN LONDON 27 MAY 1841 PRESENTED BY ZOO. SOC. OF LONDON 5 JUNE
1844   *D.* 31 mm. By W. Woodhouse. *Frazer* 1887/619; *Hyckert I*, 254/9

Georges Leopold Chrétien Frédéric Dagobert Cuvier (1769–1832), French naturalist.

1386   **Visit of Nicholas I to England 1844**

Obv. Bust r. NICOLAUS. I. TOTIUS. ROSSIAE. IMPERATOR. *Rev.* NICOLAUS I TOTIUS ROSSIAE   *AR*   60   110
IMPERATOR REGINAE BRITANNIARUM VICTORIAE AMICUS ET HOSPES 1844   *D.* 52 mm. By   *AE*   25   45
L. C. Wyon. *BHM* 2151

Nicholas Pavlovich (1796–1855), Czar Nicholas I 1825–55. This medal also occurs with another reverse recording the visit of Grand Duke Constantine to the Royal Mint in 1847.

1387   **Duke of Wellington, Equestrian Statue 1844**

Obv. Bust l. ARTHUR DUKE OF WELLINGTON. *Rev.* Equestrian statue. THE WELLINGTON STATUE   *AR*   35   60
LONDON ERECTED JUNE 18 1844. SIR F. CHANTRY SC: *Ex.* COST £9000 RAISED BY PUBLIC   *AE*   12   20
SUBSCRIPTION THE METAL WORTH £1500 GIVEN BY GOVERNMENT   *D.* 38 mm. By Allen &   *WM*   4   10
Moore. *BHM* 2191

Another reverse has a view of the Royal Exchange, outside which the statue was erected. Several medals commemorate the statue, erected on the anniversary of the battle of Waterloo.

1388   **London Missionary Society, Golden Jubilee 1844**

Obv. Fame flying above people of different nationalities. *Ex.* SANCTIONED BY THE BOARD OF   *AR*   30   50
DIRECTORS   *Rev.* Banner hanging from a trumpet, inscribed THE LONDON MISSIONARY   *AE*   10   22
SOCIETY FOUNDED IN THE YEAR 1795 HAS BEEN HONORED BY GOD IN SUCCESSFULLY DIFFUSING
THE GLORIOUS GOSPEL IN POLYNESIA, INDIA, CHINA AFRICA & THE WEST INDIES JUBILEE 22. SEP.
1844. THE GREAT TRUMPET SHALL BE BLOWN &c. ISAIAH CHAP.27 V.13; above, a radiate crown.
D. 45 mm. By J. Davis. *BHM* 2168

			£	£

1389 **Sir Edward Stanley 1844**
Obv. Bust l. SIR EDWARD STANLEY M.R.D.S. *Rev.* CHAIRMAN OF THE COMMITTEE OF IRISH
MANUFACTURE FIRST AND ZEALOUS PROMOTER OF THE EXHIBITIONS ROYAL DUBLIN SOCIETY 1ST
EXHIBITION 1833; below, 1844 *D.* 43 mm. By I. Parkes. *BHM* 2154; *Frazer* 1893/13

AR	30	50
AE	15	25

Sir Edward Stanley, 14th Earl of Derby (1799–1869), Irish Secretary under Earl Grey. This medal recognizes his services
to the Royal Dublin Society.

1390* **The Royal Exchange Opened 1844**
Obv. Bust l., wearing a cap and draped, of Thomas Gresham. EMPORIVM REGIVM A. THOMA
GRESHAM EQ. AVR. CIVE LONDINENSI CONDITVM A.S. MDLXXI *Rev.* Façade of the Royal
Exchange; statue of Victoria, inscribed on plinth A:S. MDCCCXLIV XXVIII OCT., in the
forecourt. REST. ET. APERT. AVSP. VICTORIA REG *Ex.* W: TITE F.R.S. ARCHT *D.* 74 mm. By
W. Wyon. *BHM* 2185; *Taylor* 146x. See **Plate 36**

AR	60	110
AE	25	45
WM	10	22

More than twenty medals commemorate the opening of the Royal Exchange, the major work of the architect William Tite
(1798–1873).

1391 ——
Obv. Façade of the Royal Exchange; above, Royal shield and ribbon inscribed ROYAL
EXCHANGE LONDON *Ex.* Eight-line inscription FOUNDED BY SIR THOMAS GRESHAM, A.D. 1566
... OPENED BY H.M.G. MAJESTY VICTORIA OCT: 28: 1844. *Rev.* Victoria and Albert seated upon a
platform before City dignitaries; above, a canopy decorated with shields. *Ex.* PRESENTATION
OF THE CITY ADDRESS *D.* 52 mm. By J. Davis. *BHM* 2177; *Taylor* 146s

AR	40	70
AE	12	22
WM	4	10

1392
Obv. Bust l., diademed. ROYAL EXCHANGE OPENED BY H:M: QUEEN VICTORIA OCT. 28
1844 *Rev.* Three shields upon a wreath; grasshopper above. FIRST STONE LAID BY H.R.H.
PRINCE ALBERT JANY 17 1842 *D.* 28 mm. By W. Wyon. *BHM* 2186

AR	10	15
AE	5	8
WM	2	4

1393 **British Archaeological Association 1844**
Obv. Hand pouring oil into an antique lamp. BRITISH ARCHÆOLOGICAL ASSOCIATION.
MDCCCXLIII. *Rev.* 1844 divided by arms of Canterbury. FIRST MEETING, CANTERBURY. LORD
ALB. CONYNGHAM, PRES. *D.* 35 mm. By W. J. Taylor. *BHM* 2106; *D & W* 102/11–12

AR	12	20
AE	3	7
WM	2	4

Albert Denison, Baron (Conyngham) Londesborough (1805–60), first President of the Association. Meetings held in
Winchester and Gloucester in 1845 and 1846, and in Manchester in 1850, are recorded on similar medals, each with their
respective arms on the reverse.

1394* **'Tom Thumb', Charles Stratton 1844**
Obv. 'Tom Thumb' standing on a desk amongst books, flasks and an inkwell. CHARLES S:
STRATTON. KNOWN AS GENL TOM THUMB. *Ex.* 25 1N HGH *Rev.* Busts r., conjoined and draped.
SHERWOOD E. & CYNTHIA STRATTON. PARENTS OF GENL TOM THUMB. *D.* 38 mm. By Allen &
Moore. *BHM* 2157. See **Plate 36**

AE	20	30
WM	12	18

One of a group of medals recording Charles Sherwood Stratton (1838–83), the celebrated dwarf. This medal occurs with
another reverse depicting his equipage. 'Tom Thumb' was exhibited by the showman, Phinaeus T. Barnum, who also
published this medal, in London, 1844.

1395 **Hungerford Foot Bridge Opened 1845**
Obv. Suspension bridge spanning river. HUNGERFORD AND LAMBETH *Ex.* SUSPENSION FOOT
BRIDGE OPENED MAY. I. MDCCCXLV BRUNEL ENGINEER CHADWICK BUILDER *Rev.* Façade of
building. HUNGERFORD MARKET LONDON *Ex.* OPENED JULY 2 1833 *D.* 25 mm. By J. Davis.
BHM 2213; *D & W* 75/218

AE	6	10
WM	3	5

1396 **Royal Visit to Germany 1845**
Obv. Busts l., conjoined, she diademed and draped. QUEEN VICTORIA AND PRINCE
ALBERT *Rev.* Winged female figure, facing, above two shields which she festoons. ROYAL
VISIT TO GERMANY *Ex.* AUGUST 1845 *D.* 39 mm. By Allen & Moore. *BHM* 2201A

AE	8	15
WM	3	8

Chiefly undertaken to visit Coburg where Albert grew up.

1397 **Death of William Knibb 1845**
Obv. As No. 1300. *Rev.* THE FRIEND OF THE AFRICAN BORN SEPR 7TH 1803 LANDED IN JAMAICA
FEBY 12. 1825 DIED AT KETTERING JAMAICA NOVR 15. 1845 in the centre. "WHATEVER MAY BE THE
CONSEQUENCE I WILL SPEAK & C NOR WILL I DESIST TILL THE GREATEST OF CRIMES SLAVERY IS
ABOLISHED". MISSIONARY MEETING LONDON JUNE 1832 *D.* 41 mm. By J. Davis. *BHM* 2206

AR	75	120
AE	35	55
WM	18	30

1398* **Prince Albert 1845**
Obv. Bust r. ALBERTUS PRINCEPS VICTORIAE REGINAE CONJUX. 1845. *Rev.* St. George and the
Dragon. TREU UND FEST *D.* 56 mm. By W. Wyon. *BHM* 2204; *Jones* 1979, 289. *See*
Plate 37

AV	1100	1500
AR	75	120
AE	30	55

Examples of this medal were presented by Prince Albert; they are sometimes inscribed on the edge for services.

                                                                              £   £

1399   **Joshua Reynolds 1845**
Obv. Head l., REYNOLDS behind; palette and brushes, below. *Rev.* Detail from Reynolds'   *AR*   60   130
painting *The Infant Hercules* (seated cherub strangling two snakes). ART UNION OF LONDON   *AE*   15   30
1845 *D.* 58 mm. By A. J. Stothard. *BHM* 2207; *Beaulah* 2
See No. 1381.

1400   **Smithfield Club 1845**
Obv. Bust l., draped. JOHN CHARLES EARL SPENCER PRESIDENT. 1825-1845. *Rev.* Bust r.   *AR*   12   22
CHARLES DUKE OF RICHMOND K: G: PRESIDENT OF THE SMITHFIELD CLUB. *D.* 49 mm. By
W. Wyon. *BHM* 2218; *Hocking* 255/73
Used as a prize for many years; later specimens display indistinct lettering through heavy use of the dies. Charles Gordon
Lennox, Duke of Richmond (1791–1860), succeeded Earl Spencer (1782–1845) as President. They were both
instrumental in the formation of the Royal Agricultural Society.

1401   **James Woodhouse 1845**
Obv. English royal crest, lion upon crown, within a central wreath: seven medallions   *AR*   170   250
around, named and containing a symbol of each of the seven principal Ionian islands: Corfu,   *AE*   70   120
Zante, Cephalonia, Ithaca, Santa Maura, Paxo and Cerigo. *Rev.* Nine-line Greek
dedicatory inscription within a wreath; above, badge of the Order of St. Michael and St.
George. *D.* 56 mm. By N Λ (?) *Parkes Weber* 245o
James Woodhouse (*c*.1785–1866), Treasury official and administrator in the Ionian Islands. This medal may have been
struck on his retirement.

1402   **School of Mines, de la Beche Medal** *c*.1845
Obv. Bust r.; H.T. DE LA BECHE., behind. *Rev.* Crossed mining axes within a wreath. SIS   *AR*   45   65
MEMOR USQUE MEI   *D.* 45 mm. By W. Wyon/L. C. Wyon. *BHM* 2264; *Müseler* 16/12   *AE*   20   35
Henry Thomas de la Beche (1796–1855), geologist; one of the founders of the [Royal] School of Mines. This medal was
awarded annually, in bronze, from 1857.

1403   **Gloucester Cathedral** *c*.1845
Obv. Exterior view of cathedral. *Ex.* GLOUCESTER CATHEDRAL/DEDICATED BY PERMISSION TO   *AE*   12   22
H.R.H. PRINCE ALBERT   *Rev.* Interior view. THE CHOIR GLOUCESTER CATHEDRAL   *D.* 60 mm.   *WM*   5   10
By J. Davis. *BHM* 2369; *Taylor* 5a
Uniform medals by J. Davis, all dedicated to Prince Albert, commemorate cathedrals at Canterbury, Ely, Lichfield,
Lincoln, Oxford, London (St. Paul's and Westminster Abbey), Worcester, and York. Examples of some bronze medals
have a 'grainy' appearance and may have been struck some years later.

1404   **Henry Hardinge, Treaty of Lahore 1846**
Obv. Bust l.; HARDINGE, behind. *Rev.* Victory standing, l., presents an olive-branch to a   *AR*   60   110
kneeling warrior. MENS AEQUA REBUS IN ARDUIS *Ex.* MDCCCXLVI *D.* 58 mm. By   *AE*   18   35
G. G. Adams. *BHM* 2228; *EPM* 1892, 228
Henry Hardinge (1785–1856), raised to the peerage as Viscount Hardinge of Lahore; appointed Commander-in-Chief on
the death of Wellington in 1852.

1405   **Brompton Hospital Opened 1846**
Obv. Heads l., conjoined, of Victoria, diademed, and Albert. PATRON HER MOST GRACIOUS   *AE*   25   38
MAJESTY QUEEN VICTORIA. XVIII JUNE MDCCCXLVI *Rev.* Façade of the hospital. HIS ROYAL   *WM*   8   18
HIGHNESS PRINCE ALBERT LAID THE FOUNDATION STONE ON THE 11TH OF JUNE 1844 *Ex.* THE
NEW HOSPITAL FOR CONSUMPTION AND DISEASES OF THE CHEST BROMPTON. *D.* 64 mm. By
J. Davis. *BHM* 2241; *Taylor* 153b
A similar medal commemorates the laying of the foundation stone in 1844.

1406*   **Repeal of the Corn Laws 1846**
Obv. A man wielding a twisted sword and displaying the CORN LAWS prevents a destitute   *AR*   45   80
family from reaching a boat laden with produce. CORN MONOPOLY; A NATION'S CURSE. *Ex.*   *AE*   15   28
THOU HAST WITHHOLDEN BREAD FROM THE HUNGRY JOB 22.C:V.V. *Rev.* A family unload goods   *WM*   5   12
from a boat; shipping beyond. *Ex.* FREE TRADE THE PEOPLE'S RIGHT'S. *D.* 54 mm. By J. Allen/
J. Taylor. *BHM* 1972; *Brettauer* 2151. See **Plate 37**
Several medals record the Repeal of the Corn Laws.

1407   ——
Obv. Portrait medallion of SIR ROBERT PEEL, BART: below, symbols of agriculture and   *AR*   35   60
produce. TO COMMEMORATE THE PASSING OF SIR RBT PEEL'S FREE TRADE MEASURES JUNE 25   *AE*   12   20
ROYAL ASSENT JUNE 26 1846 *Rev.* CORN BILL PASSED JUNE 25 1846 on a central scroll. Around,   *WM*   4   10
four oval portrait medallions of R. COBDEN ESQ. M.P./J. BRIGHT ESQ. M.P./G. WILSON ESQ.
CHAIRMAN/HON. C. PELHAM VILLIERS M.P., and symbols of agriculture and produce. ANTI-
CORN LAW LEAGUE ESTABLISHED 1839. *D.* 51 mm. By Allen & Moore. *BHM* 2233
John Bright (1811–89), orator and statesman. Richard Cobden (1804–65), statesman and economist; champion of the
working classes. Charles Pelham Villiers (1802–98), statesman.

				£	£
1408	——				

Obv. Bust almost facing, draped. RICHARD COBDEN ESQ^R M.P. THE CHAMPION OF FREE TRADE *Rev.* Rudder, inscribed FREE, barrel, bales and cornucopia. TO COMMEMORATE THE PASSING OF SIR ROBERT PEEL'S FREE TRADE MEASURES JUNE 25 RECEIVED THE ROYAL ASSENT JUNE 26 1846 *D.* 39 mm. By Allen & Moore. *BHM* 2238; *EPM* 1890, 62/1

           AR   30   55
           AE   10   18
           WM   3   8

1409   **Royal Visit to Guernsey 1846**

Obv. Busts l., conjoined and draped. QUEEN VICTORIA & PRINCE ALBERT OF SAXE COBURG & GOTHA *Rev.* IN COMMEMORATION OF THE VISIT OF H.M.G. MAJESTY QUEEN VICTORIA AND PRINCE ALBERT TO GUERNSEY AUG. 24 1846, within a wreath, crowned. *D.* 31 mm. (By?) *BHM* 2223

           AE   25   40
           WM   15   28

1410   **Royal Visit to Jersey 1846**

Obv. Victoria and Albert, mounting steps of the quayside, are welcomed by two lines of female figures bearing floral tributes; above, a canopy inscribed VICTORIA HARBOUR *Ex.* VICTORIA & ALBERT LANDED AT S^T HELIERS JERSEY 3RD SEPT^R 1846 *Rev.* EN COMMEMORATION DE L'ARRIVÉE DE SA MAJESTÉ LA REINE VICTORIA ET DE SON ILLUSTRE EPOUX SAR LE PRINCE ALBERT À S^T HELIER, ILE DE JERSEY LE 3 SEPT^R 1846, within a wreath. *D.* 51 mm. By J. Le Gallais. *BHM* 2224

           AR   90   150
           AE   40   70
           WM   15   30

1411   **Christopher Wren 1846**

Obv. Bust r., draped; WREN behind. *Rev.* Façade of St. Paul's Cathedral. CHRISTOPHER WREN ARCHITECT – MDCCX *Ex.* SI MONUMENTUM REQUIRIS CIRCUMSPICE *Edge.* ART UNION OF LONDON 1846 (incuse). *D.* 58 mm. By B. Wyon and (begun by) W. Wilson. *BHM* 2232; *Taylor* 39h; *Beaulah* 3

Struck in 1850; *see* No. 1381.

           AR   60   130
           AE   15   30

1412   **Macclesfield Sunday School 1846**

Obv. Bust three-quarters r. JOHN WHITAKER ESQ. BORN NOV^R 24TH 1772. DIED OCT^R 29TH 1820. *Rev.* Façade of building. MACCLESFIELD SUNDAY SCHOOL *Ex.* FOUNDED MAY 6TH 1796 JUBILEE CELEBRATED MAY 6TH 1846 *D.* 48 mm. By Allen & Moore. *Taylor* 66a

           AE   12   18
           WM   4   10

1413   **Opening of the House of Lords 1847**

Obv. Bust r., within a wreath. HER MOST GRACIOUS MAJESTY VICTORIA *Rev.* View of THE HOUSES OF PARLIAMENT from the river Thames. *Ex.* WESTMINSTER N.E. VIEW *D.* 74 mm. By Ottley. *BHM* 2295

The House of Commons was opened in 1852. Several medals commemorate the Houses of Parliament; designed by Charles Barry (*q.v.*) after the original complex of buildings had burnt down in 1834.

           AR   80   140
           AE   35   60
           WM   10   25

1414   **Jenny Lind 1847**

Obv. Bust almost facing, draped; 1847 on truncation. JENNY LIND *Rev.* A nightingale perched on a lyre decorated with flowers. NESCIT OCCASUM NATA 1821 *D. a* 55 mm.; *b* 45 mm.; *c* 39 mm. By Allen & Moore. *BHM* 2267; *Hyckert II*, 200/7–8; *Svarstad* 308–9

Struck from more than one pair of dies, and with minor varieties. Jenny Lind (1820–87), celebrated Swedish soprano; in 1847 she appeared in London.

      a AE   18   32
      WM   5   12
      b,c AR   30   55
      AE   9   15
      WM   3   6

1415   **Death of Daniel O'Connell 1847**

Obv. Figure standing, crowned by Religion. DANIEL O'CONNELL *Ex.* BORN AUG. 6. 1775 *Rev.* Funerary urn upon a mausoleum, inscribed D. O'CONNELL DIED AT GENOA MAY 15 1847 *Ex.* HIS HEART WAS INTERRED AT ROME AND HIS BODY IN HIS NATIVE LAND *D.* 51 mm. By R. Capner. *BHM* 2275

A similar obverse occurs with a scroll, inscribed CATHOLIC EMANCIPATION, on a table. O'Connell's death is recorded on more than fifteen medals.

           AR   45   75
           AE   25   40
           WM   12   22

1416   ——

Obv. Bust almost facing, draped. DANIEL O'CONNELL ESQ^{RE} M.P. *Rev.* Hibernia seated, mournfully, beside a mausoleum inscribed D. O'CONN BORN 6 AUGUST 1775 DIED 15 MAY 1847 *Ex.* CATHOLIC EMANCIPATION REPEAL *D.* 39 mm. By Allen & Moore, *obv.* from a daguerreotype by R. Beard. *BHM* 2270

           AR   40   70
           AE   15   25
           WM   7   12

1417   **Prince Albert, Chancellor of Cambridge University 1847**

Obv. Bust l. ALBERTUS PRINCEPS *Rev.* CELSISSIMUM PRINCIPEM ALBERTUM CANCELLARIUM SUUM FAUSTO FELIQUE OMINE INAUGURATUM LAETA CONSPICIT ACADEMIA CANTABRIGIENSIS JULII VI MDCCCXLVII *D.* 58 mm. By G. G. Adams. *BHM* 2255

           AV   700   850
           AR   45   85
           AE   15   25

1418   **Freehold Land Societies 1847**

Obv. Bust three-quarters r., draped. JAMES TAYLOR JN^R FOUNDER OF FREEHOLD LAND SOCIETIES 1847. *Rev.* Façade of house with an orderly garden. SOCIAL IMPROVEMENT

           WM   20   32

			£	£

POLITICAL INDEPENDENCE on a ribbon. *Ex.* A beehive. FREEHOLD FRANCHISE. *D.* 44 mm. By J. Taylor Sr. *BHM* 2288

James Arthur Taylor (1817–89), political reformer. Whether there is any kindred connection between the sitter and the medallist, who has signed the piece Jas. Taylor Sen. Birm., is unclear.

1419* Theobald Mathew 1847

Obv. Bust r., draped. FATHER MATHEW *Rev.* Mathew standing, r., blessing a group of six kneeling figures. HE REASONED ON TEMPERANCE *Ex.* MDCCCXLVII *D.* 58 mm. By L. C. Wyon. *BHM* 2269; *Frazer* 1887/325. *See* **Plate 37**

AR	60	110
AE	25	45
WM	8	15

1420 Society of Arts 1847

Obv. Bust r. PRINCE ALBERT PRESIDENT *Rev.* SOCIETY OF ARTS, MANUFACTURES AND COMMERCE within a wreath. FOUNDED 1754 – INCORPORATED BY ROYAL CHARTER 1847 *D.* 56 mm. By W. Wyon/L. C. Wyon. *BHM* 2285; *D & W* 148/366

AV	800	1000
AR	50	70

Awarded from *c.*1853, in gold and silver. *See* No. 643.

1421 Orphan Working School, Hampstead 1847

Obv. Façade of building. THE ORPHAN WORKING SCHOOL *Ex.* HAVERSTOCK HILL HAMPSTEAD ROAD FOR 240 CHILDREN *Rev.* FOR CHILDREN OF BOTH SEXES, OF EVERY DENOMINATION, AND FROM ALL PARTS OF THE KINGDOM. FOUNDED 1758 AT HOXTON, REBUILT 1773 IN CITY ROAD, AND REMOVED TO HAVERSTOCK HILL HAMPSTEAD ROAD 1847. *D.* 50 mm. (By Allen & Moore?) *Taylor* 157a; *D & W* 232/233

AE	15	22
WM	5	12

Other orphan schools commemorated on medals include: Clapham Rise, Lambeth 1827; Cholera Orphan School, Bilston 1833; Holly Bush Hill, Wanstead 1843; Orphan Asylum, Wolverhampton 1850.

1422 Church Missionary Society, Golden Jubilee 1848

Obv. St. Paul standing, r., his arms raised. CHURCH MISSIONARY SOCIETY FOUNDED A.D. 1799 *Rev.* ALL THE ENDS OF THE EARTH SHALL SEE THE SALVATION OF OUR GOD in the centre, within a band inscribed, JUBILEE COMMEMORATED 1848 Around, twelve vignettes inscribed with the name of a missionary station and date of its establishment. *D.* 58 mm. By B. Wyon. *BHM* 2310

AR	55	85
AE	15	28
WM	8	15

1423 The Ten Hours Bill 1848

Obv. Bust l., diademed, of Victoria. GOD SAVE THE QUEEN Below, ROYAL ASSENT 8TH JUNE 1847. *Rev.* Family seated around a table. *Ex.* EVENINGS AT HOME TEN HOURS BILL 1ST MAY 1848 *D.* 39 mm. (By?) *BHM* 2306

AE	15	25
WM	8	15

This limited the amount of hours which young people could work in a factory in any one shift.

1424 Transportation of John Mitchel 1848

Obv. Bust r., draped. JOHN MITCHEL *Rev.* THE BRAVE, HONEST, AND NOBLE ADVOCATE OF REPEAL; WHO WAS PROSECUTED BY GOVERNMENT FOR HIS WRITINGS, AND SENTENCED AS A "FELON", TO 14 YEARS TRANSPORTATION; MAY 27 1848 *D.* 26 mm. (By?) *BHM* 2304

WM	15	28

John Mitchel (1815–75), solicitor; Irish nationalist.

1425* Arrival of the Chinese Junk *Keying* 1848

Obv. Broadside view of the junk. *Ex.* THE CHINESE JUNK KEYING *Rev.* THE CHINESE JUNK KEYING LENGTH 160 F^T, BREADTH 33 F^T, DEPTH OF HOLD 16 F^T, HER STERN IS 35 F^T, HIGH OUT OF THE WATER, HER MAIN CABIN IS 30 F^T LONG, 25 F^T WIDE, & 12 F^T HIGH, BURTHEN ABOUT 800 TONS, HER RUDDER IS OF IMMENSE SIZE & WEIGHT, BEING MADE OF IRON WOOD, HER ANCHORS ARE MADE OF WOOD, THE CABLES ARE MADE OF BAMBOO, THE ROPES OF BAMBOO RATTAN & INDIAN GRASS. ARRIVED IN THE RIVER THAMES MARCH 27. 1848. *D.* 44 mm. By J. Davis. *BHM* 2314. *See* **Plate 37**

AR	55	80
AE	20	35
WM	8	15

More than ten medals record the arrival of the *Keying*.

1426 Lord John Russell 1848

Obv. Bust r. LORD JOHN RUSSELL *Rev.* Female figure, seated, suckling two infants and flanked by two figures, one chained and leaning on the Commandments. HAVE WE NOT ALL ONE FATHER, HAVE NOT ONE GOD CREATED US *Ex.* PUB: BY H. HYAMS. LONDON 1848. *D.* 31 mm. By Allen & Moore. *BHM* 2637

WM	15	28

This medal may have been published by H. Hyams as a tribute to Russell. He had attempted to bring a bill, on behalf of Lionel N. Rothschild, which would remove the disabilities preventing Jews from swearing their own oath when entering Parliament. *See* No. 1522.

1427* William Hogarth 1848

Obv. Bust r., wearing cap and draped; HOGARTH behind. *Rev.* Hogarth's painting *The Election* (two rival canvassers solicit a voter). HE THROUGH THE EYE CORRECTS THE HEART. *Ex.* ART-UNION OF LONDON 1848 *D.* 55 mm. By L. C. Wyon, [*obv.* after L. F. Roubiliac] *BHM* 2302; *Beaulah* 4. *See* **Plate 37**

AR	60	130
AE	15	30

William Hogarth (1697–1764), painter, engraver and political satirist. *See* No. 1381.

1428   **William Wordsworth 1848**
Obv. Bust r., draped, of Wordsworth. *Rev.* WILLIAM WORDSWORTH in the centre. FRIEND OF THE WISE AND TEACHER OF THE GOOD. 1848. *D.* 36 mm. By L. C. Wyon. *BHM* 2305; *Forrer* VI/629
William Wordsworth (1770–1850), poet.

	£	£
AR	25	45
AE	10	18

1429*   **Institution of Civil Engineers, Stephenson Medal 1848**
Obv. Bust l. GEORGE STEPHENSON B. 1781 D. 1848 THE INST. C.E. INCORP. 1828   *Rev.* View of locomotive, marked Nº 2 on its side. LOCOMOTIVE ENGINE BUILT BY GEORGE STEPHENSON 1816   *D.* 47 mm. By J. S. & A. B. Wyon. *BHM* 2311; *Moyaux* 52. See **Plate 37**
Struck *c.*1880; awarded annually, usually in gold, from 1881. *See* No. 1206.

AV	500	600
AR	55	85
AE	25	45

1430   **Dr. Albert Coffin 1849**
Obv. Bust almost facing, spectacled and draped. ALBERT ISAIAH COFFIN. M.D. FOUNDER OF THE SYSTEM OF MEDICAL BOTANY IN ENGLAND. *Rev.* THIS MEDAL WAS PRESENTED TO ALBERT I. COFFIN M.D. PROFESSOR OF MEDICAL BOTANY AS A SINCERE TESTIMONIAL OF GRATITUDE FROM HIS FRIENDS IN BIRMINGHAM. WHO HAVE BEEN BENEFITED BY HIS SYSTEM. JAN 12. 1849. *D.* 49 mm. By J. Taylor. *BHM* 2347; *Storer* 656
Albert Isaiah Coffin (*c.*1800–66).

AE	18	30
WM	12	25

1431   **Richard Carmichael 1849**
Obv. Bust l., draped. RICHARD CARMICHAEL   *Rev.* Beaded circle (space within, for recipient's name). ROYAL COLLEGE OF SURGEONS IN IRELAND. *D.* 39 mm. By J. Woodhouse. *BHM* 3390; *Brettauer* 198
The portrait also occurs on other prize medals. Richard Carmichael (1779–1849), surgeon.

AR	28	40
AE	8	12

1432   **Royal Visit to Ireland 1849**
Obv. Similar to No. 1337. *Rev.* Harp within a wreath of shamrocks. TO COMMEMORATE THE FIRST VISIT OF HER MAJESTY AND PRINCE ALBERT TO IRELAND AUGUST 1849 *D.* 45 mm. By T. Halliday. *BHM* 2329
The visit is commemorated by more than fifteen medals.

AR	40	70
AE	15	28
WM	6	14

1433   **Professor Anderson 1849**
Obv. Bust three-quarters r., draped. PROFESSOR ANDERSON "GREAT WIZARD OF THE NORTH" COMMANDED TO PERFORM BEFORE HER MAJESTY QUEEN VICTORIA AT BALMORAL CASTLE AUGUST 28. 1849 *Rev.* Head l. Same inscriptions as the obverse. *D.* 51 mm. By J. Moore. *BHM* 2346
John Henry Anderson (1815–74), magician and actor.

AE	45	60
WM	28	40

1434*   **York, Newcastle and Berwick Railway 1849**
Obv. Railway bridge spanning river. NEWCASTLE UPON TYNE & GATESHEAD HIGH LEVEL BRIDGE *Ex.* LENGTH OF WATERWAY 512 FEET HIGH WATER TO RAILS 112 FEET YORK, NEWCASTLE & BERWICK RAILWAY   *Rev.* HER MAJESTY QUEEN VICTORIA PRINCE ALBERT AND THE ROYAL FAMILY PASSED THROUGH NEWCASTLE UPON TYNE FRIDAY 28 SEPTEMBER 1849 RECEIVED ADDRESSES ON THE HIGH LEVEL BRIDGE FROM BOTH CORPORATIONS in the centre; a crown, above. J. DENT WEATHERLEY ESQ^R MAYOR OF NEWCASTLE GEORGE HAWKS ESQ^R MAYOR OF GATESHEAD   *D.* 46 mm. (By?) *BHM* 2341; *Moyaux* 35. See **Plate 37**
A similar medal commemorates the opening of the bridge in 1850.

AR	65	110
AE	35	55
WM	15	30

1435   **The Coal Exchange Opened 1849**
Obv. Central portrait medallion of Victoria, surrounded by those of Prince Albert, the Prince of Wales and Princess Royal. NEW COAL EXCHANGE OPENED OCT. 30TH 1849 BY H.R.H. PRINCE ALBERT ON BEHALF OF HER MAJESTY QUEEN VICTORIA *Rev.* Interior of the Coal Exchange; heraldic devices on either side. Below, City of London shield and motto. THE R^T HON^{BLE} SIR JAMES DUKE LORD MAYOR – JOHN WOOD ESQ^{RE} CHAIRMAN OF THE COMMITTEE – JAMES B. BUNNING ESQ^{RE} ARCHITECT   *D.* 89 mm. By B. Wyon. *BHM* 2357; *Taylor* 161c; *Welch* 6
Issued by the Corporation of London. *See* No. 1245.

AE	30	65

1436   **Death of Queen Adelaide 1849**
Obv. Half-length bust, facing, wearing a bonnet and draped. HER MAJESTY THE QUEEN DOWAGER ADELAIDE. BORN 13 AUG: 1792. *Rev.* ADELAIDE BORN 13 AUG: 1792 DIED 9 DEC: 1849 on a tomb; above, BELOVED LAMENTED   *D.* 27 mm. By Allen & Moore. *BHM* 2343

AE	12	22
WM	4	10

1437*   **Inigo Jones 1849**
Obv. Bust l., draped and wearing a cap. INIGO JONES   *Rev.* Façade of building. *Ex.* BANQUETING HOUSE WHITEHALL 1616. *Edge.* ART-UNION OF LONDON 1849 (incuse). *D.* 54 mm. By C. F. Carter. *BHM* 2348; *Taylor* 34a; *Beaulah* 5. See **Plate 37**
Struck in 1852. *See* No. 1381.

AR	60	130
AE	15	30

1438   Lambert Jones 1849   £   £
Obv. Bust r. R. LAMBERT JONES A.D. MDCCCXLIX   *Rev.* PRESENTED BY HIS GRATEFUL FELLOW   *AE*   10   15
CITIZENS TO COMMEMORATE EXERTIONS BY WHICH THE CITY OF LONDON WAS IMPROVED ART
ENCOURAGED HEALTH & CONVENIENCE PROMOTED   *D.* 64 mm. By W. Wyon. *BHM* 2349;
Storer 1820
<small>Richard Lambert Jones, member of the Court of Common Council in the City of London; represented Cripplegate Ward Without 1820–52.</small>

1439   Members of Parliament 1849
Obv. Bust l., diademed. VICTORIA   An outer border containing the names of sixteen   *AE*   50   85
members and their positions in Lord Russell's administration. *Rev.* Fifty-line inscription
listing MEMBERS OF THE HOUSE OF COMMONS YEAR 1849   *D.* 95 mm. By L. C. Lauer. *BHM*
2351
See No. 1792.

1440   Britannia Tubular Bridge 1850
Obv. Bridge spanning the Menai Strait; beyond, Telford's earlier suspension bridge. *Ex.*   *WM*   30   55
THE MENAI SUSPENSION, AND BRITANNIA TUBULAR BRIDGES. *Rev.* Details of the two bridges
listing the specifications in a sixteen line inscription divided into two vertical sections
DETAILS OF THE BRIDGES. SUSPENSION TOTAL LENGTH 910 FT HEIGHT OF ROADWAY ABOVE WATER
100 FT . . . WEIGHT OF EACH OF THE FOUR LARGE TUBES 1800 TNS DO SMALL TUBES 700 TNS TOTAL
WEIGHT 10000 TNS   *D.* 64 mm. By Allen & Moore. *BHM* 2403; *Taylor* 164b; *Moyaux* 55
<small>The bridge was built by Robert Stephenson.</small>

1441* —
Obv. Bust r. ROBERT STEPHENSON   *Rev.* Britannia tubular bridge spanning the Menai Strait,   *AV*   900   1200
a train having just crossed. *Ex.* 1846–1850   *D.* 58 mm. By L. C. Wyon. *BHM* 2402; *Taylor*   *AR*   80   140
164a; *Moyaux* 36. *See* **Plate 37**   *AE*   35   65

1442*   Albert Edward, Prince of Wales 1850
Obv. Head r., of the Prince of Wales; AUG: 1850, below. *Rev.* ALBERT EDWARD BORN NOV. IX.   *AR*   60   110
MDCCCXLI; above, Prince of Wales' plumes. *D.* 32 mm. By L. C. Wyon. *BHM* 2384;   *AE*   25   40
Hocking 258/103. *See* **Plate 38**
<small>From a uniform group portraying seven of the nine Royal children of Victoria and Albert. *See* Nos. 1443–8.</small>

1443   Prince Alfred 1850
Obv. Head l., of Alfred; AUG: 1850 below. *Rev.* ALFRED ERNEST ALBERT BORN AUG: 6 1844   *AR*   60   110
within a wreath. *D.* 32 mm. By L. C. Wyon. *BHM* 2385; *Hocking* 258/106   *AE*   25   40
<small>Alfred, Duke of Edinburgh (1844–1900), 2nd son of Queen Victoria. *See* No. 1442.</small>

1444   Princess Alice 1850
Obv. Head l., of Alice; AUG: 1850 below. *Rev.* ALICE MAUD MARY BORN APRIL 25 1843 within a   *AR*   60   110
wreath. *D.* 32 mm. By L. C. Wyon. *BHM* 2388; *Hocking* 258/105   *AE*   25   40
<small>Alice Maud Mary (1843–78), 2nd daughter of Queen Victoria. *See* No. 1442.</small>

1445   Princess Helena 1850
Obv. Head r., of Helena; AUG: 1850 below. *Rev.* HELENA AUGUSTA VICTORIA BORN MAY 25 1846   *AR*   60   110
within a wreath. *D.* 32 mm. By L. C. Wyon. *BHM* 2389; *Hocking* 258/107   *AE*   25   40
<small>Helena Augusta Victoria (1846–1923), 3rd daughter of Queen Victoria. *See* No. 1442.</small>

1446   Victoria, Princess Royal 1850
Obv. Head l., of Victoria; AUG: 1850 below. *Rev.* VICTORIA ADELAIDE MARY LOUISA BORN NOV.   *AR*   60   110
21 1840 within a wreath. *D.* 32 mm. By L. C. Wyon. *BHM* 2387; *Hocking* 258/104   *AE*   25   40
See No. 1442.

1447   Prince Arthur 1850
Obv. Head r., of Arthur; SEPT: 1850 below. *Rev.* ARTHUR WILLIAM PATRICK ALBERT BORN MAY   *AR*   60   110
1 1850 within a wreath. *D.* 32 mm. By L. C. Wyon. *BHM* 2386; *Hocking* 258/110   *AE*   25   40
<small>Arthur William Albert, Duke of Connaught and Strathearn (1850–94), 3rd son of Queen Victoria. *See* No. 1442.</small>

1448   Princess Louise 1850
Obv. Head l., of Louise, draped; SEPT.ᴿ 1850 below. *Rev.* LOUISE CAROLINE ALBERTA BORN   *AR*   60   110
MARCH 18 1848 within a wreath. *D.* 32 mm. By L. C. Wyon. *BHM* 2390; *Hocking* 258/108   *AE*   25   40
<small>Louise Caroline Alberta (1848–1939), 4th daughter of Queen Victoria. *See* No. 1442.</small>

1449   Cardinal Wiseman 1850
Obv. Bust r., of Wiseman, clerically robed and wearing a skull-cap. *Rev.* Armorial shield;   *AE*   8   15
cardinal's hat above. NICOLAUS CARDINALIS ARCHIEPISCOPUS WESTMONASTERIENSIS   *D.*   *WM*   4   7
47 mm. By W. E. Bardelle.
<small>Nicholas Patrick Stephen Wiseman (1802–65), Cardinal of Westminster.</small>

PLATE 37

1398

1419

1406

1427

1425

1429

1434

1437

1441

PLATE 38

1442

1456 (× ⅔)

1469

1464

1488

1480

1493

1500

1492

1494

1450 **Death of Sir Robert Peel 1850**
Obv. Bust r. SIR ROBᵗ PEEL BARᵗ *Rev.* BORN FEBRUARY THE 5ᵀᴴ 1788 FIRST SAT IN THE HOUSE OF
COMMONS IN THE YEAR 1809 FOR CASHEL IN THE COUNTY OF TIPPERARY DIED JULY 2ᴺᴰ 1850 *D.*
45 mm. By T. R. Pinches, *obv.* after H. Weekes. BHM 2398

This portrait was prepared in 1840, and is accordingly dated. Several medals commemorate Peel's death.

		VF (£)	EF (£)
	AE	12	20
	WM	6	10

1451 **Opening of the Hahnemann Hospital 1850**
Obv. Bust l. SAMUEL HAHNEMANN BORN AT MEISSEN X APRIL MDCCLV *Rev.* THE HAHNEMANN
HOSPITAL PROJECTED X. APRIL MDCCCL OPENED IN BLOOMSBURY SQUARE LONDON 1. NOVEMBER
MDCCCL *D.* 41 mm. (By?) BHM 2407; *Storer* 5082

Samuel Christian Friedrich Hahnemann (1755–1843), German physician; founder of homeopathy.

		VF	EF
	AR	30	50
	AE	12	22
	WM	9	15

1452 **St. George's Hospital London, Hunter Medal 1850**
Obv. Bust almost facing, draped. JOHN HUNTER *Rev.* Two men assist a stricken female in a
hospital forecourt. ΑΝΔΡΑ Δ᾿ΩΦΕΛΕΙΝ ΚΑΠΠΙΣΤΟΣ ΠΟΝΩΝ *Ex.* Sᵗ GEORGE'S HOSPITAL
1850 *D.* 55 mm. By L. C. Wyon, [*obv.* after J. Reynolds] BHM 2395; *Storer* 1717

Usually found awarded in silver.

		VF	EF
	AR	40	65
	WM	15	22

1453 **International Currencies** *c.*1850
Obv. Two triangles in the centre, one radiate, enclosing an inscription GOLDGE WIGHT TROY
WEIGHT POIDS DE TROYES. EINE UNZE ONE OUNCE UNE ONCE. Around, three compartments
inscribed FRANCE NAPLES 1 = 6 FRANCS 39 CENTIMES 1 = 1 DUCAT 50 GRANI/AUSTRIA PRUSSIA
1 = 2 FLORINS 27 KREUTZERS 1 = 1 THALER 21 SILBERGROSCHEN/ENGLAND AMERICA 1 = 5
SHILLINGS 2 PENCE 1 = 1 DOLLAR 19¾ CENTS. *Rev.* A globe in the centre, enclosed by a border,
inscribed SILBER 37 ZUSATZ 3/SILVER 37 ALLOY 3/ARGENT 37 ALLOI 3 Around, three
compartments inscribed HINDOSTAN CHINA 1 = 2 RUPEES 10 ANNAS 10 PICE, 1 = 7 MACE 8
CANDAREENS 4⅘ CASH/SPAIN PORTUGAL 1 = 1 DOLLAR 5 REALS 28 MARAVEDIS, 1 = 1 MILREIS 71½
REIS/RUSSIA HOLLAND 1 = 1 ROUBLE 60 COPECS, 1 = 2 GULDEN 99 CENTS *D.* 38 mm. (By?)

		VF	EF
	WM	18	30

1454 **City of London School, Beaufoy Medal 1851**
Obv. Bust l., draped. WILLIAM SHAKESPEARE BORN APRIL 23. 1564 DIED APRIL 23. 1616. *Rev.* A
group of characters from his plays; Prospero and Ariel, Cardinal Wolsey, Lady Macbeth,
Falstaff, Poins and Henry IV. *Ex.* CITY OF LONDON SCHOOL SHAKESPEARIAN PRIZE FOUNDED
1851 BY HENRY B.H. BEAUFOY F.R.S. BORN APRIL 23. 1785 *D.* 77 mm. By B. Wyon. MI i,
213/57; *Ogden* 48

Henry Benjamin Hanbury Beaufoy (1785–1851), philanthropist; endowed scholarships at various academies and gave the
City of London School £10,000. A number of other prize medals awarded by the school bear his name.

		VF	EF
	AR	80	140
	AE	30	55

1455 **Great Exhibition, Council Medal 1851**
Obv. Busts l., conjoined, Victoria laureate: trident behind; two dolphins below. VICTORIA D:
G: BRIT: REG: F: D. ALBERTUS PRINCEPS CONJUX. MDCCCLI. *Rev.* Standing figures of Commerce
and Industry, their hands clasped, each crowned by Britannia, facing, upon a platform
before flags of nations. On either side are symbols of Commerce and Industry. EST ETIAM IN
MAGNO QUAEDAM RESPUBLICA MUNDO *Ex.* MDCCCLI *D.* 89 mm. By W. Wyon/
J. F. Domard, *rev.* after H. Bonnardel. BHM 2461; *Parkes Weber* 70

This was the highest prize of the Council (approximately 170 were given) who awarded medals in different categories for
original products and invention (see Nos. 1457,9, 61,2). For details of the recipients, awards and objects exhibited, see
*Exhibition of the Works of Industry of all Nations 1851, Reports by the Juries on the subjects in the thirty classes in to which the
Exhibition was divided*, London, 1852. More than fifty medals commemorate the Great Exhibition, which is more usually
referred to as the Crystal Palace.
　It provided the inspiration behind the many local exhibitions which were subsequently held throughout Britain. They
were variously entitled Fine Art, Local Industry, Apprentices, Working Classes, Industrial, &c. and frequently served as a
showcase of local manufactures. Those which medals commemorate, or at which medals were awarded, include:
Maidenhead, 1865; Plymouth, 1865; East London, 1865; Reading, 1865; Preston, 1865; Wisbech, 1866; York, 1866;
Lichfield, 1874; Exeter, 1882; Derby, 1882; Oldham, 1883; Cork, 1883; Wolverhampton, 1884; Glasgow, 1886; Rugby,
1891; Sheffield, 1892; Halifax, 1893; Belfast, 1895; Dorking, 1899. See Nos. 1467, 1473, 1513, 1577–8, 1727, 1730, and
1760.

		VF	EF
	AE	110	180

1456* **Great Exhibition 1851**
Obv. Bust r. PRINCE ALBERT. CONSORT OF QUEEN VICTORIA. *Rev.* In a large upper semi-
circular section a three-dimensional view of the exhibition building. THE INTERNATIONAL
INDUSTRIAL EXHIBITION 1851. In the lower section, a seated figure of Industry, facing, holds
two wreaths in each outstretched arm over four female figures flanking her. *D.* 89 mm. By
Allen & Moore. *See* **Plate 38**

Usually found gilt.

		VF	EF
	AE	80	120
	WM	40	70

1457 **Great Exhibition, Prize Medal 1851**
Obv. Similar to No. 1455. *Rev.* BRITANNIA seated, r., confers a wreath upon the head of
INDUSTRIA, kneeling; Africa, America, Asia and Europe in attendance. To r., bust of

		VF	EF
	AE	25	42

			£	£

FLAXMAN on a socle. DISSOCIATA LOCIS CONCORDI PACE LIGAVIT. *D.* 77 mm. By W. Wyon/
L. C. Wyon. *BHM* 2462; *Hocking* 261/3
See No. 1455.

1458 **Great Exhibition 1851**
Obv. Bust l., within a wreath. HIS ROYAL HIGHNESS PRINCE ALBERT. *Rev.* View of the
exhibition building. THE BUILDING FOR THE GREAT EXHIBITION IN LONDON. 1851 *Ex.*
PROPOSED BY H.R.H. PRINCE ALBERT, DESIGNED BY JOSEPH PAXTON ESQ. F.L.S. ERECTED BY FOX,
HENDERSON, & C.º – DIMENSIONS – LENGTH 1848 FEET, WIDTH 456 FEET, HEIGHT OF PRINCIPAL
ROOF 66 FEET, HEIGHT OF TRANSEPT 108 FEET, GLAZED SURFACE 900000 FEET, OCCUPIES 18 ACRES
OF GROUND *D.* 74 mm. By Ottley. *BHM* 2446; *Taylor* 165y
AE 40 70
WM 18 32
There are a number of varieties of this medal. Joseph Paxton (1801–65), architect and designer.

1459 **Great Exhibition, Jurors' Medal 1851**
Obv. Similar to No. 1455. *Rev.* Industry, seated, receives a wreath from Fame attended by
Commerce. PULCHER ET ILLE LABOR PALMA DECORARE LABOREM *Ex.* Bust of Athena and
objects. *D.* 64 mm. By W. Wyon/G. G. Adams. *BHM* 2464; *Hocking* 261/4
AE 30 55
See No. 1455.

1460 **Great Exhibition 1851**
Obv. Similar to No. 1375. *Rev.* View of the exhibition building. THE INTERNATIONAL
INDUSTRIAL EXHIBITION LONDON, 1851. *Ex.* PROPOSED BY H.R.H. PRINCE ALBERT, DESIGNED BY
JOSEPH PAXTON ESQ. F.L.S., ERECTED BY FOX, HENDERSON & C.º. LENGTH 1848 FEET, WIDTH 456
FEET, HEIGHT OF PRINCIPAL ROOF 66 FEET, HEIGHT OF TRANSEPT 108 FEET, GLAZED SURFACE
900,000 SUP FEET OCCUPIES 18 ACRES OF GROUND. ESTIMATED VALUE £150,000. *D.* 51 mm. By
Allen & Moore. *BHM* 2419; *Taylor* 165k
AE 15 28
WM 5 10
Another obverse has a single portrait of Prince Albert.

1461 **Great Exhibition, Services Medal 1851**
Obv. Bust l. H:R:H: PRINCE ALBERT PRESIDENT OF THE ROYAL COMMISSION. *Rev.* FOR SERVICES
within a wreath. EXHIBITION OF THE WORKS OF INDUSTRY OF ALL NATIONS. MDCCCLI. *D.*
48 mm. By W. Wyon. *BHM* 2465; *Hocking* 261/5
AE 5 8
See No. 1455.

1462 **Great Exhibition, Exhibitor's Medal 1851**
Obv. Similar to No. 1461. *Rev.* A globe, decorated with a scroll inscribed EXHIBITOR, within
a wreath. EXHIBITION OF THE WORKS OF INDUSTRY OF ALL NATIONS. MDCCCLI. *D.* 44 mm. By
W. Wyon. *BHM* 2463
AE 3 5
Presented to all exhibitors. *See* No. 1455.

1463 **Great Exhibition 1851**
Obv. Bust l. H.R.H. PRINCE ALBERT Below, STRUCK IN THE BUILDING OF THE EXHIBITION.
Rev. Royal arms and supporters. GREAT EXHIBITION OF THE INDUSTRY OF ALL NATIONS.
LONDON 1851. *D.* 38 mm. By W. J. Taylor. *BHM* 2459; *Taylor* 165aa
AR 18 32
AE 12 20
WM 1 3
William Joseph Taylor (1802–85), medallist and die-sinker, exhibited his own screw-press at the Exhibition, on which
these medals were probably struck.

1464 **Diedrich Uhlhorn's Coining-Press 1851**
Obv. A coining machine press. COINING-PRESS. INVENTED. 1817. AND MADE BY D. UHLHORN AT
GRAVENBROICH. *Ex.* NEAR COLOGNE ON THE RHINE *Rev.* EXHIBITION OF THE INDUSTRY OF ALL
NATIONS 1851 LONDON within a wreath. *Edge.* MAY INDUSTRY BE CROWNED WITH SUCCESS *D.*
37 mm. (By D. Uhlhorn?) *BHM* 2471; *D & W* 69/182. *See* **Plate 38**
AR 45 75
AE 28 40
The press was on display at the Exhibition. Diedrich Uhlhorn (1767–1837), German engineer whose improved coining-
press was adopted by the Royal Mint in 1828.

1465 **Entertainment at Guildhall 1851**
Obv. Head l., diademed. VICTORIA REGINA. *Rev.* ROYAL ENTERTAINMENT AT GUILDHALL 9ᵀᴴ
JULY 1851., in the centre. EXHIBITION OF THE WORKS OF INDUSTRY OF ALL NATIONS. *D.* 36 mm.
By W. Wyon.
AR 35 55
The obverse is that of the Military General Service medal. This medal is usually found with a suspension clasp and
sometimes occurs named on the edge.

1466 **Royal Academy of Arts, Turner Medal 1851**
Obv. Bust l., draped. JOSEPH MALLORD WILLIAM TURNER R:A: NAT: 1775 OB: 1851. *Rev.* A
student of nature, reclining in a landscape; beyond, rainbow and sun over a coast. Above,
three female figures personifying the primary colours. *D.* 55 mm. By L. C. Wyon, *obv.* after
D. Maclise. *BHM* 2416
AV 700 900
AR 55 90
AE 20 30
Awarded from 1857 in gold by the R.A. Schools for the best landscape in oils. Joseph Mallord William Turner
(1775–1851), landscape painter; bequeathed £20,000 to the Royal Academy. *See* No. 724.

1467 **Cork Fine Art Exhibition 1852**
Obv. Interior view of the exhibition hall, within a wreath of shamrocks. *Ex.* FINE ARTS HALL OPENED JUNE 10 1852 SIR T. DEANE & J. BENSON ARCHT?. *Rev.* Industry raising the seated figure of Hibernia. THE DARKEST HOUR IS THAT BEFORE THE DAWN. *D.* 43 mm. By W. Woodhouse. *BHM* 2506; *Frazer* 1887/616

> Another obverse shows an exterior view of the exhibition building. Sir John Benson (1812–74), Irish architect; built the Industrial Exhibition, Dublin, in 1853. Sir Thomas Deane (1792–1871), Irish architect; responsible for many major buildings in his native Cork.

	£	£
AE	12	20
WM	4	9

1468 **Death of the Duke of Wellington 1852**
Obv. Bust l., uniformed. ARTHUR DUKE OF WELLINGTON. A wreath border. *Rev.* BORN MAY 1, 1769. DIED SEPR 14. 1852 in the centre. Below, standards of ASSAYE and WATERLOO decorate a funerary urn. BOTH AS SOLDIER AND STATESMAN HE EARNED THE TITLE OF FATHER OF HIS COUNTRY *D.* 64 mm. By Allen & Moore. *BHM* 2474

> Wellington's death is recorded on more than thirty medals.

AE	30	55
WM	10	22

1469* ——
Obv. Bust r.; WELLINGTON behind. *Rev.* Britannia seated mournfully, l., before a column decorated with plumed helmet and dagger. PLORANT IN FVNERE GENTES *Ex.* SEPT. XIV MDCCCLII *D.* 58 mm. By G. G. Adams. *BHM* 2473; *Bramsen* 2027. See **Plate 38**

> The same portrait occurs on a version by Messrs J. Pinches. G. G. Adams also made Wellington's death mask, later used on a marble statue.

AR	60	110
AE	25	40

1470 ——
Obv. Bust l. DUKE OF WELLINGTON *Rev.* Monument, inscribed TO BRITAIN'S HERO, surmounted by a weeping willow. BORN MAY 1ST 1769 DIED SEP 14 1852 *D. a* 56 mm.; *b* 45 mm. By J. Hinks. *BHM* 2487

> Type *b* is unsigned.

a AE	20	35
WM	5	12
b AE	15	25
WM	4	10

1471 **Royal Institute of British Architects, Pugin Medal 1852**
Obv. A decorated column with a turreted crown supported by two lions; crest and motto of the ROYAL: INSTITUTE: OF: BRITISH: ARCHITECTS: ANNO: SALUTIS: MDCCCXXXIV. *Rev.* Arms of Pugin within a floral device. IN: MEMORY: OF: AUGUSTUS: WELBY: PUGIN: DIED: SEPT: XIV: MDCCCLII *D.* 57 mm. By J. T. Foot

> Struck c.1865 and awarded in silver and bronze for the study of medieval architecture. Augustus Welby Northmore Pugin (1811–52), architect; son of Augustus Charles, architect, illustrator and draughtsman. *See* No. 1280.

AR	35	55
AE	15	25

1472 **Pharmaceutical Society of Great Britain 1852**
Obv. HABENDA RATIO VALETUDINIS on an oval tablet supported by Galen and Avicenna; above, medicinal plants, pestle and mortar. *Rev.* PHARMACEUTICAL SOCIETY OF GREAT BRITAIN INCORPORATED A: D: 1843 CHARTER CONFIRMED 15TH & 16TH VICT: CAP: 56 1852, within a wreath. *D.* 70 mm. By L. C. Wyon. *BHM* 2509; *Storer* 6550

> Awarded in silver and bronze to students at the school of pharmacy. The obverse is based on the Society's arms. Avicenna, or ibn-Sina (980–1037), Arab physician and philosopher.

AR	45	70
AE	18	30

1473 **Great Industrial Exhibition, Dublin 1853**
Obv. Bust r.; DARGAN behind. *Rev.* View of the exhibition buildings. GREAT INDUSTRIAL EXHIBITION. IN CONNEXION WITH THE ROYAL DUBLIN SOCIETY *Ex.* ERECTED AT THE SOLE EXPENSE OF WILLIAM DARGAN OPENED THE 12TH MAY 1853 SIR J. BENSON ARCHT *D.* 44 mm. By W. Woodhouse. *BHM* 2521; *Went* 1973, 36; *Eidlitz* 1927, 71

> A number of medals record the Exhibition. William Dargan (1799–1867), Irish railway projector.

AR	35	60
AE	12	22
WM	5	10

1474 **Royal Visit to the Great Industrial Exhibition, Dublin 1853**
Obv. Busts l., conjoined, she diademed. QUEEN VICTORIA AND PRINCE ALBERT *Rev.* TO COMMEMORATE HER MAJESTY'S VISIT TO THE GREAT INDUSTRIAL EXHIBITION IN CONNEXION WITH THE ROYAL DUBLIN SOCIETY THE 30TH OF AUGT. 1853 *D.* 44 mm. By W. Woodhouse. *BHM* 2522; *Frazer* 1887/616

AE	12	20
WM	4	9

1475 **Cessation of Transportation 1853**
Obv. Bust l., laureate. VICTORIA QUEEN MDCCCLIII *Rev.* Arms of Tasmania. CESSATION OF TRANSPORTATION 1853 *Ex.* TASMANIA FOUNDED 1803 *D.* 57 mm. (By?) *Carlisle* 1853/2

> Transportation was superseded by penal servitude.

AE	250	400
WM	70	120

1476 **James Gilbart 1853**
Obv. Bust l.; Æ 59 below. J.W. GILBART, F.R.S. THE FIRST MANAGER OF THE FIRST JOINT STOCK BANK ESTABLISHED IN LONDON *Rev.* Fourteen-line inscription THE LONDON & WESTMINSTER BANK OPENED MAR. 10, 1834. WESTMINSTER BRANCH MAR. 10, 1834. BLOOMSBURY BRANCH JAN. 4, 1836. ... WORKS BY J.W. GILBART, F.R.S A PRACTICAL TREATISE ON BANKING. THE HISTORY &

AR	28	45
AE	15	25

PRINCIPLES OF BANKING LECTURES ON ANTIENT COMMERCE LOGIC FOR THE MILLION 1853 *D.*
51 mm. By W. J. Taylor. *BHM* 2512; *EPM* 1891/384

James William Gilbart (1794–1863), statistician; writer on banking and commerce.

			£	£

1477 **Blantyre Suspension Bridge 1853**
Obv. View of bridge. BLANTYRE SUSPENSION BRIDGE *Ex.* 1853 *Rev.* HENRY MONTEITH & CO.
GLASGOW *D.* 20 mm. (By?)   —   WM 6 10

1478 **Photographic Society of London Medal 1853**
Obv. Bust l. H.R.H. THE PRINCE CONSORT PATRON *Rev.* Female figure driving a quadriga in
clouds. PHOTOGRAPHIC SOCIETY OF LONDON 1853 *D.* 63 mm. By W. J. Taylor. *BHM* 2525
  AR 60 85
  AE 20 35

Awarded, usually in bronze, at the annual exhibitions for outstanding work. Another obverse, by J. A. Restall and dated 1861, was introduced as a memorial to Prince Albert and also served as a prize. The Society, latterly Photographic Society of Great Britain, have awarded other medals; see *The Photographic Journal*, section A, January 1953, 20–25.

1479 **John Flaxman 1854**
Obv. Bust l., draped; FLAXMAN behind. *Rev.* Representation of Flaxman's bas-relief
Mercury and Pandora Edge. ART-UNION OF LONDON 1854 (incuse). *D.* 56 mm. By
H. Weigall. *BHM* 2530; *Beaulah* 6
  AR 60 130
  AE 15 30

See No. 1381.

1480* **William Wyon 1854**
Obv. Bust r., draped. WILLIAM WYON R:A: *Rev.* Representation of William Wyon's design:
Britannia, holding an olive-branch, standing, drives four sea-horses. *Ex.* ART-UNION OF
LONDON 1854 *D.* 56 mm. By L. C. Wyon. *BHM* 2535; *Forrer* VI/628; *Beaulah* 7. *See*
Plate 38
  AR 75 170
  AE 20 40

William Wyon (1795–1851), medallist and Chief Engraver at the Royal Mint. *See No.* 1381.

1481 **Pharmaceutical Society of Great Britain, Pereira Medal 1854**
Obv. Bust l., draped. JONATHAN PEREIRA M.D. F.R.S. F.L.S. NAT. 1804 OB. 1852. *Rev.* MATERIA
MEDICA AWARDED BY THE PHARMACEUTICAL SOCIETY OF GREAT BRITAIN. PRIZE MEDAL FOUNDED
1854, within a wreath. *D.* 58 mm. By L. C. Wyon. *BHM* 2534; *Storer* 2796
  AR 60 90
  AE 20 35

Awarded in silver to students at the school of pharmacy. Jonathan Pereira (1804–53), pharmacologist; one of the first professors of the school.

1482 **Birmingham & Midland Institute, Siemens Medal 1854**
Obv. Bust three-quarters l., draped. SIR WILLIAM SIEMENS, D.C.L., LL.D., F.R.S.,
PRESIDENT *Rev.* Façade of building; a panel on either side, inscribed BIRMINGHAM &
MIDLAND INSTITUTE/BIRMINGHAM-INCORPORATED 1854 *D.* 63 mm. By J. Moore. *BHM*
2543; *Taylor* 200a
  AR 35 55
  AE 15 25

Struck *c.*1882 and awarded in silver and bronze. William Siemens (1823–83), engineer; invented a regenerative steam engine. Designed the ship *Faraday* which laid the Atlantic Cable. He is commemorated on a number of prize medals issued by the City and Guilds of London Institute.

1483 **Royal School of Mines, Forbes Medal 1854**
Obv. Bust r., draped. EDVARDUS FORBES *Rev.* NATURAE ACER INVESTIGATOR ET DILIGENS NAT.
MDCCCXV OB. MDCCCLIV *D.* 51 mm. By L. C. Wyon, *obv.* after J. G. Lough. *BHM* 2531;
Storer 1082
  AR 30 50
  AE 15 30

Awarded annually in bronze for natural history. Edward Forbes (1815–54), naturalist.

1484 **Dr. Kane's Arctic Expedition 1854**
Obv. Bust l., diademed. VICTORIA D: G: BRITANNIARUM REGINA F: D: *Rev.* THE BRITISH
GOVERNMENT TO THE OFFICERS & MEN ENGAGED IN THE AMERICAN ARCTIC EXPEDITION within a
wreath, crowned. AS A TOKEN OF GRATITUDE FOR THEIR GENEROUS SERVICES *D.* 32 mm. By
L. C. Wyon. *MH* 1928, 622; *Storer* 1847; *Payne* 302
  AV — —
  AR 200 350
  AE 20 35

Elisha Kent Kane (1820–57), American Arctic explorer and medical officer; led the Arctic expedition in the search for John Franklin. Awarded in silver to the expedition members.

1485 **Crystal Palace, Sydenham 1854**
Obv. Busts l., conjoined, Victoria crowned. VICTORIA D: G: BRITANNIARUM REGINA F: D:
ALBERTUS PRINCEPS CONJUX. MDCCCLIV. *Rev.* Britannia standing, facing, between the seated
figures of Industry and Commerce; beyond, exhibition building. Above, Fame flying.
ORNATUR PROPRIIS INDUSTRIA DONIS *Ex.* MDCCCLIV *D.* 64 mm. By G. G. Adams. *BHM*
2545
  AR 75 140
  AE 25 40
  WM 8 15

This medal, together with Nos. 1486–7, sometimes occurs in a brass-bound leather case, inscribed C.P.C. on the lid. The Crystal Palace Company purchased the materials of the Great Exhibition building and re-erected the Crystal Palace on a site near Sydenham, south-east London, in 1854; its rebuilding and opening is commemorated by more than fifteen medals. Various festivals and exhibitions were subsequently held there; those recorded on medals include the Fast Day for the Indian Mutiny (No. 1515), Handel centenary festival (No. 1527), Schiller centenary festival in 1859, the Reform Banquet (No. 1593) and the International Universal Exhibition in 1884. The building was destroyed by fire in 1936.

				£	£

1486 ——
Obv. Bust l.; PAXTON behind. *Rev.* View of exhibition building. CRYSTAL PALACE *Ex.* OPENED MDCCCLIV *D.* 64 mm. By L. C. Wyon. BHM 2552; *Taylor* 171g

AR	80	150
AE	28	45
WM	10	20

Another reverse has only an inscription: THE CRYSTAL PALACE DESIGNED BY SIR JOSEPH PAXTON OPENED JUNE. 10. 1854. *See* No. 1485.

1487 ——
Obv. Female figure, lamb and helmet at her feet, opens the doors of INDUSTRY and SCIENCE to the exhibition. *Rev.* As No. 1486. *D. a* 64 mm.; *b* 41 mm. By Messrs J. Pinches. BHM 2549; *Taylor* 171h,i

a AR	70	130
AE	20	35
WM	8	15

See No. 1485.

b AR	25	45
AE	8	12
WM	2	5

1488* Sir Charles Napier 1854
Obv. Uniformed figure standing upon a ship's quarter-deck. SIR CHARLES NAPIER. "LADS, WAR IS DECLARED." *Ex.* 1854. *Rev.* Broadside view of a fully-rigged ship. "THE DUKE OF WELLINGTON" *Ex.* FLAG SHIP *D.* 44 mm. By Allen & Moore. BHM 2533; *MH* 1919, 610.
See **Plate 38**

AE	55	80
WM	25	45

The quotation is Napier's much-criticised response to news of the declaration of war with Russia, which continued 'with a numerous and bold enemy. Should they meet us and offer battle, you know how to dispose of them …'. A medal struck c.1860, by W. J. Taylor, commemorates the raising of the Russian fleet from the harbour of Sebastopol (*MH* 1928, 233a).

1489 Crimean War, Holy Alliance 1854
Obv. British grenadier and French soldier stand before their unified standards. THE HOLY ALLIANCE. LA SAINTE ALLIANCE. *Ex.* 1854 *Rev.* ENGLAND AND FRANCE UNITED TO DEFEND THE OPPRESSED, AND AVENGE INSULTED EUROPE within a wreath. *D.* 45 mm. By Allen & Moore. BHM 2536

AR	35	60
AE	10	18
WM	3	7

Another reverse has a French inscription. Various medals commemorate the Crimea; both generally and for specific actions at Alma, Balaklava, and Inkermann.

1490 Battle of Alma 1854
Obv. Troops advance behind the armed figure of a standard-bearer. ALMA (incuse) SEPTEMBER 20ᵀᴴ 1854 *Rev.* Eighteen-line inscription listing the participating regiments 1ˢᵀ. DIVISION GRENADIER GUARDS … ROYAL ARTILLERY AND ROYAL ENGINEERS *D.* 41 mm. By Messrs J. Pinches. BHM 2539

AR	35	60
AE	15	25
WM	6	10

This medal and Nos. 1491 and 1492 are sometimes found together cased; they were probably struck by Pinches at the Crystal Palace and sold to the public as a souvenir of their visit. Single medals sometimes occur in an embossed metallic case.

1491 Battle of Balaklava 1854
Obv. View of a cavalry charge. BALAKLAVA *Rev.* Sixteen line inscription listing the participating regiments ROYAL ARTILLERY & ROYAL ENGINEERS 1ˢᵀ DIVISION GRENADIER GUARDS … OCTᴿ 25ᵀᴴ 1854 *D.* 41 mm. By Messrs J. Pinches. BHM 2540
See No. 1490.

AR	35	60
AE	15	25
WM	6	10

1492* Battle of Inkermann 1854
Obv. A fierce bayonet engagement. INKERMANN *Rev.* Rᴸ. ARTILLERY. Rᴸ. ENGINEERS NOVᴿ 5. 1854. upon a central shield. Around, six compartments naming the participating regiments, the divisions of which are identified, respectively, on a continuous ribbon: 1ˢᵀ DIVISION, 2ᴺᴰ DIVISION, 3ᴿᴰ DIVISION, 4ᵀᴴ DIVISION, 5ᵀᴴ DIVISION and Lᵀ CAVALRY *D.* 41 mm. [By Messrs J. Pinches] BHM 2541. *See* **Plate 38**
See No. 1490.

AR	35	60
AE	15	25
WM	6	10

1493* Florence Nightingale 1854–55
Obv. Bust l., draped, reading a book, within an oval frame. FLORENCE NIGHTINGALE *Rev.* Oval badge in the centre, inscribed VR on a cross, and BLESSED ARE THE MERCIFUL on its border; CRIMEA on a ribbon below. AS A MARK OF ESTEEM AND GRATITUDE FOR HER DEVOTION TO. THE QUEEN'S BRAVE SOLDIERS. *D.* 42 mm. By Messrs J. Pinches. *Brettauer* 3709; *Storer* 2611. *See* **Plate 38**

AE	20	35
WM	10	18

Florence Nightingale (1820–1910), nurse, served with distinction in the Crimea. As a tribute to her work, funds were raised to establish an institution for the training of nurses.

1494* Siege of Sebastopol 1854–55
Obv. Plan of Sebastopol and coastal area; marked with positions of the military and of a fleet. MER NOIRE *Rev.* SIÉGE DE SÉBASTOPOL PAR LES ARMÉES FRANÇAISE, ANGLAISE ET TURQUE 1854–1855 within a wreath. *D.* 41 mm. By Blachère. *Parkes Weber* 9a. *See* **Plate 38**

AE	12	22
WM	8	15

			£	£

1495 **Death of Lord Raglan 1855**
Obv. Mausoleum inscribed PENINSULA WATERLOO CRIMEA, and decorated with a portrait medallion. FIELD MARSHAL LORD RAGLAN *Ex.* BORN A.D. 1788 *Rev.* Panoramic view of an encampment. DIED IN THE SERVICE OF HIS COUNTRY *Ex.* AT HEAD QUARTERS BEFORE SEBASTOPOL JUNE 23ʳᴰ, 1855 *D.* 41 mm. [By Messrs J. Pinches] *BHM* 2570
AE 18 30
WM 8 15
Lord Fitzroy James Henry Somerset, 1st Baron Raglan (1788–1855), Commander of the British forces in the Crimea.

1496 **Napoleon III and Eugénie, Visit to the City of London 1855**
Obv. Busts three-quarters l., conjoined, she draped. NAPOLEON III ET EUGENIA GALLORUM IMPERATOR ET IMPERATRIX *Rev.* Britannia introduces France to Londinia. CONCORDES SERVAT AMICITIA *Ex.* LONDINI RECEPTI 19. APR. 1855 *D.* 77 mm. By B. Wyon. *BHM* 2561; *Forrer* V/582; *Welch* 7
AE 25 48
Issued by the Corporation of London; *see* No. 1245. Charles Louis Napoleon Bonaparte (1808–73), Emperor of France 1852–70. Eugénie (1826–1920), married Napoleon III in 1853.

1497 **South Devon Railway 1855**
Obv. Locomotive engine. BRADLEY WOOD FETE JUNE 28ᵀᴴ & 29ᵀᴴ 1855 *Ex.* SOUTH DEVON RAILWAY *Rev.* Façade of building. TEIGNMOUTH & DAWLISH INFIRMARY, SUPPORTED BY VOLUNTARY CONTRIBUTIONS. *Ex.* ESTABLISHED 1848. *D.* 36 mm. (By?) *Moyaux* 57
AR 40 60
AE 20 32
WM 10 15

1498 **Royal Visit to France 1855**
Obv. Busts l., conjoined, she diademed. VICTORIA REGINA. ALBERTVS PRINCEPS GALLIAM INVISVNT AVG: MDCCCLV *Rev.* Busts r., conjoined. NAPOLEON III IMPERATOR. EVGENIA IMPERATRIX ANGLIAM INVISVNT APR: MDCCCLV *D.* 41 mm. By L. C. Wyon. *BHM* 2560
AR 28 45
AE 7 12
WM 2 4

1499 **Victor Emmanuel II, Visit to the City of London 1855**
Obv. Bust l. VICTORIUS EMMANUEL II REX SARDINIAE IN LONDINIUM A PRAESIDE CIVIBUSQUE RECEPTUS *Rev.* Britannia seated, r., Londinia standing at her side, welcomes the standing figure of Sardinia. LIBERI LIBERIS GRATULANTUR SOCIIS *Ex.* DEC. 4 1855, divided by the City shield. *D.* 76 mm. By B. Wyon. *BHM* 2567; *Welch* 8
AE 25 48
Issued by the Corporation of London. *See* No. 1245. Victor Emmanuel II (1820–78), king of Sardinia 1849–61. A 17 mm. version was also struck.

1500* **Sir John Vanbrugh 1855**
Obv. Bust almost facing, draped. SIR JOHN VANBRUGH *Rev.* Façade of Vanbrugh's Blenheim Palace. *Ex.* BLENHEIM *Edge.* ART-UNION OF LONDON 1855 (incuse). *D.* 55 mm. By B. Wyon. *BHM* 2572; *Taylor* 42a; *Beaulah* 8. See **Plate 38**
AR 60 130
AE 15 30
Sir John Vanbrugh (1664–1726), architect and dramatist. *See* No. 1381.

1501 **Richard Sainthill 1855**
Obv. Bust r. RICHARD. SAINTHILL. OF. TOPSHAM. DEVONSHIRE. NUMISMATIST. BORN. JAN. 28. 1787 Below, 1855 *Rev.* Female figure, greeting another, pulls a curtain to reveal the seated figure of Time. IRRADIATING THE PRESENT. RESTORING THE PAST. *Ex.* NUMISMATA *D.* 58 mm. By L. C. Wyon. *BHM* 2571; *Frazer* 1887/324
AR 40 75
AE 15 28
Richard Sainthill (1787–1869), antiquary, genealogist and numismatist.

1502 **Sydney Mint, Presentation Medal 1855**
Obv. Bust l., diademed and veiled. VICTORIA REGINA *Rev.* Royal arms, motto and crest, decorated with the Mint badge. SYDNEY BRANCH OF THE ROYAL MINT ESTABLISHED 1855 *D.* 41 mm. By L. C. Wyon [*rev.* after J. B. Merlen]. *BHM* 2574; *Carlisle* V/7
AV 800 1100
AR 220 380
AE 80 140
The portrait and particular form of lettering are consistent with that of No. 1694. The die for this medal was supplied in 1886 by the Royal Mint, who did not make a charge for the reverse, as it was only a slight modification of that of the 1826 Crown piece of George IV (*Seaby* 3806). Examples of this medal were probably presented to dignitaries visiting the Sydney Mint. Uniform medals with this reverse were also struck of Edward VII and George V.

1503* **Board of Trade, Sea Gallantry Medal 1855**
Obv. Bust l., laureate, of Victoria. AWARDED BY THE BOARD OF TRADE FOR GALLANTRY IN SAVING LIFE V.R. *Rev.* Three men and a woman with infant, upon a raft in tempestuous seas; beyond, a life-boat approaches. *D.* 58 mm. By B. Wyon. *MH* 1919, 815; *Brettauer* 3925. See **Plate 39**
a AR 180 250
AE 90 150
b AR — —
AE — —
The 'Gallantry' Medal (type a) was awarded to those who risked their own lives. Another issue, the 'Humanity' medal (type b), omits FOR GALLANTRY, and was awarded to those indirectly connected with an action, such a ship's captain who despatched a boat to carry out the rescue. Both these medals were awarded in silver and bronze and do not usually have a suspender. In 1905 a smaller version was introduced which could be worn with a ribbon. *See* P. E. Abbott and J. M. A. Tamplin, *British Gallantry Awards*, pp. 271–2, London, 1981.

1504 **Lincoln Cathedral c. 1855**
Obv. Façade of the cathedral. *Ex.* LINCOLN CATHEDRAL *Rev.* Interior of the cathedral. *Ex.* FOUNDED 1085. BURNT 1141. OFTEN REBUILT 1135–1250. SOUTH TRANSEPT 1306. *D.* 59 mm. By J. Wiener. *BHM* 2591; *Taylor* 7b
AR 50 90
AE 12 25
This medal and Nos. 1505–8 form part of a large series depicting European cathedrals and churches, struck c.1855–65.

			VF	EF
			£	£

1505   St. Paul's Cathedral *c.*1855

Obv. Façade of the cathedral. *Ex.* Sᵀ PAUL'S CATHEDRAL LONDON   *Rev.* Interior of the cathedral. *Ex.* FOUNDED VII CENTURY. BURNT XI CENTURY. REBUILT IN STONE XII AND XIII CENTᵞ AGAIN BURNT 1666. REBUILT IN ITS PRESENT STATE 1675–1710: ARCHIT. CHRIST. WREN. *D.* 59 mm. By J. Wiener. BHM 2363; *Taylor 39i*   AR 50 90 / AE 12 25

See No. 1504.

1506   Westminster Abbey *c.*1855

Obv. Façade of the cathedral. WESTMINSTER ABBEY   *Rev.* Interior of the cathedral. THE PRESENT CHURCH CONSTRUCTED 1220–1285. RESTORED END OF XVII CENTURY./WESTMINSTER HALL BUILT 1397. THE CHAPEL OF HENRY VII COMMENCED 1503 RESTORED 1809. *Ex.* ST. PETER'S CHURCH FOUNDED ABOUT 612. REBUILT AND ERECTED AN ABBEY 958 AND 1049–1066. *D.* 59 mm. By J. Wiener. BHM 2592; *Taylor 8b*   AR 50 90 / AE 12 25

See No. 1504.

1507   Winchester Cathedral *c.*1855

Obv. Façade of the cathedral. *Ex.* WINCHESTER CATHEDRAL FOUNDED AT THE EPOCH OF THE SAXON KINGS. THE PRESENT CATHEDRAL BUILT 1079–1093. THE NAVES AND THE AISLES CONSTRUCTED BY WYKEHAM 1370–1400. *Rev.* Interior of the cathedral. *D.* 59 mm. By J. Wiener. BHM 2593; *Taylor 11b*   AR 50 90 / AE 12 25

See No. 1504.

1508   York Cathedral *c.*1855

Obv. Façade of the cathedral. *Ex.* YORK CATHEDRAL BUILT 630–642. BURNT 1069. REBUILT 1070. AGAIN BURNT 1137. RECONSTRUCTED 1171–1361. RESTORATION FINISHED 1832. *Rev.* Interior of the cathedral. *D.* 59 mm. By J. Wiener. BHM 2558; *Taylor 13d*   AR 50 90 / AE 12 25

See No. 1504

1509   Peace in Europe 1856

Obv. THE ALLIES GIVE PEACE TO EUROPE MARCH 30ᵀᴴ 1856 within a wreath decorated with a ribbon, inscribed ENGLAND FRANCE SARDINIA TURKEY   *Rev.* A rectangular plaque with scene of ships sinking in a harbour; above, radiate scales between flags of England, France, Sardinia and Turkey. FALL OF SEBASTOPOL SEP 8ᵀᴴ 1855   *Ex.* A snake in undergrowth. SINOPE – HANGO   *D.* 52 mm. [By Messrs J. Pinches] BHM 2581   AR 35 65 / AE 15 25 / WM 5 12

1510   British Association for the Advancement of Science 1856

Obv. Bust l. C.G.B. DAUBENY M.D. F.R.S. PRESIDENT. BRITISH ASSOCIATION FOR THE ADVANCEMENT OF SCIENCE   *Rev.* MEETING AT CHELTENHAM AUGUST 6 1856 within a wreath; an antique lamp, above. *D.* 54 mm. By J. Moore, *obv.* after R. E. & C. Marshall. BHM 2586; *Storer* 795.   AR 30 55 / AE 10 18

Charles Giles Bridle Daubeny (1795–1867), chemist and botanist.

1511   Department of Science and Art, Queen's Medal 1856

Obv. Bust l., diademed. VICTORIA BY THE GRACE OF GOD QVEEN MDCCCLVI. *Rev.* LOCAL PRIZE FOR SVCCESS IN ART AWARDED BY THE DEPARTMENT OF SCIENCE AND ART, within a wreath. *D.* 55 mm. By W. Wyon. *Hocking* 219/27; *D & W* 255/395   AV 600 700 / AR 15 28 / AE 4 9

Another reverse reads NATIONAL MEDAL (in place of LOCAL PRIZE). The obverse portrait is found on a number of prize medals issued by the Department, which was an amalgamation of the Departments of Practical Art, and Science and Art, established in 1852, as proposed by the Royal Commissioners of the Great Exhibition. A fixed amount of public funds was voted by Parliament in order to found a self-supporting system of scientific instruction. Medals were given at the public examinations in gold (1), silver (2) and bronze (3), for each of eight main groups of subjects (a few with sub-divisions). However, these proportions do not always appear to have been observed. These medals were intended to encourage and stimulate talent at local schools throughout Britain amongst the industrial classes. A number of similar medals have been awarded by the National Art Training School (No. 1660) and the Board of Education (No. 1865).

1512*   National Art Competition 1857

Obv. Bust l., diademed. VICTORIA QUEEN BY THE GRACE OF GOD. 1857. within a central circle. Around, a continuous scene of allegorical figures, and an oval (blank, for recipient's name). A narrow outer border decorated with running devices and putti. FOR SUCCESS IN THE NATIONAL ART COMPETITION. *D.* 145 mm. By A. Vechte. *Parkes Weber* 211; *Burt* 48–9. *See* **Plate 39**   AE 45 75

Awarded between 1857 and 1865; made as an electrotype, without a reverse.

1513   Exhibition of Art Treasures, Manchester 1857

Obv. View of exhibition buildings. EXHIBITION OF ART TREASURES   *Ex.* OPENED AT MANCHESTER BY HIS ROYAL HIGHNESS PRINCE ALBERT MAY 5ᵀᴴ 1857. Broad floral border decorated with shields of Manchester, Ireland, Scotland and Gt. Britain, and a continuous ribbon bearing artists' names: MURILLO FLAXMAN VAN DYKE RUBENS CELLINI RAPHAEL M.ANGELO TURNER   *Rev.* Allegorical group of three muses symbolizing the Arts. *Ex.*   *a* AE 18 32 / WM 5 12 / *b* AE 12 20 / WM 3 6

MDCCCLVII *D. a* 63 mm.; *b* 41 mm. [By Messrs J. Pinches] *BHM* 2605; *Taylor* 173*a*

£ £

Another reverse carries only an inscription. Type *b* is without the floral border. Medals are sometimes found in embossed metallic cases, inscribed with the name of Pinches.

1514 Crumlin Viaduct Opened 1857
Obv. Train upon a viaduct spanning valley. NEWPORT, ABERGAVENNY & HEREFORD RAILWAY EXTENSION TO TAFF VALLEY *Ex.* CRUMLIN VIADUCT *Rev.* MR T.W. KENNARD ENGINEER & CONTRACTOR FOR THE VIADUCT. THIS VIADUCT IS ENTIRELY OF IRON AND IS 200 FEET HIGH, AND ONE THIRD OF A MILE IN LENGTH: FIRST COLUMN ERECTED IN DECEMBER 1853, BY LADY ISABELLA FITZMAURICE. OPENED ON 1ST JUNE 1857., in the centre. MESS^RS LIDDLE & GORDON ARE THE ENGINEERS OF THE RAILWAY. *D.* 38 mm. By J. Hinks. *BHM* 2603; *Moyaux* 59; *Boon* 27

AR	75	140
AE	35	55
WM	15	28

1515 The Indian Mutiny 1857
Obv. Justice standing, r., in a landscape near kneeling captive and prostrate tiger. JUSTICE *Rev.* DURING THE SEPOY MUTINIES A.D. MDCCCLVII., within a wreath. DEDICATED TO THE BRAVE DEFENDERS OF OUR INDIAN EMPIRE *D.* 63 mm. [By Messrs J. Pinches] *BHM* 2601
On 7 October 1857 a Fast day for the Indian Mutiny was held at Crystal Palace, attended by more than 23,000 people. *See* No. 1485.

AR	65	130
AE	25	40
WM	10	22

1516 William Chambers 1857
Obv. Bust r. CHAMBERS 1725–1796 *Rev.* Façade of building. *Ex.* SOMERSET HOUSE 1781 SIR WILLIAM CHAMBERS R.A. ARCHITECT *Edge.* ART-UNION OF LONDON 1857 (incuse) *D.* 55 mm. By B. Wyon, *obv.* after R. Westmacott. *BHM* 2596; *Taylor* 52*a*; *Beaulah* 9
William Chambers (1725–96), architect. *See* No. 1381.

AR	60	130
AE	15	30

1517* Marriage of Princess Victoria and Frederick William 1858
Obv. Busts conjoined, l., she laureate. VICTORIA PRINCESS ROYAL OF ENGLAND * FREDERICK WILLIAM PRINCE OF PRUSSIA *Rev.* JANUARY XXV MDCCCLVIII within a wreath. *D.* 63 mm. By L. C. Wyon. *BHM* 2627; *RWE* 34. See **Plate 39**
Frederick William (1831–88), became Frederick III of Prussia in 1888. More than ten different medals commemorate this marriage. The marriages of several of the Royal children are commemorated on similar medals. *See* Nos. 1562, 1583, 1613, 1662, 1687 and 1718.

AR	60	130
AE	15	32

1518 ——
Obv. Busts, facing each other, in two oval frames, of FRID. GVIL. BORVSS. PRINC. REG. r., and VICTORIA BRIT. PRINC. REGIA, l., upon a platform decorated with their royal shields. Between stands a winged female figure, facing, her arms outstretched. D. XXV JANVARII MDCCCLVIII. *Rev.* VICTORIA and ALBERT, standing in a galley, together with Princess Victoria, are welcomed by Germania. Above, SALVE. *D.* 54 mm. By W. Kullrich, *rev.* after F. A. Fischer.

AR	55	100
AE	15	30

1519 ——
Obv. Bust l., laureate, of Princess Victoria. *Rev.* VICTORIA PRINCESS ROYAL OF ENGLAND JAN. 25 1858 *D.* 16 mm. By L. C. Wyon. *BHM* 2628
A companion to this medal was struck of Frederick William.

AV	35	55
AR	12	22

1520 Inauguration of Aston Hall 1858
Obv. Bust r., within a wreath. HER MOST GRACIOUS MAJESTY QUEEN VICTORIA *Rev.* Façade of the building. H.M.G. MAJESTY QUEEN VICTORIA VISITED BIRMINGHAM TO INAUGURATE ASTON HALL & PARK AS A PLACE FOR RECREATION. JUNE 15TH 1858 SIR JOHN RATCLIFF. MAYOR *Ex.* ASTON HALL ERECTED 1618–35 *D.* 74 mm. By Ottley. *BHM* 2615; *Taylor* 35*d*
Several medals commemorate Aston Hall and the Queen's visit to Warwick.

AE	20	38
WM	10	18

1521 Newport Dock Extension 1858
Obv. Panoramic view of ships in the docks. LENGTH 950 F^T BREADTH 350 F^T DEPTH 26 F^T COST £64000, AREA OF NEW & OLD DOCKS 57000 Y^DS. *Rev.* Twelve-line inscription CHAIRMAN S. HOMFRAY, ESQ. SECRETARY CAPT^N FOOTE ... MAYOR W^M WILLIAMS, ESQ., in the centre. IN COMMEMORATION OF THE OPENING OF THE NEWPORT DOCK EXTENSION. MARCH 2ND 1858 *D.* 51 mm. By J. Moore. *Boon* 28; *Fearon* 309.5
Newport's Dock was originally opened in 1842; the extension greatly enhanced trade in all South Wales ports.

AR	28	55
AE	8	15
WM	3	7

1522 Rothschild Foundation Prize 1858
Obv. FOUNDED TO COMMEMORATE THE ADMISSION OF JEWS INTO PARLIAMENT IN THE PERSON OF BARON L. DE ROTHSCHILD JULY 26TH 1858 *Rev.* A wreath (space within, for recipient's name). *D.* 55 mm. (By?)
The scholarship, endowed at the City of London School, commemorates the outcome of an eleven year struggle for Jews to be allowed to swear their own oath of allegiance, having been passed by the House of Commons on nine previous submissions but each time rejected by the Lords. *See* No. 1426.

AE	45	75

PLATE 39

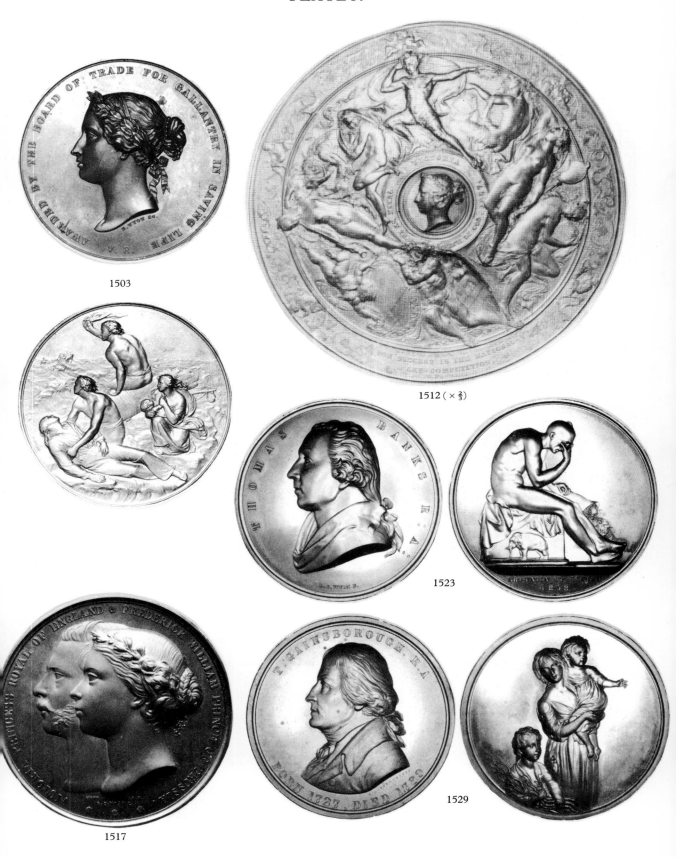

1503

1512 (× 2/3)

1523

1517

1529

PLATE 40

1530

1531

1558

1561

1568

1569

1575

			£	£

1523*   Thomas Banks 1858

Obv. Bust l., draped. THOMAS BANKS R:A: *Rev.* Part of Banks' decoration of Sir Eyre   *AR*   60   130
Coote's tomb (an American Indian seated upon a pedestal). *Ex.* ART-UNION OF LONDON 1858   *AE*   15   30
(incuse). *D.* 55 mm. By L. C. Wyon, [*obv.* after G. Dance] BHM 2633; *Beaulah* 10. *See*
Plate 39

Thomas Banks (1735–1805), sculptor. *See* No. 1381.

1524   British Horological Society 1858

Obv. A large astrolabe. SOCIETAS: HOROLOGICA: BRITANNICA: MDCCCLVIII: *Rev.* OB: *AR*   45   70
HOROLOGIAM: EXERCITATIONE: PROMOTAM DOCTRINAQUE: ERUDITAM within a wreath. *D.*   *AE*   15   22
70 mm. By J. J. Hall. BHM 2639; *Hocking* 217/30

A prize medal usually found awarded in silver; the society was established for the benefit of watch and clock makers.

1525   Thomas Holloway 1858

Obv. Bust l., of Holloway. *Rev.* MEMORIAL MEDAL OF HOLLOWAY'S PILLS & OINTMENT   *AR*   45   70
INTRODUCED TO THE PUBLIC 15 OCTᴿ 1837 PROFILE OF THE PROPRIETOR THOˢ HOLLOWAY   *AE*   20   30
ENGRAVED FROM LIFE BY JOSEPH MOORE BIRMINGHAM 1858   *D.* 62 mm. By J. Moore. BHM
2635; *Storer* 1585

Thomas Holloway (1800–83), patent medicine manufacturer and vendor; founder of a hospital for the insane poor and a college for women.

1526   Robert Burns, Centenary of Birth 1859

Obv. Bust l., draped. ROBERT BURNS   *Rev.* THE FIRST CENTENARY OF THE BIRTH OF ROBERT   *AR*   20   35
BURNS THE SCOTTISH BARD XXV JANUARY MDCCCLIX, within a wreath; a lyre, radiate, above. *D.*   *AE*   6   10
41 mm. By J. Moore. BHM 2651; *CP* 127/84   *WM*   2   4

Examples occur with and without an obverse legend. Robert Burns (1759–96), Scottish national poet.

1527   Handel Centenary Festival 1859

Obv. Bust l., wearing a cap and draped. GEORGE FREDERIC HANDEL   *Rev.* CENTENARY   *AE*   5   8
COMMEMORATION CRYSTAL PALACE MDCCCLIX within a wreath. *D.* 51 mm. By W. J. Taylor.
BHM 2656; *Niggl* 804

Over 25,000 people attended the Festival which was organized by the Sacred Harmonic Society (No. 1688). It was held over four days during which various pieces of Handel were played and bronze medals presented to performers. Similar prize medals had been given at the rehearsals held in the previous two years. *See* No. 1485.

1528   Llanidloes & Newton Railway 1859

Obv. View of steam locomotive and train. *Ex.* Two clasped hands. *Rev.* OPENING OF THE   *AE*   80   130
LLANIDLOES AND NEWTON RAILWAY AUGUST 31ˢᵀ 1859   *D.* 39 mm. By J. Moore. BHM 2662;   *WM*   45   70
Moyaux 38; *Boon* 26

1529*   Thomas Gainsborough 1859

Obv. Bust l., draped. T. GAINSBOROUGH. R.A BORN 1727. DIED 1789   *Rev.* Detail of   *AR*   60   130
Gainsborough's painting *The Wood Gatherers*. *Edge.* ART-UNION OF LONDON 1859 (incuse).   *AE*   15   30
D. 55 mm. By E. Ortner, [*obv.* after J. Zoffany] BHM 2653; *Beaulah* 11. *See* **Plate 39**

Thomas Gainsborough (1727–88), painter. *See* No. 1381.

1530*   Lord Dudley Stuart, Memorial 1859

Obv. Bust r. DVDLEY C. STVART CAVSÆ POLONÆ INDEFESSVS VINDEX EXVLVM POLONORVM   *AR*   65   120
AMICVS ET FAVTOR NAT. A. 1803. OB. HOLMIÆA. 1854 CIVES POLONI HOC MONVMENTVM PIETATIS   *AE*   25   45
PVBLICÆ F.C.A. 1859. *Rev.* Relief map of POLONIA with her towns, rivers and neighbouring
countries identified. ILLIC HONOS NOMENQVE TVVM LAVDESQVE MANEBVNT   *D.* 63 mm. By
J. F. A. Bovy. BHM 2659; *CP* 126/81. *See* **Plate 40**

Lord Dudley Coutts Stuart (1803–54), politician and a staunch advocate of Polish independence.

1531*   Death of Isambard Kingdom Brunel 1859

Obv. Bust three-quarters l., draped. ISAMBARD KINGDOM BRUNEL BORN 1806. DIED SEP. 15.   *AR*   70   130
1859   *Rev.* Broadside view of ship. THE "GREAT EASTERN" STEAM SHIP. SCREW, PADDLE AND   *AE*   30   55
SAIL. – FOUR DECKS WOULD ACCOMMODATE 10,000 TROOPS. *Ex.* 692 F. LONG. 83 F. WIDE. HEIGHT   *WM*   15   25
OF HULL 60 F. 24,000 TONS BURDEN. 2,600 HORSE POWER   *D.* 36 mm. By J. Moore. BHM 2650.
See **Plate 40**

A similar reverse occurs on two 45 mm. medals: obverses with bust of Brunel three-quarters r.; and conjoined busts, l., of Victoria and Albert.

1532   First Volunteer Court 1860

Obv. Bust l., diademed and draped. VICTORIA   *Rev.* TO COMMEMORATE THE FIRST VOLUNTEER   *AE*   3   6
COURT HELD BY HER MAJESTY AT Sᵀ JAMES'S PALACE MARCH 7ᵀᴴ 1860. *D.* 28 mm. By Messrs   *WM*   2   3
J. Pinches. BHM 2684

1533   Thomas Sayers 1860

Obv. Bust l., draped. THOMAS SAYERS, THE CHAMPION OF ENGLAND   *Rev.* THE GREAT   *WM*   15   28
INTERNATIONAL PRIZE FIGHT BETWEEN HEENAN & SAYERS FOR THE CHAMPIONSHIP OF THE

WORLD FOUGHT APRIL 1860, within a wreath. *D.* 34 mm. By F. B. Smith & Hartmann. £ £

The match took place at Farnborough, Hampshire; it was interrupted after several hours with both men receiving a silver belt. Thomas Sayers (1826–65); champion 1849–60. John Heenan was an American.

1534 Royal Dramatic College 1860
Obv. Distant view of building. FOUNDATION STONE LAID BY THE PRINCE CONSORT JUNE 1. *AR* 20 30
1860 *Rev.* Bust of Shakespeare in a portico, flanked by characters from his plays. ALL THE *AE* 8 12
WORLD'S A STAGE & ALL THE MEN & WOMEN MERELY PLAYERS Below, ROYAL DRAMATIC *WM* 3 5
COLLEGE FOUNDED A D 1858 *D.* 23 mm. By H. Brown. *BHM* 2692

The college was situated at Maybury near Woking.

1535 Prince of Wales, Visit to Canada 1860
Obv. Bust l. ALBERT EDWARD PRINCE OF WALES *Rev.* Prince's plumes and coronet within a *AV* 500 800
wreath interlaced by a ribbon inscribed WELCOME thrice. VISITED CANADA AND INAUGURATED *AR* 50 90
THE VICTORIA BRIDGE. 1860. *D.* 48 mm. By J. S. Wyon, *rev.* after M. D. Wyatt. *BHM* 2669; *AE* 12 22
Leroux 641; *Moyaux* 85

Several medals commemorate the visit. *See* No. 1347.

1536 Prince of Wales, Opening of Victoria Bridge, 1860
Obv. Bust facing, uniformed. H.R.H. THE PRINCE OF WALES BORN 9 NOV 1841 *Rev.* View of *AE* 20 35
bridge; a train just crossing. OPENED BY THE PRINCE OF WALES 1860 *Ex.* VICTORIA BRIDGE *WM* 15 28
MONTREAL *D.* 44 mm. (By?) *Leroux* 642; *Moyaux* 47

Struck from more than one pair of dies. This commemorates the opening of the bridge of the Grand Trunk Railway Company.

1537 Richard Trevithick 1860
Obv. Bust l., draped; RICHARD TREVITHICK behind. GRAND TRUNK RAILWAY COMPANY OF *AR* 45 70
CANADA *Rev.* Panels, inscribed PRESENTED BY THE DIRECTORS TO (space for recipient's *AE* 10 20
name) FOR GENERAL EFFICIENCY AND GOOD CONDUCT DURING THE YEAR (space for date), within
maple leaves. *D.* 45 mm. By J. S. Wyon. *BHM* 2681; *Moyaux* 49

1538 Dr. Arthur Jacob 1860
Obv. Bust l., draped; JACOB behind. *Rev.* IN COMMEMORATION OF EMINENT SERVICES *AE* 20 35
RENDERED TO SCIENCE AND THE MEDICAL PROFESSION IN IRELAND 1860, within a wreath.
.ARTHUR JACOB. M.D. F.R.C.S. PROF. OF ANAT. & PHYS. ROY. COLL. OF SURG. IN IRELAND *D.*
64 mm. By J. Woodhouse (although signed W. Woodhouse) *BHM* 2675; *Frazer* 1887/191;
Storer 1753

Arthur Jacob (1790–1874), oculist.

1539 Thomas Lawrence 1860
Obv. Bust l.; LAWRENCE behind. *Rev.* Standing figure of WELLINGTON, uniformed (from a *AR* 60 130
painting by Lawrence). ART UNION OF LONDON. 1860. *D.* 56 mm. By G. G. Adams, [*obv.* after *AE* 15 30
E. H. Baily] *BHM* 2676; *Beaulah* 12

See No. 1381.

1540 William Joseph Taylor 1860
Obv. Bust l.; WILLIAM JOSEPH TAYLOR 1860 behind. *Rev.* Man seated at a work-bench *AE* 28 45
engraving a die; bust on socle before him. Beyond, a medal-press. *D.* 45 mm. By *WM* 20 30
W. E. Bardelle. *BHM* 2680

William Joseph Taylor (1802–85) medallist and die-sinker. A similar medal occurs dated 1884 and signed W.J.T & Sons.

1541 Royal National Life-Boat Institution 1860
Obv. Head l., laureate. VICTORIA PATRONESS. ROYAL NATIONAL LIFE-BOAT INSTITUTION. *AV* 700 1000
FOUNDED IN 1824 – INCORPORATED 1860. *Rev.* As No. 1174. *D.* 36 mm. By L. C. Wyon. *MH* *AR* 150 230
1919, 836; *D & W* 142/319 *AE* 15 25

See No. 1174.

1542 National Rifle Association 1860
Obv. THE NATIONAL RIFLE ASSOCIATION 1860 within a wreath. *Rev.* An ancient bowman and a *AR* 12 18
rifle volunteer, side by side; 1300. 1500 and 1860 in the field. *Ex.* SIT PERPETUUM *D.* 48 mm. *AE* 6 9
By G. G. Adams. *BHM* 2682; *Payne* 187.

One of many prize medals awarded by the N.R.A.

1543 Order of Druids 1860
Obv. Two male figures standing in a thickly-wooded landscape, amidst symbols and *AR* 60 110
objects; Stonehenge in distance. THE ORDER OF DRUIDS. *Rev.* A wreath (space within, for
recipient's name). *D.* 69 mm. By Ottley.

The Order was founded in 1781, in London, as an institution for ancient Druids who adopted masonic rites.

1544 *Great Eastern* 1861

Obv. Broadside view of ship. THE GREAT EASTERN   *Ex.* 1861   *Rev.* 2,600 HORSEPOWER 4, DECKS 10, BOILERS 112, FURNACES 10, ANCHORS. WILL CARRY 10,000 TROOPS., in the centre. TONNAGE 24,000 LENGTH 692 F.T BREDTH 83 F.T DEPTH 60 F.T *   *D.* 33 mm. (By?) *Fearon* 312.3

	£	£
AE	20	30
WM	12	18

1545 Royal College of Physicians, Baly Medal 1861

Obv. Bust three-quarters l., draped. IN HONOREM GULIELMI BALY M.D. OB.T 1861   *Rev.* Façade of the College building (in Pall Mall, London). OB PHYSIOLOGIAM FELICITER EXCULTAM. Below, SIR R. SMIRKE R.A. ARCH.T   *Ex.* COLL. REG. MED. LOND. *D.* 57 mm. By J. S. Wyon/J. S. & A. B. Wyon. *BHM* 2707; *Storer* 154

AV	gold value
AR	40 70
AE	18 30

Awarded biennially from 1869 for distinction in physiology, usually in gold; since 1977 it has been given in silver. William Baly (1814–61), physician. Robert Smirke (1781–1867) architect; he also designed the façade of the British Museum.

1546 Augustus Frederick, Duke of Sussex 1861

Obv. Bust r. AUGUSTUS FREDERICK   *Rev.* CONSTITUTED BY WARRANT FROM THE GRAND LODGE OF IRELAND IN 13 NOVEMBER 1861 within a wreath, crowned; a harp below. THE DUKE OF LEINSTER'S LODGE OF FREEMASONS. CLI. LIMA. PERU. *D.* 40 mm. By J. Moore. *Poole* 100

AE	15	25

1547 Prince Albert, Death and Obsequies 1861

Obv. Bust l. HIS ROYAL HIGHNESS PRINCE ALBERT   *Rev.* Britannia, mournful, seated upon a recumbent lion beside a tomb, inscribed THE PRINCE CONSORT DIED DECE 14 1861 AGED 42, on facia. IN MEMORY OF HIS OBSEQUIES AT WINDSOR DECEM. 1861 Wreath border. *D.* 64 mm. By Ottley. *BHM* 2700

AR	60	110
AE	18	32
WM	5	12

1548 Dr. Steevens Hospital, Cusack Medal 1861

Obv. Bust r., draped. JAMES WILLIAM CUSACK BORN 1788 DIED 1861   *Rev.* Façade of hospital building. D.R STEEVENS HOSPITAL DUBLIN   *Ex.* Two armorial shields. CUSACK PRIZE FOUNDED 1861   *D.* 76 mm. By J. S. Wyon. *Frazer* 1887/325; *Storer* 720

AR	55	85

Only found awarded in silver. Richard Steevens (1653–1710), physician.

1549 David Wilkie 1861

Obv. Bust r., draped. SIR DAVID WILKIE R.A. 1785–1841   *Rev.* A detail from Wilkie's painting *The Village Politicians.*   *Ex.* ART UNION OF LONDON 1861   *D.* 55 mm. By L. C. Wyon. *BHM* 2704; *Forrer* VI/627; *Beaulah* 13

AR	60	130
AE	15	30

Sir David Wilkie (1785–1841), painter. *See* No. 1381.

1550 Royal Hibernian Academy of Arts 1861

Obv. Bust r., diademed. VICTORIA REGINA ROYAL HIBERNIAN ACADEMY OF ARTS. 1823 1861   *Rev.* PRIZE MEDAL within a wreath, crowned. An outer border (plain, for recipient's name). *D.* 64 mm. By J. Woodhouse. *Frazer* 1887/196

AR	60	100
AE	20	35

Awarded in silver and bronze.

1551 Hartley Colliery, Service Medal 1862

Obv. Winged female guardian prevents a miner from hacking at rocks while a rescuer attempts to recover two bodies beneath. *Rev.* PRESENTED TO THOSE/WHO RISKED THEIR OWN LIVES IN ATTEMPTING TO SAVE THE LIVES OF THEIR FELLOW WORKMEN BURIED IN HARTLEY COLLIERY/JANUARY 1862   in three panels upon a wreath. *D.* 51 mm. By J. S. & A. B. Wyon. *Müseler* 1614

AV	—	—
AR	150	220
AE	50	70

An example in gold, forty in silver and an unspecified number in bronze are reported as being given. The medal occurs with a suspension loop. This disaster in Northumberland cost the lives of 204 miners. The medals were presented at a public ceremony in Newcastle. For full details and a list of recipients, *see* T. E. Forster, *Memoir of the Hartley Colliery Accident,* Newcastle-on-Tyne, 1912.

1552 Prince Albert, Memorial 1862

Obv. Head l. ALBERT PRINCE CONSORT, BORN AUGUST 26 1819, DIED DECEMBER 14 1861. *Rev.* FOUNDER OF THE INTERNATIONAL EXHIBITIONS OF 1851 AND 1862. within a wreath. *D.* 68 mm. By C. Wiener. *BHM* 2710; *Parkes Weber* 218

AR	55	90
AE	15	25
WM	5	12

Another reverse commemorates the inauguration of the Albert Memorial in 1863.

1553 International Exhibition, Prize Medal 1862

Obv. Britannia seated, l., surrounded by female figures bearing the products of Art, Science, Industry and Agriculture; a lion in foreground. *Rev.* 1862 LONDINI – HONORIS CAUSA within a wreath. *D.* 77 mm. By L. C. Wyon, *obv.* after D. Maclise. *BHM* 2747; *Jones* 1979, 291

AE	12	22

The official prize medal, awarded in thirty-six classes of subject-matter. *See* No. 1555. For details of the recipients and awards, *see* Reports of the International Exhibition, Medals and Honourable Mentions Awarded by the International Juries, London, 1863. More than forty different medals commemorate the exhibition, which was situated in South Kensington on a site now occupied by the Natural History Museum.

1554 International Exhibition, London 1862

Obv. Bust three-quarters, l., diademed and draped. HER MOST GRACIOUS MAJESTY VICTORIA QUEEN OF GREAT BRITAIN   *Rev.* View of the exhibition building. THE BUILDING FOR THE

AE	40	65
WM	15	30

			VF	EF
			£	£

INTERNATIONAL EXHIBITION (SOUTH FRONT VIEW) OPENED MAY 1ST 1862   *Ex.* COVERS A SPACE OF 26 ACRES, LENGTH 1200 FT WIDTH 700 FT, HEIGHT 100 FT, NAVE 85 FT WIDE THE BUILDING IS OF BRICK, THE DOMES ARE OF IRON AND GLASS, HEIGHT 250 FT AND 160 FT DIAM: AT BASE (THE LARGEST DOMES EVER ERECTED) COST £300,000   *D.* 73 mm. By G. Dowler. *BHM* 2720; *Taylor* 182*h*

1555   **International Exhibition, Services Medal 1862**
Obv. Bust l., diademed. HER MAJESTY QUEEN VICTORIA   *Rev.* FOR SERVICES within a wreath. INTERNATIONAL EXHIBITION. 1862   *D.* 55 mm. By W. Wyon.   *AE*   5   8
See No. 1553.

1556   **International Exhibition, London 1862**
Obv. Bust l. TO THE COMMEMORATION OF HIS LATE R.H. THE PRINCE CONSORT ALBERT   *Rev.*   *AR*   28   45
Façade of the exhibition building. INTERNATIONAL EXHIBITION 1862. *Ex.* STAMPED IN THE   *AE*   8   15
BUILDING BY H. UHLHORN OF GREVENBROICH. PRUSSIA   *D.* 41 mm. By C. Schnitzspahn/   *WM*   3   5
J. Wiener. *BHM* 2743; *Taylor* 182*u*
Bronze and white metal examples frequently occur gilt. Another reverse has an interior view of the building.

1557   **Marriage of Princess Alice and Louis of Hesse 1862**
Obv. Busts l., conjoined and draped. H.R.H. PRINCESS ALICE AND H.G.D.H. PRINCE LOUIS OF   *AE*   45   70
HESSE   *Rev.* View of the marriage ceremony. *Ex.* MARRIED JULY 1ST 1862   *D.* 51 mm. (By?)   *WM*   20   35
Prince Louis (1837–92), Louis IV Grand Duke of Hesse (-Darmstadt) 1877–92. Few medals record this marriage.

1558*   **Charles Barry 1862**
Obv. Bust r., draped. SIR C. BARRY R.A. ARCHITECT. ART-UNION OF LONDON 1862   *Rev.* River-   *AR*   75   170
front view of the Houses of Parliament. *Ex.* COMMENCED 1837. INAUGURATED 1847. *D.* 60 mm.   *AE*   20   40
By L. Wiener/J. Wiener. *BHM* 2712; *Taylor* 171*i*; *Beaulah* 14. *See* **Plate 40**
Sir Charles Barry (1795–1860), architect. *See* No. 1381.

1559   **Duke of Devonshire, Chancellor of Cambridge University 1862**
Obv. Bust l., draped. PRINCEPS ILLUSTRISS: GULIELMUS CAVENDISH DEVONIÆ DUX ACAD: *AR*   20   35
CANTAB: CANCELL: 1862. *Rev.* Similar to No. 1282. *D.* 44 mm. [By J. Peters] *BHM* 2713;   *AE*   5   9
Taylor 45*e*   *WM*   2   4
William Cavendish, 7th Duke of Devonshire (1808–91). *See* No. 1282.

1560   **Exploration of the Nile 1863**
Obv. Bust l., diademed. VICTORIA REGINA *Rev.* River with wooded banks; sun on horizon.   *AR*   80   140
VICTORIA NYANZA SOURCE OF THE NILE   *Ex.* EXPLORED BY SPEKE & GRANT 1860–3   *D.* 37 mm.   *AE*   50   80
By J. S. & A. B. Wyon. *BHM* 2792   *WM*   25   40
James Augustus Grant (1827–92), soldier and African explorer. John Hanning Speke (1827–64), African explorer; previously accompanied Richard Burton on expeditions into Somaliland and Lake Nyasa.

1561*   **Princess Alexandra, Entry into the City of London 1863**
Obv. Bust l. ALEXANDRA   *Rev.* Londinia, with attendants, welcomes Alexandra accom-   *AE*   25   48
panied by the Prince of Wales. WELCOME ALEXANDRA   *Ex.* MAR. 1863 divided by the City
shield. *D.* 77 mm. By J. S. Wyon/J. S. & A. B. Wyon. *BHM* 2783; *Forrer* VI/589; *Welch* 9.
See **Plate 40**
Issued by the Corporation of London; *see* No. 1245. Alexandra Caroline Marie (1844–1925), eldest daughter of Christian IX of Denmark. A 17 mm. version of this medal was also struck.

1562   **Marriage of Alexandra and the Prince of Wales 1863**
Obv. Busts r., conjoined. ALBERT EDWARD PRINCE OF WALES. ALEXANDRA PRINCESS OF   *a AR*   60   130
DENMARK. *Rev.* Royal arms of the couple. Prince's plumes and coronet, above; motto below.   *AE*   15   32
MARCH 10 1863   *D. a* 63 mm.; *b* 33 mm. By L. C. Wyon. *BHM* 2770
Type *b* differs slightly. The marriage is commemorated by more than twenty-five different medals. *See* No. 1517.   *b AV*   200   350
                                                               AR   25   40
                                                               AE   7   12

1563   ——
Obv. Busts r., conjoined and draped. H.R.H. THE PRINCE OF WALES AND H.R.H. THE PRINCESS   *a AR*   40   75
ALEXANDRA   *Rev.* H.R.H. THE PRINCE OF WALES BORN NOV. 9. 1841 MARRIED MARCH 10. 1863 AT   *AE*   15   25
ST GEORGE'S CHAPEL WINDSOR TO H.R.H. ALEXANDRA PRINCESS OF DENMARK BORN DEC. 1. 1844   *WM*   3   7
within a wreath; Prince's crest, above. *D. a* 51 mm.; *b* 39 mm. By Ottley. *BHM* 2768
                                                                 b AE   10   15
                                                                WM   2   5

1564   ——
Obv. Busts l., conjoined. ALBERT EDWARD AND ALEXANDRA. *Rev.* Crowned shields of the   *AR*   28   55
couple; 1863 below. *D.* 42 mm. By Dodd & Sons. *BHM* 2762   *AE*   10   18
                                                                 WM   2   5

1565   **Prince and Princess of Wales, Visit to Halifax 1863**

Obv. Busts r., conjoined and draped. ALBERT EDWARD PRINCE OF WALES. PRINCESS ALEXANDRA OF DENMARK. *Rev.* Façade of a church.. ALL SOULS' CHURCH HALIFAX. VISITED BY THE PRINCE & PRINCESS OF WALES, AUGT 4TH 1863. *D.* 38 mm. By J. Moore. *BHM* 2786

This obverse occurs on a number of medals commemorating other visits: Glasgow, 1868; Ireland, 1868; Chester, 1869 (No. 1603); Bolton, 1873; and Plymouth, 1874.

	£	£
AR	28	45
AE	10	15

1566   **Society of Arts, Albert Medal 1863**

Obv. Bust l. ALBERT PRINCE CONSORT PRESIDENT 1842–61 *Rev.* Art, holding a palette, presents a flower to Industry, seated facing her; Commerce seated, r. SOCIETY OF ARTS MANUFACTURES AND COMMERCE   *Ex.* MDCCCLXIII. *D.* 56 mm. By L. C. Wyon. *BHM* 2795; *Hocking* 257/102

Established in 1864 and awarded annually in gold for outstanding contributions to the promotion of Arts, Manufactures and Commerce. *See* No. 643.

AV	800	1000
AR	35	50
AE	10	18

1567   **Society of Arts 1863**

Obv. Bust r. ALBERT EDWARD PRINCE OF WALES PRESIDENT MDCCCLXIII   *Rev.* Similar to No. 1420. *D.* 56 mm. By L. C. Wyon. *BHM* 2794; *D & W* 149/368

See No. 643.

AV	800	1000
AR	30	45
AE	8	15

1568*   **Free Russian Press in London 1863**

Obv. Head r. ALEXANDER HERZEN   *Rev.* A bell, inscribed zemlya i volga [= the Earth and the Will]/VIVOS VOCO!; 1853 1863 in the field, either side. FIRST DECENNIUM OF THE FREE RUSSIAN PRESS IN LONDON. *D.* 51 mm. By C. Wiener. *EPM* 1892, 236. See **Plate 40**

Alexander Herzen (1816–70), Russian author; founder of the *Kolokol* (the Bell), a radical journal.

AE	35	55

1569*   **Missions of Sir Moses Montefiore 1864**

Obv. Heads l., conjoined. JUDITH LADY MONTEFIORE. SIR MOSES MONTEFIORE BART. F.R.S. *Rev.* Hebrew inscription [= Jerusalem. Damascus 5600 Russia 5606 Roumania 5610 Morocco 5624], within a wreath interlaced with a ribbon inscribed in Hebrew [= And Moses grew up and he went out to his brethren and he beheld their burdens (*Exodus* ii, 11), And the wise shall shine like the brightness of the firmament and they that turn many to righteousness shall be as the stars forever (*Daniel* xii,3)]   *D.* 68 mm. By C. Wiener. *BHM* 2802A; *JMC* 1171. See **Plate 40**

The dates of the respective missions are stated in the Jewish calendar, calculated as beginning 3760 years before the Christian; i.e. 5600 = 1840. Judith Montefiore (*c.*1795–1862), married Moses in 1812; his missions were made on behalf of international Jewry.

AR	180	350
AE	90	150

1570   **Visit of Garibaldi to England 1864**

Obv. Bust almost facing, draped. GIUSEPPE GARIBALDI   *Rev.* TO COMMEMORATE THE VISIT TO GREAT BRITAIN OF THE BRAVE AND GOOD GARIBALDI, WHOSE EXALTED VIRTUES, NOBLE PATRIOTISM, AND UNSELFISH HEROISM, HAVE WON FOR HIM THE LOVE AND ADMIRATION OF ALL. Above, cap of LIBERTY, radiate. LANDED AT SOUTHAMPTON 3RD APRIL 1864 *D.* 42 mm. By J. Moore. *BHM* 2798

Giuseppe Garibaldi (1807–82), Italian patriot. A number of medals commemorate his visit, during which he was given a triumphant reception in London.

AE	8	15
WM	3	7

1571   **William Shakespeare, Tercentenary of Birth 1864**

Obv. Bust of Shakespeare draped, l., encircled by titles of his thirty-nine works *Ex.* His signature, within wreath. *Rev.* Shakespeare seated upon clouds, facing, with three female figures, one of whom places a wreath upon his head. TERCENTENARY ANNIVERSARY. 1864 *D.* 64 mm. By L. C. Wyon, *rev.* after J. Bell. *BHM* 2815; *Ogden* 48

The portrait is from Gerard Johnson's Stratford monument.

AR	65	120
AE	18	35

1572   **Clifton Suspension Bridge 1864**

Obv. View of bridge spanning Avon Gorge; shipping beneath. SPAN 702 FEET *Ex.* COMMENCED 1836 I.K. BRUNEL F.R.S. ENGR COMPLETED 1864 J. HAWKSHAW F.R.S. W.H. BARLOW F.R.S. ENGRS MESSRS COCHRANE CONTRACTORS. *Rev.* Seventeen-line inscription COMPLETED BY THE CLIFTON SUSPENSION BRIDGE COMPANY 1864 CHAIRMAN MARK HUISH ... SECRETARY CAPN. CLAXTON R.N., in the centre. FOUNDED BY WILLIAM VICK. 1753 *D.* 41 mm. (By?) *BHM* 2827

William Henry Barlow (1812–1902) and Sir John Hawkshaw (1811–91) were civil engineers.

AE	25	40
WM	15	25

1573   **John Bacon 1864**

Obv. Bust facing, draped, head r. I. BACON R.A. 1740–1799 *Rev.* Bacon's statue of SAMUEL JOHNSON; below, ART-UNION OF LONDON 1864 *D.* 55 mm. By J. S. Wyon. *BHM* 2797; *Beaulah* 15

John Bacon (1740–99), sculptor. *See* No. 1381.

AR	60	130
AE	15	30

                                                        £   £

1574   **Restoration of St. Patrick's Cathedral, Dublin 1865**
Obv. Bust l., draped. BENJAMIN LEE GUINNESS L.L.D. *Rev.* Façade of the cathedral. *Ex.* ST   *AR*   80   140
PATRICK'S CATHEDRAL. DUBLIN. ERECTED 1190 RESTORED BY BENJAMIN LEE GUINNESS L.L.D.   *AE*   30   55
1865   *D.* 65 mm. By W. T. Parkes. *BHM* 2846   *WM*   12   25
A 52 mm. version was also struck. Sir Benjamin Lee Guinness (1798–1868), brewer; public benefactor.

1575*   **Solway Junction Railway, Annan 1865**
Obv. Train crossing a bridge; below, shields of England and Scotland. Continuous border   *WM*   35   55
of roses and thistles. *Rev.* IN COMMEMORATION OF CUTTING THE FIRST SOD OF THE SOLWAY
JUNCTION RAILWAY AT ANNAN, BY W^M EWART ESQ. M.P. 28TH MARCH 1865   *D.* 38 mm. (By?)
BHM 2848. *See* **Plate 40**
William Ewart (1798–1869), M.P. for Dumfries.

1576   **Anglo-French Working Class Exhibition: Death of Richard Cobden 1865**
Obv. Bust three-quarters r., draped. RICHARD COBDEN BORN 1804 DIED 1865   *Rev.* PEACE   *AR*   20   35
JUBILEE ANGLO-FRENCH WORKING-CLASS EXHIBITION LONDON 1865 LAUS LABORI, within a   *AE*   5   8
wreath. *D.* 41 mm. By E. Weigand. *BHM* 2839; *EPM* 1890, 63/2   *WM*   2   4

1577   **Dublin International Exhibition 1865**
Obv. Winged female figure flying, l., with a cornucopia; below, Athena, seated before a   *AE*   12   20
temple with various objects. ARTS AND MANUFACTURES   *Rev.* DUBLIN INTERNATIONAL
EXHIBITION 1865 within a wreath. *D.* 75 mm. By A. Geefs. *Parkes Weber* 101*b*; *D & W* 56/93
A prize medal.

1578   **Wakefield Industrial Exhibition 1865**
Obv. Female figure seated, l., upon a platform inscribed UNION IS STRENGTH, confers a   *AE*   15   28
wreath upon kneeling figures bearing products of industry, and attended by Science and   *WM*   10   15
Art. *Rev.* Town shield between objects of art and science at the base of an ornamental sexfoil
(space above, for recipient's name). WAKEFIELD. INDUSTRIAL. EXHIBITION. AND. FINE-ART.
EXHIBITION. A.D. MDCCCLXV   *D.* 77 mm. By Ottley.
A prize medal, found awarded in bronze and white metal.

1579   **Death of Viscount Palmerston 1865**
Obv. Bust three-quarters l., draped. RIGHT HONOURABLE VISCOUNT PALMERSTON, K,G. G,C,B.   *AE*   12   20
M.P. AND P,C.   *Rev.* BORN OCT^R 20TH 1784 DIED OCTOBER 18^T,H 1865 within a wreath. *D.* 44 mm.   *WM*   5   9
By W. Mack. *BHM* 2834
This medal also occurs with another reverse commemorating an industrial exhibition at Bristol in 1865. Hugh John
Temple, 3rd Viscount Palmerston (1784–1865), statesman.

1580   **Royal Horticultural Society, Lindley Medal 1865**
Obv. Bust l., bespectacled and draped. DR JOHN LINDLEY F.R.S. BORN FEB^Y 5. 1799. DIED NOV^R.1.   *AR*   12   22
1865   *Rev.* Female figure standing, r., upon platform, holding a wreath. ROYAL
HORTICULTURAL SOCIETY   *D.* 45 mm. By J. N. Hakowski. *BHM* 2833
Awarded from 1874, in gilt silver, for fine exhibits and cultivation skills. Dr. John Lindley (1799–1865), botanist and
horticulturalist. *See* No. 955.

1581   **Royal Engineers, Fowke Medal 1865**
Obv. Bust l., uniformed. FRANCIS FOWKE   *Rev.* MEMORIAL MEDAL ESTABLISHED BY THE   *AR*   40   70
OFFICERS OF ROYAL ENGINEERS AS AN ARCHITECTURAL PRIZE IN THE CORPS., within a decorative   *AE*   20   35
border. *D.* 58 mm. By G. T. Morgan. *BHM* 2940; *Taylor* 233*a*
Struck and awarded from 1872 in silver and bronze by the School of Military Engineering, Chatham. Francis Fowke
(1823–65), captain in the Royal Engineers; architect. He planned the International Exhibition building in 1862, and the
original design for the Albert Hall.

1582   **University College London, Donaldson Medal 1865**
Obv. Head r. THOMAS. LEVERTON. DONALDSON. PH: D: EMERITUS. PROF: UNIV: COLL: LOND: *AR*   30   55
1865. *Rev.* TO COMMEMORATE LONG & ZEALOUS SERVICES IN PROMOTING THE STUDY OF   *AE*   15   28
ARCHITECTURE, within a wreath. *D.* 57 mm. By J. S. & A. B. Wyon. *BHM* 2832; *Eidlitz* 1927,
304; *Taylor* 232*a*
Found awarded in silver. *See* No. 1280.

1583   **Marriage of Princess Helena and Prince Christian of Schleswig-Holstein 1866**
Obv. Busts l., conjoined. PRINCESS HELENA OF ENGLAND: PRINCE CHRISTIAN OF SCHLESWIG   *a AR*   60   130
HOLSTEIN   *Rev.* Arms of the couple; crown above, dividing JULY 1866: all within an   *AE*   15   32
ornamental sexfoil. *D. a* 64 mm.; *b* 32 mm. By J. S. & A. B. Wyon. *BHM* 2859–60
Frederick Christian Charles Augustus (1831–1917), Prince of Schleswig-Holstein. The reverse of type *b* has a crown in the   *b AR*   25   40
centre dividing the date and inscription. *See* No. 1517.   *AE*   7   12

			£	£

1584 **Foundation of the Cobden Club 1866**
Obv. Bust l. draped. RICHARD COBDEN 1804–1865 *Rev.* COBDEN CLUB FOUNDED 1866 within a wreath. FREE TRADE PEACE GOODWILL AMONG NATIONS *D.* 57 mm. By J. S. & A. B. Wyon. BHM 2864; *D & W* 116/127

AR 28 45
AE 7 12

Established to assimilate Cobden's ideas of free trade, as champion of the industrial classes.

1585 **Atlantic Submarine Telegraph Cable 1866**
Obv. Upright trident between shields of Britain and the United States, encircled by a looped cable. SUBMARINE TELEGRAPH *Rev.* THE ATLANTIC CABLE COMMENCED JULY 7TH COMPLETED JULY 27. 1866 Above, motto on a ribbon. *D.* 26 mm. By Messrs J. Pinches. *Fearon* 317.3

AR 20 30
AE 8 12

1586 **Fenian Brotherhood 1866**
Obv. F B divided by a fully-rigged ship. IRISH REPUBLIC *Rev.* Two clasped hands dividing a shamrock and radiate sun. IRELAND 1866 AMERICA Thirteen stars around the edge. *D.* 30 mm. By Sewell. BHM 2863; *Forrer* V/485

AR 45 60
AE 20 30

Sometimes found pierced and suspended from a ribbon. The Fenians (*Fionna :* ancient Irish national heroes) were a brotherhood, in the United States and Ireland, pledged to liberate Ireland and establish a republic, by any means. This medal may refer to the rumoured sailing from the United States of James Stephens, a central organizer, for whose apprehension the British Government had offered £2000.

1587 **Victoria, Visit to Wolverhampton 1866**
Obv. Bust l., diademed and draped. HER MOST GRACIOUS MAJESTY QUEEN VICTORIA. *Rev.* TO COMMEMORATE THE VISIT OF H,M,G, MAJESTY QUEEN VICTORIA TO WOLVERHAMPTON, TO INAUGURATE THE STATUE OF THE LATE PRINCE CONSORT 30 NOᵛ 1866., in the centre. JOHN MORRIS, ESQ, MAYOR. *D.* 64 mm. By Ottley. BHM 2851

AR 40 70
AE 15 25
WM 7 12

One of several medals recording this visit.

1588 **Geological Society of London, Murchison Medal 1866**
Obv. Bust l., draped. SIR RODERICK I. MURCHISON BART. K.C.B. 1866. *Rev.* Silurian fossils and two geological hammers in saltire, within a border of Graptolites. SILURIA *D.* 55 mm. By L. C. Wyon. BHM 2869; *Woodward* 247

AE 15 28

Awarded annually from 1871 in bronze. Sir Roderick Impey Murchison (1792–1871), geologist.

1589 **Benjamin West 1866**
Obv. Bust l.; WEST behind. Below, 1738–1820 *Rev.* Central group of West's painting *Death of Wolfe at Quebec.* *Ex.* 1759 *Edge.* ART-UNION OF LONDON 1866 (incuse). *D.* 55 mm. By W. Wilson. BHM 2862; *Forrer* VI/510; *Beaulah* 16

AR 60 130
AE 15 30

See No. 1381.

1590 **Confederation of Canada 1867**
Obv. Bust l., diademed, veiled and draped. VICTORIA D : G : BRITT : REG : F : D : *Rev.* Britannia, seated beside the British lion, displays a scroll inscribed CONFEDERATION to four female figures representing each of the original provinces. JUVENTAS ET PATRIUS VIGOR CANADA INSTAURATA 1867 *D.* 76 mm. By J. S. & A. B. Wyon. BHM 2875; *Leroux* 1191

a AR 500 900
AE 80 170

b AR — —

Type *b* was adapted for use as a presentation medal for North American Indian chiefs by the addition of a 25 mm. outer border inscribed DOMINION OF CANADA CHIEFS MEDAL 1872/INDIANS OF THE NORTH WEST TERRITORIES. See *Jamieson* 37; *Leroux* 1190.

1591 **Abdul Aziz, Visit to the City of London 1867**
Obv. Bust r., wearing a fez and draped. ABDUL AZIZ OTHOMANORUM IMPERATOR. LONDINIUM INVISIT MDCCCLXVII *Rev.* Londinia, standing before a burning altar decorated with the City shield and inscribed WELCOME, greets the figure of Turkey. Beyond, St. Paul's Cathedral, l., and the mosque of St. Sophia, r. *D.* 76 mm. By J. S. & A. B. Wyon. BHM 2872; *Welch* 10

AE 25 55

Issued by the Corporation of London (*see* No. 1245). Abdul Aziz (1830–76), Sultan of Turkey 1861–76.

1592 **Michael Faraday 1867**
Obv. Bust r. MICHAEL FARADAY *Rev.* A student and two angels lay wreaths before a plinth, inscribed FARADAY, on which rests electrical apparatus. INTERROGATE NATURE *D.* 77 mm. By L. C. Wyon. BHM 2874

AR 50 80
AE 20 30

Awarded trienially by the Chemical Society in bronze. Michael Faraday (1791–1867), chemist and physicist.

1593 **Passing of the New Reform Bill 1867**
Obv. A lion standing, victorious, over hydra. FACTION DEFEATED THE PEOPLE TRIUMPHANT *Ex.* REFORM BILL PASSED AUG. 15. 1867 *Rev.* NO CLASS LEGISLATION, within a central triangle: LIBERTY IN RIGHT/EQUALITY IN LAW/FRATERNITY IN INTEREST, around each of its edges. JUST MEASURES & HONEST MEN *Ex.* REFORM BANQUET CRYSTAL PALACE SEPT. 30. 1867 *D.* 38 mm. By W. J. Taylor. BHM 2876

AR 25 38
AE 8 12
WM 4 7

See No. 1485.

		£	£

1594 William Dyce 1867
Obv. Bust l.: DYCE behind. Below, 1806–1864 *Rev.* Detail from Dyce's painting *The Good Shepherd*. ART-UNION OF LONDON 1867 *D.* 57 mm. By G. G. Adams. *BHM* 2873; *Beaulah* 17
  AR 60 130
  AE 15 30
<small>William Dyce (1806–64), historical and portrait painter. *See* No. 1381.</small>

1595 Royal Visit to Ireland 1868
Obv. As No. 1563. *Rev.* TO COMMEMORATE THE VISIT OF HIS ROYAL HIGHNESS THE PRINCE OF WALES TO IRELAND APRIL 1868, within a wreath. Above, Prince's plumes and motto; below, Irish harp. *D.* 51 mm. By Ottley. *BHM* 2884
  AR 40 70
  AE 15 25
  WM 4 10
<small>One of several medals recording the visit.</small>

1596 Prince of Wales, Knight of the Order of St. Patrick 1868
Obv. Bust r., draped. H.R.H. ALBERT EDWARD PRINCE OF WALES, KNIGHT OF Sᵀ PATRICK &ᶜ . *Rev.* Irish harp upon wreath decorated with the Prince's plumes and the Order (collar chain, star and motto). TO COMMEMORATE THE VISIT TO IRELAND OF H.R.H. ALBERT EDWARD PRINCE OF WALES AND HIS INSTALLATION AS KNIGHT OF THE MOST ILLUSTRIOUS ORDER OF Sᵀ PATRICK *D.* 51 mm. By F. H. Mares. *BHM* 2882
  AR 50 90
  AE 15 25
  WM 12 18

1597 William Gladstone, Candidature 1868
Obv. Bust three-quarters l., draped. RIGHT HON, W.E. GLADSTONE. M.P. *Rev.* IN COMMEMORATION OF Mᴿ GLADSTONE'S CANDIDATURE FOR SOUTH WEST LANCASHIRE 1868 within a wreath. *D.* 44 mm. (By ?) *BHM* 2890
  WM 7 12
<small>William Ewart Gladstone (1809–98), statesman and author. He was defeated in south-west Lancashire but subsequently elected for Greenwich.</small>

1598 Duke of Edinburgh, Visit to Australia 1867–8
Obv. Bust l., uniformed. H.R.H. DUKE OF EDINBURGH *Rev.* Broadside view of a fully-rigged ship. TO COMMEMORATE THE VISIT OF H.R.H. PRINCE ALFRED, DUKE OF EDINBURGH K.G. TO AUSTRALIA. *Ex.* H.M.S. GALATEA 1867–8 *D.* 48 mm. By T. Stokes. *MH* 1919, 627; *Carlisle* 167–8/1
  WM 35 60
<small>There are several varieties of this piece.</small>

1599 Whitworth Scholarship 1868
Obv. Bust l., draped. SIR JOSEPH WHITWORTH. BART. FRS. DCL. LLD. Bᴺ DECᴿ XXI. MDCCCIII *Rev.* A precision machine tool. A DIFFERENCE OF ONE MILLIONTH OF AN INCH IS MEASVRED BY VSING FOVR TRVE PLANES IN CONCERT *Ex.* WHITWORTH SCHOLARSHIPS FOVNDED MDCCCLXVIII *D.* 57 mm. By A. Wyon/J. S. & A. B. Wyon, *obv.* after E. J. Poynter. *BHM* 2899; *Inglis* 13
  AE 8 15
<small>Joseph Whitworth (1803–87), mechanical engineer and public benefactor; developed the 'Whitworth' rifle. In 1868 he endowed the Science & Art Department with £100,000, to award a number of scholarships, annually. This medal was struck in 1883 for Whitworth's eightieth birthday, and used as an award, backdated, to each holder of a Whitworth scholarship.</small>

1600 Richard Westmacott 1868
Obv. Bust r., draped. SIR RICHARD WESTMACOTT R.A. 1775–1856 *Rev.* Westmacott's sculpture, *Charity* (three infants around mother). ART-UNION OF LONDON 1868 *D.* 55 mm. L. C. Wyon, *obv.* after R. Westmacott Jr. *BHM* 2894; *Beaulah* 18
  AR 60 130
  AE 15 30
<small>Sir Richard Westmacott (1775–1856), sculptor. *See* No. 1381.</small>

1601 Henri Giffard, Captive Ascents 1869
Obv. A tethered balloon in an arena. *Rev.* CAPTIVE ASCENTS/DIMENSIONS OF THE BALLOON DIAMETER 90. FT. CUBE 300,000. FT. HEIGHT OF ASCENTS 2000. FT. POWER OF ENGINE 200. H.P. NUMBER OF PASSENGERS 30/LONDON *D.* 51 mm. By Labouche. *BHM* 2896
  AE 50 75
  WM 30 45
<small>Henri Giffard (1825–82), French engineer; in 1851 he constructed a steam-engine with which to propel an elongated balloon.</small>

1602 Death of Thomas Graham 1869
Obv. Bust l., draped. THOMAS GRAHAM. BORN DECᴿ 21ˢᵀ 1805 DIED SEPᵀᴿ 16ᵀᴴ 1869 *Rev.* THOˢ. GRAHAM M.A. F.R.S. D.C.L. OXON CORRᴰᴳ MEMBER INSTᵀᴱ FRANCE MASTER OF THE MINT Compartments around, inscribed DIALYSIS HYDROGENIUM PHOSPHATES DIFFUSION *D.* 46 mm. By J. W. Minton, *obv.* after T. J. Minton. *BHM* 2902; *Hocking* 237/18
  AR 50 85
  AE 25 40
<small>Thomas Graham (1805–69), chemist; Master of the Mint.</small>

1603 Prince and Princess of Wales, Visit to Chester 1869
Obv. As No. 1565. *Rev.* Façade of building. CHESTER TOWN HALL. *Ex.* T.G. FROST. MAYOR 1869 *D.* 38 mm. By J. Moore. *BHM* 2900; *Taylor* 188a
  AR 28 45
  AE 10 15

			£	£

1604   Blackfriars Bridge and Holborn Valley Viaduct Opened 1869
Obv. Bust l., crowned. VICTORIA D: G: BRIT: REGINA F: D: *Rev.* City shield in the centre linking two wreaths, each containing a view: HOLBORN VIADUCT above, and BLACKFRIARS BRIDGE below. On either side; Londinia, l., with a scroll inscribed OPENED NOV. 6, and Britannia, r. 1869 at the top. *D.* 76 mm. By G. G. Adams. *BHM* 2906; *Welch* 11   *AE*   25   45
<small>Issued by the Corporation of London. *See* No. 1245.</small>

1605   New Town Hall, Ryde, Isle of Wight 1869
Obv. Façade of building. NEW TOWN HALL, OPENED APRIL 14, 1869. F. NEWMAN. ARCH   *Rev.* Arms dividing date 1868; motto below. BOROUGH OF RYDE, I. OF WIGHT. THO.ᶳ DASHWOOD, MAYOR   *D.* 32 mm. (By?)   *WM*   4   7

1606*   Death of Charles Dickens 1870
Obv. Bust l., draped. CHARLES DICKENS   *Rev.* INTERRED IN WESTMINSTER ABBEY 1870 in the centre. * BORN FEBRUARY 7ᵀᴴ 1812 DIED JUNE 9ᵀᴴ 1870 *   *D.* 64 mm. By J. W. Minton. *EPM* 1890, 95 (sim.). *See* **Plate 41**   *AR*   30   55   *AE*   15   28
<small>Charles John Huffam Dickens (1812–70), novelist.</small>

1607   Charles Dickens, Memorial 1870
Obv. Bust of Dickens, facing, draped. *Rev.* Full-length figure, facing, leaning upon a pile of books. CHARLES DICKENS. 1812–1870. (incuse). *D.* 71 mm. Cast. By R. Searle. *The Medal 4*   *AE*   —   22
<small>Issued in 1985 by the British Art Medal Society. *See* No. 2141.</small>

1608   Charles Leslie 1870
Obv. Bust r. C.R. LESLIE R.A. BORN 1794 DIED 1859. ART-UNION OF LONDON 1870.   *Rev.* Detail from Leslie's painting THE SENTRY BOX (incuse). *D.* 55 mm. By A. B. Wyon. *BHM* 2911; *Forrer* VI/575; *Beaulah* 19   *AR*   60   130   *AE*   15   30
<small>Charles Robert Leslie (1794–1859), painter and author. *See* No. 1381.</small>

1609   St. Thomas' Hospital, Mead Medal *c.*1870
Obv. Bust r., draped. RICHARD MEAD M.D.   *Rev.* Hygeia standing, three-quarters l., a serpent coiled around her arm. MERERI MEDENDO   *Ex.* Sᵀ THOMAS'S HOSPITAL   *D.* 73 mm. By L. C. Wyon. *BHM* 3000; *Storer* 2408   *AR*   50   90   *AE*   20   35
<small>Awarded annually for proficiency in practical science.</small>

1610   North American Indian Chiefs' Medal *c.*1870
Obv. Bust l., diademed, veiled and draped. VICTORIA REGINA   *Rev.* Uniformed figure of the Canadian Treaty Commissioner and an Indian standing in a field shaking hands; a tomahawk buried in the ground, between them. Sun rising, beyond. In outer border INDIAN TREATY Nᴼ (space for number of Treaty) 187 (space for last figure of date) *D.* 76 mm. By J. S. & A. B. Wyon. *BHM* 2961; *Jamieson* 38   *AR*   800   1200
<small>The treaty number and last figure of the date were inscribed in the border. The first medal was presented in 1873 for treaty No. 3, and then used successively until treaty No. 7 in 1877; the last was made in 1899 for treaty No. 8. The medal usually occurs with a suspension clasp and loop. Treaty medals issued under Edward VII and George V have a similar reverse. *See* No. 472.</small>

1611   Society for the Promotion of Industry *c.*1870
Obv. Industry standing, holding oil lamp and wreath; beyond, locomotive crossing a viaduct. *Rev.* A wreath (space within, for recipient's name). SOCIETY FOR THE PROMOTION OF SCIENTIFIC INDUSTRY. MANCHESTER   *D.* 61 mm. By Elkington & Co.   *AR*   25   40   *AE*   8   15
<small>Found awarded in silver.</small>

1612   London Mathematical Society, de Morgan Medal 1871
Obv. Head l. AUGUSTUS DE MORGAN B. 1806. D. 1871   *Rev.* A syllogic zodiac. THE ZODIAC OF SYLLOGISM FIRST PRESIDENT OF THE LONDON MATHEMATICAL SOCIETY 1865. *D.* 47 mm. By J. Moore. *BHM* 2919   *AV*   gold value   *AR*   25   40   *AE*   8   15
<small>Awarded triennially in gold from 1884, for a contribution to the study of mathematics. Augustus de Morgan (1806–71), mathematician and logician; advocate of decimal coinage.</small>

1613*   Marriage of Princess Louise and the Marquis of Lorne 1871
Obv. Busts l., conjoined; a thistle, above, and a rose, below. H.R.H. PRINCESS LOUISE MARQUIS OF LORNE   *Rev.* Heraldic shields dividing 1871 21 MAR on a field decorated with roses and thistles; within an ornamental quatrefoil. *D.* 64 mm. By J. S. Wyon. *BHM* 2916; *RWE* 117. *See* **Plate 41**   *AR*   60   130   *AE*   15   32
<small>John Douglas Sutherland, 9th Duke of Argyll (1845–1914), Governor-General of Canada; unionist M.P. A small number of medals commemorate this marriage. *See* No. 1517.</small>

1614   King's College London, Jelf Medal 1871
Obv. Bust r., draped. IN HOC RIC. GUL. JELF. S.T.P. AMICI COLLEGÆ DISCIPULI   *Rev.* Arms of the College. COLL: REG: LOND: *Ex.* SANCTE ET SAPIENTER   *D.* 76 mm. By J. S. &   *AR*   40   55   *AE*   15   28

			VF	EF
			£	£

A. B. Wyon. *BHM* 2920; *Storer* 1788

Found awarded in bronze. Richard William Jelf (1798–1871), Principal of King's College. The college issued a uniform medal in memory of the surgeon Dr. Robert B. Todd, who died in 1860.

1615*   **New Trent Bridge, Nottingham 1871**
Obv. Bridge spanning river. THE NEW TRENT BRIDGE, NOTTINGHAM JOHN MANNING ESQ MAYOR J.G. WOODWARD ESQ SHERIFF 1871 S.G. JOHNSON, TOWN CLERK   *Ex.* ALD^M VICKERS CHAIRMAN ALD^M PAGE VICE CHAIRMAN OF COMMITTEE. M.O. TARBOTTON F.G.S. ENGINEER   *Rev.* View of the old stone-arched bridge. Seven-line inscription listing dimensions of both bridges THE OLD TRENT BRIDGE … NEW BRIDGE HAS 3 IRON & 4 STONE ARCHES LENGTH 700 F^T WIDTH 40 F^T   *D.* 54 mm. (By?) *BHM* 2924. *See* **Plate 41**
   AR   40   60
   AE   20   35

1616   **Channel Islands Exhibition 1871**
Obv. Two shields within a quatrefoil; 1871 below. CHANNEL ISLANDS EXHIBITION. PRIZE MEDAL. *Rev.* Industry seated upon bales amidst produce; beyond, paddle-steamer at sea. JERSEY   *D.* 51 mm. By W. J. Taylor.
   AR   60   90
   AE   35   50

Awarded in silver and bronze.

1617   **James Watt & Co. 1871**
Obv. Busts r., conjoined, of Matthew Boulton and James Watt. *Rev.* JAMES WATT & C^O LATE BOULTON & WATT ENGINEERS LONDON. & SOHO BIRMINGHAM   *D.* 39 mm. By J. Moore. *BHM* 2922; *Eidlitz* 1928, 13; *Davis* 1241
   AE   8   15

1618   **Prince of Wales, National Thanksgiving 1872**
Obv. Londinia, attended by Britannia, invites the Queen and Prince of Wales into St. Paul's Cathedral. *Ex.* I WAS GLAD WHEN THEY SAID UNTO ME LET US GO INTO THE HOUSE OF THE LORD   *Rev.* Interior of St. Paul's with the royal procession and congregation; ornamental end-panels decorated with the Royal arms and ribbon inscribed NATIONAL THANKSGIVING, l., and City shield and ribbon inscribed S^T PAUL'S LONDON, r. Two upright supports inscribed FOR THE RECOVERY OF/H.R.H. THE PRINCE OF WALES   *Ex.* 27 FEB. 1872   *D.* 77 mm. By J. S. & A. B. Wyon. *BHM* 2928; *Taylor* 39k; *Welch* 12
   AE   25   48

Issued by the Corporation of London (*see* No. 1245). The Prince of Wales had developed typhoid fever in late 1871 but the danger had passed by Christmas; more than ten medals commemorate his recovery and the thanksgiving.

1619   ——
Obv. Head l. ALBERT EDWARD PRINCE OF WALES   *Rev.* Prince's crest within a wreath. NATIONAL. THANKSGIVING. FOR. RECOVERY. OF. THE. PRINCE. OF. WALES. FEB: 1872. *D.* 58 mm. By J. S. Wyon/J. S. & A. B. Wyon. *BHM* 2929; *Storer* 6088
   AR   35   60
   AE   12   22

1620   **Royal Cinque Ports Yacht Club 1872**
Obv. Bust l. H.R.H. PRINCE ARTHUR K.G. COMMODORE   *Rev.* Crowned shield. ROYAL CINQUE PORTS YACHT CLUB FOUNDED 1872   *D.* 45 mm. By J. S. Wyon. *BHM* 2949
   AV   400   600
   AR   25   40
   AE   10   18

1621*   **William Etty 1872**
Obv. Bust l.; ETTY behind: 1787–1849 below. *Rev.* Etty's painting, *Venus and Cupid descending*. ART-UNION OF LONDON. 1872. *D.* 57 mm. By G. G. Adams, [*obv.* after a self-portrait] *BHM* 2938; *Beaulah* 20. *See* **Plate 41**
   AR   60   130
   AE   15   30

William Etty (1787–1849), figure painter. *See* No. 1381.

1622   **Fine Arts Exhibition 1873**
Obv. Bust l., draped; plumes behind. ALBERT. EDWARD. PRINCE. OF. WALES. PRESIDENT. *Rev.* Façade of buildings, including Albert Hall. LONDON. ANNUAL. INTERNATIONAL. EXHIBITION. OF. ALL. FINE. ARTS. INDUSTRIES. AND. INVENTIONS. *Ex.* MDCCCLXXIII   *D.* 70 mm. By G. T. Morgan, *rev.* after J. Gamble. *BHM* 2964; *Taylor* 180a
   AE   10   18

These medals all appear to have been gilt. The Prince of Wales helped to promote an international exhibition held annually at South Kensington; this medal was awarded to exhibitors. A number of commemorative medals were struck, some in the exhibition building itself. However, the exhibition closed in 1874 due to lack of interest. *See* No. 1633.

1623   **Nasr-Ed-Din, Visit to the City of London 1873**
Obv. Bust three-quarters l., wearing a fez decorated with a diamond aigrette, and draped. NASSER-ED-DEEN SHAH OF PERSIA   *Rev.* Londinia standing between shields of London and Persia, head l., holds a scroll in her outstretched hand inscribed 20TH JUNE 1873   Beyond, St. Paul's Cathedral, l., and the Tower, r. *D.* 77 mm. By A. B. Wyon. *BHM* 2951; *Welch* 13
   AE   30   65

Issued by the Corporation of London (*see* No. 1245). Nasr-Ed-Din (1831–96), King of Persia 1848–96.

1624   **John Stuart Mill 1873**
Obv. Bust l., draped. JOHN STUART MILL   Without reverse. *D.* 105 mm. Cast. By A. Legros. *BHM* 3067
   AE   —   50

Made *c.*1882. John Stuart Mill (1806–73), philosopher and economist. Legros produced a number of portrait medals, including those of Thomas Carlyle, Charles Darwin, William Gladstone, Cardinal Manning and George Frederic Watts; *see* P. Attwood, 'The Medals of Alphonse Legros', *The Medal* 5, 7–23.

1625   **Earl of Dufferin, Governor-General's Medal 1873**

     Obv. Busts r., conjoined, she diademed. EARL OF DUFFERIN K.P. K.C.B. GOV. GEN. OF CANADA

     COUNTESS OF DUFFERIN 1873   *Rev.* Heraldic shield, supporters, &c. PRESENTED. BY. HIS.

     EXCELLENCY. THE. GOVERNOR. GENERAL   *D.* 51 mm. By A. B. Wyon/J. S. & A. B. Wyon.

     BHM 2958; *EPM* 1890, 97

		VF	EF
		£	£
Obv. line	AV	—	—
	AR	50	80
	AE	10	15

     Frederick Temple Blackwood, 1st Marquis of Dufferin and Ava (1826–1902), diplomat and administrator; Viceroy of India in 1884. Presented, usually in silver, for services during the tenure of office. Uniform medals were awarded by successive Governor-Generals including: Earl of Dufferin 1876 (a second issue), Marquis of Lorne 1878, Marquis of Lansdowne 1884, Lord Stanley 1888, Earl of Aberdeen 1893, Earl of Minto 1898, Earl Grey 1904, Duke of Connaught 1911 (No. 1920), Duke of Devonshire 1916, Lord Willingdon 1926 and Lord Bessborough 1931.

1626   **London Missionary Society, Livingstone Medal 1873**

     Obv. Bust three-quarters r., draped. DAVID. LIVINGSTONE. BORN. BLANTYRE. 1813. DIED.

     ILALA. 1873   *Rev.* St. Paul, with attendants, preaching before an altar, inscribed ΝΩΣΤΩθΕΩ,

     at Athens. *Ex.* ΕΙΣ ΤΟΝ ΚΟΣΜΟΝ ΑπΑΝΤΑ   *D.* 43 mm. By A. Wyon. BHM 2959; *Storer* 2226

	AV	—	—
	AR	40	70
	AE	15	25

     David Livingstone (1813–73), missionary and explorer who died in Africa. This medal may have been struck some years later.

1627   **Royal Scottish Geographical Society, Livingstone Medal 1873**

     Obv. Bust three-quarters, r., draped and wearing a cap. DAVID LIVINGSTONE   *Rev.* Winged

     figure of Peace, bearing a torch, flying over a ship and landscape. FIAT LUX   *D.* 63 mm. By

     J. P. MacGillivray. BHM 3387; *Storer* 2227

	AV	600	900
	AR	45	75

     Awarded from c.1900, usually in gold.

1628   **Statistical Society, Howard Medal 1873**

     Obv. Bust l., draped. JOHN HOWARD F.R.S. SHERIFF OF BEDFORD. 1773. *Rev.* A wheatsheaf, tied.

     HOWARD. PRIZE. FOUNDED. 1873 WILLIAM A. GUY M.B. F.R.S. PRESIDENT STATISTICAL. SOCIETY

     ESTABLISHED 1834. *D.* 76 mm. By A. B. Wyon. BHM 2970; *Storer* 1662

	AE	35	60

     Awarded in bronze at irregular intervals to the writer of an essay on social statistics. *See* H. W. Macrosty, *Annals of the Royal Statistical Society* 1834–1934, London, 1934. John Howard (1725?–90), philanthropist and prison reformer. William Guy (1810–85), statistician.

1629   **St. Thomas's Hospital, Solly Medal 1873**

     Obv. Bust l. SAMUEL. SOLLY. F.R.S.   *Rev.* AWARDED FOR EXCELLENCE OF SURGICAL REPORTS TO

     (space, for recipient's name) in the centre. IN MEMORY. OF. SAMUEL. SOLLY. F.R.S. SURGEON.

     TO. S^T. THOMAS'S HOSPITAL FOUNDED. A.D. 1873   *D.* 70 mm. By J. S. & A. B. Wyon, *obv.* after

     E. B. Stephens. BHM 3001; *Storer* 3394

	AR	55	90
	AE	20	35

     Awarded annually, in silver, for certain periods. Samuel Solly (1805–71), surgeon.

1630*   **Iron & Steel Institute, Bessemer Medal 1873**

     Obv. Head l. HENRY BESSEMER   *Rev.* A crucible (Bessemer converter?), within an

     ornamental escutcheon. *D.* 58 mm. [By Messrs J. Pinches, after G. T. Morgan/L. F. Day]

     BHM 2954; *Hocking* 218/9–12. See **Plate 41**

	AV	600	800
	AR	40	65
	AE	20	35

     Awarded annually for an invention relating to a mechanical or chemical process. Sir Henry Bessemer (1813–98), engineer and inventor; obtained patents for the manufacture of steel in a specially converted blast furnace. Another prize medal by G. T. Morgan records Bessemer's Presidency of the Institute (latterly the Metals Institute).

1631   **Geological Society of London, Lyell Medal 1873**

     Obv. Bust l. CHARLES LYELL 1873   *Rev.* The three columns of the temple of Jupiter Serapis at

     Puzzuoli, which have submerged and risen again. Beyond, a hilly landscape. *D.* 60 mm. By

     L. C. Wyon. BHM 2969; *Woodward* 250–1

	AE	15	28

     Awarded annually in bronze as a mark of distinction to a geologist. Charles Lyell (1797–1875), geologist.

1632   **Marriage of Alfred, Duke of Edinburgh and Marie Alexandrowna 1874**

     Obv. Busts r., conjoined. MARIE ALEXANDROWNA. ALFRED   *Rev.* Angel standing upon the

     crowned shields of the couple, facing, displays a ribbon inscribed 23 JANUARY 1874 (incuse).

     Ex. Spray of rose, thistle and shamrock. *D.* 63 mm. By C. Schnitzspahn. *RWE* 128; *Parkes

     Weber* 208

	AR	45	75
	AE	20	35

     Grand Duchess Marie Alexandrowna (1853–1920), daughter of Emperor Alexander II. A small number of medals commemorate the marriage.

1633   **Fine Arts Exhibition 1874**

     Obv. Bust l. ALBERT. EDWARD. PRINCE. OF. WALES. PRESIDENT. *Rev.* Similar to No. 1622, but

     Ex. MDCCCLXXIV   *D.* 52 mm. By G. T. Morgan, *obv.* after J. E. Boehm/[rev. after J.

     Gamble] BHM 2992; *Taylor* 180b

	AR	25	45
	AE	8	15

     Awarded in bronze. *See* No. 1622.

1634   **Alexander II, Visit to the City of London 1874**

     Obv. Bust l., uniformed. ALEXANDER II RUSSORUM IMPERATOR   *Rev.* Londinia, attended by

     two cupids, welcomes the Czar standing opposite her; Peace, her wings outstretched, stands

     over the couple. To l., an altar decorated with the Russian eagle. SERVORUM EMANCIPATOR

	AE	25	48

LIBERAE CIVITATIS HOSPES. XVIII MAII MDCCCLXXIV. *Ex.* LONDINI   *D.* 77 mm. By C. Wiener.   £   £
BHM 2981; *Forrer* VI/481; *Welch* 14
<small>Issued by the Corporation of London (*see* No. 1245). Alexander II (1818–81), Emperor of Russia 1855–81.</small>

1635   Royal Visit to The Mint, Birmingham 1874

Obv. TO COMMEMORATE THE VISIT OF THEIR ROYAL HIGHNESSES THE PRINCE & PRINCESS OF   *AV*   —   —
WALES. Above, coat of arms. BIRMINGHAM 3 NOV. 1874; below, J. CHAMBERLAIN ESQ.   *AR*   30   55
MAYOR   *Rev.* View of manufacturing buildings. RALPH HEATON AND SONS COINERS   *Ex.* TO   *AE*   15   25
THE BRITISH FRENCH ITALIAN & OTHER GOVERNMENTS THE MINT BIRMINGHAM   *D.* 37 mm.
(By R. Heaton & Sons?) *BHM* 2973; *Taylor* 178a; *Davis* 741
<small>An example in gold is reported to have been given to the Princess of Wales. Ralph Heaton (1755–1832) founded the firm of die-sinkers in 1819, which eventually became Ralph Heaton & Sons. From 1899 the business was known as The Mint, Birmingham Limited, and produced coinage for many countries, usually designated with the H mint-mark; they also struck some medals. See *Forrer* II/446–54; James O. Sweeny, *A Numismatic History of The Birmingham Mint*, Birmingham, 1981.</small>

1636   John Gibson 1874

Obv. Bust l. JOHN GIBSON R.A. 1789–1866   *Rev.* Gibson's group sculpture, *Grecian Hunter*   *AR*   60   130
and his dog. Ex. ART UNION OF LONDON 1874   *D.* 55 mm. By J. S. Wyon. *BHM* 2982; *Forrer*   *AE*   15   30
VI/576; *Beaulah* 21
<small>John Gibson (1790–1866), sculptor. *See* No. 1381.</small>

1637*   Royal Geographical Society, Livingstone Medal 1874

Obv. Bust three-quarters r., draped. DAVID LIVINGSTONE. BORN 1813. DIED, ILALA, 1873. *Rev.*   *AR*   170   220
PRESENTED BY THE ROYAL GEOGRAPHICAL SOCIETY OF LONDON 1874   *D.* 37 mm. By A. B.   *AE*   10   15
Wyon. *Storer* 2229; *Fearon* 325.2. See **Plate 41**
<small>Presented in silver, with a suspension loop attached, to the natives who carried Livingstone's body from Ilala to the coast; the edge is most frequently found inscribed FAITHFUL TO THE END, preceded by the recipient's name. *See* F. Pridmore & D. H. Simpson, 'Faithful To The End', *SNC* May 1970, 192–6.</small>

1638   Tribute to British Nurses 1870–1874

Obv. A nurse dresses the wound of a soldier seated in bed. 'THIS IS MY COMMANDMENT THAT   *WM*   15   25
YE LOVE ONE ANOTHER AS I HAVE LOVED YOU' Sᵀ JOHN XV: XII   *Rev.* DEDICATED TO THE PIOUS
LADIES OF BRITANNIA IN COMMEMORATION OF THEIR NOBLE DEVOTION TO THE CAUSE OF THE
SICK AND WOUNDED DURING THE FRANCO-GERMAN & SPANISH WARS 1870:71:73:74: within a
wreath. *D.* 51 mm. (By?) *Storer* 7052; *Brettauer* 3665

1639   The Tichborne Claimant 1874

Obv. Bust l., of Arthur Orton, draped. THE TICHBORNE CLAIMANT   *Rev.* Bust of a child,   *AE*   8   15
draped, r. THE ALLEGED 'RIGHTFUL HEIR' AGE 5 YEARS   *D.* 31 mm. (By?) *BHM* 2985
<small>Arthur Orton (1834–98), a butcher and impostor who emigrated to Australia in 1852. He returned in 1866 on the invitation of Lady Tichborne, when he claimed to be her son Sir Roger Tichborne, who had in fact been lost at sea in 1854. In a trial lasting 102 days Orton fought an unsuccessful case; he was subsequently committed for perjury and, after another trial lasting 188 days, found guilty and sentenced to fourteen years. It was the longest trial in English legal history.</small>

1640   Holborn Restaurant 1874

Obv. A group of figures congregated around a grand entrance. HOLBORN   *Ex.* RESTAURANT   *Pb.*   10   —
ESTᴰ 1874   *Rev.* Couples dancing on a large ballroom floor. Below, PRESENTED BY THE
PROPRIETORS (space below, for the recipient's name) on a scroll. *D.* 69 mm. (By?) *BHM*
2990; *Taylor* 207a
<small>Struck c.1895 from more than one pair of dies. Examples occur with a bronzed finish.</small>

1641   Kingsley Medal 1875

Obv. Head r. CHARLES KINGSLEY BORN 1819. DIED 1875. *Rev.* CHESTER SOCIETY OF NATURAL   *AR*   25   45
SCIENCE MEMORIAL PRIZE within a wreath. *D.* 60 mm. By M. Vermeiren, *obv.* after R. Belt.   *AE*   15   25
BHM 3008; *Parkes Weber* 210a
<small>Awarded in bronze. Charles Kingsley (1819–75), clergyman and novelist.</small>

1642   Pharmaceutical Society of Great Britain, Hanbury Medal 1875

Obv. Bust r. DANIEL HANBURY F.R.S. BORN 1825 – DIED 1875   *Rev.* A wreath (space within, for   *AV*   800   1000
recipient's name). AWARDED FOR ORIGINAL RESEARCH IN THE NATURAL HISTORY AND   *AR*   30   55
CHEMISTRY OF DRUGS   *D.* 58 mm. (By?) *Storer* 6549
<small>Awarded from 1881, biennially in gold. Daniel Hanbury (1825–75), pharmacist.</small>

1643   Prince of Wales, Grand Master of English Freemasonry 1875

Obv. Bust of the Prince of Wales, three-quarters l., draped. *Rev.* INSTALLATION OF H.R.H.   *AR*   30   55
ALBERT EDWARD PRINCE OF WALES AS GRAND MASTER OF ENGLISH FREEMASONS APRIL 28 1875.   *AE*   15   25
LOYALTY AND CHARITY   *D.* 48 mm. By G. Kenning. *BHM* 3002; *Shackles* 18

1644   Samuel Plimsoll 1875

Obv. Bust l., draped. HOUSE OF COMMONS 22 JULY 1875 LONDON. S. PLIMSOLL. *Rev.* Ship,   *AE*   4   7
flying the 'skull and cross-bones', in a stormy sea. *Ex.* COFFIN SHIP   *D.* 36 mm. By A.

PLATE 41

1606

1613

1615

1621

1637

1630

PLATE 42

1648

1655

1657

1668 (× ⅔)

1660

1680

1685

1681A

Chevalier. *MH* 1919, 633   £   £

Occurs with a suspension loop; a 25 mm. medal was also struck. Samuel Plimsoll (1824–98), politician; leader of shipping reform.

1645   **Royal Institution of Cornwall, Henwood Medal 1875**

Obv. Bust l. HENWOOD   *Rev.* Shield of Cornwall, crowned. ROYAL INSTITUTION OF CORNWALL   *D.* 49 mm. By J. A. Restall.

     AV   500   700
     AR   30   50

Found awarded in gold. William Jory Henwood (1805–75), mineralogist; assay-master of tin for the Duchy of Cornwall.

1646   **Daniel O'Connell, Centenary of Birth 1875**

Obv. Head almost facing. DANIEL O'CONNELL BIRTH CENTENARY 1875   *Rev.* O'Connell, standing, delivers an oration. CLARE ELECTION. EMANCIPATION. MUNICIPAL REFORM 'I AT ONCE REFUSE TO MAKE THIS DECLARATION PART OF IT I BELIEVE TO BE UNTRUE THE REST I KNOW TO· BE FALSE, BORN CAHIRCIVEEN AUGUST 6 1775. DIED GENOA MAY 15 1847. *D.* 54 mm. By O'Hanlon. *BHM* 3010

     AE   25   40
     WM   12   22

A few medals commemorate O'Connell's centenary.

1647   **Prince of Wales, Visit to India 1875**

Obv. PRESENTED IN LOYAL COMMEMORATION OF THE VISIT OF H.R.H. THE PRINCE OF WALES TO MADRAS 1875 BY THE JAGIRDAR OF ARNI; above, arms and motto. *Rev.* A E divided by the Prince's plumes and motto. *D.* 43 mm. By J. S. & A. B. Wyon.

     AR   35   50
     AE   20   30

A few medals commemorate the Prince's visit, at least one of which was struck in India. *See* Magor.

1648*   **Thomas Carlyle, 80th Birthday 1875**

Obv. Bust l., draped. THOMAS CARLYLE   *Rev.* IN COMMEMORATION. 1875 DECEMBER 4. *D.* 56 mm. By G. T. Morgan, *obv.* after J. E. Boehm. *BHM* 3006; *EPM* 1888, 276. *See* **Plate 42**

     AR   35   65
     AE   15   28

Thomas Carlyle (1795–1881), essayist and historian. *See* M. Stocker, 'Edgar Boehm's medal of Thomas Carlyle', *The Medal 6*, 14–15.

1649   **David Roberts 1875**

Obv. Bust l. DAVID ROBERTS. R.A. 1796–1864   *Rev.* A typical scene from one of Roberts' near-Eastern paintings: Moorish scribe with seated female. ART-UNION OF LONDON 1875. *D.* 56 mm. By G. T. Morgan. *BHM* 3016; *Beaulah* 22

     AR   60   130
     AE   15   30

David Roberts (1796–1864), painter. *See* No. 1381.

1650   **Samuel Owen 1875**

Obv. Bust l., draped. SAM. OWEN MACHINARUM INVENTOR. N. 1774. D. 1854. *Rev.* Broadside view of a paddle-steamer. NOVAS DEDIT ALAS. *Ex.* SOCIO MECHANICO REG. ACAD. SC. SVEC. MDCCCLXXV. *D.* 32 mm. By L. Ahlborn. *MH* 1928, 308; *Hyckert II*, 135

     AR   15   25

Samuel Owen (1774–1854), mechanical engineer; designed engines for paddle-steamers. Struck by the Swedish Academy of Science, which issued medals of several eminent scientists.

1651   **Alexandra Palace 1875**

Obv. View of the exhibition building and grounds. THE ALEXANDRA PALACE   *Ex.* THE GROUND PLAN OF THIS BUILDING OCCUPIES AN AREA OF 7½ ACRES. DIMENSIONS OF GRAND CENTRAL HALL 386 F^T BY 184 F^T *Rev.* THE ALEXANDRA PALACE OPENED TO THE PUBLIC MAY DAY 1875, within a wreath. *D.* 51 mm. (By?) *Taylor* 196a

     AE   12   20
     WM   3   7

The site was named after the Princess of Wales. The original palace was fully completed in May 1873, but destroyed by fire only two weeks later. The new building hosted numerous exhibitions and festivals; it was North London's answer to Crystal Palace, and became known as 'Ally Pally'. It was from here that the first outside television broadcast took place in 1936. In 1980 the building was destroyed by another fire.

1652   **Royal Geographical Society *c.*1875**

Obv. Britannia holding a wreath and scroll standing, l., beside a globe and sextant. OB TERRAS RECLUSAS   *Rev.* A beaded circle (space within, for recipient's name). ROYAL GEOGRAPHICAL SOCIETY   *D.* 40 mm. (By?)

     AR   12   20

Examples of this unofficial prize occur awarded in silver, with a suspension clasp and loop.

1653   **Geological Society of London, Bigsby Medal 1876**

Obv. Head l. J. J. BIGSBY M.D. F.R.S. BIENNIAL PRIZE MEDAL FOUNDED 1876   *Rev.* An Echinoderm (starfish). AGELACRINITES DICKSONI FOUND. 1822. CANADA. AWARDED BY THE GEOLOGICAL SOCIETY OF LONDON. FOR WORKS OF GREAT MERIT. *D. a* 64 mm. *b* 46 mm. By J. S. Wyon/J. S. & A. B. Wyon. *BHM* 3033; *Woodward* 252

     a AR   35   55
     AE   15   28
     b AV   500   600
     AR   25   45
     AE   18   30

John Jeremiah Bigsby (1792–1881), pioneer of geology in Canada. Type *b* was awarded biennially in gold, and latterly in bronze, for geological work.

1654   **Ruan Temperance Society 1876**

Obv. Bust l., draped. THE VERY REV^D. THEOBALD MATHEW   *Rev.* RUAN within a beaded circle. TEMPERANCE SOCIETY A.M.D.G. ESTABLISHED JAN^Y 23RD 1876   *D.* 43 mm. By J. Woodhouse. *Frazer* 1887/207

     WM   10   15

                                                      £   £

1655*   **J. M. W. Turner 1876**
Obv. Bust l., draped. JOSEPH MALLORD WILLIAM TURNER R.A. 1775–1851   *Rev.* Detail from   *AR*   85   180
Turner's painting *The Fighting Téméraire.* ART-UNION OF LONDON. 1876. *D.* 55 mm. By L. C.   *AE*   25   45
Wyon, [*obv.* after C. Turner] BHM 3030; *Forrer* VI/626; *Beaulah* 23. *See* **Plate 42**
See No. 1381.

1656   **Queen Victoria, Empress of India 1877**
Obv. Bust l., crowned, veiled and draped. VICTORIA 1ST JANUARY 1877   *Rev.* EMPRESS OF   *AV* 900 1200
INDIA; the same inscription, above and below, in Hindustani and Persian. A narrow   *AR*   80   150
ornamental border. *D.* 57 mm. By G. G. Adams. BHM 3036; *Payne* 31   *AE*   25   45
Examples in gold and silver were presented at the celebrations in Delhi and usually occur with a suspension clasp; they are
not normally found named.

1657*   **William Mulready 1877**
Obv. Head l. MULREADY 1786–1863   *Rev.* Detail from Mulready's painting *The Haymakers.*   *AR*   60   130
ART-UNION OF LONDON. 1877. *D.* 55 mm. By G. G. Adams. BHM 3037; *Beaulah* 24. *See*   *AE*   15   30
Plate 42
William Mulready (1786–1863), genre painter and illustrator; designed the first penny-postage envelope in 1840. *See*
No. 1381.

1658   **Removal of Temple Bar from the City of London 1878**
Obv. Elevation of the decorative façade. TEMPLE BAR: ERECTED 1672, DEMOLISHED 1878: THIS   *Pb.*   —   170
EFFIGY OF IT WAS STRUCK FROM THE LEAD FORMERLY ON THE ROOF. H J (Horace Jones)
monogram, in a shield. *Ex.* Ribbon inscribed SIR C. WREN ARCHᵀ (incuse). Without reverse.
D. 101 mm. By Foot and Tebay (after C. H. & J. Mabey). BHM 3051; *Taylor* 37a; *Welch* 15
Issued by the Corporation of London (*see* No. 1245). Examples of this medal are usually found mounted under glass,
within a circular brass frame, forming a paperweight. Temple Bar was re-erected at the entrance to private grounds in
Waltham Cross, Hertfordshire, where it remains in a dilapidated state. In 1880 a memorial, designed by Sir Horace Jones
(1819–87), City architect, was erected to mark its original site, where it formed the western boundary of the City of London
with that of Westminster.

1659   **Daniel Maclise 1878**
Obv. Bust l., draped. DANIEL MACLISE R.A. B. 1811 D. 1870 ART UNION OF LONDON 1878   *Rev.*   *AR*   60   130
Detail of Maclise's painting *The Play Scene from Hamlet. D.* 55 mm. By A. B. Wyon. BHM   *AE*   15   30
3047; *Forrer* VI/577; *Beaulah* 25
Daniel Maclise (1806–70), historical painter. *See* No. 1381.

1660*   **National Art Training School, Queen's Medal 1878**
Obv. Bust l., similar to No. 1511. VICTORIA BY THE GRACE OF GOD QVEEN MDCCCLXXVIII   *Rev.*   *AV* 500   700
NATIONAL ART TRAINING SCHOOL, SOVTH KENSINGTON within a wreath. *D.* 50 mm. By W.   *AR*   18   30
Wyon. BHM 3049. *See* **Plate 42**   *AE*   8   12
A prize awarded in gold, silver and bronze.

1661   **Gunnery School, Goodenough Medal 1878**
Obv. Head l. JAMES. GRAHAM. GOODENOUGH SANTA CRUZ 1875 Below, AD. SANGUINEM on a   *AV* 500   600
ribbon. *Rev.* Female figure seated, l., before breech of a gun; above, stern view of H.M.S.   *AR*   30   55
EXCELLENT firing both broadsides (crest of the Gunnery School). MEMORIAL. PRIZE. FOR.   *AE*   12   18
GUNNERY INSTITUTED. A.D. 1878. *D.* 48 mm. By L. C. Wyon, *rev.* after F. P. Cockerell. BHM
3045; *MH* 1919, 632
Awarded annually by the Gunnery School in gold; from 1939 in gilt silver, and latterly in bronze. James Graham
Goodenough (1830–75), commodore; investigated various aspects of naval gunnery.

1662   **Marriage of Duke of Connaught and Princess Louise of Prussia 1879**
Obv. Busts l., conjoined. PRINCESS LOUISE MARGARET OF PRUSSIA * ARTHUR, DUKE OF   *AR*   60   130
CONNAUGHT & STRATHEARNE K.G. *Rev.* Armorial shields of the couple, crowned; ribbon   *AE*   15   32
below, inscribed MAR: 13 1879. Within an ornamental quatrefoil. *D.* 64 mm. By J. S. & A. B.
Wyon. BHM 3052; *RWE* 133
Louise Alexandra Margaret (1860–1917), daughter of Prince Frederick Charles Nicholas of Prussia. Few medals record
this marriage. *See* No. 1517.

1663   **Albert and Battersea Bridges 1879**
Obv. Bust l., diademed. VICTORIA REGINA   *Rev.* Prince of Wales' plumes and motto. ALBERT   *AR*   15   28
& BATTERSEA BRIDGES FREED BY ACT OF PARLIAMENT 1877. OPENED BY H.R.H. PRINCE OF WALES   *AE*   8   12
MAY 24. 1879. *D.* 38 mm. By W. J. Taylor. BHM 3059   *WM*   3   6

1664   **New Bridge, Maidstone 1879**
Obv. Three-arched stone bridge spanning river. NEW BRIDGE   *Ex.* OPEN,ED 6. AUG: *AR*   22   35
1879   *Rev.* Borough shield. BOROUGH OF MAIDSTONE CHARLES ELLIS ESQᴿ MAYOR   *D.* 41 mm.   *AE*   7   15
By R. Heaton. BHM 3060   *WM*   5   8

			£	£

1665   William Gladstone, 70th Birthday 1879
Obv. Bust r., draped. WILLIAM EWART GLADSTONE AET. 70. *Rev.* 29TH DECEMBER 1879   *AR*   25   40
LIVERPOOL within a wreath. SERUS IN COELUM REDEAS DIUQUE LAETUS INTERSIS POPULO   *D.*   *AE*   10   18
44 mm. By L. C. Wyon. *BHM* 3054; *EPM* 1891, 385
A birthday reception in his honour was held in Liverpool.

1666   David Cox 1879
Obv. Bust almost facing, draped. DAVID COX   *Rev.* Detail from Cox's painting *Returning*   *AR*   60   130
from market. Ex. ART UNION OF LONDON 1879   *D.* 57 mm. By G. T. Morgan [*obv.* after J. W.   *AE*   15   30
Gordon] *BHM* 3053; *Beaulah* 26
David Cox (1783–1859), landscape painter. *See* No. 1381.

1667   Ackworth School 1879
Obv. Bust r., draped. DR JOHN FOTHERGILL, FOUNDER OF ACKWORTH SCHOOL / BORN 1712 – DIED   *WM*   3   7
1780   *Rev.* Distant view of ACKWORTH SCHOOL and grounds. IN COMMEMORATION OF THE
CENTENNIAL OF ACKWORTH SCHOOL. 1879. *Ex.* FOUNDED 1779   *D.* 51 mm. By J. Moore.
Taylor 50a

1668*   George I of Greece, Visit to the City of London 1880
Obv. Head l. GEORGE 1ST. KING OF THE HELLENES   *Rev.* Londinia, accompanied by Britannia,   *AE*   40   75
welcomes Hellas; beyond, St. Paul's Cathedral, l., and Parthenon, r. *Ex.* JUNE 16. 1880   *D.*
76 mm. By G. G. Adams. *BHM* 3077; *Welch* 16. *See* **Plate 42**
Issued by the Corporation of London (*see* No. 1245). Christian William Ferdinand Adolphus George (1845–1913), king of
Greece 1863–1913; 2nd son of Christian IX of Denmark.

1669   Sunday Schools Centenary 1880
Obv. Bust l., diademed, veiled and draped. SUNDAY SCHOOL CENTENARY. 1880 QUEEN   *AR*   25   40
VICTORIA. PATRON   *Rev.* Open bible inscribed FEED MY LAMBS JOHN XXI v. 15 within a   *AE*   8   15
wreath. CHURCH OF ENGLAND SUNDAY SCHOOL INSTITUTE FOUNDED 1843   *D.* 51 mm. By J. S.
& A. B. Wyon. *BHM* 3085
Several medals, some with the bust of Robert Raikes, commemorate the centenary. From 27 June a week of national
celebrations took place, promoted by the Royal Family and the Church.

1670   Mason Science College 1880
Obv. Bust three-quarters r., draped. SIR JOSIAH MASON BORN FEB: XXIII MDCCXCV THE   *AR*   25   40
FOUNDER OF THE ALMSHOUSES & ORPHANAGE AT ERDINGTON & SCIENCE COLLEGE BIRMINGHAM.   *AE*   12   18
Rev. Façade of building. FIRST STONE LAID FEB. XXIII MDCCCLXXV AND OPENED OCT. 1.
MDCCCLXXX BY SIR JOSIAH MASON   *Ex.* THE MASON SCIENCE COLLEGE J. A. COSSINS
ARCHITECT   Below, helmet and visor. *D.* 51 mm. By J. Moore. *BHM* 3083; *Taylor* 199a
Josiah Mason (1795–1881), manufacturer and businessman; public benefactor.

1671   City of London School, New Buildings 1880
Obv. Façade of the new buildings. *Rev.* PRESENTED TO THE COMMITTEE BY MESSRS DAVIS &   *AR*   20   35
EMANUEL THE ARCHITECTS IN COMMEMORATION OF LAYING THE FOUNDATION STONE OF THE   *AE*   7   12
NEW BUILDINGS FOR THE CITY OF LONDON SCHOOL ON THE THAMES EMBANKMENT 14TH
OCTOBER, 1880   *D.* 45 mm. By Waterlow & Sons. *BHM* 3082

1672   Thomas Stothard 1880
Obv. Bust r., draped: STOTHARD behind; 1755–1834 below. *Rev.* Central detail from   *AR*   60   130
Stothard's painting *The Canterbury Pilgrims*. *Ex.* ART UNION OF LONDON 1880   *D.* 55 mm.   *AE*   15   30
By L. C. Wyon. *BHM* 3080; *Forrer* VI/625; *Beaulah* 27
Thomas Stothard (1755–1834) painter and book-illustrator; father of the sculptor and medallist Alfred Joseph. *See*
No. 1381.

1673   Boycott Expedition 1880
Obv. THE BOYCOTT EXPEDITION LOUGH MASK 1880. central space (for recipient's name);   *AR*   170   220
wreath below. *Rev.* IN HONOUR OF THE LOYAL & BRAVE ULSTERMEN; imperial crown above. *D.*
40 mm. By J. Woodhouse. *Frazer* 1887/200; *Payne* 229
Awarded in silver and sometimes found with a suspension loop. Charles Cunningham Boycott (1832–97), Irish land agent.
He was ostracised by tenants who refused to pay rent or work for him (from which the term 'Boycott' originates). The
dispute resulted in agitation by the Irish Land League. A purely commemorative medal was also made by J. Woodhouse.

1674   Charles Parnell c.1880
Obv. Bust almost facing, draped. CHARLES S. PARNELL M.P. *Rev.* A crown, radiate, above a   *AE*   8   12
harp and branches of shamrock. HOME RULE   *Edge.* Grained. *D.* 25 mm. By W. T. Parkes.
Went 1978, 112
Charles Stewart Parnell (1846–91), Irish nationalist leader; united the Fenians (*see* No. 1586) and the Land League in a
fight for home rule. *See* No. 1675.

			VF	EF
			£	£

1675 Irish-American Political Propaganda *c.*1880

Obv. An eagle flying, l.; a harp below. Around, a long ribbon, inscribed AMERICAN MANUFACTURES AND IRELANDS INDEPENDENCE SOLIDARITY *Rev.* WE PURPOSE 'FORE HIGH HEAVEN 'TILL ERINS CHAINS ARE RIVEN FOR WORKS BY BRITAIN MADE NO MORE WITH HER WE'LL TRADE, between two clusters of stars. *D.* 38 mm. (By?)

		AR	35	50
		AE	20	30
		WM	10	18

In 1880 Charles Parnell went to New York, from where this medal may originate, for help to relieve Ireland politically and financially.

1676 Building Trades Exhibition *c.*1880

Obv. Female figure standing, facing, holds two wreaths over seated figures of two builders; beyond, façade of a building in the Greek style. BUILDING TRADES EXHIBITION *Rev.* AWARDED BY THE SOCIETY OF ARCHITECTS (space, for recipient's name) FOR SUPERIORITY IN WORKMANSHIP AND MATERIAL *D.* 51 mm. By J. Moore.

| | | AR | 18 | 25 |
| | | AE | 6 | 10 |

Awarded in silver and bronze.

1677 Pitt-Rivers *c.*1880

Obv. OPENED BY A. PITT RIVERS F.R.S. *Rev.* An urn, skull and theodolite. *Ex.* Blade of an antique sword. *D.* 38 mm. (By?) *BHM* 3079

| | | AE | 25 | 35 |

Augustus Henry Pitt-Rivers, original surname Lane Fox (1827–1900), army officer and archaeologist; assumed the name of Pitt-Rivers on inheriting the estates of his great-uncle. He excavated British battle sites and deposited these medals as evidence of their examination.

1678 Balloon Society of Great Britain *c.*1880

Obv. Balloon in flight at cloud level. BALLOON SOCIETY OF GREAT BRITAIN. *Rev.* A wreath (space within, for recipient's name). *D.* 32 mm. (By?)

| | | AR | 90 | 120 |
| | | AE | 55 | 80 |

Awarded in bronze, and possibly silver. In September 1880 five balloons, starting from various places around London, competed for a medal awarded by the Society.

1679 David Livingstone and Henry Stanley *c.*1880

Obv. Busts l., conjoined and draped. HEROES OF THE DARK CONTINENT LIVINGSTONE & STANLEY *Rev.* Equestrian figure of an American Indian, l., looking back over his shoulder and firing an arrow. *D.* 31 mm. (By?) *BHM* 3388; *Storer* 2231

| | | AE | 18 | 25 |

Henry Morton Stanley (1841–1904), commissioned by James Gordon Bennett, proprietor of the *New York Herald*, to lead an expedition into central Africa to find Livingstone.

1680* Death of Benjamin Disraeli 1881

Obv. Bust three-quarters l., draped. RT. HON EARL OF BEACONSFIELD *Rev.* DIED APRIL 19TH 1881 BORN DEC. 21ST. 1804. INTERRED AT HUGHENDEN CHURCH APRIL 26TH 1881 in the centre. ONE OF ENGLAND'S GREATEST STATESMEN "NOTHING IS DIFFICULT TO THE BRAVE" *D.* 44 mm. By Ottley. *BHM* 3094; *Friedenberg* 1963, 56. *See* **Plate 42**

| | | AE | 40 | 55 |
| | | WM | 20 | 35 |

Benjamin Disraeli, 1st Earl of Beaconsfield (1804–81), Prime Minister and statesman. A few portrait medals commemorate his death, although none are known to have been struck during his lifetime.

1681A* George Stephenson, Centenary 1881

Obv. Bust l., draped. GEORGE STEPHENSON. BORN JUNE 9. 1781. AT WYLAM. NEWCASTLE-ON-TYNE. DIED AUG. 12. 1848. Rev. Locomotive pulling wagons, l., on section of viaduct. GEORGE STEPHENSON CENTENARY MEDAL *Ex.* THE ROCKET 1830 *D.* 45 mm. By T. P. Chapman. *BHM* 3097; *Moyaux* 39. *See* **Plate 42**

		AV	500	600
		AE	25	38
		WM	10	18

1681B ——

Obv. As *A. Rev.* Locomotive engine (similar to *A*); below, N° 1 1825 on a plaque. GEORGE STEPHENSON CENTENARY MEDAL *Ex.* THE FIRST LOCOMOTIVE ENGINE THAT EVER PULLED A PASSENGER TRAIN *D.* 45 mm. By T. P. Chapman. *BHM* 3096; *Moyaux* 40

		AV	500	600
		AR	50	80
		AE	25	38
		WM	10	18

Several medals commemorate the centenary.

1682 Volunteer Movement, 21st Anniversary 1881

Obv. Bust of the Queen, almost facing, crowned, veiled and draped, dividing letters V R in the field. XXI. ANNIVERSARY. OF. THE. VOLVNTEER. MOVEMENT. MDCCCLXXXI *Rev.* A warrior, standing, protects the kneeling figures of Anglia, Hibernia and Scotia, in defence of their mother Kingdom. PRO ARIS ET FOCIS *D.* 63 mm. By N. Macphail, *rev.* after J. N. Paton. *BHM* 3104; *CP* 191/12

| | | AR | 30 | 55 |
| | | AE | 10 | 18 |

More than 52,000 volunteers were reviewed by Victoria at Windsor in July 1881, and a further 40,000 at Queen's Park, Edinburgh, in August.

1683 International Medical Congress, London 1881

Obv. Bust l., crowned, veiled and draped. VICTORIA QUEEN OF GREAT BRITAIN AND IRELAND: EMPRESS OF INDIA *Rev.* Three supplicant figures, one holding an infant, kneeling before Aesculapius; beyond, a globe and the departing figures of Death. INTERNATIONAL MEDICAL CONGRESS, LONDON. JAMES PAGET, PRES. WILLIAM MAC CORMAC, HON. SEC. GEN. *Ex.* 1881

| | | AR | 45 | 70 |
| | | AE | 20 | 35 |

D. 77 mm. By L. C. Wyon, *rev.* after J. Tenniel. BHM 3110; *Storer* 6307   £   £

Silver examples sometimes occur frosted and set within a watch-style glass bound by a silver frame. James Paget (1814–99), surgeon to Queen Victoria. William MacCormac (1836–1901), surgeon; edited the *Transactions of the Congress.*

1684   **City and Guilds of London Institute 1881**
Obv. City of London shield in centre; around, shields of sixteen City livery companies. *Rev.*   *AR*   18   25
TECHNOLOGICAL EXAMINATION. HONOURS. in the centre. TECHNICAL EDUCATION. CITY AND   *AE*   4   7
GUILDS OF LONDON INSTITUTE   *D.* 51 mm. By E. D. Jackman. *Hocking* 219/34

The 'City and Guilds' was founded by the City Companies in 1878 for the advancement of technical education. This medal is the first which was awarded. The Institute presented a number of various medals; details of the recipient and the subject were usually engraved on the edge, while those of the grade (Grade I, Grade II, Final, Ordinary, Honours, etc.) and examination were struck, each from a different die, in the centre of the reverse. *See* Nos. 1764 and 1864.

1685*   **Military Hospital, Netley: Montefiore Medal 1881**
Obv. Armorial shield; THINK AND THANK on a pennant, above. EX DONIS N. MONTEFIORE.   *AR*   70   120
F:R:C:S:SCHOL:MIL:MED:1881   *Rev.* Field ambulance in a rugged landscape; soldier lying   *AE*   35   60
on stretcher attended by doctor and orderlies. ΙΗΤΡΟΣ ΓΑΡ ΑΝΗΡ ΠΟΜΩΝ ΑΝΤΑΞΙΟΣ ΑΜΩΝ
[= For a doctor is a man abler than many others]. *D.* 60 mm. By A. Dubois, [*rev.* after T. Longmore] *Storer* 2471; *Parkes Weber* 82. See **Plate 42**

Awarded in bronze from 1882, for proficiency in military surgery. Nathaniel Montefiore (1819–83), surgeon.

1686   **The Royal Society, Darwin Medal 1882**
Obv. Bust l., draped, of Darwin. *Rev.* MDCCCIX CAROLVS DARWIN MDCCCLXXXII, within a   *AR*   45   70
wreath of plants identified in Darwin's research. *D.* 57 mm. By A. Wyon. BHM 3136;   *AE*   12   20
Storer 783

Awarded from 1890 in silver, biennially, for biological research. Charles Robert Darwin (1809–82), naturalist; originated the theory of natural selection.

1687   **Marriage of Duke of Albany and Princess Helen of Waldeck 1882**
Obv. Busts r., conjoined. LEOPOLD, DUKE OF ALBANY, K.G. PRINCESS HELEN OF   *AR*   70   150
WALDECK   *Rev.* Armorial shields of the couple; ribbon below, inscribed 27 APRIL 1882: all   *AE*   18   35
within an ornamental quatrefoil. *D.* 64 mm. By J. S. & A. B. Wyon. BHM 3113; *RWE* 142

Leopold George Duncan Albert, Duke of Albany (1854–84), fourth and youngest son of Victoria. Princess Helen Frederica (1861–1922), daughter of H.S.H. George Victor, Prince of Waldeck-Pyrmont. Few medals commemorate the marriage. *See* No. 1517.

1688   **Sacred Harmonic Society 1882**
Obv. An open music score of THE MESSIAH upon a lyre and crossed cornets, within a wreath.   *AR*   18   28
SACRED HARMONIC SOCIETY. FOUNDED 1832. *Rev.* Statue of HANDEL seated with a lyre; cherub   *AE*   7   12
below. TO COMMEMORATE THE FIFTIETH AND LAST SEASON. 1882. *D.* 51 mm. [By Messrs. J. Pinches] BHM 3137; *Niggl* 802

Awarded in silver and bronze. *See* No. 1527.

1689   **Epping Forest, Royal Visit and Dedication 1882**
Obv. Bust of Queen Victoria, l., crowned, veiled and draped. Continuous border of roses,   *AE*   25   48
thistles and shamrocks. *Rev.* Londinia standing opposite the Queen, seated, holds a gate
open at the edge of a forest, allowing passage along its winding pathway. IT. GIVES. ME. THE.
GREATEST. SATISFACTION. TO. DEDICATE. THIS. BEAUTIFUL. FOREST. FOR. THE. USE. AND.
ENJOYMENT. OF. MY. PEOPLE. FOR. ALL. TIME. EPPING. FOREST. 6. MAY. 1882. *D.* 75 mm. By C.
Wiener. BHM 3128; *Welch* 17

Issued by the Corporation of London. *See* No. 1245.

1690   **City of London School, New Buildings 1882**
Obv. Busts r., conjoined. ALBERT EDWARD ALEXANDRA   *Rev.* Façade of school building,   *AE*   25   45
flanked by the shields of the Prince of Wales, l., and City of London, r. CITY OF LONDON
SCHOOL NEW BUILDINGS OPENED   *Ex.* BY HIS ROYAL HIGHNESS THE PRINCE OF WALES 12 DEC.
1882   *D.* 77 mm. By J. S. & A. B. Wyon. BHM 3133; *Taylor* 202a; *Welch* 18

Issued by the Corporation of London. *See* No. 1245.

1691   **Edward Baily 1882**
Obv. Head l. E. H. BAILY R.A. 1788–1867   *Rev.* Baily's statue, *Eve at the Fountain. Ex.* 1882   *AR*   60   130
ART-UNION OF LONDON   *D.* 55 mm. By A. B. Wyon. BHM 3115; *Forrer* VI/578; *Beaulah* 28   *AE*   15   30

Edward Hodges Baily (1788–1867), sculptor; many of his designs appear on medals. *See* No. 1381.

1692*   **Lillie Langtry 1882**
Obv. Bust of Langtry almost facing, loosely draped, head r.; a miniature dagger in her   *AE*   —   150
cleavage. L. L in the field, either side of the bust. Without reverse. *D.* 142 mm. Cast. By E. J.
Poynter. BHM 3120; *Forrer* IV/680; *Inglis* 10. See **Plate 43**

Lillie Langtry (1853–1929), actress and socialite; known as the 'Jersey Lily'. The dagger is probably an allusion to the theatre; she made her first stage appearance in 1881.

			VF	*EF*
			£	£

1693 **Princess Victoria and Frederick William, Silver Wedding 1883**
Obv. Heads r., conjoined. FR. WILH. KRONPRINZ. VICTORIA KRONPRINZESSIN D. DEUTSCH.
REICHS. *Rev.* Armorial shields of the couple upon scrolls, crowned. Below, 1858. 1883 on a
plaque. ZUR ERINNERUNG AN DIE SILBERNE HOCHZEIT D. 25. JANUAR 1883   D. 31 mm. By H.
Weckwerth. *Parkes Weber* 215e

      AR   25   38
      WM   8   15

1694 **International Fisheries Exhibition, London 1883**
Obv. Head l., diademed and veiled. VICTORIA REGINA   *Rev.* Various fish, some within a net.
INTERNATIONAL FISHERIES EXHIBITION 1883   D. 45 mm. By L. C. Wyon, *rev.* after L. F. Day.
BHM 3153; *Hocking* 262/24

      AV   350   450
      AR   20   35
      AE   8   15

Awarded to exhibitors in gold, silver and bronze, in various classes. The obverse is common to prize medals awarded at
several exhibitions held in South Kensington: National Fisheries 1881, Smoke Abatement 1882, Health (No. 1704) and
Inventions (No. 1715).

1695 **John Bright, M.P. for Birmingham 1883**
Obv. Bust of Bright, three-quarters l., draped. *Rev.* THE RIGHT HON: JOHN BRIGHT ELECTED
M.P. FOR BIRMINGHAM AUGUST 1857   Below, ribbon inscribed PEACE. RETRENCHMENT.
REFORM. A shield and motto. BIRMINGHAM LIBERAL ASSOCIATION. BRIGHT CELEBRATION JUNE
1883   D. 45 mm. By J. Moore. *BHM* 3145

      AR   15   25
      AE   6   10

John Bright (1811–89), orator and statesman.

1696 **Captain Matthew Webb 1883**
Obv. Bust almost facing, draped. CAPᵀ WEBB'S MEDAL. BORN 19ᵀᴴ JAN. 1848. DIED JULY 24ᵀᴴ
1883. *Rev.* A wreath (space within, for recipient's name). D. 34 mm. By W. Holmes.

      AR   25   40

Matthew Webb (1848–83), known as Captain Webb; became the first to swim the Channel in 1875, a feat which aroused
much public interest. It is unclear for or by whom this medal was issued.

1697 **Statue of Francis Drake 1883**
Obv. Statue of Drake holding compass points over a globe. FIRST ENGLISH STATUE TO FRANCIS
DRAKE UNVEILED AT TAVISTOCK SEPTEMBER 27. 1883   *Rev.* PRESENTED TO HIS BIRTHPLACE
TAVISTOCK BY HASTINGS IXᵀᴴ DUKE OF BEDFORD   D. 53 mm. By J. E. Boehm. *BHM* 3149;
MH 1919, 3

      AR   25   38
      AE   8   15

Francis Drake (1540?–96), admiral and circumnavigator. *See* M. Stocker, 'Edgar Boehm's medal commemorating Sir
Francis Drake'. *The Medal 5*, 30–1.

1698 **Thomas Coats 1883**
Obv. Bust l. THOMAS COATS 1883   *Rev.* An observatory building. OBSERVATORY PAISLEY   D.
49 mm. By N. Macphail. *BHM* 3147

      AR   45   60
      AE   25   35
      WM   12   20

Thomas Coats (1809–83), thread manufacturer and public benefactor; a native of Paisley, to which he gave the
observatory.

1699 **Birmingham School of Art, Chamberlain Medal 1883**
Obv. Bust r., draped. JOHN HENRY CHAMBERLAIN BORN 24 JUNE 1831 DIED 22. OCT. 1883   *Rev.*
Façade of Birmingham School of Art. GIVEN FOR DESIGN. IN MEMORY OF A MASTER OF DESIGN.
Ex. BIRMINGHAM MUNICIPAL SCHOOL OF ART   D. 60 mm. By J. Moore. *BHM* 3146

      AR   38   55
      AE   15   25

Awarded in silver and bronze. John Henry Chamberlain (1831–83), architect.

1700 **Numismatic Society of London 1883**
Obv. The three Monetae standing, facing, each with a pile of coins at their feet. TESTIS
TEMPORVM: NVNCIA VETVSTATIS: VITA MEMORIAE   *Ex.* MON. AVG. *Rev.* SOC. NVMISM. LOND.
OPTIME MERENTI within a wreath. D. 57 mm. (By Messrs J. Pinches?)

      AR   30   45
      AE   8   15

Awarded annually in silver for a significant contribution to numismatics. A similar medal was instituted in 1936, the
Society's centenary, and awarded thereafter. For a list of the recipients of 'the world's premier numismatic distinction', see
NC 1983, xxxii–iv. *See* No. 1320.

1701 **University of Glasgow, Balfour Medal 1884**
Obv. Bust l., draped. JOHN HUTTON BALFOUR   *Rev.* UNIVERSITY OF GLASGOW CLASS OF
BOTANY – FOR HERBARIUM   Below, a spray of thistle. D. 38 mm. by 46 mm. Oval. By
Maclure & MacDonald. *BHM* 3074; *Storer* 153

      AR   50   75
      AE   20   30

John Hutton Balfour (1808–84), botanist.

1702 **Centenary of Methodism in the Channel Islands 1884**
Obv. Similar to No. 1330. *Rev.* 1884 CENTENARY OF THE INTRODUCTION OF WESLEYAN
METHODISM INTO THE CHANNEL ISLANDS 1784, within a beaded circle. WESLEY. BRACKENBURY.
COKE. DE QUETTEVILLE. CLARKE. D. 38 mm. By J. Carter.

      AR   55   80
      AE   25   40
      WM   12   18

Examples occur with a suspension loop and an attached clasp with ribbon.

1703 **Death of Leopold, Duke of Albany 1884**
Obv. Head l. H.R.H. PRINCE LEOPOLD. DUKE OF ALBANY. K.G. BORN APRIL 7ᵀᴴ 1853   *Rev.*
House in a hilly landscape. DIED AT CANNES   *Ex.* MARCH 28ᵀᴴ 1884   D. 25 mm. By Benson.
BHM 3160

      AR   18   28
      AE   8   12

D. 77 mm. By L. C. Wyon, *rev.* after J. Tenniel. *BHM* 3110; *Storer* 6307

£   £

Silver examples sometimes occur frosted and set within a watch-style glass bound by a silver frame. James Paget (1814–99), surgeon to Queen Victoria. William MacCormac (1836–1901), surgeon; edited the *Transactions of the Congress.*

1684   **City and Guilds of London Institute 1881**

Obv. City of London shield in centre; around, shields of sixteen City livery companies. *Rev.*   *AR*   18   25
TECHNOLOGICAL EXAMINATION. HONOURS. in the centre. TECHNICAL EDUCATION. CITY AND   *AE*   4   7
GUILDS OF LONDON INSTITUTE   *D.* 51 mm. By E. D. Jackman. *Hocking* 219/34

The 'City and Guilds' was founded by the City Companies in 1878 for the advancement of technical education. This medal is the first which was awarded. The Institute presented a number of various medals; details of the recipient and the subject were usually engraved on the edge, while those of the grade (Grade I, Grade II, Final, Ordinary, Honours, etc.) and examination were struck, each from a different die, in the centre of the reverse. *See* Nos. 1764 and 1864.

1685*   **Military Hospital, Netley: Montefiore Medal 1881**

Obv. Armorial shield; THINK AND THANK on a pennant, above. EX DONIS N. MONTEFIORE.   *AR*   70   120
F:R:C:S: SCHOL: MIL: MED: 1881   *Rev.* Field ambulance in a rugged landscape; soldier lying   *AE*   35   60
on stretcher attended by doctor and orderlies. ΙΗΤΡΟΣ ΓΑΡ ΑΝΗΡ ΠΟΜΩΝ ΑΝΤΑΞΙΟΣ ΑΜΩΝ
[= For a doctor is a man abler than many others]. *D.* 60 mm. By A. Dubois, [*rev.* after T. Longmore] *Storer* 2471; *Parkes Weber* 82. See **Plate 42**

Awarded in bronze from 1882, for proficiency in military surgery. Nathaniel Montefiore (1819–83), surgeon.

1686   **The Royal Society, Darwin Medal 1882**

Obv. Bust l., draped, of Darwin. *Rev.* MDCCCIX CAROLVS DARWIN MDCCCLXXXII, within a   *AR*   45   70
wreath of plants identified in Darwin's research. *D.* 57 mm. By A. Wyon. *BHM* 3136;   *AE*   12   20
Storer 783

Awarded from 1890 in silver, biennially, for biological research. Charles Robert Darwin (1809–82), naturalist; originated the theory of natural selection.

1687   **Marriage of Duke of Albany and Princess Helen of Waldeck 1882**

Obv. Busts r., conjoined. LEOPOLD, DUKE OF ALBANY, K.G. PRINCESS HELEN OF   *AR*   70   150
WALDECK   *Rev.* Armorial shields of the couple; ribbon below, inscribed 27 APRIL 1882: all   *AE*   18   35
within an ornamental quatrefoil. *D.* 64 mm. By J. S. & A. B. Wyon. *BHM* 3113; *RWE* 142

Leopold George Duncan Albert, Duke of Albany (1854–84), fourth and youngest son of Victoria. Princess Helen Frederica (1861–1922), daughter of H.S.H. George Victor, Prince of Waldeck-Pyrmont. Few medals commemorate the marriage. *See* No. 1517.

1688   **Sacred Harmonic Society 1882**

Obv. An open music score of THE MESSIAH upon a lyre and crossed cornets, within a wreath.   *AR*   18   28
SACRED HARMONIC SOCIETY. FOUNDED 1832. *Rev.* Statue of HANDEL seated with a lyre; cherub   *AE*   7   12
below. TO COMMEMORATE THE FIFTIETH AND LAST SEASON. 1882. *D.* 51 mm. [By Messrs. J. Pinches] *BHM* 3137; *Niggl* 802

Awarded in silver and bronze. *See* No. 1527.

1689   **Epping Forest, Royal Visit and Dedication 1882**

Obv. Bust of Queen Victoria, l., crowned, veiled and draped. Continuous border of roses,   *AE*   25   48
thistles and shamrocks. *Rev.* Londinia standing opposite the Queen, seated, holds a gate
open at the edge of a forest, allowing passage along its winding pathway. IT. GIVES. ME. THE.
GREATEST. SATISFACTION. TO. DEDICATE. THIS. BEAUTIFUL. FOREST. FOR. THE. USE. AND.
ENJOYMENT. OF. MY. PEOPLE. FOR. ALL. TIME. EPPING. FOREST. 6. MAY. 1882. *D.* 75 mm. By C.
Wiener. *BHM* 3128; *Welch* 17

Issued by the Corporation of London. *See* No. 1245.

1690   **City of London School, New Buildings 1882**

Obv. Busts r., conjoined. ALBERT EDWARD ALEXANDRA   *Rev.* Façade of school building,   *AE*   25   45
flanked by the shields of the Prince of Wales, l., and City of London, r. CITY OF LONDON
SCHOOL NEW BUILDINGS OPENED   *Ex.* BY HIS ROYAL HIGHNESS THE PRINCE OF WALES 12 DEC.
1882   *D.* 77 mm. By J. S. & A. B. Wyon. *BHM* 3133; *Taylor* 202a; *Welch* 18

Issued by the Corporation of London. *See* No. 1245.

1691   **Edward Baily 1882**

Obv. Head l. E. H. BAILY R.A. 1788–1867   *Rev.* Baily's statue, *Eve at the Fountain. Ex.* 1882   *AR*   60   130
ART-UNION OF LONDON   *D.* 55 mm. By A. B. Wyon. *BHM* 3115; *Forrer* VI/578; *Beaulah* 28   *AE*   15   30

Edward Hodges Baily (1788–1867), sculptor; many of his designs appear on medals. *See* No. 1381.

1692*   **Lillie Langtry 1882**

Obv. Bust of Langtry almost facing, loosely draped, head r.; a miniature dagger in her   *AE*   —   150
cleavage. L. L in the field, either side of the bust. Without reverse. *D.* 142 mm. Cast. By E. J.
Poynter. *BHM* 3120; *Forrer* IV/680; *Inglis* 10. See **Plate 43**

Lillie Langtry (1853–1929), actress and socialite; known as the 'Jersey Lily'. The dagger is probably an allusion to the theatre; she made her first stage appearance in 1881.

			VF £	*EF* £

1693   **Princess Victoria and Frederick William, Silver Wedding 1883**

Obv. Heads r., conjoined. FR. WILH. KRONPRINZ. VICTORIA KRONPRINZESSIN D. DEUTSCH.   *AR*   25   38

REICHS. *Rev.* Armorial shields of the couple upon scrolls, crowned. Below, 1858. 1883 on a   *WM*   8   15

plaque. ZUR ERINNERUNG AN DIE SILBERNE HOCHZEIT D. 25. JANUAR 1883   *D.* 31 mm. By H.

Weckwerth. *Parkes Weber* 215e

1694   **International Fisheries Exhibition, London 1883**

Obv. Head l., diademed and veiled. VICTORIA REGINA   *Rev.* Various fish, some within a net.   *AV*   350   450

INTERNATIONAL FISHERIES EXHIBITION 1883   *D.* 45 mm. By L. C. Wyon, *rev.* after L. F. Day.   *AR*   20   35

BHM 3153; *Hocking* 262/24   *AE*   8   15

Awarded to exhibitors in gold, silver and bronze, in various classes. The obverse is common to prize medals awarded at several exhibitions held in South Kensington: National Fisheries 1881, Smoke Abatement 1882, Health (No. 1704) and Inventions (No. 1715).

1695   **John Bright, M.P. for Birmingham 1883**

Obv. Bust of Bright, three-quarters l., draped. *Rev.* THE RIGHT HON: JOHN BRIGHT ELECTED   *AR*   15   25

M.P. FOR BIRMINGHAM AUGUST 1857   Below, ribbon inscribed PEACE. RETRENCHMENT.   *AE*   6   10

REFORM. A shield and motto. BIRMINGHAM LIBERAL ASSOCIATION. BRIGHT CELEBRATION JUNE

1883   *D.* 45 mm. By J. Moore. *BHM* 3145

John Bright (1811–89), orator and statesman.

1696   **Captain Matthew Webb 1883**

Obv. Bust almost facing, draped. CAP⸆ WEBB'S MEDAL. BORN 19ᵀᴴ JAN. 1848. DIED JULY 24ᵀᴴ   *AR*   25   40

1883. *Rev.* A wreath (space within, for recipient's name). *D.* 34 mm. By W. Holmes.

Matthew Webb (1848–83), known as Captain Webb; became the first to swim the Channel in 1875, a feat which aroused much public interest. It is unclear for or by whom this medal was issued.

1697   **Statue of Francis Drake 1883**

Obv. Statue of Drake holding compass points over a globe. FIRST ENGLISH STATUE TO FRANCIS   *AR*   25   38

DRAKE UNVEILED AT TAVISTOCK SEPTEMBER 27. 1883   *Rev.* PRESENTED TO HIS BIRTHPLACE   *AE*   8   15

TAVISTOCK BY HASTINGS IXᵀᴴ DUKE OF BEDFORD   *D.* 53 mm. By J. E. Boehm. *BHM* 3149;

MH 1919, 3

Francis Drake (1540?–96), admiral and circumnavigator. *See* M. Stocker, 'Edgar Boehm's medal commemorating Sir Francis Drake'. *The Medal* 5, 30–1.

1698   **Thomas Coats 1883**

Obv. Bust l. THOMAS COATS 1883   *Rev.* An observatory building. OBSERVATORY PAISLEY   *D.*   *AR*   45   60

49 mm. By N. Macphail. *BHM* 3147   *AE*   25   35

   WM   12   20

Thomas Coats (1809–83), thread manufacturer and public benefactor; a native of Paisley, to which he gave the observatory.

1699   **Birmingham School of Art, Chamberlain Medal 1883**

Obv. Bust r., draped. JOHN HENRY CHAMBERLAIN BORN 24 JUNE 1831 DIED 22. OCT. 1883   *Rev.*   *AR*   38   55

Façade of Birmingham School of Art. GIVEN FOR DESIGN. IN MEMORY OF A MASTER OF DESIGN.   *AE*   15   25

Ex. BIRMINGHAM MUNICIPAL SCHOOL OF ART   *D.* 60 mm. By J. Moore. *BHM* 3146

Awarded in silver and bronze. John Henry Chamberlain (1831–83), architect.

1700   **Numismatic Society of London 1883**

Obv. The three Monetae standing, facing, each with a pile of coins at their feet. TESTIS   *AR*   30   45

TEMPORVM: NVNCIA VETVSTATIS: VITA MEMORIAE   *Ex.* MON. AVG. *Rev.* SOC. NVMISM. LOND.   *AE*   8   15

OPTIME MERENTI within a wreath. *D.* 57 mm. (By Messrs J. Pinches?)

Awarded annually in silver for a significant contribution to numismatics. A similar medal was instituted in 1936, the Society's centenary, and awarded thereafter. For a list of the recipients of 'the world's premier numismatic distinction', see *NC* 1983, xxxiii–iv. *See* No. 1320.

1701   **University of Glasgow, Balfour Medal 1884**

Obv. Bust l., draped. JOHN HUTTON BALFOUR   *Rev.* UNIVERSITY OF GLASGOW CLASS OF   *AR*   50   75

BOTANY – FOR HERBARIUM   Below, a spray of thistle. *D.* 38 mm. by 46 mm. Oval. By   *AE*   20   30

Maclure & MacDonald. *BHM* 3074; *Storer* 153

John Hutton Balfour (1808–84), botanist.

1702   **Centenary of Methodism in the Channel Islands 1884**

Obv. Similar to No. 1330. *Rev.* 1884 CENTENARY OF THE INTRODUCTION OF WESLEYAN   *AR*   55   80

METHODISM INTO THE CHANNEL ISLANDS 1784, within a beaded circle. WESLEY. BRACKENBURY.   *AE*   25   40

COKE. DE QUETTEVILLE. CLARKE. *D.* 38 mm. By J. Carter.   *WM*   12   18

Examples occur with a suspension loop and an attached clasp with ribbon.

1703   **Death of Leopold, Duke of Albany 1884**

Obv. Head l. H.R.H. PRINCE LEOPOLD. DUKE OF ALBANY. K.G. BORN APRIL 7ᵀᴴ 1853   *Rev.*   *AR*   18   28

House in a hilly landscape. DIED AT CANNES   *Ex.* MARCH 28ᵀᴴ 1884   *D.* 25 mm. By Benson.   *AE*   8   12

BHM 3160

			£	£

1704   International Health Exhibition, London 1884

Obv. As No. 1694. *Rev.* A globe, bearing the fruits of the world, flanked by HEALTH, holding a serpent, and EDUCATION, holding a wreath. THE INTERNATIONAL HEALTH EXHIBITION. *Ex.* LONDON 1884 *D.* 45 mm. By L. C. Wyon (*rev.* after L. F. Day?) BHM 3175; *Storer* 4811

   AV   350   450
   AR   18   30
   AE   8   12

Awarded to exhibitors in various classes, in gold, silver and bronze. *See* No. 1694.

1705   New Council Chamber, Guildhall 1884

Obv. A detailed interior view of the Council Chamber, flanked by two heraldic panels. THE NEW COUNCIL CHAMBER. GUILDHALL OF LONDON. OPENED 2ND OCTOBER 1884. *Ex.* City of London shield. *Rev.* Londinia standing before the civic chair, r., attended by Mercury and Commerce, addressing her Council, standing and seated before her. *Ex.* City sword and mace, entwined by a ribbon bearing the City motto. *D.* 77 mm. By J. S. & A. B. Wyon. BHM 3177; *Taylor* 206a; *Welch* 19

   AE   25   48

Issued by the Corporation of London. *See* No. 1245.

1706   National Liberal Club 1884

Obv. Bust three-quarters l., draped. IN COMMEMORATION OF THE FOUNDATION STONE OF THE NATIONAL LIBERAL CLUB BEING LAID BY THE RT: HON: W. E. GLADSTONE. M.P. OC^{TR} 1884. *Rev.* Perspective view of building. *D.* 76 mm. By G. Kenning. BHM 3176; *Taylor* 214a

   AE   20   35

1707   Sir Moses Montefiore, 100th Birthday 1884

Obv. Bust three-quarters r., of Montefiore, draped. Hebrew legend [= Happy are all who fear God and walk in his ways 1884]. *Rev.* A UNIVERSAL TRIBUTE OF RESPECT & ESTEEM TO SIR MOSES MONTEFIORE BART. PHILANTHROPIST FROM HIS ADMIRERS & FRIENDS – CENTENARY 27th OCTOBER 1884, in the centre. HOLY LAND, EGYPT, DAMASCUS, CONSTANTINOPLE, RUSSIA, POLAND, ROME, MOROCCO, ROUMANIA. *D.* 41 mm. By A. D. Loewenstark & Sons. BHM 3166; *JMC* 1169

   AR   120   170
   AE   60   100
   WM   25   45

1708   Extension of the Electoral Franchise 1884

Obv. British lion standing resolutely before rocks. THE CONSTITUTION IN ALL ITS FULLNESS FOR THE PEOPLE OF THE UNITED KINGDOM *Ex.* GLADSTONE AND THE FRANCHISE FOR TWO MILLIONS 1884. *Rev.* A crown decorated with two ribbons inscribed JUSTICE FOR ALL / PEACE, LAW, ORDER within a wreath. OUR QUEEN OUR COUNTRY AND OUR RIGHTS. *D.* 43 mm. By Maher & Son.

   AR   15   28
   AE   7   10

The bill extended household and lodger suffrage to counties uniform with boroughs.

1709*   George Gilbert Scott 1884

Obv. Bust l. SIR G. GILBERT SCOTT. R.A. 1811–1878 *Rev.* Façade of Scott's St. Mary's Episcopal Cathedral, Edinburgh. ART-UNION OF LONDON *Ex.* EDINBURGH 1884 *D.* 57 mm. By G. G. Adams. BHM 3170; *Eidlitz* 1927, 942; *Beaulah* 29. See **Plate 43**

   AR   75   170
   AE   20   40

Sir George Gilbert Scott (1811–78), architect. *See* No. 1381.

1710   Marquis of Lansdowne, Governor-General's Medal 1884

Obv. Busts r., conjoined. MARQUESS OF LANSDOWNE G.C.M.G. GOV: GEN: OF CANADA. MARCHIONESS OF LANSDOWNE. 1884. *Rev.* Arms, supporters, etc. PRESENTED. BY. HIS. EXCELLENCY. THE. GOVERNOR. GENERAL *D.* 51 mm. By J. S. & A. B. Wyon. BHM 3164

   AV   —   —
   AR   50   80
   AE   10   15

Henry Charles Keith Petty-Maurice, 5th Marquis of Lansdowne (1845–1927), diplomatist and administrator. *See* No. 1625.

1711   John Wisden 1884

Obv. Standing figure of a cricketer, three-quarters r., holding a ball; below, a scroll inscribed JOHN WISDEN 1826–1884 Without reverse. *D.* 51 mm. by 96 mm. Rectangular. (By?)

   AE   45   —

John Wisden (1826–84), chronicler of cricket.

1712*   Centenary of *The Times* 1885

Obv. Busts r., conjoined and draped, of the Walter family: John Sr., John Jr., and John III. *Rev.* Clockface upon an open book, inscribed THE TIMES, over a wreath. CENTENARY CELEBRATION BEARWOOD. 1885 *D.* 45 mm. By [Longman] & Strongi'th'arm. BHM 3202. *See* **Plate 43**

   AR   25   40
   AE   12   18

John Walter Sr. (1739–1812), founder of *The Times*; John Walter Jr. (1776–1847), 2nd son of John Sr. and chief proprietor; John Walter III (1818–94), eldest son of John Jr. and chief proprietor.

1713   Sunday School Centenary, Wales 1885

Obv. Bust almost facing, draped. THOMAS CHARLES O'R BALA, SYLFAENYDD YR YSCOL SABBOTHOL YN NCHYMRU. CANWYD HYD. 14, 1755. BU FARW HYD. 5, 1814 *Rev.* Eight-line inscription (from St. John, v,39) CHWILIWCH YR YSGRYTHYRAU . . . AM DANAF FI – IESU GRIST, in the centre. CANMLWYDDIANT YR YSGOL SABBOTHOL YN NGHYMRU, 1885 *D.* 45 mm. (By?) BHM 3201

   AR   15   25
   AE   5   7
   WM   2   4

Thomas Charles (1755–1814), of Bala; Welsh preacher and writer.

                                                  £   £

1714   General Gordon, Memorial 1885

Obv. Bust almost facing, wearing a fez and uniformed. GENERAL C. G. GORDON. C.B., R.E. ✻ THE   *AR*   40   70
LATEST CHRISTIAN MARTYR ✻   *Rev*. SENT BY THE GLADSTONE GOVERNMENT TO THE SOUDAN   *AE*   20   32
WITH ONE COMPANION, JAN.^Y 1884. IN MARCH HE ASKED FOR 200 BRITISH TROOPS BUT WAS   *WM*   8   15
DELIBERATELY ABANDONED TO HIS FATE UNTIL TOO LATE, within a wreath. *D*. 45 mm. By W. O.
Lewis. *BHM* 3187

Charles George Gordon (1833–85), soldier; known also as 'Chinese Gordon' and 'Gordon Pasha' through his campaigns
in China and Egypt; killed at the fall of Khartoum. A few medals commemorate Gordon and the circumstances of his
death.

1715   International Inventions Exhibition, London 1885

Obv. As No. 1694. *Rev*. The figures of INVENTION and MUSIC, holding a compass and a lyre,   *AV*   350   450
upon a platform displaying a plaque, inscribed 1885 INTERNATIONAL INVENTIONS   *AR*   18   30
EXHIBITION   *D*. 45 mm. By L. C. Wyon/(L. F. Day?) *BHM* 3198   *AE*   8   12

Awarded to exhibitors in gold, silver and bronze. For a list of recipients, medals and subject-matter, *see* International
Inventions Exhibition, official catalogue, *The Awards of the Juries*, London, 1885. *See* No. 1694.

1716   William Gladstone: Lord Salisbury 1885

Obv. Bust three-quarters l., draped. THE R.^T HON. W. E. GLADSTONE M.P. *Rev*. Bust r., draped.   *AE*   2   4
THE MOST HON. THE MARQUIS OF SALISBURY K.G. *D*. 33 mm. By Oldacre & Co. *BHM* 3191

Another medal by Oldacre has the bust of Salisbury to left. Robert Arthur Talbot Gascoyne-Cecil, 3rd Marquis of
Salisbury (1830–1903), statesman; first became Prime Minister in 1885.

1717   Prince Albert Victor of Wales, Freedom of the City of London 1885

Obv. Bust r., within a wreath of roses, thistles and shamrocks. H.R.H. PRINCE ALBERT VICTOR   *AE*   25   45
EDWARD OF WALES. BORN JANUARY 8TH 1864. *Rev*. The Prince and Princess of Wales, together
with the Lord Mayor, watch as Prince Albert Victor receives the Freedom from the
Chamberlain. RECEIVING THE FREEDOM OF THE CITY OF LONDON JUNE 29TH 1885   *Ex*. City
arms. *D*. 77 mm. By G. G. Adams. *BHM* 3182; *Welch* 20

Issued by the Corporation of London (*see* No. 1245). Albert Victor Christian Edward, Duke of Clarence and Avondale
(1864–92), eldest son of Edward, Prince of Wales, and Alexandra.

1718   Marriage of Princess Beatrice and Prince Henry of Battenberg 1885

Obv. Busts l., conjoined. PRINCESS BEATRICE OF ENGLAND. PRINCE HENRY OF BATTENBERG.   *AR*   60   130
Rev. Armorial shields of the couple; ribbon below, inscribed .23. JULY. 1885. All within an   *AE*   15   32
ornamental quartrefoil. *D*. 64 mm. By A. Wyon. *BHM* 3183

Princess Beatrice Mary Victoria Feodore (1857–1944), youngest daughter of Victoria. Prince Henry Maurice of
Battenberg (1858–96), naturalized British subject; governor of the Isle of Wight. He died of fever during the Ashanti
expedition. Few medals commemorate the marriage. *See* No. 1517.

1719   Earl of Shaftesbury 1885

Obv. Head l. ANTHONY, EARL OF SHAFTESBURY, K.G. .BORN 28 APR. 1801. DIED 1 OCT. 1885. *Rev*.   *AR*   22   35
A wreath (space within, for recipient's name). *D*. 37 mm. By A. Wyon. *BHM* 3192   *AE*   8   15

Anthony Ashley Cooper, 7th Earl of Shaftesbury (1801–85), public benefactor; champion of the rights of working
children. It is unclear by or for whom this medal was struck.

1720   Cardinal Henry Newman 1885

Obv. Bust l., wearing a skull-cap and clerical robes. IOHANNES. HENRICVS M.D. S.R.E. NEWMAN   *AE*   —   60
A.D MDCCCLXXXV   *Rev*. Equestrian figure of St. George; ribbon, inscribed COR ADCOR
LOQVETVR, decorated by a heraldic shield in the field. S GIORGII. IN VELABRO DIAC   *D*.
112 mm. Cast. By E. Hallé. *Attwood* 3

Cardinal John Henry Newman (1801–90), theologian; Anglican leader and latterly a Roman Catholic cardinal. Other cast
portrait medals by E. Hallé include those of Charles Hallé (her father), T. H. Huxley, C. S. Parnell and H. M. Stanley
(No. 1763).

1721   Henry Irving: Ellen Terry *c*.1885

Obv. Bust l., draped. MR HENRY IRVING   *Rev*. Bust r., draped. MISS ELLEN TERRY   *D*.   *AE*   15   25
35 mm. Cast. (By?) *Svarstad* 110

Sir Henry Irving, original name John Henry Brodribb (1838–1905), actor; from 1878 to 1902, professionally associated
with the actress Ellen Alice Terry (1847–1928).

1722*   Lord Randolph Churchill: Colonel Frederick Burnaby *c*.1885

Obv. Bust three-quarters l., draped. LORD RANDOLPH CHURCHILL M.P. STATESMAN &   *AR*   30   45
ORATOR   *Rev*. Bust three-quarters r., draped. COL. FRED BURNABY SOLDIER & PATRIOT   *D*.   *AE*   15   25
39 mm. By W. O. Lewis. *BHM* 3161. *See* **Plate 43**

Frederick Gustavus Burnaby (1842–85), traveller and soldier. Randolph Henry Spencer Churchill (1849–95), statesman.

1723   Young Men's Christian Institute *c*.1885

Obv. INDUSTRIAL EXHIBITION 309 REGENT ST. POLYTECHNIC LONDON in the centre. YOUNG   *AR*   12   22
MENS' CHRISTIAN INSTITUTE Wreath border decorated with symbols of Art, Industry,   *AE*   6   10

			VF	EF
	Literature and Music. *Rev.* St. George slaying the Dragon. THE LORD IS OUR STRENGTH *D.* 57 mm. By J. A. Restall/J. S. & A. B. Wyon. *BHM* 3426		£	£

One of several medals awarded by the Institute, in silver and bronze.

1724   Heriot's Hospital School 1886

Obv. Bust of Heriot, l., draped. URBI PATER EST, URBIQUE MARITUS. *Rev.* AWARDED TO (space, for recipient's name) within a wreath. GEORGE HERIOT'S HOSPITAL SCHOOL   Below, façade of building dividing dates, 1628 1886   *D.* 47 mm. By A. Kirkwood & Son.   *AR*   12   18

George Heriot (1563–1624), goldsmith and public benefactor; founder of Heriot's Hospital, Edinburgh. Usually found with a large scroll mount on the edge.

1725   Colonial and Indian Exhibition, London 1886

Obv. Bust l. ALBERT EDWARD PRINCE OF WALES EXECUTIVE PRESIDENT   *Rev.* COLONIAL AND   *AR*   25   45
INDIAN EXHIBITION 1886 within a wreath. *D.* 52 mm. By L. C. Wyon. *BHM* 3209; *Hocking*   *AE*   6   10
262/34

A prize medal usually found awarded in bronze. The exhibition was for the products, manufactures and arts of India and the Colonies; it was held at South Kensington on a site adjacent to the Albert Hall.

1726   Colonial and Indian Reception, Guildhall, London 1886

Obv. A mantle decorated with the Royal shield, crowned, from which hang three Colonial   *AE*   25   45
shields upon crossed flags; PEACE UNITY CONCORD on a ribbon, below. TO COMMEMORATE THE COLONIAL & INDIAN RECEPTION AT THE GUILDHALL. LONDON 1886. *Rev.* Detailed interior view of the Guildhall. *Ex.* City shield and motto. *D.* 77 mm. By Elkington & Co. *BHM* 3214; *Taylor* 185a; *Welch* 21

Issued by the Corporation of London. *See* No. 1245.

1727   International Exhibition, Liverpool 1886

Obv. Bust l., crowned. OPENED. BY. HER. MAJESTY. QVEEN. VICTORIA. MAY. 1886. *Rev.*   *AE*   7   12
Industry, standing, holds caduceus and wreath; below, arms of Liverpool. Beyond, shipping at sea. INTERNATIONAL. EXHIBITION. OF. NAVIGATION. TRAVELLING. COMMERCE. &. MANUFACTURES. LIVERPOOL. 1886. *Ex.* SIR DAVID RADCLIFFE MAYOR CHAIRMAN   *D.* 51 mm. By Elkington & Co. *BHM* 3216

1728   Sister Dora 1886

Obv. Bust r., in nurse's uniform. SISTER DORA THE FRIEND OF THE SUFFERING   *Rev.* IN   *WM*   15   25
COMMEMORATION OF UNVEILING THE STATUE OF SISTER DORA AT WALSALL BY B. BEEBEE, ESQ^R J.P. OCTOBER 11TH 1886 THOMAS EVANS, ESQ^R MAYOR   *D.* 41 mm. By Kirby. *BHM* 3204

Dorothy Wyndlow Pattison (1832–78), known as Sister Dora, philanthropist and member of the sisterhood of the Good Samaritan. In later life she worked in the Municipal Epidemic Hospital, Walsall.

1729   Numismatic Society of London, Golden Jubilee Completed 1887

Obv. Bust r., draped. IOH. EVANS. D.C.L. S.R.S. PRAESIDI   *Rev.* SIC L SIC C. within a wreath.   *AR*   28   45
SOCIETAS NVMISM. LOND. ANNOS CONST. LI. MDCCCLXXXVII   *D.* 57 mm. By Messrs. J.   *AE*   8   15
Pinches. *BHM* 3344; *Forrer* IV/549

Sir John Evans (1823–1908), archaeologist and numismatist; President of the Society since 1874, and recipient of their medal (No. 1700) in 1887. *See* No. 1320.

1730   Mining, Engineering and Industrial Exhibition, Newcastle-upon-Tyne 1887

Obv. City arms; 1887 above. NEWCASTLE-UPON-TYNE ROYAL MINING, ENGINEERING &   *AR*   25   35
INDUSTRIAL EXHIBITION 1887   *Rev.* View of the high-level bridge spanning river; city   *AE*   10   18
beyond. QUEEN'S JUBILEE YEAR   *D.* 51 mm. By Reid & Sons. *BHM* 3343

Awarded in bronze and silver, often unnamed.

1731   John Dillon, 'Plan of Campaign' 1887

Obv. Bust three-quarters l., between two sprigs of shamrock. JOHN DILLON   *Rev.* Irish harp   *WM*   15   25
and 1887, divided by two clasped hands. PLAN OF CAMPAIGN. GOD SAVE IRELAND   With integral suspension loop. *D.* 30 mm. (By?)

John Dillon (1851–1927), Irish nationalist politician. The Plan called for the payment of rent to the National League instead of to landlords; tenants were to be supported by a general fund if evicted. In 1887 Dillon was unsuccessfully prosecuted for collecting these rents.

1732   Golden Jubilee of Queen Victoria 1887

Obv. Busts l., conjoined, crowned and draped, of the young and jubilee heads of the Queen.   *AE*   30   50
VICTORIA REGINA. IMPERATRIX. 1837. 1887   *Rev.* Britannia standing in a car drawn by two lions and led by a genius; Justice and Prudence on either side. .ANNUS. JUBILÆUS. 1887. *Ex.* City arms and motto. *D.* 80 mm. By A. Scharff. *BHM* 3284; *Parkes Weber* 206; *Welch* 22

Issued by the Corporation of London. *See* No. 1245. The Jubilee was commemorated by well over one hundred national and local medals (*see* No. 1739); others were struck in Commonwealth countries.

1733 ——

Obv. Bust l., crowned and veiled. VICTORIA REGINA ET IMPERATRIX   *Rev.* Enthroned figure of Empire, facing, flanked by standing figures of Science, Letters and Art, l., opposite those of Industry and Agriculture, r. At their feet, below Empire, are Mercury, reclining, and Time. Above, two cherubs displaying shields inscribed MDCCCLXXXVII and MDCCCXXXVII, and V.R.I. in a wreath, between. IN. COMMEMORATION   *Ex.* Five linked shields, inscribed ASIA AMERICA EUROPE AUSTRALASIA and AFRICA   *D. a* 77 mm.; *b* 58 mm. By J. E. Boehm/F. Leighton. *BHM* 3219: *Wollaston* 39

		£	£
a	AR	60	110
	AE	12	25
b	AV	600	900
	AR	—	—

The official Royal Mint issue. *See* M. Stocker, 'Edgar Boehm and the Jubilee Medals of 1887', *The Medal* 5, 25–9.

1734* ——

Obv. Bust l., crowned, veiled and draped. VICTORIA D: G: BRITT: REGINA F: D: ET IND: IMPERATRIX   *Rev.* Victoria enthroned, facing, flanked by Industry and Neptune; behind, shields of Britain and Saxe-Coburg-Gotha. In foreground, a scroll inscribed 1837–87, displayed by Britannia. GLORIOUS REIGN OF FIFTY YEARS COMPLETED   *Ex.* 20 JUNE 1887   *D.* 64 mm. By A. Wyon. *BHM* 3290. *See* **Plate 43**

AR	70	120
AE	20	35

1735 ——

Obv. Bust r., crowned and draped. VICTORIA QUEEN OF GREAT BRITAIN & IRELAND & EMPRESS OF INDIA Below bust, ANN. IVBIL. 1887   *Rev.* Winged female figure of Fortune standing upon stern of medieval ship holds billowing sails. ART SAILETH THOUGH LIFE FAILETH ART UNION OF LONDON 1837–1887   *D.* 63 mm. [By A. Gilbert] *BHM* 3246; *Beaulah* 30

AR	140	250
AE	90	170

This medal also commemorates the Golden Jubilee of the Art-Union of London. *See* No. 1381.

1736 ——

Obv. Bust l., diademed and veiled. VICTORIA D: G: BRITANNIARUM REGINA F:D: INDIÆ IMPERATRIX. *Rev.* IN COMMEMORATION OF THE FIFTIETH YEAR OF THE REIGN OF H.G.M. QUEEN VICTORIA ASCENDED THE THRONE JUNE 20TH 1837, within a wreath; above, a radiate crown. *D.* 45 mm. By J. Carter. *BHM* 3232–5

AR	14	22
AE	4	6
WM	2	4

Struck from several pairs of dies, and in different diameters. The portrait was used on a number of local issues.

1737* ——

Obv. Bust l., crowned, laureate, veiled and draped. VICTORIA REGINA ET IMPERATRIX   *Rev.* Exterior view of building; a curved pennant, around, inscribed THE IMPERIAL INSTITUTE TO COMMEMORATE THE JUBILEE OF VICTORIA R. ET I. 1887   *Ex.* ALBERT EDWARD P. PRESIDENT   *D.* 38 mm. [By G. W. de Saulles] after T. Brock/J. H. Pinches. *BHM* 3226; *Taylor* 221*b*. *See* **Plate 43**

AV	280	350
AR	15	28
AE	5	10

Struck in 1893, when the building was opened by the Queen. The portrait is from Brock's rejected coinage design of 1892.

1738 ——

Obv. Bust l., diademed and veiled. IN COMMEMORATION OF THE JUBILEE REIGN OF H.G.M. QUEEN VICTORIA. 1837–1887. *Rev.* VICTORIA E.I. BORN MAY 24. 1819 ASCENDED JUNE 20. 37 CROWNED JUNE 28. 38 MARRIED FEB. 10. 40 JUBILEE 1887 within a wreath displaying colonial shields. *D.* 38 mm. By J. Moore. *BHM* 3262

AR	10	18
AE	3	5
WM	1	3

A 33 mm. version of this medal was also struck. The portrait was used on several local issues.

1739 ——

Obv. Bust l., diademed and veiled. VICTORIA QUEEN OF GT BRITAIN & IRELAND & EMPRESS OF INDIA   *Rev.* Arms of Brighton. BOROUGH OF BRIGHTON REEVES MAYOR, around. IN COMMEMORATION OF QUEEN VICTORIA'S JUBILEE. 1887   *D.* 38 mm. (By?) *BHM* 3298

AR	12	20
AE	5	8
WM	2	4

The first royal event to see a large issue of local medals; well over one hundred localities throughout Britain commemorated the Jubilee with a medal. Many are of local manufacture and use a portrait based on one of the general issues, such as those by J. Carter or J. Moore, and a reverse with the district's arms and motto. Most were produced in white metal and were worn during the festivities; they are often found holed and with suspension loops. Localities which issued medals include: Bideford, Bromsgrove, Croydon, Derby, Dorchester, Farncombe, Ilford, Kirkcaldy, Leyland, Lichfield, Lostwithiel, Mortlake, Norwich, Portsmouth, Reading, Stafford, Surbiton, Tintwistle, Warwick, West Hartlepool, Whitby Abbey, Wigan, Worcester.

1740   Victoria Bridge, Stockton-upon-Tees, Opened 1887

Obv. Bust l., crowned, laureate and veiled. QUEEN VICTORIA BORN MAY 24TH 1819 ASCENDED THE THRONE 20TH JUNE 1837. *Rev.* Three-arched bridge spanning river. Arms of STOCKTON-UPON-TEES above. VICTORIA BRIDGE OFFICIALLY OPENED JUNE 20. 1887   *Ex.* JOSEPH RICHARDSON MAYOR. *D.* 36 mm. [By Messrs J. Pinches] *BHM* 3281

AR	25	38
AE	12	20

1741   Tay Bridge Opened 1887

Obv. Bridge spanning river. STEEL TO THE BANE on scroll, above. THE TAY BRIDGE   *Ex.* OPENED JUNE 1887   *Rev.* Shields with supporters. Two scrolls, inscribed DEI DONUM, above, and PRUDENTIA ET CONDORE, below. *D.* 39 mm. (By?) *BHM* 3350

WM	12	20

PLATE 43

1692 (× $\frac{2}{3}$)

1709

1712

1734

1743

1722

1737

1753

PLATE 44

1754

1755

1770

1783 (× ⅔)

1791

1796

1805

1806

		£	£

1742   **Consecration of Truro Cathedral 1887**
Obv. Façade of cathedral. *Ex.* TRURO CATHEDRAL   *Rev.* FOUNDATION STONE LAID BY H.R.H. PRINCE OF WALES MAY 20TH 1880 CONSECRATED BY THE LORD BISHOP OF TRURO NOV 3RD 1887, within a wreath; above, shield of bishopric and mitre. *D.* 44 mm. (By?) *BHM* 3351; *Taylor* 216*a*   *WM*   3   8

1743*   **Prince and Princess of Wales, Silver Wedding 1888**
Obv. Busts l., conjoined and draped, she diademed; below, their heraldic shields. TH. R.H. THE PRINCE AND PRINCESS OF WALES   *Rev.* IN COMMEMORATION OF THE SILVER WEDDING 10 MARCH 1888 within a wreath; above, the Prince's crest and motto. *D.* 34 mm. By H. Grueber. *BHM* 3354; *Parkes Weber* 251. *See* **Plate 43**   *AR*   20   35   *AE*   12   18
A few medals commemorate the silver wedding.

1744   **Victoria, Visit to Florence 1888**
Obv. Bust l., of Victoria, crowned, veiled and draped. *Rev.* RICORDO DEL SOGGIORNO IN FIRENZE PRIMAVERA 1888 within a wreath. *D.* 46 mm. By L. Giorgi.   *AE*   18   30

1745   **Spanish Armada, Tercentenary 1888**
Obv. Busts, draped, of Elizabeth I and Victoria, each within an oval frame and almost facing; ribbon between, inscribed 1588 1888 Radiate crown, above; royal shields, below. *Rev.* Victory seated, l., inscribing HOWARD SEYMOUR DRAKE HAWKYNS WYNTER FROBISHER on a column. DESTRUCTION OF THE SPANISH ARMADA   *Ex.* TERCENTENARY COMMEMORATION A.D. 1888   *D.* 45 mm. By J. Carter. *BHM* 3364   *AR*   20   32   *AE*   6   10   *WM*   2   5
Martin Frobisher (1535?–94), navigator. John Hawkyns (1532–95), naval commander. Charles Howard, Baron Effingham (1536–1624), Lord High Admiral. William Wynter (d.1589), admiral.

1746   **John Pope-Hennessy 1888**
Obv. Bust r., draped. SIR JOHN POPE HENNESSY   *Rev.* Female figure of Mauritius seated, l., beside her shield, scatters a floral tribute to a departing steamer. A SIR JOHN POPE HENNESSY, K.C.M.G. GOUVERNEUR DE L'ILE MAVRICE ET DE SES DEPENDANCES LES MAVRICIENS RECONNAISSANTS. XXII DECEMBRE MDCCCLXXXVIII   *D.* 69 mm. By O. Roty. *BHM* 3360; *Parkes Weber* 201   *AR*   60   90   *AE*   25   45
Struck on the retirement of John Pope-Hennessy (1834–91), colonial Governor of Mauritius.

1747   **Queen Victoria, 70th Birthday 1889**
Obv. Bust three-quarters l., crowned, veiled and draped. VICTORIA BY THE GRACE OF GOD QUEEN OF GREAT BRITAIN EMPRESS OF INDIA   *Rev.* Britannia seated on a parapet beside a lion holding the British arms. 1889 in the field. *D.* 65 mm. By Messrs L. C. Lauer. *BHM* 3365   *AR*   25   45   *AE*   8   15

1748   **Opening of Barry Dock and Railways 1889**
Obv. Panoramic view of Barry Island and ships within the harbour and docklands area. BARRY DOCK AND RAILWAYS   *Rev.* Ten-line inscription listing dignitaries, etc. DIRECTORS LORD WINDSOR CHAIRMAN DAVID DAVIES . . ., in the centre. FIRST SOD CUT BY LORD WINDSOR 14TH NOVR 1884. OPENED FOR PUBLIC TRAFFIC BY LADY WINDSOR 18TH JULY 1889. *D.* 51 mm. By Barry & Sons. *BHM* 3374; *Boon* 29   *AE*   18   30   *WM*   8   15
Sir John Wolfe Barry (1836–1918), consulting engineer, who also worked on Tower Bridge (No. 1790); youngest son of the architect Charles.

1749   **The Aluminium Company Ltd. 1889**
Obv. THE ALUMINIUM COMPANY LIMITED LONDON 1889 in the centre. MANUFACTURERS BY THE DEVILLE-CASTNER PROCESS. *Rev.* Vulcan attended by Science working at a forge. LABOUR SCIENCE   *Ex.* INDUSTRY   *D.* 50 mm. (By?) *BHM* 3373   *Al.*   3   5
Aluminium medals issued by other companies involved in its manufacture include the British Aluminium Co., 1896; Foyers Aluminium 1897; Kinlochleven Aluminium 1907.

1750   **Naval Review at Spithead 1889**
Obv. A fleet in line formation. NAVAL REVIEW Above, a portrait medallion of the Queen decorated with a ribbon, inscribed VICTORIA REGINA 1889   *Rev.* Bust three-quarters l., uniformed. THE GERMAN EMPEROR WILHELM II VISITS ENGLAND AUGUST 1889 *   *D.* 60 mm. By Messrs L. C. Lauer. *BHM* 3368; *MH* 1919, 643   *AR*   30   55   *AE*   12   20

1751   **James Prescott Joule 1889**
Obv. Bust three-quarters l., draped. JAMES PRESCOTT JOULE PRIZE FOUNDED BY SIR W. H. BAILEY   *Rev.* A flaming torch in the form of a steelyard; a weight at one end, inscribed FT. 772 LBS, in pan. Below, AWARDED TO (space, for recipient's name). TO COMMEMORATE THE DISCOVERY OF THE MECHANICAL EQUIVALENT OF HEAT. *D.* 57 mm. (By?)   *AR*   35   60
Awarded annually, being alternately presented by the Institution of Civil Engineers and Salford University for a paper dealing with the transformation of energy. James Prescott Joule (1818–89), physicist; observed that the quantity of heat capable of increasing the temperature of one pound of water by 1° Fahrenheit requires the expenditure of 772 foot-pounds of mechanical energy. He gave his name to a unit of work or energy.

1752   **Mayoralty of the City of London, 700th Anniversary 1889**

         £   £

Obv. Busts, crowned and draped, of RICHARD I. 1189 and VICTORIA 1889, facing towards each other in two open circular frames; a vignette of seven interlaced circles, above, and one of St. George and Dragon, below. TO COMMEMORATE THE 700TH ANNIVERSARY OF THE MAYORALTY OF THE CITY OF LONDON. MDCCCLXXXIX. *Rev.* Londinia seated, r., receives symbols of Mayoralty from St. Michael standing before her; above, radiate crown. Beyond, St. Paul's and the Tower. THE POWERS THAT BE ARE ORDAINED OF GOD   *Ex.* 1189–1889   *D.* 81 mm. By A. Kirkwood & Son. *BHM* 3377; *Welch* 23   *AE*   25   45

Issued by the Corporation of London. *See* No. 1245.

1753*   **Guy's Hospital Nursing Medal 1889**

Obv. Bust almost facing, draped. THOMAS GUY. FOUNDER OF GUY'S HOSPITAL 1720   *Rev.* TO (space, for recipient's name) CERTIFIED NURSE ON COMPLETING FIVE YEARS SERVICE in the centre. MEDAL INSTITUTED BY JOSHUA W. BUTTERWORTH F.S.A. GOVERNOR. 1889   *D.* 32 mm. By Adams. *BHM* 3376; *Storer* 7096. See **Plate 43**   *AR*   10   15
                                                              AE   4   7

Awarded in silver, usually with a suspension loop. Thomas Guy (1645?–1724), book dealer and philanthropist.

1754*   **Forth Bridge Opened 1890**

Obv. View of the cantilever bridge, shipping beneath. THE FORTH BRIDGE   *Ex.* 1890   *Rev.* THE BRIDGE WAS OPENED BY H.R.H. THE PRINCE OF WALES ON TUESDAY MARCH 4. 1890. LENGTH ONE MILE AND 1,005 YARDS. FROM THE BASE OF THE DEEPEST PIER TO THE TOP OF THE CANTILEVERS THE TOTAL HEIGHT IS 450 FEET, THE TWO LONGEST SPANS ARE EACH 1,710 FEET WIDE. THE BRIDGE WAS BEGUN IN DECEMBER 1882, AND ITS CONSTRUCTION HAS COST TWO MILLIONS & A QUARTER STERLING. *D.* 64 mm. By Messrs L. C. Lauer. *BHM* 3399; *Moyaux* 42. See **Plate 44**   *AE*   45   70

1755*   **William Blades 1890**

Obv. Head l. WILLIAM BLADES BORN 1824. APPRENTICED 1840. JUBILEE 1890   *Rev.* A printing press; MAY 1ST 1890 on a ribbon in field. IN. LABORE. FRUCTUS   *D.* 41 mm. By Heming & Co. *BHM* 3394. See **Plate 44**   *AR*   30   55
                                                               AE   15   22

William Blades (1824–90), printer and bibliographer; author of *Printer's Medals*, 1869.

1756   **Penny Postage Jubilee 1890**

Obv. A stamped envelope, inscribed POST OFFICE JUBILEE OF UNIFORM PENNY POSTAGE AT SOUTH KENSINGTON MUSEUM, 2ND JULY, 1890.: stage-coach the NORTH MAIL MAKING FOR HIGHGATE 1790 AT 8 MILES AN HOUR, above; a train THE NORTH MAIL 1890, APPROACHING CARLISLE AT 48 MILES AN HOUR., below. On either side are two figures displaying postal rates in 1840, l., and 1890, r. In the field, around the envelope: bust of Victoria, crowned and veiled, above; V R crowned, on either side; Royal arms, below. JUBILEE 2ND JULY 1890   *Rev.* An envelope in the centre, inscribed W. MULREADY. R.A. POSTAGE ONE PENNY JOHN THOMPSON. In the field, around the envelope: VR crowned, on either side; draped bust almost facing, of ROWLAND HILL ORIGINATOR OF THE PENNY POSTAGE SYSTEM, above; rose, thistle and shamrock, 1840, below. *D.* 65 mm. By Messrs L. C. Lauer. *BHM* 3407

      AR   80   150
      AE   35   65
      WM   20   40
      Al.   25   45

This elaborate medal was struck from several dies, each showing slight variances. Rowland Hill (1795–1879), originator of the 'penny post' and a postal authority. John Thompson (1785–1866), wood-engraver, cut the relief on brass of William Mulready's design for the envelope.

1757   **Charles Roach Smith 1890**

Obv. Bust l., of Roach Smith, draped. *Rev.* TO CHARLES ROACH SMITH F.S.A. FROM FELLOW ANTIQUARIES AND FRIENDS IN RECOGNITION OF LIFELONG SERVICES TO ARCHAEOLOGY 1890   *D.* 57 mm. By J. H. Pinches. *BHM* 3396   *AR*   35   55
                                                               AE   12   20

Charles Roach Smith (1807–90), antiquary and founder-member of the British Archaeological Association. This medal, in silver, was presented to him by the Society of Antiquaries just three days before he died. Roach Smith was a frequent contributor to the *Numismatic Chronicle*, journal of the [Royal] Numismatic Society of London, and was the first recipient of their medal (No. 1700). A medal dated 1858 honours his archaeological work in preserving the Roman walls of Dax, the Roman Acquae Tarbellicae, in France.

1758   **Royal Visit to Llandudno 1890**

Obv. Bust r., draped, seen partially from behind. TO COMMEMORATE THE VISIT OF ELIZABETH QUEEN OF ROUMANIA TO LLANDUDNO. SEPT. 1890   *Rev.* NIHIL SINE DEO within a wreath. *D.* 32 mm. By W. Mayler?   *AR*   15   25
                                                    AE   4   7

Pauline Elisabeth Ottilie Luise (1843–1916), Queen of Roumania 1881–1916; writer under the pseudonym Carmen Sylva. This medal has the name W. Mayler in large letters below the wreath; this may be an incorrect spelling of W. Mayer, engraver.

1759   **Royal Asiatic Society, Burton Medal 1890**

Obv. Bust l., draped. SIR. RICHARD. F. BURTON. K.C.M.G. 1821–1890. *Rev.* PRESENTED TO (space, for recipient's name) RICHARD BURTON MEMORIAL MEDAL within a wreath. *D.* 53 mm. By   *AR*   —   35

H. W. Page.   £   £

Struck and awarded from *c.*1920, no more than triennially, in gilt silver for work in Asiatic exploration or research. Richard Burton (1821–90), explorer; Orientalist and scholar.

1760   **Electric Exhibition, Edinburgh 1890**

Obv. Magnet, inscribed ΔγNAMAI on its keep, discharging an electric current. INTERNATIONAL ELECTRIC EXHIBITION EDINBURGH. 1890. *Rev.* Industry seated, l., amidst bridge, locomotive and other attributes; beyond, Edinburgh. *D.* 51 mm. By A. Kirkwood & Son. *BHM* 3401

	VF	*EF*
AV	400	500
AR	22	35
AE	10	15

A prize medal awarded in silver and bronze.

1761   **Prince Albert Victor of Wales, Visit to India 1890**

Obv. Bust almost facing, uniformed. HIS ROYAL HIGHNESS PRINCE ALBERT VICTOR *Rev.* IN COMMEMORATION OF THE VISIT OF HIS ROYAL HIGHNESS PRINCE ALBERT VICTOR OF WALES TO INDIA 1889–1890, within a wreath. Above, Prince's crest and motto; below, a Bengal lion. *D.* 36 mm. By W. Mayer. *BHM* 3391

	VF	*EF*
AR	18	30
AE	5	8

1762   **Royal Mint, Visit of Prince Henry of Battenberg 1890**

Obv. Head l., diademed. VICTORIA REGINA ET IMPERATRIX *Rev.* H.R.H. PRINCE HENRY OF BATTENBERG, K.G. VISITED THE ROYAL MINT 19 NOVEMBER 1890, within a wreath. *D.* 36 mm. By L. C. Wyon. *BHM* 3393

	VF	*EF*
AR	—	100

The obverse was also used to commemorate the Mint visits of the Prince and Princess of Saxe-Meiningen 1883, Crown Prince of Portugal 1883, and the Duchess of Albany in 1890.

1763   **Royal Geographical Society, Stanley Medal 1890**

Obv. Bust l., draped; MDCCCXC. behind. H M STANLEY PRESENTED BY THE ROYAL GEOGRAPHICAL SOCIETY *Rev.* Africa seated r., in elephant head-dress, empties waters of the Congo and Nile from two vases; beyond, lake and mountains. CONGO NILE RVWENZORI 1887–1889 *D.* 124 mm. Cast. By E. Hallé. *BHM* 3410; *Atwood* 11

	VF	*EF*
AE	—	220

Examples of this medal were presented to members of Stanley's Emin Pasha relief expedition on their return in 1890, and to the families of those that had died. A reduced 75 mm. version was also made.

1764   **City and Guilds of London Institute *c.*1890**

Obv. Bust l. H.R.H. THE PRINCE OF WALES K.G. PRESIDENT *Rev.* TECHNOLOGICAL EXAMINATION on a central plaque. Above, City of London arms, and a ribbon (blank, for the grade). + CITY AND GUILDS OF LONDON INSTITUTE + TECHNICAL EDUCATION *D.* 51 mm. By L. C. Wyon. *Hocking* 220/35–7

	VF	*EF*
AR	12	20
AE	5	8

See No. 1684.

1765   **St. Stephen's School, Westminster: Burdett-Coutts Medal, *c.*1890**

Obv. Bust r., draped. ANGELA GEORGINA BURDETT COUTTS *Rev.* FOR MISSING NO ATTENDANCE in the centre. ST. STEPHEN'S SCHOOL WESTMINSTER *D.* 37 mm. By Jones & Co. *D & W* 259/416

	VF	*EF*
AR	10	15
AE	3	5

Usually found awarded in silver with a suspension loop. Angela Georgina Burdett-Coutts (1814–1906), philanthropist; daughter of Francis Burdett. In 1865 she proposed the establishment of small village schools.

1766   **Surgeons' Hall (Edinburgh) *c.*1890**

Obv. Shield decorated with a cadaver and surgical implements, upon ribbon with motto. Caduceus above. SCHOOL. OF. MEDICINE. SURGEONS'. HALL. EDINBURGH. *Rev.* A wreath (space within, for recipient's name). *D.* 49 mm. By A. Kirkwood & Son. *Storer* 5869

	VF	*EF*
AR	20	35
AE	8	15

Awarded in silver and bronze.

1767   **Royal Naval Exhibition, London 1891**

Obv. IN COMMEMORATION OF THE ROYAL NAVAL EXHIBITION PATRON H.M. THE QUEEN 1891 within a wreath. *Rev.* View of the Eddystone Lighthouse; beyond, two ships on an open sea. *Ex.* H.M.S. VICTORY 1805 H.M.S. CAMPERDOWN 1891 *D.* 38 mm. By A. E. Warner. *BHM* 3419; *MH* 1919, 811

	VF	*EF*
AR	15	22
AE	5	8
WM	1	3

The exhibition was held on Chelsea Embankment and lasted for six months.

1768   **Wilhelm II, Visit to the City of London 1891**

Obv. Busts three-quarters r., conjoined, of the Empress, draped, and Emperor, helmeted and uniformed. GULIELMUS II IMPERATOR ET REX *Rev.* Londinia, leaning against a stone balustrade of the Embankment, indicates to Prussia, seated beside her, shipping on the Thames, beyond, with St. Paul's Cathedral on the opposite bank. At their feet, stone facia inscribed JULY 10TH 1891 (incuse). *D.* 80 mm. By Elkington & Co. *BHM* 3412; *Welch* 24

	VF	*EF*
AE	25	48

Issued by the Corporation of London (*see* No. 1245). Friedrich Wilhelm Viktor Albert (1859–1941), Wilhelm II, King of Prussia 1888–1918; grandson of Queen Victoria. Princess Augusta Victoria (1858–1921), of Schleswig-Holstein-Sonderburg-Augustenburg.

			£	£
1769	**Henry Irving 1891** *Obv.* Bust of Irving l., draped. *Rev.* HENRY IRVING 1891 *D.* 60 mm. [By Messrs L. C. Lauer] *BHM* 3416; *Parkes Weber* 132; *Svarstad* 112	AR AE *Al.*	35 12 15	60 20 25
1770*	**Joseph Moore 1891** *Obv.* Bust three-quarters l., draped. JOSEPH MOORE *Rev.* THIS MEDAL WAS ENGRAVED, AT THE EARNEST REQUEST OF HIS FAMILY AND MANY FRIENDS, BY JOSEPH MOORE IN HIS 75TH YEAR 1891 *D.* 51 mm. By J. Moore. *BHM* 3417. *See* **Plate 44** Joseph Moore (1817–92), medallist and die-sinker; formerly in partnership with J. Allen (Allen & Moore).	AR AE	25 10	40 15
1771	**Joseph Edgar Boehm 1891** *Obv.* Bust r., draped; behind, sculptor's tools. SIR EDGAR. J. BOEHM. BARONET. R.A. MDCCCLXXXXI. SC. Without reverse. *D.* 117 mm. Cast. By E. Lantéri. *BHM* 3414; *Parkes* *Weber* 258a; *Forrer* VII/533 Sir Joseph Edgar Boehm (1834–90), sculptor and medallist; son of the Viennese medallist Josef Daniel Boehm.	AE	—	50
1772	**Death of Albert Victor, Duke of Clarence & Avondale 1892** *Obv.* Bust facing, uniformed. H.R.H: THE. DUKE. OF. CLARENCE. & AVONDALE *Rev.* IN MEMORIAM DIED AT SANDRINGHAM JAN. 14. 1892 within a wreath. *D.* 24 mm. (By?) *BHM* 3429	AE	2	4
1773	**Ulster Unionist Convention 1892** *Obv.* Hibernia standing, beside lion, displays a pennant inscribed 17 JUNE 1892; a harp at her side. ULSTER UNIONIST CONVENTION *Ex.* Spray of shamrock. *Rev.* Shields of Ireland, England and Scotland upon a wreath of rose, thistle and shamrock. A crown, above; shield of Ulster, below. QUIS SEPARABIT 1892 *D.* 38 mm. By Gibson & Co. *BHM* 3433 Bronze examples frequently occur gilt.	AR AE	15 4	25 7
1774	**Baptist Missionary Society, Centenary 1892** *Obv.* Exterior view of the mission house. BAPTIST MISSION CENTENARY 1792–1892 *Ex.* THE HOUSE AT KETTERING IN WHICH THE BAPTIST MISSIONARY SOCIETY WAS FORMED OCT 2ND 1792 *Rev.* Four vignettes containing views of missionary stations at INDIA AFRICA CHINA and the WEST INDIES; symbols of EMANCIPATION around. CAREY FULLER MARSHMAN WARD *D.* 45 mm. (By?) *Taylor* 40c Several medals commemorate the Society's centenary. Andrew Fuller (1754–1815), theologian and missionary. Joshua Marshman (1768–1837), orientalist and missionary. William Ward (1769–1823), missionary.	AR AE WM	25 12 3	40 18 8
1775	**Death of Alfred, Lord Tennyson 1892** *Obv.* Bust of Tennyson three-quarters r., wearing a beret and draped. *Rev.* TENNYSON *D.* 60 mm. [By Messrs L. C. Lauer] *Parkes Weber* 133 Alfred Tennyson, 1st Baron Tennyson (1809–92), poet.	AR AE *Al.*	35 12 15	60 20 25
1776	**Trinity College Dublin, Tercentenary Medal 1892** *Obv.* Busts l., conjoined, of Elizabeth I, wearing bandeau and ruff, and Victoria, crowned, veiled and draped. AB ELIZABETHA AD VICTORIAM 1592 1892 *Rev.* Armorial shield of the College between rose and portcullis. COLL. SS. TRINITATIS. IVXTA. DVBLIN. CCC. ANNOS FLORET. MDCCCXCII *D.* 63 mm. By E. Johnson. *BHM* 3438; *Went* 1978, 147 Awarded in gold, silver and bronze.	AV AR AE	800 35 12	1000 55 20
1777	**St. Thomas' Hospital, Bristowe Medal 1892** *Obv.* Bust l., draped. JOHN SYER BRISTOWE M.D. F.R.S. *Rev.* Student seated, r., in a pathology laboratory, examining a pathological specimen(?) held in his hand. Above, armorial shield. *Ex.* ST THOMAS'S HOSPITAL *D.* 73 mm. By A. Wyon. *BHM* 3475; *Storer* 480 First struck in 1894, and awarded annually for pathology and morbid anatomy, usually in silver. Subscriptions were collected on Bristowe's retirement in 1892 and used to fund this medal. John Syer Bristowe (1827–95), physician.	AR AE	60 25	90 45
1778	**Centenary of Portland Wesleyan Chapel 1892** *Obv.* Half-length figure of John Wesley, standing at pulpit. THE BEST OF ALL, GOD IS WITH US. *Rev.* PORTLAND WESLEYAN CHAPEL KINGSDOWN BRISTOL CENTENARY COMMEMORATION 1892 R. WALLIS BOYNS MINISTER IN CHARGE. *D.* 52 mm. (By?) Several Wesleyan chapels and schools have been recorded on medals, including those at Peel 1863, Cheadle 1872, Banbury 1883, Newcastle-on-Tyne 1890, Oldham 1890, Padiham 1897.	AR AE WM	30 15 8	50 22 12
1779	**Marriage of Princess Marie and Prince Ferdinand 1893** *Obv.* Busts l., conjoined and draped. FERDINAND PRINCIPE MOSTENITOR AL ROMANIEI MARIA PRINCIPESA DE MAREA BRITANIA SI IRLANDA *Rev.* Cupid crowns the shields of the couple, draped with a ribbon inscribed 29 DECEMBRE 1892 10 IANUARIE 1893 *D.* 51 mm. By A. Scharff. *BHM* 3453; *Parkes Weber* 206b The date of 29 December 1892 is that according to the Greek Church. Princess Marie Alexandra Victoria (1875–1938), eldest daughter of Alfred, Duke of Edinburgh. Crown Prince Ferdinand of Hohenzollern (1865–1927), King of Roumania 1914–27.	AR AE	40 18	60 25

1780   **Marriage of Duke and Duchess of York 1893**
Obv. Busts l., conjoined, she draped. T.R.H. THE DUKE AND DUCHESS OF YORK.   *AE*   25   45
MDCCCXCIII *Rev.* The couple, advancing in a triumphal car driven by Cupid and drawn by
two horses, l., approach an archway, inscribed FELICITAS G M, and are welcomed by
Londinia. *Ex.* JULY 6. 1893. *D.* 76 mm. By G. G. Adams. *BHM* 3452; *Welch* 25

Issued by the Corporation of London. *See* No. 1245. Prince George of Wales, Duke of York (1865–1936), George V
1910–36; second son of Edward, Prince of Wales and Alexandra. Princess Victoria Mary (1867–1953), only daughter of
Prince Francis, Duke of Teck. More than twelve medals commemorate the marriage.

1781   ——
Obv. Busts draped, of H.R.H. PRINCE GEORGE DUKE OF YORK K.G. and H.S.H. PRINCESS VICTORIA   *AR*   35   60
MARY OF TECK, each in an oval frame linked by a monogrammed heart G M, almost facing   *AE*   12   20
towards each other. *Rev.* Britannia attending the couple, who stand at an altar, their hands
clasped. MARRIED. AT. CHAPEL. ROYAL. S.ᵀ JAMES'S. PALACE. 6. JULY. 1893   *Ex.* Shields of the
couple. *D.* 51 mm. By Spink & Son. *BHM* 3446; *RWE* 176
The medal also occurs with another reverse.

1782   ——
Obv. Busts l., conjoined and draped. H.S.H. PRINCESS VICTORIA MARY H.R.H. GEORGE DUKE OF   *AR*   30   55
YORK   *Rev.* MARRIED JULY 6ᵀᴴ 1893 between two festoons. Crowns, above; monogram G V,   *AE*   8   15
below. *D.* 38 mm. By J. Moore. *BHM* 3444   *WM*   2   4

1783*   **Christian IX and Louise, Visit to the City of London 1893**
Obv. Busts r., conjoined and draped; she diademed, he uniformed. CHRISTIANUS IX ET LOUISE   *AE*   25   45
D: G: DANIÆ V: G: REX ET REGINA +   *Rev.* Londinia seated, l., almost facing, beside a
pedestal decorated with the Danish shield, r., holds a streaming pennant inscribed WELCOME
CHRISTIAN IX TO LONDON Beyond, façade of the Guildhall. *Ex.* 8ᵀᴴ JULY 1893   *D.* 75 mm. By
F. Bowcher. *BHM* 3454; *Welch* 26. *See* **Plate 44**

Issued by the Corporation of London (*see* No. 1245). Christian IX (1818–1906), King of Denmark 1863–1906. Princess
Louise (1817–98), daughter of William, Prince of Hesse-Cassel.

1784   **North Cornwall Railway Opened 1893**
Obv. A platform and nameplate, inscribed CAMELFORD BOSCASTLE AND TINTAGEL; beyond,   *WM*   12   18
perimeter fencing. NORTH CORNWALL RAILWAY OPENED AUGUST 1893 *Ex.* MAY WE
PROSPER *Rev.* Cornish shield and motto. *D.* 39 mm. (By?) *BHM* 3462

1785   **Winchester College, 500th Anniversary 1893**
Obv. William of Wykeham seated, holding crozier and model of chapel, surrounded by   *AR*   35   55
scholars. THIS MEDAL WAS STRUCK IN COMMEMORATIO[N] OF THE FIVE HVNDREDTH   *AE*   12   25
ANNIVERSARY 1393 1893 MANNERS MAKYTH MAN WILLIAM WYKEHAM *Rev.* Chapel and
College buildings in a landscape; shield r., and motto STET FORTVNA DOMVS on ribbon,
above. *D.* 76 mm. By G. Frampton. *BHM* 3464; *Taylor* 27*a*
Examples in bronze are found silver-plated.

1786   **Great Yarmouth Golf Club, Blackheath Medal 1893**
Obv. Shield upon crossed golf clubs; below, ribbon inscribed GREAT YARMOUTH GOLF CLUB   *AR*   30   55
and two balls. THE BLACKHEATH MEDAL *Rev.* Two golf clubs in a saltire, quartered by a
crown, thistle, two figures, and an emblem; motto below. PRESENTED BY THE ROYAL
BLACKHEATH GOLF CLUB. 1893. *D.* 58 mm. By Baddeley Bros.
Usually found with a suspension clasp and loop. Various medals were awarded by golf clubs throughout Britain
c.1880–1930.

1787   **Royal Mint, Visit of the Duke of York 1894**
Obv. Bust l., diademed, veiled and draped. VICTORIA. DEI. GRA. BRITT. REGINA. FID. DEF. IND.   *AR*   —   250
IMP. *Rev.* H.R.H. THE DUKE OF YORK, K.G. VISITED THE ROYAL MINT 25 APRIL 1894 within a
wreath, crowned. *D.* 39 mm. By T. Brock. *BHM* 3465; *Hocking* 240/60
The obverse is that of the currency crown (*Seaby* 3937); it also occurs on a medal recording the visit of Queen Wilhelmina
of Holland to the Mint in 1895.

1788   **Manchester Ship Canal Opened 1894**
Obv. Bust l., veiled. OPENED BY H.M. QUEEN VICTORIA MAY 21, 1894. in a central circle.   *AR*   30   45
Around, a circular inscription enumerating details TOTAL LENGTH OF CANAL 36 MILES . . . 8000   *AE*   12   20
TONS OF CEMENT *Rev.* Shipping on the waterway. SUCCESS TO THE SHIP CANAL AND THE   *WM*   5   8
THIRLMERE WATER SUPPLY. *Ex.* Foul anchor in a wreath. *D.* 36 mm. (By A. Miesch?)

1789   **Young Men's Christian Association, Jubilee 1894**
Obv. Bust l., draped. GEORGE WILLIAMS 1894 FOUNDER IN 1844 OF THE Y.M.C.A. *Rev.* An open   *AR*   12   20
bible, radiate, within a wreath. YOUNG MEN'S CHRISTIAN ASSOCIATION. JUBILEE 6 JUNE   *AE*   6   10

1894 *D.* 51 mm. By A. Wyon. *BHM* 3479; *Forrer* VI/579		£	£

George Williams (1821–1905) evangelist and advocate of temperance; founded the Y.M.C.A. as a mutual improvement and young men's missionary society. This medal also occurs with another reverse, which served as a prize of the Association.

1790   Tower Bridge Opened 1894

Obv. Busts l., conjoined and draped, of Queen Victoria, crowned, between the Prince and Princess of Wales. *Rev.* View of the bridge, its bascules raised and a steam-yacht passing through; above, Bridge-House Estates badge. TOWER BRIDGE OPENED 30TH JUNE 1894 *Ex.* ON BEHALF OF HER MAJESTY QUEEN VICTORIA BY HRH THE PRINCE OF WALES City of London shield in centre. *D.* 76 mm. By F. Bowcher. *BHM* 3476; *Taylor* 225a   AE   30   55

Issued by the Corporation of London (*see* No. 1245). The bridge was designed by Horace Jones; the consulting engineer was John Wolfe Barry.

1791*   William Gladstone, Four Ministries 1894

Obv. Bust r., draped. WILLIAM. EWART. GLADSTONE. *Rev.* PRIME MINISTER OF THE UNITED KINGDOM OF GREAT BRITAIN AND IRELAND Below, scrolls each inscribed with a term of office 1868–74 1880–85 1886 1892–94, upon branches. *D.* 47 mm. By A. Wyon. *BHM* 3469. *See* **Plate 44**   AR   22   35 / AE   8   15

1792   Members of Parliament 1894

Obv. Bust of Gladstone, three-quarters l., draped. *Rev.* Fifty-line inscription listing MEMBERS OF THE HOUSE OF COMMONS YEAR 1894 *D.* 95 mm. By Messrs L. C. Lauer. *BHM* 3468; *Parkes Weber* 142a   AR   150   280 / AE   50   80

A companion piece to No. 1439.

1793   Earl of Elgin, Viceroy's Medal 1894

Obv. Busts l., conjoined and draped. THE EARL OF ELGIN G.M.S.I. G.M.I.E. VICEROY OF INDIA * THE COUNTESS OF ELGIN * 1894 * *Rev.* Arms, supporters, motto, etc. PRESENTED. BY. HIS. EXCELLENCY. THE. GOVERNOR. GENERAL *D.* 51 mm. By A. Wyon. *BHM* 3467   AV   —   — / AR   50   80 / AE   10   15

Victor Alexander Bruce, 9th Earl of Elgin (1849–1917), statesman. Presented for services during the tenure of office. Uniform medals were awarded by successive Viceroys. *See* H. Pownall, 'Viceroys' Medals', *OMRS* 1980, 3–24; 1985, 27–35.

1794   Royal Anthropological Institute, Huxley Medal 1895

Obv. Bust l., draped. THOMAS HENRY HUXLEY B: 1825 D: 1895 *Rev.* Female figure of Progress, l., holds oil lamp and wreath above a pedestal, inscribed ΕΠΙΣΤΗΜΗ *D.* 63 mm. By F. Bowcher [*obv.* after E. O. Ford] *BHM* 3488; *Storer* 1734   AE   20   35

Awarded annually in bronze from 1900. Thomas Henry Huxley (1825–95), eminent biologist.

1795   Severn Street School, Jubilee 1895

Obv. Bust r., draped; JOSEPH STURGE, below. JUBILEE OF THE SEVERN STREET AND PRIORY FIRST DAY ADULT SCHOOLS 13 OCTOBER 1845–95. *Rev.* Two pupils seated before a teacher. FAITH HOPE LOVE BUT THE GREATEST OF THESE IS LOVE LET BROTHERLY LOVE CONTINUE *D.* 45 mm. By J. Moore, *obv.* after A. Watson. *BHM* 3492   AR   20   35 / AE   6   10 / WM   3   5

1796*   Four Generations of the Royal Family 1895

Obv. Victoria, seated in the centre, flanked by standing figures of Edward, Prince of Wales and George, Duke of York, holds her great-grandson Prince Edward. FOUR GENERATIONS OF THE BRITISH ROYAL FAMILY. *Rev.* Shields of Britain upon a decorated scroll; above, radiate crown. 1895 *D.* 38 mm. By H. Grueber. *BHM* 3480; *Parkes Weber* 251a. See **Plate 44**   Al.   —   8

A hollow 'shell' comprising two plates of metal joined at the edge by a flange. A number of similar medals of the Royal Family and national events were produced at this time. Prince Edward (1894–1972), eldest son of George (V), Duke of York. Abdicated in 1936 as the uncrowned Edward VIII; later, Duke of Windsor.

1797   *Challenger* Expedition 1895

Obv. A knight standing, l., points to the gauntlet he has thrown down; behind, an upright trident from which unfurls a ribbon, inscribed REPORT ON THE SCIENTIFIC RESULTS OF THE CHALLENGER EXPEDITION 1886.95 *Rev.* Neptune standing beside an oval framed bust of Athena, l., and an owl. Below, two mermaids display a ribbon, inscribed VOYAGE OF H.M.S. CHALLENGER 1872–76 *D.* 75 mm. Cast. [By B. Rhind after W. S. Black] *BHM* 3487   AE   —   45

An expedition to examine conditions of the great ocean basins, and the direction of their currents. Awarded to naval officers on the expedition, contributors to the report on the scientific results, and to members of the civilian scientific staff. *See* the magazine *Nature*, 1895, August 417. The medal was cast in Paris.

1798   Royal College of Physicians, Bisset Hawkins Medal 1895

Obv. Bust facing, draped; 1796 1895 either side. FRANCIS. BISSET HAWKINS. M.D. F.R.C.P. *Rev.* Aesculapius seated, r., greets Hercules, standing. OB SEDVLO CVLTAM MEDICINAE CIVILIS DISCIPLINAM *D.* 76 mm. By F. Bowcher. *BHM* 3491; *Storer* 1484   AE   15   25

Awarded for a contribution to sanitary science. Francis Bisset Hawkins (1796–1895), physician.

1799   **The Royal Society, Buchanan Medal 1895**

Obv. Head l. SIR GEORGE BUCHANAN M.D. F.R.C.P. F.R.S. *Rev.* Hygeia and attendant ward Death away from a prostrate body. IN SALVTEM PVBLICAM AVDACIA ET INDVSTRIA *Ex.* Staff and chalice. *D.* 55 mm. [By G. W. de Saulles] *Storer* 508; *Hocking* 215/11; *D & W* 159/454

	VF £	EF £
AV	600	700
AR	25	45
AE	10	15

George Buchanan (1831–95), physician. Subscriptions were collected on his retirement to found a medal, awarded triennially (first in 1897) in gold, for distinguished service in hygienic science.

1800   **Cardiff Photographic Society** *c.*1895

Obv. Female figure, camera on her lap, seated in a galley, inscribed Y. DDRAIG. COCH. A. DDRYR. GYCHWYN Beyond, ships at sea. CARDIFF PHOTOGRAPHIC SOCIETY *Ex.* EXHIBITION *Rev.* A wreath (space within, for recipient's name). *D.* 51 mm. (By?)

AR	20	35
AE	8	15

This period saw a huge growth of interest in photography; more than forty clubs and societies throughout Britain issued prize medals, *c.*1890–1930.

1801   **Lord Walsingham** *c.*1895

Obv. Bust r., draped. AUSP. THOMA. BAR. DE. WALSINGHAM. ACADEM. SUMMI. SENESCH. *Rev.* Animals in a sea and mountain landscape; above, heraldic shield. PROPTER. AUCTAM. NATURAE. SCIENTIAM *D.* 70 mm. By E. O. Ford.

AR	40	65
AE	20	35

Thomas de Grey, 6th Baron Walsingham (1843–1919), natural historian and sportsman. Bequeathed his library and collection of insects to the Natural History Museum.

1802   **Royal Geographical Society, Nansen Medal 1896**

Obv. Bust l., draped; FRIDTJOF NANSEN behind. A wreath around. PRESENTED BY THE ROYAL GEOGRAPHICAL SOCIETY. FOR ARCTIC EXPLORATION 1893–1896. *Rev.* Broadside view of Nansen's ship FRAM in sea ice. *Ex.* Arctic canoe and paddle. *D.* 69 mm. By A. Wyon. *MH* 1928, 328; *Poulsom* 86

AV	—	—
AR	75	120
AE	30	55

Fridtjof Nansen (1861–1930), Norwegian explorer, zoologist and statesman; awarded this medal in gold for his journey on the drifting *Fram*.

1803   **Robert Burns, Centenary 1896**

Obv. Bust three-quarters l., draped. ROBERT BURNS 1796–1896 *Rev.* A domed and columned monument. DUMFRIES. CENTENARY. CELEBRATION. *Ex.* JULY. 21ST. 1896. *D.* 44 mm. By Messrs J. Pinches

AR	12	20
AE	5	8
WM	2	4

1804   **School of Military Engineering, Haynes Medal 1896**

Obv. Bust three-quarters r., uniformed. CAPTAIN. A. E. HAYNES. R.E. 1861–96 *Rev.* Two figures standing on a pontoon bridge in a rugged landscape. FIELD. FORTIFICATION. S.M.E. *D.* 56 mm. By F. Bowcher. *Hocking* 210/3

AE	8	12

Awarded annually from 1902, in bronze, for a contribution to field-work. Alfred Ernest Haynes (1861–96), military engineer; killed during the assault on Makoni's stronghold in Mashonaland.

1805*   **Royal Astronomical Society, Herschel Medal 1896**

Obv. Bust r., draped. WILLIAM. HERSCHEL. MDCCXXXVIII. MDCCCXXII. *Rev.* Female figure standing upon globe. Around, the moon and Saturn amongst stars. ROYAL. ASTRONOMICAL. SOCIETY. JACKSON-GWILT. GIFT MDCCCXCVI *D.* 78 mm. Cast [By Messrs J. Pinches] *BHM* 3502. See **Plate 44**

AE	—	65

Awarded from 1897 in bronze for outstanding observational work, such as the discovery of new objects. It has been given at intervals of between three and seven years.

1806*   **William Morris 1896**

Obv. Head three-quarters l. WILLIAM MORRIS; field simulating a foliage-pattern wallpaper, rolled at the edge *Rev.* TILES FURNITURE BOOK DESIGN STAINED GLASS WALLPAPER ARCHITECTURE PROSE WRITING POLITICS TEXTILES POETRY, upon fragment of foliage-pattern wallpaper. A border simulating a book's spine and pages. *D.* 90 mm. Cast. [By R. Elderton] *The Medal* 6/42. See **Plate 44**

AE	—	22

Issued in 1985 by the British Art Medal Society (*see* No. 2141). William Morris (1834–96), artist and poet.

1807   **Geological Society of London, Prestwich Medal 1896**

Obv. Bust l., draped. JOSEPH PRESTWICH BORN 1812 DIED 1896 *Rev.* Representation of the fossil Arachnid ('Prestwichiana'). THE. GEOLOGICAL. SOCIETY. OF. LONDON. TO. (space, for recipient's name). *D.* 57 mm. By F. Bowcher, *obv.* after H. Pinker. *BHM* 3501; *Woodward* 254–5

AV	600	800
AE	15	28

Awarded triennially from 1900 in gold, and latterly bronze, for stratigraphy or physical geology. Joseph Prestwich (1812–96), geologist and wine merchant.

1808   **London Missionary Society, Centenary 1896**

Obv. A fully-rigged ship. *Ex.* THE SHIP DUFF SAILED FOR THE SOUTH SEAS 1796 *Rev.* Four vignettes, each containing an unidentified missionary station. NEW GUINEA. WEST INDIES. CHINA. SOUTH SEAS. AFRICA. INDIA. MADAGASCAR. MONGOLIA. *D.* 45 mm. (By?)

AR	20	35
AE	8	12
WM	3	5

				£	£

1809   **Conquest of Trinidad, Centenary 1897**
Obv. Bust three-quarters l., uniformed. SIR RALPH ABERCROMBY   *Rev.* Ships at anchor in mole of Port of Spain; hills beyond. TO COMMEMORATE THE CENTENARY OF THE CONQUEST OF TRINIDAD BY THE BRITISH 1797   *Ex.* MISCERIQUE PROBAT POPULOS ET FOEDERA JUNGI   *D. a* 48 mm.; *b* 39 mm. (By?) *BHM* 3623; *MH* 1919, 457

      a AR   25   40
      AE   12   22
      b AV   350   550

1810   **Centenary of the Last Foreign Invasion of Britain, 1897**
Obv. Column of women dressed in Welsh national costume, holding crooks and pitchforks, descending a cliff; beyond, ships at sea in distance. A LADDO A LEDDIR. 1797 * FISHGUARD * 1897. *Rev.* 1897 CENTENARY OF THE LAST FOREIGN INVASION OF BRITAIN 1797 IN COMMEMORATION OF THE SURRENDER OF THE FRENCH ON CARREG WASTAD POINT PENGAER FEB^Y. 24TH 1797 within a wreath   *D.* 39 mm. By H. B. Sale. *BHM* 3608

      AE   15   25
      WM   8   12

1811   **Augustus W. Franks 1897**
Obv. Bust l., draped; SIR AVG. WOLLASTON FRANKS. KCB. PSA below. In field, 1826 1897 (incuse); below, shield and crest. Without reverse. *D.* 40 mm. by 52 mm. Rectangular, cast. By C. J. Prætorius. *BHM* 3607; *The Medal 6*, 10/7

      AE   —   60

Augustus Wollaston Franks (1826–97), archaeologist, medievalist and numismatist; co-editor of *Medallic Illustrations*. This piece also occurs in another size.

1812   **Blackwall Tunnel Opened 1897**
Obv. Bust l., crowned, laureate, veiled and draped; IN COMMEMORATIONEM ANNI REGNI LX in the field. VICTORIA. DEI. GRA: BRITT: REGINA. FID: DEF: IND: IMP MDCCCXCVII   *Rev.* Cross-sectional view of tunnel; carriages and pedestrians within. BLACKWALL TUNNEL. CONSTRUCTED BY THE LONDON COUNTY COUNCIL AND OPENED BY H.R.H. THE PRINCE OF WALES ON BEHALF OF H.M. THE QUEEN MAY XXII MDCCCXCVII   *D.* 76 mm. By F. Bowcher. *BHM* 3615

      AR   80   140
      AE   28   50
      WM   12   22

1813   **Nelson and the *Foudroyant* 1897**
Obv. Bust facing, uniformed, head three-quarters l. HORATIO VISCOUNT NELSON. *Ex.* BORN, 29TH SEPTEMBER, 1758. DIED. 21ST OCTOBER, 1805   *Rev.* Ship at anchor, without rigging. "FOUDROYANT". LORD NELSON'S "FLAGSHIP". *Ex.* COMMENCED BUILDING, 1789. LAUNCHED AT PLYMOUTH, APRIL, 1798. WRECKED AT BLACKPOOL JUNE 16TH. 1897 MEDAL STRUCK FROM COPPER OF VESSEL AFTER BREAKING UP   *D.* 37 mm. (By?) *BHM* 3613; *MH* 1919, 537

      AE   3   5

1814   **Diamond Jubilee of Queen Victoria 1897**
Obv. Bust l., crowned, veiled and draped. VICTORIA REGINA   *Rev.* Britannia seated beside British lion holds a radiate crown aloft. IN COMMEMORATIONEM ANNI REGNI LX 1837–1897   *Ex.* GOD BLESS OUR QUEEN   *D.* 78 mm. [after T. Brock] *BHM* 3581

      Pb.   12   20

Examples occur bronzed, silvered or gilt, the obverse with a stippled field. The Jubilee is commemorated on well over one hundred national and local medals (*see* No. 1822); many were also struck in the colonies, as well as a few by non-Commonwealth countries.

1815 *   ——
Obv. Bust l., crowned, veiled and draped. IN. HONOREM. VICTORIAE R: ET. I: EXCUD: CUR: CIVITAS. LOND: *Rev.* Londinia, with attendants, presents a garland to Britannia, seated before her on a dais. FROM MY HEART I THANK MY BELOVED PEOPLE MAY GOD BLESS THEM V.R.I. *Ex.* 1837–1897   *D.* 76 mm. By F. Bowcher. *BHM* 3510. *See* **Plate 45**

      AE   25   45

Issued by the Corporation of London. (*See* No. 1245).

1816   ——
Obv. As No. 1812. *Rev.* Royal arms in the centre; below, THE BRITISH EMPIRE A.D. 1897 and a vignette containing four clasped hands, inscribed PEACE LOVE AND UNION. A border with fifty shields of British Colonies and Protectorates, each identified. *D.* 76 mm. By F. Bowcher. *BHM* 3511

      AR   70   120
      AE   15   25
      WM   12   20

1817   ——
Obv. Bust l., crowned, veiled and draped. VICTORIA ANNVM REGNI SEXAGESIMVM FELICITER CLAVDIT XX IVN. MDCCCXCVII. *Rev.* Young head of the Queen, l., dividing inscription LONGI-TVDO DIERVM IN DEXTERAEIVS ET IN SINISTRA GLORIA. Below, 1837 upon branch tied with ribbon. *D. a* 56 mm.; *b* 26 mm. [By G. W. de Saulles], after T. Brock/[W. Wyon] *BHM* 3506; *Wollaston* 40

      a AV   600   700
      AR   15   22
      AE   3   5
      b AV   90   110
      AR   2   3

The official Royal Mint issue.

1818   ——
Obv. Bust l., crowned, laureate, veiled and draped. VICTORIA D: G: BRITT: REGINA F: D: IND: IMP: IN. COMMEMOR. AN. REG. SEXAGESIMI MDCCCXCVII   *Rev.* Steam-ship advancing, l. *Ex.* Vignette with a locomotive within a life-buoy, inscribed BRITISH COMMERCE 1837 1897; a

      AR   25   45
      AE   10   18
      WM   4   7

		VF	EF

globe either side. *D*. 51 mm. By F. Bowcher. *BHM* 3515   £   £

This obverse is coupled with other reverses commemorating the Jubilee: *a* Prime Ministers 1837–97. *b* Primates of England 1837–97. *c* The Army & Navy. *d* Exhibition of the Victorian Era. *e* Royal Family. See *SNC* 1897, 2155/2–6.

1819 ——

Obv. Conjoined young and old heads of the Queen, l. VICTORIA REG: IMP: 1837 1897   *Rev*.   AR   25   48
Royal arms. UNITED IN LOYALTY, IN PROSPERITY, IN ENTERPRISE within a central frame.   AE   12   22
Around, various flora separating fifteen compartments each inscribed with a British colony
or protectorate. *D*. 47 mm. By G. G. Adams. *BHM* 3507

1820 ——

Obv. Bust l., crowned, laureate, veiled and draped. VICTORIA QUEEN AND EMPRESS In field, TO   AR   20   35
COMMEMORATE THE 60TH YEAR OF HER MAJESTY'S REIGN   *Rev*. Four oval cameo portraits,   AE   8   12
facing, of H.I.M QUEE[N] VICTORIA / H.R.H. PRI[NCE] OF WALES / H.R.H. DUKE OF YORK / H.R.H.   WM   3   5
PR[INCE] EDWARD In the centre JUBILATE BRITANNI, on a scroll. MAY. GOD. PRESERVE. OUR.
QUEEN AND. THE. HEIRS. TO. THE. THRONE   *D*. 38 mm. By F. Bowcher. *BHM* 3529

This obverse is coupled with other reverses commemorating the Jubilee: *a* Victory upon globe. *b* Australia. *c* Canada. *d* Cape Colony. *e* India. *f* New Zealand. *g* Four longest reigns. *h* Peace. *i* Britons Rejoice. See *SNC* 1897, 2158/7–16.

1821 ——

Obv. Bust of the Queen, veiled, l. SEMPER HONOR, NOMENQUE TUUM LAUDESQUE MANEBUNT   AR   12   22
1837–1897. *Rev*. Flags of Great Britain and Argentina, crossed. IN COM. LX ANN. ACC.
VICTORIÆ BRITT. REG. IND. IMP. BUENOS AIRES. *D*. 34 mm. By J.D. (?)

One of a small number of non-Commonwealth medals which commemorate the Jubilee.

1822 ——

Obv. Bust l., crowned, veiled and draped. VICTORIA QUEEN AND EMPRESS. DIAMOND JUBILEE   AR   12   18
1897. *Rev*. Town shield. TEIGNMOUTH DIAMOND JUBILEE CELEBRATION. 1837–97. *D*. 32 mm.   AE   3   5
(By?)

A large number of localities throughout Britain celebrated the Jubilee with a medal; many are of local manufacture and used a portrait based on one of the national issues. They occur most frequently in white metal, pierced with a suspension loop, to be displayed during the festivities. Localities which issued medals include: Aston Manor, Belfast, Birmingham, Bournemouth, Bradford, Burnley, Coventry, Gloucester, Higham Ferrers, Ilkeston, Lancaster, Northampton, Nottingham, Rochdale, Sheffield, Southend, Stafford, Thornaby, Warrington, Windsor.

1823 **North Bridge, Edinburgh, Opened 1897**
Obv. Bust l., draped. RIGHT HONBLE SIR ANDREW MC DONALD LORD PROVOST 1897   *Rev*. Road   AR   45   70
bridge over railway lines, beneath which a train passes. NORTH BRIDGE EDINBURGH   AE   25   38
FOUNDATION STONE LAID 25 MAY 1896, OPENED 15. SEP. 1897   *D*. 64 mm. By A. Kirkwood &
Son. *BHM* 3619

1824 **Maidstone Typhoid Epidemic, Service Medal 1897**
Obv. Armorial shield with crest. MAIDSTONE. KENT. *Rev*. WITH GRATITUDE TO (space, for   AR   40   70
recipient's name) FOR LOVING SERVICES 1897 *D*. 32 mm. (By?) *Fearon* 348.9

Sometimes found with a suspension clasp and loop. The outbreak occurred in October 1897 and was attributed to bad water supply. A Maidstone epidemic fund was opened by the Mansion-House Funds and more than £27,000 raised.

1825 **Department of Science & Art, Queen's Medal 1897**
Obv. Bust l., crowned, veiled and draped. VICTORIA BY THE GRACE OF GOD QVEEN & EMPRESS   AV   500   600
1897   *Rev*. NATIONAL MEDAL FOR SVCCESS IN ART AWARDED BY THE DEPARTMENT OF SCIENCE   AR   18   25
AND ART within a wreath. *D*. 51 mm. By F. Bowcher.   AE   3   7
See No. 1511.

1826 **Theobald Wolfe Tone 1898**
Obv. Bust l., uniformed. THEOBALD WOLFE TONE 1798–1898   *Rev*. An Irish harp. .WHO FEARS   AE   18   25
TO SPEAK OF. 98. *D*. 33 mm. (By?)

Theobald Wolfe Tone (1763–98), Irish revolutionary; founder of the *United Irishman*. Captured by the British off Lough Swilly in 1798 and charged with treason, he was sentenced to death but committed suicide before the order was carried out.

1827 **Death of William Gladstone 1898**
Obv. Bust three-quarters l., draped. WILLIAM EWART GLADSTONE   *Rev*. Britannia stands   AE   6   10
mournfully beside a tomb, inscribed BORN DEC. 29TH – 1809 – DIED MAY 19TH 1898 Lion, shield   WM   2   4
and anchor in foreground. *D*. 39 mm. By H. B. Sale. *BHM* 3629

This medal also occurs with another reverse.

1828 **Imperial Penny Postage 1898**
Obv. Bust l., crowned and laureate; ROWLAND HILL and H. HEATON below, on two ribbons of   AR   30   50
a wreath. VICTORIA DEI: GRA: BRITT REG: IND: FID: IMP: *Rev*. Britannia hands a scroll to   AE   15   25
Neptune advancing, l., in a marine car; beyond globes of the two hemispheres. IMPERIAL
PENNY POSTAGE *Ex*. A.D. 1898 *D*. 31 mm. [By F. Bowcher] *BHM* 3638

Sir John Henniker Heaton (1848–1914), M.P. and postal reformer; his twelve-year campaign for a universal penny postage came to fruition on Christmas Day 1898.

			£	£

1829   **Joseph Hooker, Laudatory Medal 1898**
Obv. Bust l., draped, dividing inscription J.D.H. ÆT LXXX   *Rev.* TO SIR JOSEPH HOOKER M.D.   **AV**   —   —
R.N., G.C.S.I., C.B., D.C.L., L.L.D., P.P.R.S., F.L.S., F.G.S IN RECOGNITION OF HIS SERVICES TO   **AR**   55   80
SCIENCE FROM THE LINNEAN SOCIETY OF LONDON 1898 within a wreath. *D.* 76 mm. By F.   **AE**   20   35
Bowcher. *BHM* 3632; *Storer* 1596   **Pb.**   15   25

Joseph Dalton Hooker (1817–1911) botanist; collaborated with Darwin in research on his theory of natural selection. At an anniversary meeting of the Linnean Society he was presented with this medal in gold for having completed a survey of the flora of British India.

1830   **National Eisteddfod Association 1898**
Obv. Figure of the bard TALIESIN standing, r., in landscape playing a harp; cromlech   **AR**   40   70
(megalithic tomb) and sun on horizon. *Rev.* A dragon, curled into a ball. CYMDEITHAS. YR.   **AE**   20   35
EISTEDDFOD GENEDLAETHOL. THE. NATIONAL. EISTEDDFOD. ASSOCN. *D.* 75 mm. By W.
Goscombe John. *BHM* 3637; *Pearson* 49; *Forrer* III/78

Examples in silver are sometimes found awarded. Taliesin, Welsh bard of the 6th century (perhaps a mythical figure).

1831*   **S.S. *Maine* 1899**
Obv. Broadside view of S.S. MAINE, steamship. LENT TO BRITISH GOVᵗ FOR USE IN TRANSVAAL   **AR**   60   90
WAR BY PRES. OF ATLANTIC TRANSPORT COY   *Ex.* BERNARD N. BAKER ESQ 1899   *Rev.* FOR THE   **AE**   28   45
AMERICAN LADIES HOSPITAL SHIP FUND CHAIRMAN LADY R. CHURCHILL HON. SEC. MRS A. BLOW   **WM**   12   20
HON. TRES. MRS RONALDS in the centre, divided by the crossed flags of Britain and the United
States. FITTED AS HOSPITAL SHIP BY MESSRS FLETCHER SON & FEARNALL Lᵀᴰ LONDON   *D.*
45 mm. (By?) *BHM* 3650; *MH* 1919, 652; *Payne* 238. *See* **Plate 45**

1832   **Royal Military Academy, Armstrong Medal 1899**
Obv. Bust facing, draped, head l. COL: R.Y. ARMSTRONG. C.B. ROYAL. ENGINEERS. *Rev.* An   **AR**   60   90
upright hand issuing from a turreted crown grasps a winged thunderbolt. ARMSTRONG   **AE**   25   35
MEMORIAL PRIZE   *D.* 57 mm. By F. Bowcher. *Hocking* 210/5–6

Awarded in silver from 1902, to the Gentleman Cadet at the Royal Military Academy most proficient in electrical engineering. Colonel Robert Young Armstrong (1839–94).

1833   **Death of Thomas Edward Ellis 1899**
Obv. Bust l., draped; GANWYD CHWEFROR 16. 1859 HVNODD EBRILL 5. 1899 in the field.   **AE**   25   40
THOMAS. EDWARD ELLIS. *Rev.* House in a landscape. AHJER DYN YW EI GYNYSGAETH. *Ex.*
CYNLAS   *D.* 63 mm. By W. Goscombe John. *Pearson* 57

Thomas Edward Ellis (1859–99), politician; member of the Welsh Language Society.

1834   **George Stokes 1899**
Obv. Bust l., draped. GEORGE GABRIEL STOKES B. 1819   *Rev.* Seventeen-line laudatory   **AR**   25   40
inscription VIRO ILLVSTRI ET DE PHILOSOPHIA ... TANTO INGENIO GRATVLANTES KAL. IVN. A.S.   **AE**   10   15
MDCCCXCIX within a wreath. *D.* 63 mm. By G. W. de Saulles. *BHM* 3644

Sir George Gabriel Stokes, 1st Baronet (1819–1903), mathematician and physicist.

1835   **Lord Curzon, Viceroy's Medal 1899**
Obv. Busts l., conjoined. * LORD CURZON OF KEDLESTON G.M.S.I. G.M.I.E. VICEROY OF INDIA *   **AV**   —   —
LADY CURZON OF KEDLESTON * 1899   *Rev.* Heraldic arms, supporters, motto, etc. PRESENTED.   **AR**   50   80
BY. HIS. EXCELLENCY. THE. GOVERNOR. GENERAL. *D.* 51 mm. By A. Wyon. *BHM* 3643   **AE**   10   15

George Nathaniel Curzon, Marquess of Kedleston (1859–1925), statesman. *See* No. 1793.

1836   **Victoria's Reign Enters a New Century 1900**
Obv. Bust almost facing, draped, head l., crowned, laureate and veiled; VICTORIA R.I. 1900,   **AR**   70   130
behind. *Rev.* An angel standing, facing, upon a globe, parades a plaque inscribed with the   **AE**   25   45
Queen's signature. *D.* 76 mm. By E. Fuchs. *BHM* 3658; *Jones* 1985, 24/3

Fuchs made two other medals of 35 mm. and 27 mm. diameter for this occasion; the portraits similar to this piece and reverses with only a date and the Queen's signature.

1837   **University College of South Wales & Monmouthshire, Hughes Medal 1900**
Obv. Bust almost facing, draped; PRO PATRIA MORTWS MDCCCC across field decorated with   **AR**   28   40
wreath. ALFRED. WILLIAM. HVGHES. MAGISTER. DILECTVS   *Rev.* Female figure seated, l.,   **AE**   18   30
holding wreath. VNIVERSITY COLLEGE OF SOVTH. WALES & MONMOVTHSHIRE., across field. FOR
ANATOMY, on scroll below. JUVAT. INTEGROS. ACCEDERE. FONTES. NERTH. GWLAD. EI.
GWYBODAV. *D.* 58 mm. By W. Goscombe John. *Storer* 1678; *Forrer* III/77; *Pearson* 58

Alfred William Hughes (1861–1900), anatomist; professor at University College of South Wales & Monmouthshire 1893–7. Set up a hospital during the Boer War; contracted a disease and died on his way home aboard ship.

1838*   **Visit of the Minister for China to The Mint, Birmingham 1900**
Obv. Bust three-quarters l., wearing cap and draped in oriental dress. SIR CHICHEN LO FENG   **AR**   40   70
LUH, K.C.V.O. .MINISTER FOR CHINA. *Rev.* TO COMMEMORATE THE VISIT OF HIS. EXCELLENCY   **AE**   20   32
THE MINISTER FOR CHINA TO THE MINT, BIRMINGHAM, LIMITED JANUARY 1900   *D.* 39 mm. (By   **WM**   8   15
The Mint, Birmingham?) *BHM* 3666. *See* **Plate 45**

1839   **The Royal Society, Hughes Medal 1900**

                                                 £   £

Obv. Bust r. DAVID. EDWARD. HUGHES. B. 16. MAY. 1830. D. 19.IAN. 1900   *Rev.* Eagle in flight.   *AV*   600   800

ΦΡΟΝΤΙΔΟΣ ΓΕΛΕΣΟΡΟΝ ΣΕΛΑΣ   *D.* 56 mm. By J. H. M. Furse. *BHM* 3687; *Hocking* 215/16   *AR*   25   40

   Awarded annually in gold and silver from 1902, for original discoveries in electricity or magnetism. David Hughes   *AE*   10   18
   (1830–1900), electrical engineer and inventor.

1840   **Royal Visit to Ireland 1900**

Obv. Head l., crowned, laureate and veiled. VICTORIA. R.I. 1900   *Rev.* TO COMMEMORATE   *AR*   15   27

THE VISIT OF HER MOST GRACIOUS MAJESTY TO IRELAND IN THE SIXTY-THIRD YEAR OF HER   *AE*   7   12

REIGN   To l., a crowned harp upon wreath. *D.* 38 mm. By F. Bowcher. *BHM* 3662   *WM*   3   6

   The visit was undertaken to pay tribute to the valour of her Irish troops in South Africa.

1841   ————

Obv. Bust l., diademed, veiled and draped. VISIT OF H.M. QUEEN VICTORIA TO IRELAND. 1900.   *AR*   40   55

Rev. A ribbon, decorated with shamrocks, inscribed TO COMMEMORATE IRISH VALOUR. A   *AE*   20   35

continuous ropework border decorated with four masks. *D.* 32 mm. By E. Johnson. *BHM* 3660

1842*   **Siege of Peking, Defence of Legations 1900**

Obv. Fortress engulfed in smoke and flames; a cannon in foreground. JUNII XX – AUGUSTI XIV.   *AR*   70   120

– A.D. MDCCCC. – *Rev.* Female figures of Europe, America and Japan, their hands united,   *AE*   30   50

trample upon the imperial Chinese dragon. MENE. MENE. TEKEL. UPHARSIN. – ICHABOD! – *D.*

57 mm. By J. Tayler Foot. *BHM* 3672. *See* **Plate 45**

   Examples are sometimes named on the edge.

1843   **Lord Baden-Powell, Defence of Mafeking 1900**

Obv. Bust facing, uniformed and holding binoculars. BADEN-POWELL   *Rev.* Three British   *a AV*   350   450

soldiers of the armed services advancing, r., are greeted by a soldier waving his hat. *Ex.*   *AR*   35   55

MAFEKING 1899–1900   *D. a* 45 mm.; *b* 22 mm. [By F. Bowcher]   *BHM* 3677   *AE*   20   35

   Type *b* differs slightly; it sometimes occurs with a suspension loop. Robert Stephenson Smyth, 1st Baron Baden-Powell of   *WM*   8   18
   Gilwell (1857–1941). Several medals commemorate Baden-Powell, a number of which were issued in Australia; *see*
   Carlisle.   *b AV*   40   55

                                                             AR   3   5

1844   **Lord Roberts, Relief of Bloemfontein and Pretoria 1900**

Obv. Bust facing, uniformed and holding a baton. LORD ROBERTS   *Rev.* Three British   *a AV*   400   500

soldiers of the armed services advancing, r., are greeted by a soldier waving his hat.   *AR*   35   55

1900   *Ex.* BLOEMFONTEIN – PRETORIA   *D. a* 45 mm.; *b* 22 mm. [By F. Bowcher]   *BHM*   *AE*   20   35

3678   *WM*   8   18

   Type *b* differs slightly; it sometimes occurs with a suspension loop. Frederick Sleigh Roberts, 1st Earl Roberts
   (1832–1914), Field Marshal. Several medals commemorate Roberts, a number of which were issued in Australia; *see*   *b AV*   40   55
   Carlisle.   *AR*   3   5

1845   **Princess Alexandra, 'The Princess of Pity', 1900**

Obv. Bust l., draped, seen partially from behind; ALEXANDRA (incuse) on shoulder. THE   *AR*   60   110

PRINCESS OF PITY 1900 (incuse); all within a cameo decorated with ribbon and flowers. *Rev.*

Standing figures of HOPE FAITH and CHARITY in a landscape.: all within a cameo, similar to

obv. *D.* Square. 70 mm. by. 70 mm. By E. Fuchs. *BHM* 3665; *Jones* 1985, 24/8

   'The Princess of Pity' was a soubriquet used by various newspapers in recognition of her work during the South African
   War and for numerous needy causes.

1846*   **Princess Alexandra's Private Military Hospital 1900**

Obv. Bust l., draped, of Princess Alexandra; beyond, a waterline with steamship on the   *AR*   70   130

horizon. TRANSVAAL WAR 1899–1900 SOUVENIR OF THE PRINCESS OF WALES' PRIVATE MILITARY   *AE*   40   70

HOSPITAL. THE GABLES. SURBITON. *Rev.* Façade of the hospital building, flying the Red Cross.   *WM*   30   50

MAINTAINED BY Mʀ & Mʀˢ ALFRED COOPER AS AN ADJUNCT TO H.R.H.'s HOSPITAL-SHIP. *Ex.* FOR

SICK & WOUNDED FROM S. AFRICA   *D.* 57 mm. By Warrington & Co. *BHM* 3664; *Storer* 5319.

See **Plate 45**

   Examples in white metal frequently occur silvered.

1847   **George White 1900**

Obv. Bust r., uniformed, of White. *Rev.* HONISTE PARTA GEO S WHITE 1900 (White's motto and   *AR*   12   20

signature, in running script). *D.* 31 mm. By E. Fuchs. *BHM* 3671; *Forrer* II/166   *AE*   5   8

   Sir George Stuart White (1835–1912), Field Marshal. Fuchs made a similar medal of Lord Roberts: Bust facing/Victory
   on a galley.

1848   **City of London Imperial Volunteers 1900**

Obv. A soldier of the C.I.V., proclaimed by a fanfare and welcomed by Londinia, seated on a   *AE*   25   45

dais. Around, oak branches entwined with fourteen labels commemorating the C.I.V.s

various actions in the South African War. *Ex*. PRO PATRIA REGINA ET VRBE   *Rev*. The Union
and C.I.V. flags flying, upon a hill surrounded by trees; sun on horizon and a cannon in
foreground. *Ex*. THE CITY OF LONDON IMPERIAL VOLVNTEERS RAISED AND EQVIPPED FOR THE
WAR IN SOVTH AFRICA BY THE CITIZENS OF LONDON FORMED DECEMBER 1899 RETVRNED TO
LONDON OCTOBER 1900   *D*. 76 mm. By G. Frampton. *BHM* 3684; *Hibbard* A15

    Issued by the Corporation of London (*see* No. 1245). Examples are occasionally found with the edge inscribed to a member
    of the C.I.V. *See* M. Aldred and W.S. Stitt, 'The City of London Imperial Volunteers', *OMRS* 1976, 64–71, and J.V.
    Webb, *Further Notes*, 71–4.

		£	£
1849 ———			

Obv. Bust almost facing, uniformed. IN MEMORY OF THEIR GALLANT DEEDS IN SOUTH AFRICA
COLONEL W.H. MACKINNON   *Rev*. SOUTH AFRICA C.I.V. 1899–1900 within a wreath. *D*. 29 mm.
(By?)   WM   15   25

    Sir William Henry Mackinnon (1852–1929), general, helped to form the C.I.V. in December 1899. The C.I.V.s left South
    Africa in October 1900. Mackinnon subsequently published the *Journal of the C.I.V. in South Africa* (1901).

1850   **South African War, Memorial 1900**

Obv. An angel with olive-branch kneels over a fallen soldier clutching a flag; beyond,   *a* AR   40   65
soldiers and tents on a battlefield. TO THE MEMORY OF THOSE WHO GAVE THEIR LIVES FOR QUEEN   AE   22   38
AND COUNTRY Below, a plaque inscribed SOUTH AFRICAN CAMPAIGN 1899 1900   *Rev*.
Helmeted figure of Bellona standing on a rocky ledge sheathing her sword; below, columns   *b* AR   20   32
of departing troops march along the coast towards awaiting ships. Radiate sun, inscribed   AE   12   22
PAX, over distant mountains. *D*. *a* 70 mm.; *b* 52 mm.; *c* 44 mm. By E. Fuchs. *BHM* 3679;
Jones 1985, 25/6   *c* AR   15   25
                                                                    AE   10   18
    Examples also occur with the dates 1899 1902 on the plaque.

1851*   **South African War, National Commemorative 1900**

Obv. Soldier, his head bandaged, standing on rugged ground cocking his rifle. THE   *a* AV   300   400
NATIONAL COMMEMORATIVE MEDAL 1899–1900   *Rev*. THIS MEDAL COMMEMORATES THE   AR   12   20
MAGNIFICENT RESPONSE OF BRITAIN'S SONS TO THE EMPIRE'S CALL TO ARMS! TRANSVAAL WAR   AE   7   12
1899–1900, in the centre; to l., Union flag and palm branch tied to a staff decorated with a   WM   2   5
rose, thistle and shamrock. THE QUEEN GOD BLESS HER On bottom edge, DAILY MAIL
KIPLING POEM   *D*. *a* 45 mm.; *b* 22 mm. [By F. Bowcher] *BHM* 3680. *See* **Plate 45**   *b* AV   35   45
                                                                     AR   3   5

    The obverse is taken from Caton Woodville's painting *The Gentleman in Khaki*. The medal was advertised in the *Daily*
    Mail in conjunction with Rudyard Kipling's poem *The Absent-Minded Beggar* and sold in aid of the widows and orphans of
    soldiers. Type *b* differs slightly and sometimes occurs with a suspension clasp in the form of a bow, inscribed 1899
    TRANSVAAL 1900 and enamelled in red, white and blue.

1852   **South African War, Commanders 1900**

Obv. Cameo portraits, almost facing, of LD. ROBERTS V.C./GEN. BULLER V.C./LD.   AE   12   20
KITCHENER/QUEEN (Victoria) & EMPRESS Two scrolls upon sprigs, inscribed 1899, l., and
1900, r. Below, SOUTH AFRICA   *Rev*. Peace flying over mountains; pile of arms in
foreground. VICTORY. LIBERTY. PEACE   *D*. 38 mm. (By?). *Africana Mus.* 33

    Sir Redvers Henry Buller (1839–1908), commander of British forces in South Africa until the arrival of Lord Roberts.
    Horatio Herbert Kitchener, 1st Earl Kitchener of Khartoum (1850–1916), organized forces against Boers' guerrillas;
    mobilized British forces in the Great War 1914–16.

1853   **Gruffyd, Prince of Llewellyn** *c.*1900

Obv. Armoured figure of the Prince standing, three-quarters facing, in a landscape. PEN   AR   35   55
MILWR PEN MOLIANT RHAGLLAW PEN DRAGON PEN DRAIG OEDD ARNAW, in the field. LLYWELYN
AP GRVFFYDD   *Rev*. A nightingale in a rowan tree; Snowdon in the distance. *D*. 77 mm. By
W. Goscombe John. *Pearson* 109

    Llewelyn ap Gruffyd (died 1282), last recognized Prince of Wales; married Eleanor de Montfort at Worcester.

1854   **Great Northern Railway Company Medal** *c.*1900

Obv. Shields of England and Scotland; below, a wheel and axle. GREAT. NORTHERN.   AR   45   65
RAILWAY. PRIZE. ESSAY.   *Rev*. Mercury heralds the progress, below, of a locomotive   AE   20   30
advancing, r. *D*. 51 mm. By Elkington & Co.

    Awarded in silver.

1855   **Death of Queen Victoria 1901**

Obv. Bust l., crowned, veiled and draped. VICTORIA. QUEEN. OF. GREAT. BRITAIN. EMPR: OF.   AR   25   45
INDIA   *Rev*. A reclining female figure, winged, regards a plaque decorated with the young   AE   8   15
head of the Queen; to l., Houses of Parliament. BORN MAY 24ᵀᴴ 1819 DIED JANUARY 22ᴰ
1901   *D*. 65 mm. [By Messrs L. C. Lauer] *BHM* 3689

    Only a few medals commemorate the Queen's death.

PLATE 45

1815

1831

1838

1842

1846

1851

PLATE 46

1856

1860

1859

1871

EDWARD VII, 1901–10

                                                                       £

1856*   **Accession of Edward VII 1901**

Obv. Bust three-quarters l., draped. KING EDWARD VII OF ENGLAND AND EMPEROR OF INDIA   *Rev.* Façade of St. James's Palace. ACCESSION JANUARY 23ᴿᴰ   *Ex.* 1901   *D.* 35 mm. By Messrs L. C. Lauer. *See* **Plate 46**

     AV   350
     AR   30
     AE   15

A similar medal with a diameter of 40 mm. is dated January 22nd.

1857   **Royal Visit to the Colonies 1901**

Obv. Busts l., conjoined, Mary draped and George uniformed. T.R.H. THE DUKE & DUCHESS OF CORNWALL & YORK   Below, on a ribbon VISITED CANADA 1901   *Rev.* British shield, crowned, flanked by two soldiers. IN SOUTH AFRICA 1899–1900. Ribbon above, inscribed CANADA   *Ex.* FOR CROWN & EMPIRE   *D.* 56 mm. By G. W. de Saulles. *Hocking* 244/99

     AR   55
     AE   25

A number of medals commemorate this tour which included Australia and New Zealand; medals were struck in each country visited, including several for the opening of the first Federal Parliament in Australia.

1858   **Naval & Military Exhibition 1901**

Obv. Vignette containing busts of Edward VII and Alexandra. NAVAL & MILITARY EXHIBITION   *Ex.* CRYSTAL PALACE 1901   *Rev.* Vignette containing conjoined busts of Queen Victoria and Albert (similar to No. 1455); below, Great Exhibition building. JUBILEE OF THE GREAT EXHIBITION HYDE PARK SYDENHAM 1851 1901   *D.* 38 mm. (By ?)

     WM   3

1859*   **British Empire Medal; South African War 1901**

Obv. Bust l., crowned and draped. EDWARD. VII. D G REX. ET. I: within a wreath, in the centre. Around, supporting figures of IVSTITIA, l., and INDVSTRIA, r. Figure of Peace, above; British shield, with ribbons inscribed TRANSVAAL and ORANGE RIVER COLONIES, and view of town and landscape, below. OPPRESSORVM CONSERVATOR   *Rev.* Equestrian figure of Lord Roberts, facing, upon rocky ledge, lauded by Victory and Fame hovering above; beyond, column of troops advancing, l. VIRTVTE ET DVCTV. in the field. SOVTH AFRICA   *Ex.* PAX. QVÆRITVR. BELLO 1901   *D.* 100 mm. By F. Bowcher. *Forrer* V/642; *Africana Mus.* 66. *See* **Plate 46**

     AV   —
     AR   400
     AE   150

1860*   **Montgomeryshire Imperial Yeomanry 1901**

Obv. Armorial shield and motto. MONTGOMERYSHIRE. IMPERIAL. YEOMANRY   *Rev.* Rifleman kneeling, r., before a mounted trooper. SOUTH. AFRICAN. CAMPAIGN 1901   *D.* 39 mm. By J. A. Restall. *Hibbard* D2. *See* **Plate 46**

     AR   55
     AE   25

Examples are sometimes found with their edge named. The South African War is the first occasion in which tribute medals were given by local townships to those who had served; many were made by local jewellers or die-sinkers, and vary considerably in their style and composition. Some are struck but many are entirely hand-engraved tributes. Localities which issued struck medals include: Birmingham (No. 1867), Bridgnorth, Cheshire, Clitheroe, Coleraine, Cornwall, King's Lynn, Melton Mowbray, Newark, Northwich, Norton, Ossett, Oxfordshire, Selkirk, Stafford, Sunderland, Winsford, Worksop, and Yorkshire

1861   **The Royal Society, King's Medal 1901**

Obv. Head l. EDWARDVS VII REX SOC: REG: LOND: PATRONVS MDCCCCI   *Rev.* As No. 1186. *D.* 72 mm. By G. W. de Saulles/[W. Wyon]. *R. Mint* 1902, pl. B

See No. 1186.

     AV   —
     AR   180

1862   **Royal Academy of Arts 1901**

Obv. Bust r., draped. EDWARDVS VII D: G: REX ET IMP: PATRONVS   *Rev.* Belvedere's Torso upon plinth; STVDY behind. Beyond, classical landscape. THE ROYAL ACADEMY OF ARTS INSTITVTED MDCCLXVIII   *D.* 55 mm. By T. Brock.

Awarded in silver and bronze. *See* No. 724.

     AR   40
     AE   18

1863   **Society of Arts 1901**

Obv. Head l. EDWARD VII R & I. PATRON. MDCCCCI   *Rev.* Similar to No. 1420. *D.* 56 mm. By E. Fuchs/L. C. Wyon.

Awarded in silver and bronze. The reverse was also struck from an unsigned die. The portrait on this medal was that adopted for the definitive postage stamps. *See* No. 643.

     AR   30
     AE   12

1864   **City and Guilds Institute 1901**

Obv. Bust l. (similar to No. 1764). H.M. KING EDWARD VII. PRESIDENT 1881–1900. PATRON 1901. *Rev.* Similar to No. 1764. *D.* 51 mm. [By L. C. Wyon]. *Hocking* 220/42

Awarded in silver and bronze. *See* No. 1684.

     AR   14
     AE   6

1865   **Board of Education *c.*1901**

Obv. Bust l., crowned and draped. EDWARD VII BY THE GRACE OF GOD KING AND EMPEROR   *Rev.* NATIONAL MEDAL FOR SVCCESS IN ART AWARDED BY THE BOARD OF EDVCATION, within a wreath. *D.* 51 mm. By G. W. de Saulles. *Hocking* 219/19

Awarded in silver and bronze. A uniform medal by B. Mackennal, with a bust of George V, was awarded from 1910. *See* No. 1511.

     AR   15
     AE   6

			£
1866	**Death of Horace Seymour 1902**		
	Obv. Bust l., of Seymour, draped. *Rev.* HORACE SEYMOUR 9 APRIL 1843 – 25 JUNE 1902 Above,	*AR*	15
	crest and motto. *D.* 29 mm. By G. W. de Saulles. *Hocking* 237/19		
	<small>Horace Seymour (1843–1902), Deputy Master of the Royal Mint 1894–1902.</small>		
1867	**Mayor of Birmingham, Tribute Medal 1902**		
	Obv. Busts conjoined, r., crowned and draped. KING. EDWARD. VII. QUEEN. ALEXANDRA JUNE	*WM*	12
	26 1902 *Rev.* City arms. IN. GRATEFUL. REMEMBRANCE OF SERVICE. NOBLY. DONE		
	BIRMINGHAM *Ex.* SOUTH AFRICA *D.* 38 mm. By H. B. Sale. *Hibbard* A4; *Payne* 239		
	<small>Frequently found gilt, with an attached ribbon and clasp dated 1899 1902. *See* No. 1860.</small>		
1868	**Incorporated Law Society 1902**		
	Obv. Arms of the Society. THE. INCORPORATED. LAW. SOCIETY. OF. THE. UNITED. KINGDOM.	*AE*	40
	1902. *Rev.* PRESENTED BY THE PRESIDENT OF THE SOCIETY, SIR ALBERT KAYE ROLLIT, LLD.,		
	D.C.L., M.P., AND THE VICE PRESIDENT, JOHN EDWARD GRAY HILL, ESQ., TO SOLICITORS AND		
	ARTICLED CLERKS WHO SERVED IN THE SOUTH AFRICAN CAMPAIGN, 1899–1902, AND WHO WERE		
	ENTERTAINED BY THE SOCIETY, AT A BANQUET IN ITS HALL, ON DECEMBER 18TH, 1902.		
	superimposed upon rose, thistle and shamrock, crowned. *D.* 56 mm. (By?) *Hibbard* J3		
1869	**Coronation of Edward VII 1902**		
	Obv. Busts r., conjoined, crowned and draped. EDWARD. VII ALEXANDRA *Rev.* Helmeted	*a AV*	1400
	figure of the Mother Country holds a crown, aloft; children of the Empire, l., and Britannia	*AR*	60
	seated, r. Westminster Abbey in the distance. GOD SAVE THE KING *Ex.* JUNE 26TH 1902 *D. a*	*AE*	25
	76 mm.; *b* 46 mm.; *c* 39 mm.; *d* 32 mm. By F. Bowcher. *Forrer* I/257		
	<small>The date in the exergue is sometimes found replaced with that of August 9th 1902, to which the coronation was postponed</small>	*b AV*	450
	<small>owing to the King's appendix operation. More than one hundred national and local (*see* No. 1873) medals were struck to</small>	*AR*	18
	<small>commemorate the coronation, as well as several colonial issues; some have the original date of the ceremony on them.</small>	*AE*	10
		c,d AR	10
		AE	6
1870	——		
	Obv. Busts r., conjoined, crowned and draped. KING EDWARD VII QUEEN ALEXANDRA *Rev.*	*a AR*	40
	Female figure seated, r., displaying an oval shield, inscribed 26 JUNE 1902 and bearing the	*AE*	18
	Royal arms, looks towards Westminster Abbey, beyond; above, a radiate crown. *D. a*		
	64 mm.; *b* 39 mm.; *c* 20 mm. By E. Fuchs. *Jones* 1985 28/9	*b AR*	15
		AE	8
	<small>The Fuchs portrait was frequently used on locally-issued coronation medals.</small>		
		c AR	5
1871*	——		
	Obv. Bust r., crowned and draped. EDWARD VII CROWNED 9. AUGUST 1902 *Rev.* Bust r.,	*a AV*	700
	crowned, veiled and draped. ALEXANDRA QUEEN CONSORT. Below, ribbon inscribed 9. AUG.	*AR*	22
	1902 *D. a* 56 mm.; *b* 31 mm. By G. W. de Saulles. *R. Mint* 1902 pl. A, 1–2; *Wollaston* 27.	*AE*	6
	See **Plate 46**		
	<small>The official Royal Mint issue.</small>	*b AV*	120
		AR	3
1872	——		
	Obv. Busts l., conjoined and draped. EDWARDVS. VII. REX. ET. IMP. ET. ALEXANDRA. REG. 1902.	*a AR*	25
	Rev. Imperial crown upon radiate circle; lion above, flanked by two trees decorated with the	*AE*	10
	Scottish lion, l., and Irish harp, r. *Ex.* IN COMMEMORATION OF THE CORONATION. OF. KING.		
	EDWARD. VII AND QVEEN. ALEXANDRA 1902 *D. a* 52 mm.; *b* 39 mm.; *c* 35 mm.; *d* 24 mm. By	*b,c AR*	12
	G. Frampton.	*AE*	5
		d AR	4
		AE	2
1873	——		
	Obv. Busts l., conjoined and draped. EDWARDUS VII. REX ET IMP. ET ALEXANDRA REG. *Rev.* TO	*AR*	14
	COMMEMORATE THE CORONATION OF KING EDWARD VII AND QUEEN ALEXANDRA JUNE 26TH 1902.	*AE*	5
	BURNLEY. *D.* 39 mm. By The Mint, Birmingham.	*WM*	3
	<small>A large number of localities throughout Britain celebrated the coronation with the issue of a medal; many are of local</small>		
	<small>manufacture and used a portrait based on one of the general issues, such as that by Fuchs (No. 1870), and a reverse with the</small>		
	<small>district's arms and motto. Those in white metal are often found pierced as they were worn during the festivities. Localities</small>		
	<small>which issued a medal include: Bath, Beccles, Bristol, Cheltenham, Dartmouth, Greenock, Hammersmith, Lerwick,</small>		
	<small>Rochester, Saffron Walden, Stornoway, York. Businesses to have issued a commemorative include The Metropole Hotel</small>		
	<small>in London and the Union Castle shipping line.</small>		

1874   **Edward VII and Alexandra, Visit to the City of London 1902**
Obv. Busts l., conjoined and draped, she crowned. IN HONOUR OF THE VISIT TO THEIR MAJESTIES KING EDWARD VII & QUEEN ALEXANDRA TO THE CORPORATION OF THE CITY OF LONDON. 25. OCT. 1902. *Rev.* Londinia presents a welcoming address to the King and Queen seated, r., upon a dais. To l., a ribbon inscribed CIVIVM AMOR ET FIDES and, to r., fanfare blown by Fame; beyond, façade of the Guildhall. *Ex.* Sceptre and mace. *D.* 76 mm. By Searle & Co. *Hocking* 223/32   *AE*   £ 65

Issued by the Corporation of London (*see* No. 1245).

1875   **St. Batholomew's Hospital, Willett Medal 1902**
Obv. Bust r., draped. ALFREDVS. WILLETT. NOSOC: S: BARTHOL: CHIRVRGVS. A: D: 1865–1902. *Rev.* Façade of hospital building; armorial shield, above, and inscription QVI IN OPERATIONIBVS CHIRVRGICIS BENE MERVIT   *D.* 57 mm. By F. Bowcher. *Storer* 3783   *AR*   30   *AE*   12

Awarded in silver from 1904 for surgery. Alfred Willett (1837–1913), surgeon; head of orthopaedics at St. Batholomew's 1870–80.

1876   **Joseph Chamberlain, Visit to South Africa 1903**
Obv. Bust facing, draped, wearing a monocle. THE RIGHT HON. J. CHAMBERLAIN. M.P. *Rev.* Peace standing, l., her arm outstretched towards sun, inscribed UNITY and rising over the horizon; steamship H.M.S. GOOD HOPE at sea. SOUTH AFRICA 1903   A cartouche below, inscribed I GO TO S. AFRICA WITH THE MOST EARNEST DESIRE TO BRING TOGETHER THE PEOPLE INTO ONE GREAT AFRICAN NATION UNDER THE BRITISH FLAG   *D.* 51 mm. By J. Fray. *MH* 1919, 668   *AR*   28   *AE*   12

Joseph Chamberlain (1836–1914), statesman, father of Neville. He was the first Secretary of State to visit an overseas colony on political matters. Chamberlain arrived at Durban on *H.M.S. Good Hope* in December 1902. Bronze examples of this medal are usually silvered.

1877   **Death of Quintin Hogg 1903**
Obv. Bust three-quarters r., draped. QUINTIN HOGG   *Rev.* QUINTIN HOGG THE POOR BOY'S FRIEND FOUNDER PRESIDENT OF THE POLYTECHNIC BORN FEB. 17 1845 AT REST JAN. 17. 1903. Below, a tablet inscribed THE LORD BLESS THEE AND KEEP THEE   *D.* 45 mm. By J. A. Restall.   *AR*   12   *AE*   8   *WM*   4
Quintin Hogg (1845–1903), philanthropist.

1878   **King Edward VII Bridge, Kew, Opened 1903**
Obv. Busts three-quarters r., conjoined and crowned. H.M. EDWARD VII H.M. QUEEN ALEXANDRA 1903. *Rev.* Three-arched bridge. THE ROYAL BOROUGH OF RICHMOND SURREY IN COMMEMORATION OF THE OPENING OF KING EDWARD VII BRIDGE AT KEW BY H.M. THE KING, ACCOMPANIED BY H.M. QUEEN ALEXANDRA MAY 20TH 1903   *Ex.* ALBERT CHANCELLOR J.P. MAYOR   *D.* 38 mm. By J. A. Restall.   *AR*   25   *AE*   12   *WM*   6

1879   **Royal Visit to England 1904**
Obv. Busts l., conjoined and draped. T.M. THE KING AND QUEEN OF PORTUGAL   Ribbon below, inscribed VISIT TO ENGLAND 1904 (incuse). *Rev.* IN COMMEMORATION OF THE VISIT OF T.M. KING CARLOS & QUEEN AMELIE OF PORTUGAL TO ENGLAND AND THE PRESENTATION AND GRACIOUS RECEPTION BY THEM OF AN ADDRESS FROM MEMBERS OF PORTUGUESE ORDERS OF KNIGHTHOOD. LONDON, DECEMBER 1ST 1904   Crosses of the orders of knighthood in the field. *D.* 76 mm. By Spink & Son. *Forrer* V/639   *AR*   75   *AE*   30
Carlos I (1863–1908), King of Portugal 1889–1908.

1880   **Royal Geographical Society, Scott Medal 1904**
Obv. Bust three-quarters l., uniformed; JANUARY 2. 1902. MARCH 5. 1904 across field. TO. CAPTAIN. ROBERT. FALCON. SCOTT. RN. CVO. FRGS COMMANDER. OF. THE. EXPEDITION   *Rev.* Scott standing before a sledge, facing; on an icefield, beyond, the *Discovery* and three men and a sledge. PRESENTED. BY. THE. ROYAL. GEOGRAPHICAL. SOCIETY FOR. ANTARCTIC. DISCOVERY   *Ex.* Penguins and seals. *D.* 69 mm. By G. Bayes. *MH* 1919, 665; *Poulsom* 86, 9   *AV*   —   *AR*   150   *AE*   50
Awarded in gold to Scott, and in silver to officers, staff and crew of the *Discovery*. Robert Falcon Scott (1868–1912), antarctic explorer.

1881   **George Frederic Watts 1904**
Obv. Bust r., draped. GEORGE. FREDERICK. WATTS. RA   *Rev.* Plain. *D.* 102 mm. Cast. By T. Spicer-Simson. *Forrer* V/608   *AE*   40

George Frederic Watts (1817–1904), painter and sculptor. Spicer-Simson produced a gallery of portrait medals, mostly in the Renaissance manner.

1882   **Jewish Lads' Brigade, Goldsmid Medal 1904**
Obv. Head l. MACCABÆANS' MEMORIAL TO COLONEL ALBERT GOLDSMID M.V.O.   *Rev.* A menorah (seven-branched candelabrum). FOR SERVICE IN. THE JEWISH LADS BRIGADE. *D.* 29 mm. (By?) *JMC* 1156   *AR*   55   *AE*   22

Awarded in bronze and often found with an attached suspension loop. Colonel Albert Goldsmid (1846–1904), banker; founded the J.L.B. in 1895. 'The Maccabæans' is an association of Jewish professional men.

£

1883　**Institution of Gas Engineers, Jones Medal 1904**
Obv. Bust l., draped; WILLIAM MURDOCH, across field. INSTITUTION OF GAS ENGINEERS　*Rev.*　*AV*　—
Figure of Science standing, facing, holds a torch aloft; beyond, a gasometer and machinery.　*AR*　35
H.E. JONES LONDON MEDAL　*Ex.* 1904 I.G.E. *D.* 51 mm. By J. Pinches.

William Murdock (1754–1839), engineer; inventor of coal-gas lighting. This medal was originally endowed in gold by the president H.E. Jones. It is awarded annually for a paper dealing with the construction of works for the manufacture of gas. The Institution also awarded four other medals. *See* W.T.K. Braunholtz, *Institution of Gas Engineers 1863–1963*, 320–3, London, 1963.

1884　**Richard Phené Spiers 1905**
Obv. Bust l., draped. R. PHENE SPIERS ARCHITECT MDCCCCV　*Ex.* A. RECORD. OF. THE. ESTEEM.　*AE*　25
OF. HIS PVPILS. COLLEAGVES. AND. FRIENDS　*Rev.* An Ionic capital, compass and books;
temple in distance. THE. GREATEST. TRVST. BETWEEN. MAN. AND. MAN. IS. THE. TRVST. OF.
GIVING. COVNSEL　*D.* 59 mm. by 79 mm. Rectangular. By E. Lantéri. *Eidlitz* 1927, 963

Richard Phené Spiers (1838–1916), architect; erected schools and studios for artists. Retired in 1905 as a master from the Royal Academy of Arts architectural school.

1885　**Death of John Pinches 1905**
Obv. Bust r., draped. JOHN PINCHES. BORN JAN 1ST 1825, DIED APRIL 22ND 1905　*Rev.*　*AR*　22
.LABORARE EST ORARE., within an ornamental device. *D.* 25 mm. by 32 mm. Oval. [By G. W.　*AE*　10
de Saulles] *Hocking* 240/33

John Pinches (1824–1905), head of the firm of die-sinkers and medallists. He studied under W. J. Taylor and worked at the Mint under William Wyon. This portrait of Pinches was prepared *c.*1900 by de Saulles who, from 1884, had spent four years in his employment.

1886　**Launching of the *Katori* 1905**
Obv. View of ship. BUILT BY VICKERS SONS & MAXIM LTD BARROW IN FURNESS　*Ex.* H.I.J.M.S.　*AE*　12
"KATORI"　*Rev.* LENGTH 420 FEET. BREADTH 78 FEET. DISPLACEMENT 15,950 TONS LAUNCHED
BY HER IMPERIAL HIGHNESS PRINCESS ARISUGAWA 4TH JULY 1905, within a wreath. *D.* 38 mm.
By W. T. Story.

Other medals by Story which record launchings of British battleships at Vickers include those of *H.M.S. Powerful* in 1895 and *H.M.S. Vengeance* in 1899.

1887　**Death of Sir Henry Irving 1905**
Obv. Bust r., of Irving, draped and wearing a skull-cap. *Rev.* "MIGHTY MAGICIAN, MASTER OF　*AR*　28
THE SPELLS THAT MOVE TO GRIEF OR PITY, LOVE OR SCORN" J.R./SIR. HENRY IRVING　*AE*　12
1838–1905　*D.* 39 mm. By F. Bowcher. *Forrer* V/644; *Svarstad* 113

Irving is here portrayed in his last role as Lord Tennyson's *Becket*. The quotation is thought to be that of the art critic John Ruskin.

1888　**Anglo-French Fleets, 'Entente Cordiale' 1905**
Obv. Bust almost facing, crowned, draped and holding a sceptre. EDWARD. VII. D.G. REX. ET.　*AR*　25
IMP　*Rev.* Standing figures of Britannia and France, their hands clasped; beyond, two ships　*AE*　10
approaching. THE FRENCH & BRITISH FLEETS EXCHANGE COURTESIES　*Ex.* BREST-PORTSMOUTH
1905　*D.* 45 mm. [By F. Bowcher] *MH* 1919, 669

1889　**Dr. Barnardo's Homes *c.*1905**
Obv. Children standing around a central figure, facing. WHOSE SHALL RECEIVE ONE SUCH　*AR*　18
LITTLE CHILD IN MY NAME RECEIVETH ME　*Rev.* "DR BARNARDO'S HOMES" PRESENTED TO　*AE*　8
(space, for recipient's name) FOR GOOD CONDUCT AND LENGTH OF SERVICE　*D.* 51 mm. By
J. A. Restall. *Storer* 164

Awarded in silver and bronze. Thomas John Barnardo (1845–1905), philanthropist; established orphanages.

1890*　**Royal Visit to India 1905–6**
Obv. Busts r., conjoined and draped, of Prince George and Princess Mary, diademed, r.　*AR*　90
Rev. Prince's crest and motto upon Garter and within Order of the Star of India. T.R.H. THE
PRINCE & PRINCESS OF WALES VISIT TO INDIA 1905–6　*D.* 51 mm. By Elkington & Co. *See*
Plate 47

Usually found with a clasp and suspension loop; one of a number of medals struck to commemorate the visit. *See Magor*.

1891　**Inter-Parliamentary Union Conference 1906**
Obv. Head l. KING EDWARD VII. THE PEACEMAKER　*Rev.* Female figure standing, r., holds　*AR*　22
wreath in an outstretched hand. XIV CONFERENCE INTER-PARLIAMENTARY UNION PALACE OF　*AE*　8
WESTMINSTER 1906　*D.* 51 mm. By A. Wyon.

Examples in bronze usually occur silvered.

1892　**Royal Army Medical College, Tulloch Medal 1906**
Obv. Bust almost facing, uniformed; UGANDA 1906, in the field. LIEUT. F.M.G. TULLOCH.　*AR*　55
R.A.M.C.　*Rev.* Female figure of SCIENTIA seated, facing, holding ribbon inscribed LIBER　*AE*　30

NATVRAE (incuse). ROYAL ARMY MED: COLL: PRIZE IN PATHOLOGY   D. 45 mm. [By   £
F. Bowcher] *Storer* 3578; *Forrer* V/640

Awarded in silver. Forbes Manson Grantt Tulloch (1879–1906).

1893   **King Edward Bridge Opened 1906**
Obv. Bridge spanning river. NORTH EASTERN RAILWAY   *Ex.* KING EDWARD BRIDGE OVER THE   AR   60
RIVER TYNE   *Rev.* COMMENCED MAY 1902 LENGTH 2500 FT CENTRE SPANS 300 FT SOUTH SPAN   AE   25
191 FT NORTH SPAN 231 FT WIDTH 46 FT 6 INS HEIGHT 110 FT WEIGHT OF STEEL WORK 5782 TONS
ENGINEER C.A. HARRISON C. E. CONTRACTORS THE CLEVELAND BRIDGE & ENG^NG C^O OPENED ON
JULY 10TH 1906 BY H.M. KING EDWARD VII   D. 48 mm. By Elkington & Co. *Moyaux* 73

1894   **Austrian Exhibition, London 1906**
Obv. Bust l., of George (V), draped. .HIS. ROYAL. HIGHNESS. THE. .PRINCE. OF. WALES. *Rev.*   AE   20
AUSTRIAN EXHIBITION LONDON 1906 between two palms; above, shields of Britain and
Austria. *D.* 62 mm. By L. Hujer.

1895   **Opening of the Wilberforce Museum 1906**
Obv. Bust almost facing, draped. SLAVE TRADE ABOLISHED BY ACT OF PARLIAMENT 25TH MARCH   AR   32
1807. WILLIAM WILBERFORCE BORN 1759. DIED 1833. *Rev.* Façade of house with garden and   AE   18
gateway. BIRTHPLACE OF WILLIAM WILBERFORCE M.P.   *Ex.* HIGH STREET, HULL OPENED AS A
PUBLIC MUSEUM 24TH AUG^T 1906. *D.* 45 mm. By T. Sheppard & W. Sykes.

1896   **Royal Mint, Visit of Princess Mary 1906**
Obv. Head r. EDWARDVS VII DEI GRA: BRITT: OMN: REX FID: DEF: IND: IMP: *Rev.* H.R.H. THE   AR   180
PRINCESS MARY OF WALES VISITED THE ROYAL MINT 11 OCT: 1906, within a wreath. *D.* 39 mm.
By G. W. de Saulles. *Hocking* 241/69

The obverse is that used on the 1902 currency crown (*Seaby* 3978); it was also used to commemorate the Mint visits of
Princess Beatrice of Saxe-Coburg-Gotha, 1905; the Battenberg royal family, 1905; Prince Albert of Wales, 1906; Prince
Edward of Wales, 1906; Prince Arthur of Connaught, 1908.

1897*   **Trinity College Dublin, Bennett Medal 1906**
Obv. Bust r., draped. IN. HONOREM. EDVARDI. HALLARAN. BENNETT. PROF. CHIR. 1906. *Rev.*   AE   40
Metacarpal bone exhibiting Bennett's fracture, upon wreath; shamrock below. VIRI. IN.
FRACTIS. OSSIBVS. COLLOCANDIS. SOLLERITISSIMI   *D.* 64 mm. By O. Sheppard. *Forrer* V/495.
See **Plate 47**

Edward Hallaran Bennett (1837–1907), surgeon. One of a small group awarded in bronze by Trinity College; others
include portrait medals of Joseph Banks and Daniel Cunningham (No. 1913).

1898*   **Liverpool, 700th Anniversary of Foundation 1907**
Obv. Kneeling figure of Liverpool, l., city shield behind, receives Charter from King John,   *a* AR   35
enthroned. 700TH ANNIVERSARY OF THE FOUNDATION OF LIVERPOOL   *Rev.* A fully-rigged   AE   15
ship. DEUS NOBIS HÆC OTIA FECIT 1207 1907 (a wreath between each word and date). *D. a*
64 mm.; *b* 36 mm. By C. J. Allen. See **Plate 47**   *b* AR   8
   AE   4
   WM   2

1899*   ———
Obv. A medieval ship; PRESENTED BY THE CUNARD STEAMSHIP C^O around, on a garter. 700TH   WM   20
ANNIVERSARY OF THE INCORPORATION OF LIVERPOOL 1207   *Rev.* Four-funnelled ship under
steam. S.S. "LUSITANIA" & "MAURETANIA"   *Ex.* CUNARD LINE. 1907. *D.* 38 mm. By Elkington
& Co. See **Plate 47**

1900   **Queen Alexandra Dock, Cardiff, Opened 1907**
Obv. Busts r., conjoined. KING EDWARD VII. QUEEN ALEXANDRA   *Rev.* City arms in the centre.   AR   18
TO COMMEMORATE THE VISIT TO THE CITY OF CARDIFF OF THE KING & QUEEN & H.R.H. PRINCESS   AE   4
VICTORIA ON THE OCCASION OF THE OPENING OF THE QUEEN ALEXANDRA DOCK 13TH JULY
1907   Below, SIR. W.S. CROSSMAN K^T LORD MAYOR J.L. WHEATLEY TOWN CLERK   *D.* 52 mm.
By Spiridion & Sans. *Boon* 30

The dock was built on land reclaimed from the sea by the Bute Docks and Taff Vale Railway Companies, and was their
answer to the Barry Docks (No. 1748). Princess Victoria Alexandra Olga Mary (1868–1935), 2nd daughter of the King and
Queen.

1901*   **Death of Allan Wyon 1907**
Obv. Bust l., of Allan Wyon, draped. A continuous ornamental border. *Rev.* IN MEMORY OF   AR   30
ALLAN WYON BORN 1843 DIED 1907 upon a scrolled tablet; a wreath, below. *D.* 44 mm. By   AE   15
A. G. Wyon. See **Plate 47**

Alan Wyon (1843–1907), medallist; son of Benjamin and father of Allan Gairdner.

1902   **Glasgow University, Kelvin Medal 1907**
Obv. Bust l., draped. WILLIAM. THOMSON. BARON. KELVIN. O.M. G.C.V.O. P.R.S. P.R.S.E. P.N.P.   AE   15
1846–99. CANC. 1904–7   *Rev.* Archimedes seated at a table regarding a balance. VNIVERSITAS.

£

GLASGVENSIS *Ex.* ΛΡΧΙΜΗΔΗΣ *D.* 48 mm. By Messrs J. Pinches.

William Thomson, 1st Baron Kelvin (1824–1907), mathematician and physicist. Archimedes (287?–212 BC) Greek mathematician and inventor.

1903* **Franco-British Exhibition, London 1908**

Obv. A winged female figure of Peace encourages the alliance between Britannia and France, seated facing each other. LONDON MDCCCCVIII *Rev.* Female figure standing, r., her arm aloft, regards a plaque (blank, for recipient's name); exhibition buildings, beyond. FRANCO BRITISH EXHIBITION *D. a* 63 mm.; *b* 51 mm. By F. Bowcher. *See* **Plate 47**

a AV	900
AR	50
AE	22
b AV	600
AR	28
AE	10

Awarded in gold, silver and bronze. The *Fine Arts Souvenir Catalogue* (1909) of the exhibition mentions the award of this medal in a smaller diameter (1½ inches) but no example has been noted. The exhibition was held on a newly-prepared site at White City, West London. Others to be held there, and for which medals were awarded, include the Japan-British Exhibition in 1910, and the Anglo-American Exhibition in 1914.

1904* **Olympic Games, London 1908**

Obv. Fame standing upon a globe, facing, head r., with trumpet and palm branch. ELIS ATHENS PARIS S⸆ LOUIS LONDON IN COMMEMORATION OF THE OLYMPIC GAMES HELD IN LONDON 1908 *Rev.* A quadriga advancing, l., driven by two standing figures. *D.* 50 mm. By B. Mackennal. *Hocking* 262/39. *See* **Plate 47**

AR	120
AE	75
WM	40

The Games were held in the stadium of the Franco-British Exhibition, White City. Participants' names are occasionally found engraved, unofficially, on the edge. The reverse was subsequently used on medals commemorating the Stockholm Games in 1912, and those of 1948 which were again held in London (No. 2076).

1905* **———**

Obv. Youth standing facing, head l., crowned with a wreath held by two seated female figures, either side. OLYMPIC GAMES LONDON 1908 *Rev.* Fame advancing l., leading a warrior, as St. George slaying the Dragon. *D.* 33 mm. By B. Mackennal. *Jones* 1979, 383. *See* **Plate 47**

AV	450
AR	140
AE	70

The official prize medal, awarded in gold, silver and bronze. For a list of recipients and the disciplines in which medals were presented, *see* T. A. Cook, *The Fourth Olympiad, Official Report of the Olympic Games of 1908*, London, 1908.

1906 **Linnean Society, Darwin-Wallace Medal 1908**

Obv. Bust l., draped. LINN: SOC: LOND: 1858–1908 DARWIN *Rev.* Bust three-quarters, r. draped. LINN: SOC: LOND: 1858–1908 WALLACE *D.* 48 mm. By F. Bowcher. *Storer* 784

AV	—
AR	60
AE	25

Alfred Russel Wallace (1823–1913), trained surveyor and architect; devoted himself to natural history and originated, independently of Charles Darwin, the theory of natural selection. The medal commemorates the semi-centenary of publication of their joint paper by the Linnean Society. A special meeting was held during which Wallace was presented with an example in gold. For details of this presentation, and that of five silver medals to those who had played a part in the development of Darwinian theory, see *The Darwin-Wallace Celebrations held on 1 July 1908 by the Linnean Society of London*, London, 1908. The centenary is commemorated by a similar medal, only the dates being altered.

1907 **Cardiff School of Art, Goscombe John Medal 1908**

Obv. A nude male figure, crouched, in a life-study pose. CARDIFF. SCHOOL OF. ART *Rev.* A bird in full flight above a mountain landscape. GOSCOMBE JOHN PRIZE. FOR. MERIT. IN. MODELLING. *D.* 38 mm. By W. Goscombe John. *Pearson* 87

AR	25
AE	12

Awarded in silver. Sir William Goscombe John (1860–1952), sculptor and medallist; attended Cardiff School of Art at an early age.

1908* **Charles Darwin, Centenary of Birth 1909**

Obv. Bust three-quarters l., draped. CHARLES ROBERT DARWIN *Rev.* An ape, crouched, in a landscape, gazes quizzically at a human skull upon the ground; sun rising heralds a new day, with birds billing, serpent, bee and flowering plants. PHYTOPHYSIOLOGIE ENTOMOLOGIE ZOOLOGIE on a plinth, beyond. MDCCCIX – MCMIX *D. a* 70 mm. cast; *b* 36 mm. By K. Goetz. *Kienast* 57; *Storer* 785; *Forrer* VII/380. *See* **Plate 48**

a AE	70
b AR	50

1909 **Royal Geographical Society, Shackleton Medal 1909**

Obv. Bust three-quarters l., uniformed; 1907 1909 across the field. ERNEST. H. SHACKLETON. MVO. FRGS COMMANDER OF THE EXPEDITION *Rev.* Two figures in a polar landscape load a sleigh drawn by two ponies; glacier beyond. PRESENTED. BY. THE ROYAL. GEOGRAPHICAL. SOCIETY . . FOR . . ANTARCTIC. DISCOVERY. 1909 *D.* 70 mm. By G. Bayes. *MH* 1919, 674; *Poulsom* 86–7

AV	—
AR	150
AE	50

Awarded in gold to Ernest Henry Shackleton (1874–1922), Antarctic explorer. Members of the landing party were given examples in silver.

1910 **Queen Alexandra Bridge Opened 1909**

Obv. Suspension bridge spanning river. NORTH. EASTERN. RAILWAY. .AND. CORPORATION. OF. SUNDERLAND. *Ex.* QUEEN. ALEXANDRIA. BRIDGE, SUNDERLAND. ..COMMENCED.; SEPTEMBER. 1904.. OPENED BY THE R⸆ HON: THE EARL OF DURHAM K.G. LORD LIEUT. OF THE COUNTY JUNE 10ᵀᴴ 1909. *Rev.* Corporation arms and those of the railway company in the centre, dividing inscription: RT. HON. J.L. WHARTON CHAIRMAN N.E.R. CHARLES A. HARRISON D.SC. M.I.C.E. ENGINEER, SIR WILLIAM ARROL LTD & MITCHELL BROS CONTRACTORS/ARTHUR F. YOUNG. MAYOR. FRANCIS M. BOWEY. TOWN CLERK. *D.* 64 mm. (By?) *Moyaux* 74

AR	80
AE	45
WM	25

PLATE 47

1890

1897 (× ⅔)

1898

1899

1901

1903

1905

1904

PLATE 48

1908

1918

1919

1925

1922

1930

1933

		£

1911   Ludwig Mond 1909

Obv. Bust l., draped. D<u>R</u> LUDWIG MOND. F.R.S. ANNO. MDCCCCVIII   *Rev.* Thirteen-line inscription of academic achievements. BORN AT CASSEL–7<u>TH</u> MARCH–MDCCCXXXIX 1889–PRESIDENT OF THE SOCIETY OF CHEM. INDUSTRY. 1891–FELLOW OF THE ROYAL SOCIETY.... 1909–MEMBER CORPES<u>P</u> KÖNIG–PREUSSISCHE. AKADEMIE DER WISSENSCHAFTEN. 7<u>TH</u> MARCH–MCMIX. *D.* 115 mm. Cast. By E. Lantéri.   *AE*   90

Ludwig Mond, 1st Baron Melchett (1839–1909), academic, chemist and manufacturer.

1912   'C.Q.D.' Tribute Medal 1909

Obv. View of a holed passenger ship THE S.S. REPUBLIC, her wireless aerial telegraphing the signal C.Q.D. [= Come Quick Danger], the all stations distress. *Rev.* FOR GALLANTRY upon central panel. Around, FROM THE SALOON PASSENGERS OF THE R.M.S. BALTIC & R.M.S. REPUBLIC TO THE OFFICERS AND CREWS OF THE S.S. REPUBLIC, BALTIC & FLORIDA COMMEMORATING THE RESCUE OF OVER 1700 SOULS JAN. 24<u>TH</u> 1909   A star (emblem of the White Star Company). *D.* 46 mm. (By?) *MH* 1919, 673   *AV*   —   *AR*   60

The Italian steamer *Florida* had collided with the White Star liner *Republic* 175 miles east of New York. The *Republic's* wireless operator, using Marconi's recently developed transmitter, sent out the first ever emergency distress signal. The *Baltic* responded and saved all but six persons. The passengers on the *Baltic* decided to recognize the bravery of the seamen with a medal which was struck by Ralph Ingersoll, an American watch manufacturer who had been on board. Medals were awarded in silver, unnamed, and sometimes occur with a suspension loop. Four medals were struck in gold for the three captains and the *Baltic's* radio operator. *See* R. Anderson, *White Star*, Prescot (Lancs.), 1964.

1913   Trinity College Dublin, Cunningham Medal 1909

Obv. Bust l., draped. DANIEL. IOHANNES. CUNNINGHAM. DEFVNCTVS. ADHVC. LOQVITVR 1850–1909   *Rev.* Lateral view of temple lobe of brain, within a wreath. ANATOMIAE. STVDIOSIS. LVMEN. ACCENDIT. LVMINOSVM LVMEN. IPSE. *D.* 64 mm. By O. Sheppard. *Storer* 714   *AE*   40

Struck in 1911. Daniel John Cunningham (1850–1909), professor of anatomy. *See* No. 1897.

1914   Death of Edward VII 1910

Obv. As No. 1888. *Rev.* IN MEMORIAM MAY 6<u>TH</u> 1910 within a wreath. *D. a* 76 mm.; *b* 45 mm. [By F. Bowcher]. *Forrer* V/644.

   a AE   20
   b AR   15
   AE   8

GEORGE V, 1910–36

1915   The Royal Society, King's Medal 1910

Obv. Head l. GEORGIVS V REX SOC: REG: LOND: PATRONVS MDCCCCX   *Rev.* As No. 1186. *D.* 72 mm. By B. Mackennal/[W. Wyon].   *AV*   —   *AR*   180

See No. 1186.

1916   Royal Academy of Arts 1910

Obv. Bust l., draped. GEORGIVS V D: G: REX ET IMP: PATRONVS   *Rev.* As No. 1862. *D.* 55 mm. By T. Brock.   *AR*   35   *AE*   15

Awarded in silver and bronze. *See* No. 724.

1917   Royal Society of Arts 1910

Obv. Head l. GEORGE V KING & EMPEROR PATRON MCMX   *Rev.* Similar to No. 1420. *D.* 55 mm. By B. Mackennal/[L.C. Wyon].   *AR*   28   *AE*   10

A modified portrait was used by Mackennal for the coinage. Awarded in silver and bronze. *See* No. 643.

1918*   British Numismatic Society, Saltus Medal 1910

Obv. Britannia standing on a rocky shore, almost facing, before an open sea. THE BRITISH NUMISMATIC SOCIETY   *Rev.* MCMX and a crown within a wreath; below, THE JOHN SANFORD SALTUS MEDAL AWARDED TO (space, for recipient's name) BY THE VOTE OF THE MEMBERS FOR (space, for amount) CONTRIBUTIONS TO THE SOCIETY'S PUBLICATIONS *D.* 45 mm. By F. Bowcher. *See* **Plate 48**   *AR*   45   *AE*   —

The Society was founded in 1904 for the study of numismatics, particularly with regard to the British Isles, British Commonwealth and the United States. This medal, awarded triennially, was founded in 1910 with a gift of £200 from John Sanford Saltus, an American who was Vice-President of the Society. In 1922 Saltus was elected President, and it was on his visit to London on this occasion that his death occurred in tragic circumstances. He was cleaning some coins which he intended to present to the Society, when he mistook a glass of cyanide for one of ginger ale. *Adelson* 188, 214–5. For a list of recipients of the Saltus medal, see *BNJ*. 1983, 196–7.

1919*   London School of Economics, Brunel Medal c.1910

Obv. Bust three-quarters r., draped. ISAMBARD. KINGDOM. BRUNEL. CIVIL ENGINEER. *Rev.* Brunel's Royal Albert Bridge (a double-girder suspension) over the river Tamar, Saltash.   *AR*   55

THE LONDON SCHOOL OF ECONOMICS (UNIVERSITY OF LONDON). *D.* 51 mm. By Elkington & Co.   £
See **Plate 48**

A prize medal.

1920   **Duke of Connaught, Governor-General's Medal 1911**

Obv. Busts l., conjoined and draped, she wearing a diadem. THEIR. ROYAL. HIGHNESSES. THE.   *AV*   —
DUKE. AND. DUCHESS. OF. CONNAUGHT   *Rev.* Heraldic shield, supporters, etc. PRESENTED. BY.   *AR*   80
H.R.H. THE. DUKE. OF. CONNAUGHT. K.G. GOVERNOR. GENERAL. CANADA *D.* 51 mm. By   *AE*   15
F. Bowcher.

See Nos. 1625 and 2005.

1921   **Coronation of George V 1911**

Obv. Busts l., conjoined, crowned and draped. GEORGE. V MARY. *Rev.* King and Queen   *a AR*   400
enthroned, facing, acclaimed by Britannia, as Empire, standing l. with a wreath; in
foreground, a plaque inscribed HOMAGE OF THE BRITISH. EMPIRE 1911, festooned by two   *b AV*   900
cherubs. GOD. SAVE. THE. KING   *D. a* 103 mm.; *b* 63 mm.; *c* 36 mm.; *d* 28 mm. By F.   *AR*   40
Bowcher. *Forrer* V/643   *AE*   18

The coronation was celebrated by more than fifty national and local medals (*see* No. 1923) as well as several colonial issues.

c AV   240
AR   15
AE   8
WM   4

d WM   3

1922*   ——

Obv. Bust l., crowned and draped; an orb before. GEORGE V CROWNED JUNE 22 1911   *Rev.*   *a AV*   700
Bust l., crowned and draped. QUEEN MARY JUNE 22 1911   *D. a* 51 mm.; *b* 31 mm. By   *AR*   50
B. Mackennal. *R. Mint* 1911, pl. B, 3–4; *Wollaston* 28. *See* **Plate 48**   *AE*   12

The official Royal Mint issue. The obverse was further used on a medal, the reverse displaying a crowned Royal Cypher,   *b AV*   120
which was presented to Sudanese Chiefs (*Jamieson* 73).   *AR*   5

1923   ——

Obv. Busts l., conjoined, crowned and draped. GEORGIUS. V. D.G. REX. ET. IMP. ET. MARIA.   *AR*   40
REGINA   *Rev.* A pear tree laden with fruit. COMITATUS. WIGORNIENSIS   *Ex.* 1911   *D.*   *AE*   18
64 mm. By A. Halliday.

A large number of localities throughout Britain commemorated the coronation with the issue of a medal; many are of local
manufacture and used a portrait based on one of the general issues coupled with a reverse displaying the district's arms and
motto. Those in white metal were often pierced for wear during the coronation festivities. Localities which have issued
medals include: Accrington, Aston, Belfast, Biggleswade, Birmingham, Bolton, Carlisle, Burton-on-Trent, Derby,
Fulham, Govan, Hackney, Kings Norton & Northfield, Long Eaton, Newcastle-upon-Tyne, Richmond, Southwark,
Torquay, Wandsworth and York Minster.

1924   **Investiture of Edward, Prince of Wales 1911**

Obv. Bust three-quarters l., in naval cap and uniform. IORWERTH. TYWYSOG. CYMRU   *Rev.*   *AR*   45
Prince's crest and motto within an ornamental border. URDDWISGIAD. CASTELL.   *AE*   25
CAERNARVON. GORPH.ᶠ 1911   *D.* 39 mm. By Vaughton.

This medal also occurs with English inscriptions.

1925*   ——

Obv. Bust three-quarters l., crowned and draped. CARNARVON IVLY. XIII MCMXI across the   *AV*   350
field. INVESTITVRE. OF. EDWARD. PRINCE. OF WALES. K.G.   *Rev.* Caernarvon Castle; the Welsh   *AR*   30
dragon, below. GORPHENAF MCMXI above, on a radiate sky decorated with the Prince's crest   *AE*   —
within Garter, crowned. ARWISGIAD. IORWERTH TYWYSOG. CYMRU. M.G.   *D.* 35 mm. By
W. Goscombe John. *R. Mint* 1911, pl. B, 5–6; *Pearson* 75. *See* **Plate 48**

The official Royal Mint issue. The medallist designed the Investiture Regalia, including the chaplet which the Prince of
Wales is wearing in this portrait.

1926   ——

Obv. Bust three-quarters l., in naval cap and uniform. EDWARD PRINCE OF WALES   *Rev.*   *AE*   20
BRIDGEND on ribbon over castle gateway and Welsh dragon. INVESTITURE. CARNARVON
CASTLE. JULY 1911   *D.* 38 mm. (By?)

A few localities celebrated the Investiture with an issue of a medal, including Holyhead, Llandudno, and Llanwchllyn.

1927   **William Shakespeare 1911**

Obv. Bust almost facing, draped; WILLIAM SHAKESPEARE below. PICT. AD. VIV. APVD. Wᴹ   *AV*   400
SHARP. OGDEN MCMXI   *Rev.* The muse of Poesy standing, facing, unconsciously laureates   *AR*   35
Shakespeare's head, r.; at her feet sits Puck. EFFIG APVD. ECCL. and SA in a monogram. *Ex.*   *AE*   18

MDLXIV APOLLO MDCXVI ALTER   *D.* 44 mm. By F. Bowcher. *Forrer* V/644; *Ogden* 50   £

Sponsored by William Sharp Ogden, a Shakespeare aficionado; the obverse portrait of Shakespeare is that on a painting that had come into Ogden's possession and which he wanted to record on a medal. The portrait on the reverse is from Gerard Johnson's Stratford (SA) monument.

1928   **Centenary of Steam Shipping in Europe 1912**
Obv. Bust almost facing. HENRY BELL B. TORPHICHEN MILL 1767. D. 1830   *Rev.* Broadside view of a steamship. THE COMET 1812 FIRST SEAGOING STEAMSHIP IN EUROPE. CENTENARY MEDAL 1912   *D.* 47 mm. (By?)   *AR* 40   *AE* 18

Henry Bell (1767–1830), engineer; one of the originators of steam navigation in Europe.

1929   **Loss of the *Titanic* 1912**
Obv. Bust r., uniformed; CAPTAIN ROSTRON below. S.S. TITANIC APRIL. 15, 1912 S.S. CARPATHIA   *Rev.* Plain. *D.* 51 mm. By T. Spicer-Simson. *MH* 1928, 716   *AE* 50

The White Star liner *Titanic* struck an iceberg on her maiden voyage across the Atlantic. Captain Arthur Henry Rostron of the Cunard steamer *Carpathia* responded to distress calls and saved several hundred passengers.

1930*   **The *Titanic*, Relief Fund 1912**
Obv. Broadside view of four-funnelled passenger ship, r., under steam. BALHAM AND TOOTING TITANIC RELIEF FUND. 'HELP SURPASSETH PITY'. *Rev.* TITANIC. LENGTH 882 FT 6 IN. BREADTH 92 FT 6 IN. DISPLACEMENT 66000 TONS KEEL LAID 22ND MARCH 1909 LAUNCHED 31ST MAY 1911 SAILED FROM SOUTHAMPTON 10TH APRIL 1912. COLLIDED WITH ICEBERG 270 MILES OFF CAPE RACE 14TH APRIL 1912 in the centre. PRESENTED TO THE ACTIVE WORKERS OF THE RELIEF FUND BY THE HEAVER ESTATE, 223 BALHAM HIGH ROAD S.W.   *D.* 44 mm. (By?). *See* **Plate 48**   *Al.* 45

1931   **Royal Visit to Merthyr Tydvil 1912**
Obv. Busts l., conjoined, crowned and draped. KING GEORGE V QUEEN MARY   *Rev.* TO COMMEMORATE THEIR MAJESTIES – VISIT TO – MERTHYR TYDVIL JUNE 27TH 1912, on an escutcheon with motto on ribbon, all within chain of mayoralty. MERTHYR. TYDVIL. CHAMBER. OF. TRADE & COMMERCE   *D.* 38 mm. By Vaughton.   *AR* 12   *AE* 7

Medals were also struck for other pre-war visits by George V and Mary, including those to Bristol, 1912; Northampton, 1913; Port Sunlight, 1914; and Shrewsbury, 1914.

1932   **Millenary of Oxford 1912**
Obv. Standing figures of Queen Æthelfelda and the Mayor of Oxford, facing, with shields dated 912 and 1912, jointly hold the sands of time aloft. Below, three ribbons inscribed SIC. M./SIC. M.M./DEI. GRATIA. Beyond, sun rising over city. .OXFORD. MILLENARY. *Rev.* Towers and spires of Oxford enclosed by the old wall decorated with the city shield. FORTIS EST VERITAS   *D.* 50 mm. By H.W. Page. *Forrer* VIII/108   *AR* 20   *AE* 8   *WM* 5

1933*   **Royal Geographical Society, Scott Medal 1913**
Obv. Bust almost facing, uniformed. BRITISH ANTARCTIC EXPEDITION 1910–1913 CAPTAIN R.F. SCOTT. C.V.O. R.N. COMMANDER. *Rev.* Polar expedition advancing, r., with skis and sledge. PRESENTED BY THE ROYAL GEOGRAPHICAL SOCIETY   *Ex.* FOR ANTARCTIC DISCOVERY 1913 (incuse). *D.* 56 mm. By F. Bowcher. *MH* 1919, 683; *Poulsom* 87. *See* **Plate 48**   *AV* —   *AR* 250   *AE* 100

Presented in silver to the officers and scientific staff, and in bronze to the crew.

1934   **Hans Richter 1913**
Obv. Bust three-quarters l., draped. HANS RICHTER MUS: DOC: OXON. *Rev.* IN COMMEMORATION OF HIS SEVENTIETH BIRTHDAY, APRIL 4TH 1913, AND IN RECOGNITION OF HIS SERVICES TO MUSICAL ART IN ENGLAND. Below, laurel branches. *D.* 54 mm. By H.W. Page. *Forrer* VIII/107; *Niggl* 1681   *AV* —   *AR* 20   *AE* 10   *WM* 5

Hans Richter (1843–1916), Hungarian musical conductor.

1935   **Royal Philatelic Society, Crawford Medal 1913**
Obv. Bust almost facing. THE 26TH EARL OF CRAWFORD. K.T. *Rev.* ROYAL PHILATELIC SOCIETY LONDON FOUNDED APRIL 10TH 1869 UTILE DULCI   *D.* 44 mm. By C.W. Thomas.   *AR* 25

Awarded annually from 1920, in gilt silver, for a contribution to philately published in book form. James Ludovic Lindsay, 26th Earl of Crawford (1847–1913), Scottish astronomer, bibliophile and collector; President of the R.P.S. A uniform medal of another eminent philatelist, Thomas Keary Tapling, by Thomas, was also awarded by the Society.

1936   **Royal Mint, Visit of Prince George 1914**
Obv. Head of the King, l. GEORGIVS V D.G. BRITT: OMN: REX F.D. IND: IMP: *Rev.* H.R.H. THE PRINCE GEORGE VISITED THE ROYAL MINT 1 MAY 1914   *D.* 45 mm. By B. Mackennal.   *AR* 60

Prince George (1902–42), 5th child of George V and Mary; later Duke of Kent. A similar medal records the visit of Prince Henry, George's younger brother, on the same day.

1937   **Prince Louis Alexander of Battenberg 1914**
Obv. Bust l., uniformed. ADMIRAL. PRINCE. LOVIS. OF BATTENBERG. GCB. In field, MCMXIV ÆT LX   Without reverse. *D.* 99 mm. Cast. By F. Gleichen. *MH* 1919, frontispiece   *AE* 90

Prince Louis Alexander Mountbatten, Marquis of Milford Haven (1854–1921), eldest son of Prince Alexander of Hesse. He assembled a distinguished collection of naval medals (dispersed by Messrs Sotheby's, July and November, 1919), on which the reference catalogue *MH* (Milford Haven) is based.

£

1938   **Bombardment of Scarborough 1914**
Obv. Arms of Scarborough upon a central shield, between views of the town and beach.   *a* AR   25
Below, ribbon inscribed SCARBOROUGH STILL UNDISMAYED.; above, a coastal bombardment   AE   12
from three ships. *Rev.* BOMBARDMENT OF SCARBOROUGH & NON COMBATANTS BY THE GERMAN   WM   5
FLEET DEC. 16ᵀᴴ 1914   *D. a* 32 mm.; *b* 18 mm. (By?) *MH* 1919, p.489
Type *b* differs slightly.   *b* AR   5

1939   **Prince of Wales Fund 1914**
Obv. Bust facing, uniformed. PRINCE OF WALES FUND 1914   *Rev.* Prince's crest and motto.   AE   8
D. 32 mm. (By?)
This medal is usually found with a suspension loop.

1940*   **Heligoland Bight 1914: Dogger Bank 1915**
Obv. Two oval frames, vertically arranged, each containing a view of a sinking ship: *a* AV   400
"MAINZ" SINKING 28 AUG. 1914, above; "BLÜCHER" SINKING 24 JAN. 1915, below. On either   AR   30
side are smaller oval frames of the ships LION, l., and ARETHUSA, r., flying the flags of BEATTY   AE   12
and TYRWHITT respectively. *Rev.* Twenty-six line narrative of the actions VICE ADMIRAL SIR   WM   7
DAVID BEATTY COMMANDING ... ENEMY SHIPS DESTROYED LIGHT CRUISERS MAINZ, KÖLN
ARIADNE DESTROYER V. 187 BATTLE CRUISER BLÜCHER   *D. a* 45 mm.; *b* 22 mm. By Spink &   *b* AV   45
Son. *MH* 1919, p.490. *See* **Plate 49**   AR   6
The medal was designed by Prince Louis of Battenberg and sold in aid of Naval Orphanages. Type *b* differs slightly and
usually occurs with a suspension loop. David Beatty, 1st Earl of the North Sea (1871–1936), admiral. Sir Reginald Yorke
Tyrwhitt (1870–1951), English naval commander.

1941A*   **Sinking of the S.S. *Lusitania* 1915**
Obv. Steamship sinking in heavy seas. KEINE BANN WARE! *Ex.* DER   *a* Fe.   8
GROSSDAMPFER = LUSITANIA = DVRCH EIN DEVTSCHES TAVCHBOOT VERSENKT 5 MAY
1915   *Rev.* Skeleton figure of Death within the CUNARD ticket kiosk, marked FAHRKARTEN   *b* Fe.   12
AUSGABE, attends to a queue of passengers. GESCHAFT VBER ALLES   *D.* 56 mm. Cast. By K.
Goetz. *MH* 1928, 438; *Kienast* 156. *See* **Plate 49**   *c* Fe.   45
Type *a* is an English copy of a German medal, sold in a cardboard box with an accompanying anti-German poster in aid of
St. Dunstan's and the Red Cross. The German medal, type *b*, has the month of May spelt MAI. In addition, a large number
of copies of type *b* were made, also dated 5 MAI 1915; they usually have a rough surface and vary slightly in diameter. Both
type *a* and *b* are incorrectly dated, as the sinking actually occurred on the 7 May. Type *c* is a corrected German version
dated 7 MAI: it usually occurs on a thinner flan and with a diameter of 57 mm. It is a cleaner cast with a finer style, and has a
medium to light grey patina. See *Kienast* pp.13–8; D. Fearon, 'The Lusitania Medal', *SNC* March 1965, 82–3.

1941B*   **Manchester Manx Society 1915**
Obv. Medieval longboat in full sail; below, a wreath between compartments containing a   AV   —
sailing boat and steamship. FOR. SERVICE. TO. THE. MANX. PEOPLE   *Rev.* Four interlaced   AR   —
compartments containing a shield, triskeles, ship, and an emblem. MANCHESTER. MANX.   AE   70
SOCIETY. SON. TA. SHIU. OOILLEY. VRAARAGHYN. *D.* 39 mm. [By F.S. Graves]. *See* **Plate 49**
No official recognition had been made of the efforts of the Peel fishermen's rescue (in the *Wanderer*) of some of the
passengers of the *Lusitania* when it was sunk off the coast of Ireland. It was decided by the Society that medals would be
struck and presented to them. Only bronze medals have been noted, although examples in gold and silver are reported to
have also been struck. Examples have also been seen inscribed with the names of past Presidents of the Society, for 1912/13
and 1913/14, and would have been done so retrospectively. See *Journal of Matters Past and Present Relating to Mann*
(Manx Language Society), November 1915, 315–7.

1942*   **Sir Edward Grey 1915**
Obv. A quarter-length figure of Grey, facing, his hands clasped before him; a figure of   Fe.   30
Death displays an hourglass, his head peers menacingly over Grey's left shoulder. SIR GREY
ZEIG' DEINE MACHT!   *Rev.* A sphinx awakening; beyond, camels being ridden past
pyramids. Above, 1915 and a star and crescent. *Ex.* ÆGYPTEN ERWACHT (incuse). *D.* 58 mm.
Cast. By K. Goetz. *Kienast* 166; *Jones* 1979, 397. *See* **Plate 49**
Edward Grey (1862–1933), statesman; established a protectorate over Egypt. Goetz produced a number of satirical
portrait medals relating to Britain, including those of Lord Northcliffe, Lord Balfour, and Roger Casement (No. 1956).

1943*   **Edith Cavell and Marie Depage 1915**
Obv. Busts l., conjoined and draped, Cavell in nurse's headdress. MARIE DEPAGE EDITH   AE   25
CAVELL. *Rev.* 1915 REMEMBER! *D.* 60 mm. By A. Bonnetain. *Storer* 579. *See* **Plate 49**
A Belgian tribute, struck in 1919. Edith Louisa Cavell (1865–1915), nurse; took charge of the emergency typhoid hospital
in Maidstone (*see* No. 1824). During the War she co-operated with Dr. Depage in establishing training schools for nurses
in Brussels. She helped British and Belgian soldiers who had become detached from their units, and was subsequently
executed by the Germans for espionage.

1944   **Zeppelins over London 1915**
Obv. Bust three-quarters r. GRAF ZEPPELIN   *Rev.* Zeppelin airships over Tower Bridge and   *a* AE   90
the Thames, picked out by searchlights. *Ex.* LUFTANGRIFF AUF LONDON 17. 18. 8. 1915   *D. a*
108 mm. cast; *b* 35 mm. By F. Eue.   *b* AR   45
A number of medals commemorate Zeppelin raids over London. Count Ferdinand von Zeppelin (1838–1917), German   AE   25
soldier, aeronaut and airship designer.

PLATE 49

1940

1941A*a*

1941A*c*

1941B

1942

1943

1945

PLATE 50

1947 (× $\frac{2}{3}$)

1948 (× $\frac{2}{3}$)

1950 (× $\frac{2}{3}$)

1953

1959

1963 (× $\frac{2}{3}$)

1967

1977

1968

1945*   Prisoner of War Camp, Douglas 1915

Obv. WELTKRIEG 1914–1915 ERINNERUNG AN DIE KRIEGSCHAFT DOUGLAS ISLE OF MAN, within a wreath divided by a central band. *Rev.* An encampment of tents and huts; castle and lighthouse, beyond. Above, triskeles on an escutcheon. Border of barbed wire. Integral slot for suspension. *D.* 45 mm. (By?). *See* **Plate 49**   WM   £30

This piece is sometimes found in a shallow wooden case with a sliding lid. Examples have been noted with the name *Gunther* impressed on the edge. A similar medal records another camp on the Isle of Man, situated at Knockaloe. *See* C. Eimer, 'First World War medals commemorating prisoner-of-war camps for German soldiers', *SCMB* August 1983, 201–3. *See also* Nos. 1946, 1954, 1955.

1946   Prisoner of War Camp, Wakefield 1915

Obv. WELT KRIEG 1914–1915 ERINNERUNG AN MEINE KRIEGS CEFANGENSCHAFT LOFTHOUSE PARK WAKEFIELD, within a wreath divided by a central band. *Rev.* View of building, marked DANCING HALL LOFTHOUSE PARK WAKEFIELD; border of barbed wire. Integral slot for suspension. *D.* 31 mm. (By?)   AE   40

See No. 1945.

1947*   Winston Churchill, First Lord of the Admiralty 1915–16

Obv. A warrior, naked, attacks a huge sea monster with shield and sword. HURRA. GERMANIA BRITANNIA RULE THE. WAVES   *Rev.* A single-masted steamer. SIR WINSTON. CHURCHILL DEM. SEEGEWALTIGEN   *D.* 83 mm. Cast. By W. Eberbach. *MH* 1928, 445; *Engstrom* 1. See **Plate 50**   Fe.   60

Sir Winston Leonard Spencer Churchill (1874–1965), soldier, statesman, orator, author and artist. W. Eberbach produced a number of anti-British propaganda medals, including those of Lords Balfour, Curzon and Fisher.

1948*   Victory of Jutland Bank 1916

Obv. Broadside view of battleship *Lion*, its guns firing; shells from three hostile ships on the horizon splashing around. *Ex.* XXXI. MAY .MDCCCCXVI. between two lions. *Rev.* Upright anchor threaded through two wreaths, inscribed JELLICOE and BEATTY; naval crown, above. THE. VICTORY. OF. JUTLAND. BANK. AUSP. REG. SOC. NUMISMATICAE. *D.* 76 mm. By H. Stabler. *MH* 1919, p.492; *Forrer* VIII/215. See **Plate 50**   AV 1500 / AR 75 / AE 30

The winning design in a competition organized by Sir Arthur Evans (1851–1941), archaeologist; eldest son of Sir John, on behalf of the Royal Numismatic Society, both to celebrate the victory and raise the standard of medal making in Britain (*see* Nos. 1949 and 1950). Sir John Rushworth Jellicoe, 1st Earl Jellicoe (1859–1935), admiral of the fleet.

1949   ——

Obv. A lion standing triumphantly, l., over a large prostrate eagle. VICTORY OF JUTLAND BANK MAY 31. 1916   *Rev.* Victory standing upon dolphin, her arms outstretched. ADMIRAL JELLICOE VICE ADMIRAL BEATTY AVSP. REG. MCMXVI SOC. NVM. PRAES. A.E across the field. THE GERMAN HIGH SEA FLEET HELD AGAINST ODDS TILL ROUTED BY INVINCIBLE MIGHT   *D.* 76 mm. By A.B. Pegram. *MH* 1919, p.493; *Forrer* VIII/119   AV 1500 / AR 75 / AE 30

Runner-up in the Royal Numismatic Society competition; *see* No. 1948.

1950*   ——

Obv. Busts three-quarters r., conjoined and uniformed, of Admirals Jellicoe and Beatty. RESOLUTE IN ACTION JUTLAND MAY 31 – JUNE 1. 1916   *Rev.* THE GERMAN. HIGH-SEA. FLEET. HELD AGAINST ODDS TILL. ROUTED BY. INVINCIBLE MIGHT within a wreath. STRUCK. UNDER. THE. AUSPICES. OF. THE. ROYAL. NUMISMATIC. SOCIETY. 1916. Æ. PRESIDENT. *D.* 76 mm. By W. Gilbert/C. Wheeler. *MH* 1919, p.494; *Forrer* VI/362. See **Plate 50**   AV 1500 / AR 75 / AE 30

Both medallists shared third prize in the Royal Numismatic Society competition; *see* No. 1948.

1951   ——

Obv. Two crossed staves displaying the White Ensign and Union flag attached to an upright trident decorated with a shield, inscribed 31 MAY 1916; anchor below. TO. THE. GLORIOUS. MEMORY. OF. THOSE. WHO. FELL. THAT. DAY   *Rev.* MAY 31, 1916 THE GERMAN FLEET ATTACKED OFF THE COAST OF JUTLAND AND DRIVEN BACK INTO PORT WITH HEAVY LOSS. ADMIRAL SIR JOHN JELLICOE COMMANDER IN CHIEF, VICE ADMIRAL SIR DAVID BEATTY COMMANDING BATTLE CRUISER FLEET. within a wreath. *D. a* 45 mm.; *b* 22 mm. By Spink & Son. *MH* 1919, p.495   a AV 400 / AR 18 / AE 8 / WM 3 / b AV 38 / AR 3

Designed by Prince Louis of Battenberg and sold in aid of Naval Orphanages. Type *b* differs slightly and usually occurs with a suspension loop.

1952   Lord Kitchener, Memorial 1916

Obv. Bust three-quarters l., uniformed; field decorated with a wreath. LORD KITCHENER FIELD-MARSHAL   *Rev.* Britannia as Minerva, armed with shield and sword, standing upon an island rock, r., calling her sons to arms; in field, Union flag and inscription THOROUGH (Kitchener's motto). *D. a* 68 mm.; *b* 45 mm.; *c* 34 mm. By J.P. Legastelois, [*obv.* after J.B. Guth] *SNC* 1916, 719–720   a AR 45 / AE 15 / b,c AR 12 / AE 5

The reverse recalls Kitchener as the mobilizer of the British forces, whose portrait was used on posters carrying the slogan, 'Your Country Needs You'.

		£

1953* ——

Obv. Bust three-quarters l., of KITCHENER, uniformed; beyond, fleet of battle cruisers at sea. *AR* 35
In foreground, a column of infantry marching. *Rev.* Closequarters engagement between *AE* 18
two battle cruisers. *D.* 50 mm. By H. Huguenin. *See* **Plate 50**

Struck *c.*1918.

1954 **Prisoner of War Camp, Islington 1916**

Obv. WELTKRIEG 1914–16 ERINNERUNG AN DIE KRIEGS HAFT LONDON, within a wreath divided *WM* 40
by a central band. *Rev.* A building and garden surrounded by wire perimeter fence. Below,
ribbon inscribed ISLINGTON CAMP   Integral slot for suspension. *D.* 45 mm. (By?)

See No. 1945.

1955 **Prisoner of War Camp, Stobs, Scotland 1916**

Obv. Encampment of huts in a field; beyond, sun over hills. KRIEGSGEFANGENEN LAGER *WM* 45
STOBS   *Rev.* Imperial German eagle above a draped shield inscribed ZUR ERINNERUNG 1916
D. 43 mm. (By?)

See No. 1945.

1956 **Execution of Roger Casement 1916**

Obv. Half-length manacled figure, l., strangled from behind by a standing figure. ENGLANDS. *Fe.* 35
TATEN DRANG   *Ex.* ROGER CASEMENT   *Rev.* A spiked chair, covered with cobwebs, upon
which stands a book inscribed ENGLISC[H] GESETZ VM 1351   Beneath is a skull, attached to
chair by a thread. 3. AVG 1916 across the field. EDWARD. III. TOTE. HAND. LEGT. DEN. STRANG.
VMS. IRENLAND   *D.* 58 mm. Cast. By K. Goetz. *Kienast* 180

Roger David Casement (1864–1916), British consular agent and Irish rebel; convicted of treason and hanged. *See* No.
1942.

1957 **Sir William Ramsay, Memorial 1916**

Obv. Bust l., draped; torch and laurel branch before. WILLIAM RAMSAY 1852–1916   *Rev.* *AR* 20
Two horizontal sections: above, female seated beside laboratory workbench; below, *AE* 8
hourglass and mirror, radiate. SCIENTIA VERITAS   *D.* 55 mm. By L. Bottée.

William Ramsay (1852–1916), chemist.

1958 **Arthur Balfour** *c.*1916

Obv. Bust almost facing, draped. THE Rᵀ HON. A.J. BALFOUR. M.P.   *Rev.* Ribbon within a *WM* 12
wreath, inscribed UNION IS STRENGTH   *D.* 39 mm. By W.O. Lewis.

Arthur James Balfour, 1st Earl of Balfour (1848–1930), statesman and philosopher.

1959* **David Lloyd George 1917**

Obv. Bust three-quarters l., draped, head facing. DAVID LLOYD GEORGE MCMXVII   *Rev.* *a AR* 50
Britannia as Minerva standing, facing. VICTORIA PER LABOREM   *D. a* 65 mm.; *b* 45 mm. By *AE* 18
F. Bowcher. *See* **Plate 50**

David Lloyd George, 1st Earl Lloyd-George (1863–1945), statesman; Prime Minister in 1917.

b AR 22
AE 12

1960 **British Offensive 1917**

Obv. An infantryman advancing, r., arms at ready. OFFENSIVE BRITANNIQUE 1917   *Rev.* *AR* 60
Lion, in attitude of aggression, beside guns and the Union flag; beyond, tanks and aircraft. *AE* 18
VIMY. ARRAS. YPRES   *Ex.* MARECHAL SIR DOUGLAS HAIG GENERAUX = SIR HENRY HORNE SIR
HERBERT PLUMER SIR JULIAN BYNG SIR HERBERT GOUGH   *D.* 68 mm. By S.E. Vernier.

Struck in 1921. Julian Hedworth George Byng, Viscount Byng of Vimy (1862–1935), Field Marshal. John Edmond
Gough (1871–1915), brigadier-general. Douglas Haig, 1st Earl Haig (1861–1928), Field Marshal. Henry Sinclair Horne,
Baron Horne (1861–1929), general. Herbert Charles Onslow Plumer, 1st Viscount Plumer (1857–1932), Field Marshal.
Restrikes of this medal have been made.

1961 **Royal Flight across the English Channel 1918**

Obv. Busts l., conjoined, of Elisabeth, draped, and Albert, uniformed. KING. ALBERT. AND. *AR* 65
QUEEN. ELISABETH. OF. THE. BELGIANS. Below, FORTISSIMI. SUNT. BELGAE on a ribbon, and *AE* 25
A N S   *Rev.* Biplane in flight, l., above an open sea. COMMEMORATING. THEIR. AERIAL.
CROSSING. OF. THE. ENGLISH. CHANNEL. JVLY. MDCCCCXVIII. *D.* 63 mm. By T. Spicer-Simson.
Adelson 204, 218

The couple attended the silver wedding anniversary of George V and Mary; their return journey was also made by air. The
medal was issued by the American Numismatic Society.

1962 **Tyne Garrison, Tribute 1918**

Obv. Rose and thistle between two armorial shields. TYNE GARRISON 1914. 1918   *Rev.* IN *AR* 45
MEMORY OF THE GREAT WAR AND FOR SERVICES RENDERED TO TYNE GARRISON CHRISTMAS 1918
within a wreath. *D.* 41 mm. (By?)

Occasionally found with the edge named.

1963*	**Members of the Inner Temple, Tribute 1918**	£

Obv. A cross, decorated by a wreath of oak leaves, inscribed THE INNER TEMPLE TO MEMBERS   *AE*   12
OF THE INN WHO FOUGHT FOR THEIR COUNTRY 1914 1918   *Rev.* A winged horse, l. MCMXIV-
MCMXVIII   *D.* 52 mm. By E. Gillick. *Eimer* 13. *See* **Plate 50**
See No. 1964.

1964   **First World War, Peace 1919**

Obv. A cherub holds an olive-branch above a reposing lion. .THE. GREAT. WAR PEACE.   *a AR*   40
PROCLAIMED JVNE 1919   *Rev.* Britannia as Peace standing, facing, with dove and olive-   *AE*   15
branch; PEACE above trident and dolphins, in the field. BRITAIN. FRANCE. ITALY AMERICA.
BELGIVM   *D. a* 63 mm.; *b* 35 mm. By E. Carter Preston.   *b AR*   12
   AE   5

One of many national medals struck to celebrate the Peace. Local communities throughout Britain issued medals in
celebration (No. 1967), as did associations (No. 1963) and private firms who wished to honour their members. Many
foreign and Commonwealth countries also struck medals; the various issues far outnumber those for the South African
War, or the handful produced after the Second World War.

1965   ——

Obv. Farmer ploughing field with two oxen; sun, inscribed PAX, on the horizon. Below,   *AR*   30
shields of nine nations. EUROPEAN WAR 1914–1919   *Rev.* Peace standing, facing, before an   *AE*   12
array of standards. PAX VICTORIS   *D.* 53 mm. By The Mint, Birmingham.   *Ni.*   25

1966   **First World War, Sea Services Tribute 1919**

Obv. Britannia, standing upon rock with British lion, holds wreath and trident; beyond,   *AR*   28
shipping and aircraft. THE SURE SHIELD   *Ex.* 1914–1919   *Rev.* SEA SERVICES COMMEMORATION   *AE*   10
4TH AUGUST 1914–1919 within a wreath. *D.* 52 mm. (By?)

1967*   **First World War, Lincoln's Tribute 1919**

Obv. Armorial shield and motto. CIVITAS LINCOLNIENSIS, below. IN TOKEN OF LINCOLN'S   *AE*   7
GRATITUDE   *Rev.* Soldier kneeling, r., before Britannia who places a wreath on his head.
Beyond, landscape and sea with field gun and cruiser; above, airship and biplane. SERVED IN
THE GREAT WAR   *Ex.* 1914–1919   *D.* 36 mm. By Lidgett. *See* **Plate 50**

Sometimes found with the edge named. The Peace was celebrated with medals issued by more than sixty localities
throughout Britain; those noted include: Birmingham, Bournemouth, Bradford, Bridlington, Carlisle, Coleraine,
Coventry, Derby, Dundee, Glasgow, Herne Bay, Peebles, Plymouth, Salford, Sheffield, Skegness, Smethwick and Sutton
Coldfield. *See* No. 1964.

1968*   **Prince of Wales, Visit to the United States 1919**

Obv. Bust r., uniformed; Prince's crest and ribbon, inscribed I SERVE, in the field. EDWARD   *AR*   130
PRINCE OF WALES   *Rev.* Columbia standing upon a dais, l., her arms raised in welcome.   *AE*   50
COMMEMORATING THE VISIT OF H.R.H. THE PRINCE OF WALES TO THE UNITED STATES NOVEMBER
M.C.M. XIX   Below, A.N.S. A branch of oak at each edge. *D.* 63 mm. By J. Flanagan. *Adelson*
212, 221. *See* **Plate 50**

Issued by the American Numismatic Society. Several medals commemorate visits by the Prince of Wales to
Commonwealth and foreign countries *c.*1918–32.

1969   **Prince of Wales, Visit to Sydney 1920**

Obv. Bust three-quarters r., uniformed. HIS ROYAL HIGHNESS THE PRINCE OF WALES   *Rev.*   *AR*   90
City arms and motto. IN COMMEMORATION OF THE ROYAL VISIT TO THE CITY OF SYDNEY   *AE*   50
1920   *D.* 52 mm. By Amor. *Carlisle* 1920/1

1970   **Institute of Transport 1920**

Obv. Pegasus, l. (Institute's emblem). INSTITUTE OF TRANSPORT INCORPORATED   *AR*   22
MCMXX   *Rev.* INSTITUTE MEDAL AWARDED TO GRADUATE (space, for recipient's name) within
a wreath. *D.* 45 mm. [By A.G. Wyon]

The Institute issued several similar awards.

1971   **Birmingham Assay Office, Service Medal *c.*1920**

Obv. Armorial shield, supporters and motto. THE ASSAY OFFICE. BIRMINGHAM. *Rev.* Façade   *AR*   28
of building; ribbon around (blank, for recipient's name). IN RECOGNITION OF TWENTY-FIVE   *AE*   8
YEARS LOYAL SERVICE. *D.* 44 mm. By C.W. Thomas. *Eimer* 33

Only found presented in silver.

1972   **Andrew Marvell, Tercentenary 1921**

Obv. Bust three-quarters r., draped. ANDREW. MARVELL. TERCENTENARY. 1621–1678. *Rev.*   *AR*   25
Façade of school building. POET. PATRIOT. STATESMAN. *Ex.* EDUCATED AT THE OLD HULL   *AE*   10
GRAMMAR SCHOOL   *D.* 45 mm. By T. Sheppard.

Andrew Marvell (1621–78), poet and satirist.

1973   **Opening of Northern Ireland Parliament 1921**

Obv. Head l. GEORGIVS V DEI GRA : BRITT : OMN : REX   *Rev.* Crown surmounted by lion upon   *AR*   28
the shield of Ulster, within a wreath of roses, thistles and shamrocks; motto on ribbon,   *AE*   15
below. THE PARLIAMENT OF NORTHERN IRELAND. 22ND JUNE 1921. *D.* 51 mm. By Heill Ltd.

1974   **Royal Visit to Jersey 1921**

Obv. Bust l., crowned and draped. GEORGE. V. KING. AND. EMPEROR   *Rev.* TO COMMEMORATE THE VISIT OF. KING GEORGE V. TO JERSEY   Below, JULY 1921 divided by arms of Jersey. *D.* 32 mm. (By?)

	£
AR	32
AE	15
WM	6

1975   **Prince of Wales, Visit to Bombay 1921**

Obv. Bust r., draped. EDWARD PRINCE OF WALES   *Rev.* VISIT OF HIS ROYAL HIGHNESS BOMBAY NOVEMBER 1921   Prince's plumes above, on the top edge. *D.* 31 mm. by 56 mm. Oval. By C.W. Thomas.

AR	60
AE	28

1976   **Prince of Wales, Visit to India 1921–22**

Obv. Bust l. EDWARD PRINCE OF WALES. INDIA 1921–1922. *Rev.* Prince's plumes within the Garter and collar chain of the Star of India. *D.* 51 mm. By Elkington & Co.

AR   150

Usually found with a suspension clasp and loop. *See* Magor.

1977*   ——

Obv. Bust l., crowned and draped. H.R.H. PRINCE OF WALES   *Rev.* 1921 INDIA 1922 within a wreath decorated with elephant, cow, tiger and peacock. *D.* 37 mm. (By?) *See* **Plate 50**

AR	60
AE	28
WM	15

1978*   **Marriage of Princess Mary and Lord Lascelles 1922**

Obv. Bust r., draped. H.R.H. PRINCESS MARY   *Rev.* .H.R.H. PRINCESS MARY VISCOUNTESS LASCELLES BORN APRIL 25TH 1897 MARRIED 1922   *D.* 26 mm. (By?) *RWE* 227. *See* **Plate 51**

Al.   5

Princess Victoria Alexandra Alice Mary (1897–1965), only daughter of George V and Mary. Henry George Charles Lascelles, 6th Earl of Harewood (1882–1947), classical connoisseur; horse-racing enthusiast.

1979   **Prince of Wales, Return from India 1922**

Obv. Bust l., crowned and draped. H.R.H. EDWARD. PRINCE. OF. WALES. K.G.   *Rev.* Prince's plumes and motto. WELCOME HOME 1922. *D.* 34 mm. by 53 mm. Oval. By F. Bowcher.

AR   75

This piece has an integral suspension loop.

1980   **Marion H. Spielmann 1922**

Obv. Head in oval frame, three-quarters r. Below, MARION. H. SPIELMANN AUTHOR ART-CRITIC ÆTATIS SVÆ LXIV   *Rev.* TO M.H. SPIELMANN F.S.A., F.R.S.L., IN GRATEFUL RECOGNITION OF HIS JUDGMENT IN THE FINE-ARTS EMINENTLY IN THE MEDALLIC ART FROM FRANK BOWCHER R.B.S. LONDON 1922   *D.* 34 mm. by 49 mm. Rectangular. By F. Bowcher.

AE   20

Marion Harold Spielmann (1858–1948), art-critic and connoisseur. Frank Bowcher (1864–1938), sculptor and medallist; founding member of the Royal Society of British Sculptors.

1981   **Preston Guild Merchant 1922**

Obv. Busts r., conjoined and draped. HENRY & MABEL ASTLEY-BELL J^S P. GUILD MAYOR & MAYORESS   *Rev.* Female figure standing, l., near river-bank, THE RIBBLE in an open landscape; PP in the field below a lamb and flag. BOROUGH OF PRESTON TO COMMEMORATE THE CELEBRATION OF GUILD MERCHANT 1922   *D.* 75 mm. By F. Bowcher.

AR	35
AE	18
WM	10

The Preston Guild Merchant is a festival held every twenty years since at least 1562; the earliest medal noted commemorates that of 1822.

1982   **Newcastle-upon-Tyne Tramways Extension 1923**

Obv. Mercury standing, facing, arms outstretched. NEWCASTLE 1923 TRAMWAYS   *Rev.* THIS MEDAL WAS STRUCK TO COMMEMORATE THE COMPLETION OF THE NEWCASTLE-UPON-TYNE TRAMWAYS EXTENSION OVER THE HIGH LEVEL BRIDGE LINKING UP THE TRAMWAY SYSTEMS ON BOTH SIDES OF THE RIVER TYNE 12TH JANUARY 1923   City arms above; view of a bridge, below. *D.* 51 mm. By Lomax.

AE   25

Examples usually occur silvered.

1983   **Sybil Thorndike as Saint Joan 1923**

Obv. Half-length figure, r., in chain-mail and armour; lys decoration on breastplate. Beyond, a decorative arched screen with two end panels, each lit with a candle. Above, SAINT JOAN; below, on a ribbon SYBIL. .THORNDIKE   *Rev.* Plain. *D.* 93 mm. Cast. By M. Kitchener.

Pb.   30

Dame Sybil Thorndike (1882–1976), actress; portrayed here as Bernard Shaw's *Saint Joan*.

1984   **London University, Petrie Medal 1923**

Obv. Bust l., draped. WILLIAM. MATTHEW. FLINDERS. PETRIE   *Ex.* MCMXXIII   *Rev.* Ivory head of Khufu (from Abydos), r.; an ibis in the foreground. PRESENTED FOR WORK IN ARCHÆOLOGY   *D.* 58 mm. [By S.W. Carline]

AE   25

Sir William Matthew Flinders Petrie (1853–1942), Egyptologist. This medal was struck for his seventieth birthday, although only presented to him in 1925. It served as a prize medal, awarded every three or four years until 1957 for distinguished work in archaeology. *See* Margaret S. Drawer, *Flinders Petrie : A Life in Archaeology*, London, 1985.

1985   **British School at Rome 1923**

f

Obv. BRITISH SCHOOL AT ROME, within a wreath. *Rev.* Fame standing upon rocky ground,   *AR*   30
facing, head r. EXPECTATA. VENI   *D.* 67 mm. By F. Bowcher.   *AE*   8

<small>A prize medal, found awarded in silver.</small>

1986   **Physiological Congress, Edinburgh 1923**

Obv. Bust l., draped. WILLIAM HARVEY 1578–1657   *Rev.* INTER-NATIONAL PHYSIOLOGICAL   *AE*   10
CONGRESS. EDINBURGH 1923   *D.* 38 mm. By C. d'O. P. Jackson.

<small>Several medals commemorate the congress.</small>

1987*   **British Empire Exhibition 1924**

Obv. Bust l., crowned and draped. GEORGIVS V BRITT : OMN : REX ET IND : IMP :   *Rev.* Stylized   *AE*   10
lion seated, l.; beyond, façade of Wembley Stadium. *Ex.* BRITISH EMPIRE EXHIBITION
1924   *D.* 51 mm. By B. Mackennal/P. Metcalfe. R. *Mint* 1924 pl. C, 5–6; *Eimer* 5. See **Plate
51**

<small>The exhibition took place on a specially built site in Wembley, north-west London, and was intended to promote trade
within the Empire, and to pay tribute to the colonial forces who had fought in the Great War. With the aim of attracting
new artists to medal work, the Royal Mint organized various competitions for designs of medals; to commemorate the
exhibition itself, and illustrate London as capital city of the Empire. This medal was the winner of a competition sponsored
by the Goldsmiths' Company; it was the official medal for exhibitors and was awarded unnamed. At this time the Royal
Mint was experimenting with different lacquers; as a result, this medal, and Nos. 1997, 2003 and 2013 have a dark matt
toning.

    A number of companies with stands at the exhibition had medals struck by way of advertisement; those noted include:
Amalgamated Anthracite Collieries Ltd, Gibbs Dentifrice, HMV Gramophone Co., and the Mond Nickel Co.</small>

1988*   ——

Obv. An allegory of the peaceful assembly of the Dominions standing before the Mother   *AR*   45
Country, seated upon a dais inscribed BRITISH-EMPIRE EXHIBITION 1924 *Rev.* MAKE. ALL.
SURE WE ARE. ONE upon a tablet. *D.* 78 mm. by 50 mm. Rectangular. By E. Carter Preston. *R.
Mint* 1924 pl. B, 1; *Eimer* 3. See **Plate 51**

<small>Winner in the competition sponsored by the Armourers' and Braziers' Company for a plaquette commemorating
Wembley; the reverse carries the Company's motto. *See No.* 1987.</small>

1989   ——

Obv. Seated figure of Moneta, r., about to strike coins with a hammer and punch. BRITANNIA   *AR*   9
MONETA   *Rev.* Façade and forecourt of the Mint. .THE. .ROYAL. .MINT. .LONDON.   *D.*   *AE*   5
36 mm. [By J. Langford Jones] R. *Mint* 1924 pl. A, 4–5

<small>The Royal Mint Souvenir, struck and sold at the exhibition. *See No.* 1987.</small>

1990   ——

Obv. Head of a stylized lion, l. STRUCK AT THE BRITISH EMPIRE EXHIBITION 1924   *Rev.*   *AR*   7
Shipping at wharf; large furnaces and chimneys, beyond. *Ex.* INDUSTRY COMMERCE   *D.*   *AE*   3
28 mm. By P. Metcalfe. R. *Mint* 1924 pl. A, 9–10; *Eimer* 6   *Ni.*   4

<small>Winner in the competition for a keepsake souvenir; *see No.* 1987.</small>

1991   ——

Obv. Head of Mercury, l. COMMERCE AND INDUSTRY   *Rev.* A ship docked beside a loading   *AR*   7
gantry. THE. BRITISH. EMPIRE. EXHIBITION. 1924   *D.* 28 mm. By W. McMillan. R. *Mint* 1924   *AE*   3
pl. A, 11–12; *Eimer* 7   *Ni.*   4

<small>Runner-up in the competition for a keepsake souvenir; *see No.* 1987.</small>

1992   **Houses of Parliament 1924**

Obv. View of Westminster Abbey and the Houses of Parliament. WESTMINSTER ABBEY AND   *AE*   25
THE HOUSES OF PARLIAMENT. LONDON. *Rev.* Plain. *D.* 75 mm. by 49 mm. Semi-circular. By E.
Bradbury. *R. Mint* 1924 pl. B, 4; *Eidlitz* 1927, 59

<small>An open competition was held for a series of plaquettes illustrative of London as capital city of the Empire. This piece and
another by Bradbury (National Gallery and St. Martin's-in-the-Fields) won first prize and could be purchased, along with
the runners-up, at the Royal Mint stand at the British Empire Exhibition. *See No.* 1987.</small>

1993   **Mining & Metallurgical Congress 1924**

Obv. THE. FIRST EMPIRE. MINING & METALLURGICAL CONGRESS LONDON. JUNE. 1924 in the   *AR*   20
centre; below, two crossed geological hammers. PER. CONSTANTIAM. PROGREDIMUR   *AE*   12
1568–1924   *Rev.* Armorial shield, supporters and crest; below, 1568 upon an escutcheon.
THE. ARMS. OF. THE. SOCIETY. OF. THE. MINES. ROYAL. ANNO. 10. ELIZ. *D.* 51 mm. By
W. McMillan. *Müseler* 16/23

<small>The Congress was held during the summer, at the British Empire Exhibition.</small>

1994   **Imperial Scout Jamboree 1924**

Obv. Bust almost facing, uniformed, of Lord Baden-Powell. CHIEF SCOUT   *Rev.* IMPERIAL   *AR*   15
JAMBOREE 1924 within a wreath. *D.* 41 mm. (By?)

			£

1995 **William Burgess 1924**
Obv. Bust l., draped, within a vertical frame. WILLIAM THOMAS BURGESS F.I.C. 1924 *Rev.* *AR* 28
Stylized nude male figure in swimming pose; an overturned urn, r., spilling water. ABSQVE *AE* 18
LABORE NIHIL| Below, AQVARIVS (incuse). *D.* 41 mm. By F. Bowcher. *See* **Plate 51**

William Thomas Burgess (1861–1939), water analyst; consultant for local authorities in their new schemes for water supplies.

1996 **Montague Rendall 1924**
Obv. Bust l., in academic robes; ÆT. LXII in the field. MONTAGVE JOHN RENDALL INFORMATOR *AE* 10
MCMXI–XXIV *Rev.* Panoramic view of Winchester College. MANNERS MAKYTH MAN *Ex.*
MCMXXIV DOMUM DAY *D.* 64 mm. By F. Bowcher, after R.M. Gleadowe.

John Montague Rendall (1862–1950), headmaster of Winchester. The medal was struck on his retirement.

1997 **British Empire Exhibition 1925**
Obv. As No. 1987. *Rev.* Three stylized figures standing, r., holding objects symbolizing *AE* 10
food, transport and housing. BRITISH EMPIRE EXHIBITION 1925 *D.* 51 mm. By
B. Mackennal/P. Metcalfe. *R. Mint* 1925 pl. B, 6; *Eimer* 16

The official Award Medal issued to exhibitors, unnamed. The objects featured on the reverse were the main focus of interest for the extension of the exhibition into 1925. *See* No. 1987.

1998 **British Empire Exhibition, Torchlight Tattoo 1925**
Obv. The 'Wembley Lion', l. . . WEMBLEY TORCHLIGHT TATTOO 1925. *Ex.* HEAVEN DOTH WITH *AE* 7
US AS WE WITH TORCHES DO. NOT LIGHT THEM FOR THEMSELVES *Rev.* St. George standing,
facing, upon a globe. A cross, radiate, decorated with shields of the three armed services. *D.*
38 mm. By H. Oakes-Jones. *See* **Plate 51**

The obverse illustrates Frederick Charles Herrick's lion; the official emblem of the British Empire Exhibition. *See* No. 1987.

1999 **Prince of Wales, Visit to Cape Town 1925**
Obv. Bust l., draped. EDWARD. PRINCE OF WALES *Rev.* A seventeenth-century sailing ship; *AE* 10
CDG HOOP on waterline. CAPETOWN. 1925. KAAPSTAD *D.* 32 mm. By P. Metcalfe. *R. Mint*
1925 pl. A, 1–2; *Eimer* 17. *See* **Plate 51**

The ship represented is that of Jan van Riebeck, the Dutch naval surgeon who sailed to Cape Town in 1652.

2000 **Prince of Wales, Visit to Argentina 1925**
Obv. Bust r. EDWARD ALBERT PRINCE OF WALES *Rev.* Shields of Britain and Argentina upon *AV* 400
a wreath. VISITA A LA REPUBLICA ARGENTINA. AGOSTO 1925. *D.* 50 mm. By J.M. Lubary. *AR* 70
AE 20

2001 **Stockton & Darlington Railway, Centenary 1925**
Obv. Busts l., conjoined, between shields of Stockton and Darlington. EDWARD PEASE. *a AR* 65
GEORGE STEPHENSON *Ex.* STOCKTON & DARLINGTON RAILWAY – INCLUDED IN LONDON & *AE* 30
NORTH EASTERN RAILWAY. 1825–1925 *Rev.* Vulcan l., holding model of engine
"LOCOMOTION NO. 1" 1825; beyond, a 1925 "PACIFIC" type engine. FIRST IN THE WORLD *D. a* *b AR* 28
77 mm.; *b* 45 mm. By G. Bayes. *AE* 15

Edward Pease (1767–1858), railway projector; adopted and funded Stephenson's plans for the Stockton & Darlington railway.

2002 **National Rifle Association, King's Trophy 1925**
Obv. An archer kneeling, r. FOR SPECIAL DISTINCTION NRA *Rev.* PRESENTED BY THE KING TO *AR* 18
ENCOURAGE YOUTH IN THE HOPE THAT FRIENDLY COMPETITION AND EFFICIENT TRAINING MAY *AE* 8
HELP IT TO FORGE NEW LINKS OF EMPIRE, upon a target. KING'S TROPHY COMPETITION *D.*
51 mm. By P. Metcalfe. *R. Mint* 1926 pl. B, 4

Boys throughout the Empire were eligible for the medal, which was presented annually in silver and bronze.

2003 **General Strike, Service Medal 1926**
Obv. Helmeted figure of Britannia seated, l., hand resting on shield, holds out a laurel; in *AV* —
field, winged emblem of the London, Midland and Scottish Railway Company, between a *AE* 7
rose and thistle. FOR SERVICE IN THE NATIONAL EMERGENCY MAY 1926 *Rev.* An allegory of
three draped figures, standing, with their backs to each other; two locomotives resting upon
their outstretched hands. LARGITAS MVNERIS SALVS REIPVBLICAE *D.* 51 mm. By E. Gillick.
R. Mint 1926 p.46; *Eimer* 12. *See* **Plate 51**

Several thousand bronze medals were struck by The Royal Mint. They were presented to those who had given service on behalf of the L.M.S. Railway Co.; whose initials are formed by those of the reverse inscription. The medals were presented unnamed, in a case, accompanied by a letter of thanks. *See* No. 1987.

2004 **British Empire Union 1926**
Obv. Bust l., draped, of the Prince of Wales. OUR. EMPIRE. PRINCE 24 MAY 1926 *Rev.* *AE* 4
Antique galley seen through the archway of a stone bridge; above, radiate sun. FOR. GOD. *Al.* 3

£

KING. AND. EMPIRE   *D.* 39 mm. (By Messrs J. Pinches?) *Eimer* 19

Examples of this particular medal also occur dated with the three following years. It was issued by the British Empire Union (motto: Britain for the British) for distribution amongst children of the Commonwealth on Empire Day. The portrait is an inferior copy of No. 1999. The medal has an integral suspension loop through which is sometimes found a ribbon with red, white and blue stripes. The Royal Mint struck two similar medals for the B.E.U. *See* Nos. 2010 and 2016.

2005 Arthur, Duke of Connaught: Grand Prior, Order of St. John 1926
Obv. Bust l., wearing robes of the Order; below, badge of the Grand Prior. ARTHVRVS. CONN: *AR*   45
DVX. MAG: PRIOR. IN. BRITT: OMN: ORD: HOSP: S: IOHIS: HIER: *Rev.* Fully-rigged medieval   *AE*   22
ship, its mainsail emblazoned with the Cross of the Order. ANNO PEREGRINATIONIS ET NOVAE
CARTAE. MCMXXVI. *D.* 70 mm. By E. C. Dingli/C. Wright.

Arthur Frederick Patrick Albert (1883–1938), only son of Prince Arthur and grandson of Queen Victoria. He was Grand Prior of the Order from 1910 until his death.

2006 Henry Carslake, Memorial 1926
Obv. Three biplanes in flight, r. *Rev.* IN MEMORY OF HENRY LEIGH CARSLAKE LIEUTENANT R.N.   *AR*   60
LATE OF H.M.S. EAGLE. NAVAL OBSERVER. FLEET AIR ARM. KILLED IN AN AEROPLANE CRASH AT SEA   *AE*   28
OFF MALTA. 21. OCT. 1926 Two anchors in the field. *D.* 51 mm. By P. Metcalfe. *R. Mint* 1928
pl. C, 2–3; *Eimer* 23

Examples in silver were presented for good service. Henry Carslake served at the Battle of Jutland (on the battle-cruiser *Princess Royal*). Promoted to lieutenant in 1920, he served from 1924 on the aircraft carrier *HMS Eagle* on the Mediterranean station.

2007 Fuad I, Visit to England 1927
Obv. Bust l., uniformed and draped. Arabic legend [= King Fuad I Egypt]. *Rev.* Shoulder-   *AE*   35
length busts, conjoined and draped, of Britannia and Egypt, facing, heads l. Below, OFFICIAL
VISIT OF HIS MAJESTY FUAD I KING OF EGYPT TO BRITAIN JULY MCMXXVII within a semi-
circular compartment. *D.* 72 mm. By P. Metcalfe/C. L. J. Doman. *R. Mint* 1930 pl. B, 1;
Eimer 22

Struck in 1930. Ahmed Fuad Pasha (1868–1936), king 1922–36.

2008 Signing of the Armistice, Tenth Anniversary 1928
Obv. The Cenotaph (in Whitehall, London). THEIR NAME LIVETH FOR EVERMORE. *Rev.* An   *a AV*   gold value
allegory of Deliverance: Great Britain advancing, l., supporting a youthful warrior, head
bandaged and shackles broken, offers a wreath to the memory of fallen heroes. *Ex.*   *AR*   45
NOVEMBER 11TH MCMXVIII *D. a* 76 mm.; *b* 32 mm. By C. L. J. Doman. *R. Mint* 1928 pl. A;   *AE*   20
Eimer 14

This medal is unusual in having been sponsored by the Royal Mint, from where it could also be purchased.

           b AV   gold value
           AR   8
           AE   3

2009 Lloyd's New Buildings 1928
Obv. As No. 1921*b. Rev.* LLOYD'S TO COMMEMORATE THE OPENING OF THE NEW BUILDING BY   *AR*   40
THEIR MAJESTIES MARCH 24 1928 within a wreath. *D.* 63 mm. By F. Bowcher.   *AE*   15

2010 British Empire Union 1928
Obv. Draped bust of the Prince of Wales, l. (similar to No. 1999). FOR GOD KING AND   *AV*   150
EMPIRE *Rev.* Female figure of the Mother Country seated, r., holds caduceus and laurel;   *AR*   35
her helmet on the ground. EMPIRE DAY MAY 24TH *Ex.* BRITISH EMPIRE UNION *D.* 33 mm.   *AE*   4
[By P. Metcalfe/T. H. Paget, *rev.* after F. Derwent Wood] *R. Mint* 1928 p. 8–9, 34; *Eimer* 20
Derwent Wood's reverse was originally intended for a currency crown. *See* Nos. 2004 and 2016.

2011 Tyne Suspension Bridge Opened 1928
Obv. Broadside view of suspension bridge; shipping on river. TYNE BRIDGE *Ex.*   *AR*   30
NEWCASTLE–GATESHEAD *Rev.* Twelve-line inscription enumerating dimensions etc.
COMMENCED 1ST JULY 1925 MAIN ARCH SPAN 531 FT TOTAL LENGTH 1800 FT … OPENED 10 OCT
1928 BY H.M. KING GEORGE. V *D.* 58 mm. By The Northern Goldsmiths Co.

2012 Flight from London to Darwin 1928
Obv. Bust almost facing, in aviator's jacket and cap. BERT HINKLER AIRMAN BUNDABERG.   *AR*   90
AUSTRALIA. *Rev.* Map of the eastern hemisphere: flight path of LONDON DARWIN AUSTRALIA   *AE*   35
delineated; FEB. 1928, below. LONDON TO DARWIN XVI DAYS PRAEPETIBUS PINNIS AUSTRALES
VECTUS AD ORAS *D.* 51 mm. By Stokes [after C. D. Richardson] *Carlisle* 1928/1
Herbert John Louis Hinkler (1892–1933), Australian aviator.

2013 Joseph Fry, Bicentenary 1928
Obv. Bust l., draped and wearing a hat. JOSEPH FRY 1728–1787 *Rev.* A flourishing cocoa   *AR*   15
plant upon the globe. J. S. FRY & SONS LTD BICENTENARY 1928 *D.* 51 mm. By H. Youngman.   *AE*   8
R. Mint 1927 pl. C, 2–3; *Eimer* 18
Joseph Fry (1728–87), type-founder and chocolate manufacturer. *See* No. 1987.

                                                                       £

2014   **The Ashes, Test Cricket Series with Australia 1928–29**   *Al.*   15
Obv. An urn containing THE ASHES in the centre; inscription around, A. P. F. CHAPMAN D. R. JARDINE J. C. WHITE. DUCKWORTH. GEARY. HAMMOND. HENDREN. HOBBS. LARWOOD. MEAD. SUTCLIFFE. TATE. Above, THE ASHES; Below, AUSTRALIA 1928–29   *Rev.* Eleven-line inscription advertising J. R. Gaunt & Son Ltd., silversmiths, medallists, etc. *D.* 38 mm. [By J. R. Gaunt]

A similar 'advertising novelty' was struck by Gaunt for the 1932–33 'Ashes'.

2015*   **Launching of the R 101 1929**   *Al.*   25
Obv. View of the R 101 airship above an open landscape. *Ex.* LAUNCHED 1929 LARGEST AIRSHIP IN THE WORLD   *Rev.* R 101 732 F$^\text{T}$ LONG 132 F$^\text{T}$ DIAM. 140 F$^\text{T}$ HIGH 5 MILLION CUBIC F$^\text{T}$ 5 BEARDMORE DIESEL CRUDE OIL ENGINES 2925 H.P. COST £527,000 LIFT 150 TONS – 70 M.P.H. 180 PASSENGERS   *D.* 38 mm. By J. R. Gaunt. *See* **Plate 51**

William Beardmore, Baron Invernairn (1856–1936), shipbuilder; built the R.34, the first airship to make a double crossing of the Atlantic.

2016   **British Empire Union 1929**   *AV*   150
Obv. As No. 2010. *Rev.* Female figure of the Mother Country seated, r., encourages two   *AR*   35
children by her side to go forth and perform great deeds. EMPIRE DAY MAY 24$^\text{TH}$ *Ex.* BRITISH   *AE*   4
EMPIRE UNION   *D.* 33 mm. By [P. Metcalfe]/C. L. J. Doman. *R. Mint* 1928 p. 9; *Eimer* 21

In 1929 the Union requested the Mint, who had struck their medal in 1928 (No. 2010), to provide a new reverse; one which would appeal more to children and perhaps 'fire them with enthusiasm to emulate the deeds of their forefathers'. *See* No. 2004.

2017   **Ramsay MacDonald, Visit to the United States 1929**   *AE*   25
Obv. Bust r., draped. J. RAMSAY MACDONALD   *Rev.* COMMEMORATING THE VISIT OF J. RAMSAY MACDONALD PRIME MINISTER OF GREAT BRITAIN TO AMERICA OCTOBER 1929 between two fasces. *D.* 69 mm. By J. R. Sinnock.

James Ramsay MacDonald (1866–1937), Labour leader and statesman. Made by the Medallic Art Co., New York, for members of the English Speaking Union. Restrikes of this medal may have been made.

2018   **Liverpool Cathedral 1930**   *AR*   35
Obv. Three male figures before Mary with infant seated over the cathedral. CATHEDRAL   *AE*   18
CHURCH OF CHRIST   *Ex.* LIVERPOOL   *Rev.* A nimbate male figure, standing, beside a winged female, kneeling, both in praise; beyond, façade of the new cathedral. *D.* 38 mm. by 72 mm. Rectangular. By E. Carter Preston. *Eimer* 25

2019   **International Jewellery Congress 1930**   *AE*   12
Obv. Naked female figure, seated, drops objects into a basket held by a kneeling cherub. CONGRESS LONDON 20–22 MAY 1930   *Rev.* A flaming crucible. VIM TEMPERATAM DI QUOQUE PROVEHUNT MAIUS   *D.* 50 mm. (By?)

2020*   **Eric Gill *c.*1930**   *AR*   55
Obv. Bust three-quarters l., draped. ERIC GILL O.S.D.   *Rev.* Plain. *D.* 43 mm. (By   *AE*   25
G. Friend?) *See* **Plate 51**

The entire design and lettering on this medal is incuse. Eric Gill (1882–1940), stone-carver, engraver, typographer and author.

2021   **Institution of Civil Engineers, Baker Medal 1932**   *AV*   700
Obv. Bust r., draped. BENJAMIN. BAKER. 1840–1907   *Rev.* View of the Forth Bridge. *Ex.*   *AE*   18
FOUNDED 1932 BY FRIENDS AND ADMIRERS AWARDED BY THE INSTITUTION OF CIVIL ENGINEERS   *D.* 57 mm. [By J. R. Pinches]

Awarded triennially in gold. Benjamin Baker (1840–1907), civil engineer.

2022   **Flight over Mount Everest 1933**   *AR*   250
Obv. Biplane in flight, r.; snow-capped mountain range beyond. APRIL 1933. *Rev.* PRESENTED BY THE TIMES TO THE MEMBERS OF THE HOUSTON MOUNT EVEREST FLIGHT EXPEDITION OF 1933 IN COMMEMORATION OF THEIR ACHIEVEMENTS   *D.* 51 mm. By P. Metcalfe. *R. Mint* 1932 pl. B, 1–2; *Eimer* 24

The decision by *The Times* to commemorate this pioneer flight with a medal was made at the last moment; in order to minimise any risk to the dies on striking, medals were made in pure silver instead of the usual, but slightly harder, sterling .925 fineness. The entire project, from its conception to striking, took just two weeks.

2023A   **Falkland Islands Centenary 1933**   *AE*   30
Obv. Bust l., crowned and draped. GEORGIVS. V. D.G. BRITT. OMN. REX. ET. INDIÆ. IMP. *Rev.* Shield of arms; around, DESIRE THE RIGHT (motto). FALKLAND ISLANDS CENTENARY 1833–1933   *D.* 36 mm. By B. Mackennal.

Struck in a light-coloured bronze, sometimes referred to as *tombac*.

PLATE 51

1978

1987

1988

1995

1998

1999

2003

2015

2020

PLATE 52

2025

2029

2033

2037 (× ⅔)

2040

2045 (× ⅔)

2027

2059 (× ⅔)

2052

2066

2023B   **Pilgrimage of the Unemployed 1933**   £
Obv. A cross upon a globe; inscription below, SEPTEMBER A.D. 1933 IN COMMEMORATION THE   *AE*   15
HOLY YEAR AND THE "UNIVERSE" PILGRIMAGE OF UNEMPLOYED TO ROME PRESENTED BY SIR
MARTIN J. MELVIN   *Rev.* The Pope, seated, receives a kneeling figure. HAVING NOTHING.
AND POSSESSING ALL THINGS. *D.* 48 mm. (By?)

Martin John Melvin, 1st Baronet (1879–1952), industrialist and philanthropist; a leading Roman Catholic layman in
England.

2024   **British Empire Games 1934**
Obv. Female figure of Fame, a wreath in her raised hand, standing l., between two columns   *AE*   25
decorated with ribbons naming the participating Commonwealth nations. BRITISH EMPIRE
GAMES   *Ex.* LONDON 1934   *Rev.* A wreath (space within, for recipient's name). *D.* 44 mm.
By F. Phillips.

Medals also commemorate the British Commonwealth Games (formerly British Empire Games) held in Cardiff, 1958, and
in Edinburgh, 1970 (No. 2121).

2025*   **Liverpool Cathedral 1934**
Obv. A huge eagle above cathedral, head turned towards a radiate sun. *Ex.* LIVERPOOL   *AR*   45
CATHEDRAL   *Rev.* FOR FELLOW WORKERS F.M.R. 1901–1934 in the centre, divided by a laurel
branch. NOT UNTO US O LORD BUT UNTO THY NAME BE THE GLORY. *D.* 57 mm. By W. Gilbert.
Eimer 26. *See* **Plate 52**

Sometimes found inscribed with a recipient's name. The obverse is an allegory of John Milton's *Aeropagatican Eagle*,
'kindling her undazzled eyes at the full midday beam, purging and unscaling her sight at the fountain of Heavenly
Radiance'. Frederick Morton Radcliffe (1861–1953), treasurer and chairman of the Liverpool Cathedral Committee.

2026   **King's Medal for Poetry 1934**
Obv. Bust l., crowned and draped. PRESENTED BY HIS MAJESTY KING GEORGE V   *Rev.* Truth   *AV*   500
emerging from her well holding the divine flame of inspiration. FOR POETRY   *D.* 51 mm. By   *AE*   15
B. Mackennal/E. Dulac. *R. Mint* 1933 pl. C, 1; *Eimer* 27

Awarded annually in gold, within the Commonwealth, for poetry in the English language; uniform medals were struck
with the portraits of successive monarchs.

2027*   **Launching of the *R.M.S. Queen Mary* 1934**
Obv. Passenger ship under steam. R.M.S. "QUEEN MARY"   *Rev.* "QUEEN MARY" CUNARD   *Al.*   15
WHITE STAR WORLDS LARGEST LINER LAUNCHED ON SEP^T 26TH 1934 LENGTH 1,004 F^T HEIGHT
234 F^T GROSS TONNAGE APPROX 73,000   *Ex.* WITH LEWIS'S COMPLIMENTS   *D.* 38 mm. (By J. R.
Gaunt?). *See* **Plate 52**

2028   **Marriage of George, Duke of Kent and Marina of Greece 1934**
Obv. Busts l., conjoined, he uniformed and she diademed and draped; below, two   *AR*   80
interlinked circles. H.R.H. THE DUKE OF KENT. H.R.H. PRINCESS MARINA OF GREECE. *Rev.*   *AE*   45
Personal shields of the couple, supporters and crests. *Ex.* LONDON. 29 NOV. MCMXXXIV   *D.*
69 mm. By V. Phalirèas. *RWE* 266.

Princess Marina (1906–68), daughter of Prince Nicholas of Greece.

2029*   **George V, Silver Jubilee 1935**
Obv. Busts of George V and Mary, l., conjoined, crowned and draped. VI. MAII. MCMX   *a AV*   800
MCMXXXV   *Rev.* Formalized view of Windsor Castle. STET FORTUNA DOMUS   *D. a* 57 mm.; *b*   *AR*   20
32 mm. By P. Metcalfe. *R. Mint* 1934 pl. A, 3–4; *Eimer* 28; *Wollaston* 41. *See* **Plate 52**

The official Royal Mint issue. Examples of type *b* in silver which were struck at the colonial branch mints of Calcutta and   *b AV*   150
Pretoria, and can be identified, respectively, by the mint-marks I and P, which are situated on the reverse in the lower half   *AR*   3
of the field. Those struck in London and Ottawa bear no mark. A number of general and local issues were struck to
celebrate the Jubilee, although they are less numerous than those for the 1887 and 1897 jubilee celebrations.

2030   ——
Obv. Busts l., conjoined, crowned and draped. GEORGE. V. MARY Continuous border of six   *AR*   22
pairs of panels each containing an animal and its country of origin: kiwi NEW ZEALAND / fish   *AE*   12
NEWFOUNDLAND / lion INDIA / moose CANADA / kangaroo AUSTRALIA / springbok SOUTH
AFRICA   *Rev.* Female figure of the Mother Country standing upon a globe, facing, two
cherubs at her feet with cornucopiae filled with fruits of the Empire; behind, a procession of
Commonwealth subjects carrying produce. SILVER JUBILEE A D. 1935   *D.* 51 mm. [By
Turner & Simpson]

The medal sometimes occurs with Nos. 2040*a* (or 2044*a*), and 2047*a*, in a case entitled 'The Three British Kings of 1936'.

2031   ——
Obv. Busts l., conjoined, crowned and draped. GEORGE. V. MARY   *Rev.* MAY 1935 beneath a   *AR*   7
crown, crossed sword and sceptre, in the centre. TO COMMEMORATE THE JUBILEE OF THEIR   *AE*   4
REIGN   *D.* 32 mm. [By Turner & Simpson]

The medal sometimes occurs together with Nos. 2040*b* (or 2044*b*) and 2047*b* in a case entitled 'The Three British Kings of
1936'.

					£
2032	——				

2032 ——

Obv. Busts l., conjoined and crowned. GEORGE. V. MAY 1910 1935 *Rev.* City shield. *AR* 8
NOTTINGHAMSHIRE COUNTY COUNCIL. EDUCATION COMMITTEE *D.* 35 mm. By E. Carter *AE* 5
Preston. *WM* 2

Fewer local districts issued medals at this than at previous coronations and jubilees. Issuers include: Bebington, Bexhill-on-Sea, Birmingham, Blackpool, Braintree, Chatham, Coventry, Send and Southampton.

2033* **Prince of Wales, Honourable Company of Master Mariners 1935**

Obv. Head l. H.R.H. THE PRINCE OF WALES. MASTER. *Rev.* Arms with supporters, crest and *AR* 180
motto. HONOURABLE COMPANY OF MASTER MARINERS. *D.* 50 mm. By T. H. Paget. *R. Mint* *AE* —
1934 pl. C, 1–2; *Dyer* 169; *Eimer* 32. See **Plate 52**

Instituted on the suggestion of the Prince of Wales; presented in silver to a cadet who had distinguished himself. *See* No. 738.

2034 **Marquis of Reading 1935**

Obv. Bust l., draped. RVFVS. D. ISAACS. MARQVIS. OF. READING – G.C.B. – G.C.S.I. – G.C.I.E. – *AE* 90
G.C.V.O. 1860–1935 Without reverse. *D.* 138 mm. Cast. By A. Löwental. *JMC* 1183

Rufus Isaacs, 1st Marquis of Reading (1860–1935), diplomat and administrator.

2035 **Sir George Hill 1936**

Obv. Bust l., draped. SIR. GEORGE. F. HILL K.C.B. DIRECTOR. OF. THE. BRITISH MUSEUM *Rev.* A *AE* 90
winged mythological creature, seated, l. THESAVROPHYLAX *D.* 138 mm. Cast. By A.
Löwental.

Sir George Francis Hill (1867–1948), numismatist and classicist; authority on Italian Renaissance medals.

2036 *R.M.S. Queen Mary* **Commissioned 1936**

Obv. Passenger ship QUEEN MARY under steam. *Ex.* MARIA REGINA MARI ME COMMISIT *Rev.* *AV* —
Naturalistic view of New York's skyscrapers seen through the old Bargate of Southampton; *AR* —
COMMISSIONED 1936 on a ribbon, across. On either side, shields of Southampton, l., and New *AE* 35
York, r. Below, shield of Cunard White Star; above, QUEEN MARY *D.* 70 mm. By G. Bayes.
R. Mint 1935/6 pl. C, 1–2; *Eimer* 35.

The dedicatory inscription on the obverse, 'a Queen confided me to the ocean' (trans.), is based on Horace, and was the suggestion of Rudyard Kipling. The reverse design was proposed by Sir Robert Johnson, Deputy Master of the Royal Mint. The medal was available at the Mint and could also be purchased by passengers on board ship. An example was struck in silver for the medallist, and those in gold were presented to the King and Queen, the President of the United States and Mrs Roosevelt.

2037* **Rudyard Kipling, Memorial 1936**

Obv. Bust r., draped. RUDYARD KIPLING *Rev.* Two female figures on a mountain peak: one *AE* 25
standing, holding a lyre; the other reclining, her arm resting on a book. *D.* 76 mm. By J.
Kilenyi. See **Plate 52**

(Joseph) Rudyard Kipling (1865–1936), author.

2038 **Death of George V 1936**

Obv. As No. 2030. *Rev.* BORN 1865 SUCCEEDED TO THE THRONE 1910 DIED 1936 within a wreath. *AR* 22
D. 51 mm. [By Turner & Simpson] *AE* 12

The medal sometimes occurs together with Nos. 2040*a* (or 2044*a*) and 2047*a* in a case entitled 'The Three British Kings of 1936'.

EDWARD VIII, 1936

2039 **The Royal Society, King's Medal 1936**

Obv. Head l. EDWARDVS VIII REX SOC: REG: LOND: PATRONVS MCMXXXVI *Rev.* As No. 1186. *AV* —
D. 72 mm. By T. H. Paget/[W. Wyon]. *AR* 250

Uniform Royal medals of George VI and Elizabeth II have also been awarded. *See* No. 1186.

2040* **Abdication of Edward VIII 1936**

Obv. Bust r., crowned and draped. EDWARD. VIII. KING & EMPEROR. *Rev.* ASCENDED THE *a AR* 40
THRONE JANUARY 20ᵀᴴ 1936 ABDICATED DECEMBER 10ᵀᴴ 1936 upon a scroll within wreath. *D. a* *AE* 25
51 mm.; *b* 32 mm. [By Turner & Simpson]. See **Plate 52**

See Nos. 2030,1,8. A number of various medals were struck to commemorate the abdication. *b AR* 18
 AE 12

2041 ——

Obv. Bust l., crowned. EDWARD. VIII. KING AND EMPEROR *Rev.* ASCENDED THE THRONE JAN. *AV* 280
20ᵀᴴ 1936 ABDICATED DEC. 10ᵀᴴ 1936 IN FAVOUR OF H.R.H. DUKE OF YORK *D.* 35 mm. By L. E. *AR* 28
Pinches. *AE* 15

2042 **Coronation of Edward VIII 1937**

Obv. Bust l., draped. .EDWARD. VIII. *Rev.* IN REMEMBRANCE. OF. THE. CORONATION. 1937 in the centre. VIVAT. CRESCAT. FLOREAT * AD. MULTOS ANNOS * *D.* 81 mm. By L. Hujer. *Eimer* 36

This and No. 2043 were made in Austria, which Edward had recently visited. A large number of medals were struck in anticipation of the proposed coronation.

	£
AR	90
AE	35

2043 ——

Obv. Head l. EDVARDVS VIII: D: G: BRITT: OMN: REX *Rev.* 1937 above a crown, within a central beaded circle. FID: DEF: IND: IMP: DIADEMA: ACCEPIT: *D.* 60 mm. By J. Tautenhayn Jr. *Eimer* 37

See No. 2042.

AR	75
AE	30

2044 ——

Obv. As No. 2040. *Rev.* Britannia standing, r., upon a plaque inscribed CORONATION 1937; a wreath in her outstretched hand. Beyond, façade of Westminster Abbey. *D. a* 51 mm.; *b* 32 mm. [By Turner & Simpson]

See Nos. 2030,1,8.

a AR	45
AE	28
b AR	20
AE	14

GEORGE VI, 1937–52

2045* **Coronation of George VI 1937**

Obv. Busts r., conjoined, crowned and draped. GEORGE VI QUEEN ELIZABETH *Rev.* Britannia standing, facing, lion at her side and orb in hand; beyond, Thames and Parliament, St. Paul's, etc. TO COMMEMORATE THE CORONATION – A.D. 1937 – *D.* 76 mm. (By Turner & Simpson?). *See* **Plate 52**

A number of national medals commemorate the coronation but fewer local issues were produced than in 1911. A few Commonwealth countries issued medals, most notably Australia. Lady Elizabeth Bowes-Lyon (born 1900), youngest daughter of the 14th Earl of Strathmore; married Prince Albert (1895–1952), (George) Duke of York, in 1923. Latterly, Queen Elizabeth The Queen Mother.

AR	60
AE	25

2046 ——

Obv. Bust l., crowned and draped. GEORGE VI CROWNED 12 MAY 1937 *Rev.* Bust l., crowned and draped. QVEEN ELIZABETH 12 MAY 1937 *D. a* 57 mm.; *b* 30 mm. By P. Metcalfe. *R. Mint* 1935/6 pl. B, 3–4; *Eimer* 38; *Wollaston* 29

The official Royal Mint issue.

a AV	800
AR	20
b AV	150
AR	3
AE	2

2047 ——

Obv. Busts l., conjoined, crowned and draped. .GEORGE. VI & .QUEEN ELIZABETH. *Rev.* As No. 2044. *D. a* 51 mm.; *b* 32 mm. [By Turner & Simpson]

See Nos. 2030–1,8.

a AR	20
AE	12
b AR	6
AE	3

2048 ——

Obv. Busts l., conjoined and crowned. GEORGE VI. ELIZABETH 12 MAY 1937. *Rev.* Arms and crest. BOROUGH OF HENDON. WYKEHAM ROAD CORONATION FESTIVITIES. *D.* 38 mm. (By?)

Other localities for which medals have been noted include: Beeston, Berkshire, Bolton, Chatham, Denbigh, Hampstead, Handsworth, Sutton Coldfield, Warrington, West Bromwich, Wrexham.

AE	5

2049 **Coronation of George VI, National Maritime Museum 1937**

Obv. Busts l., conjoined, crowned and draped. CORONATION OF KING GEORGE VI & QUEEN ELIZABETH 12 MAY 1937 *Rev.* Façade of building. QUEEN'S HOUSE *Ex.* THE NATIONAL MARITIME MUSEUM OPENED BY HIS MAJESTY KING GEORGE VI 27TH APRIL 1937 *D. a* 57 mm.; *b* 32 mm. [By J. Langford Jones] *R. Mint* 1935/6 pl. B, 5

The National Maritime Act passed in 1934 appropriated the vacant Queen's House to house the museum and the work was completed in 1936. The conjoined portraits on this medal were originally produced for the Royal Mint; permission was given for their use on coronation medals issued by private manufacturers, such as this medal struck by Spink & Son (*Eimer* 11).

a AR	30
b AR	9

2050 **Births & Deaths Registration; Marriage Acts, Centenary 1937**

Obv. Busts l., conjoined, of Queen Victoria (her young head, after W. Wyon) and George VI; 1837 1937 on either side. BIRTHS & DEATHS REGISTRATION & MARRIAGE ACTS *Rev.* The

AV	—
AR	10

Lampadephorian Torch. BIRTH – MARRIAGE – DEATH   *D.* 32 mm. By J. Langford Jones. *R.*   £
Mint 1937 pl. D, 1

The torch is that used at the Lampadephoria, the relay races in ancient Greece, and symbolizes the continuity of life. It
occurs on the coinage of Amphipolis, *c.*400 BC.

2051   Neville Chamberlain 1938

Obv. Bust l., draped. NEVILLE. CHAMBERLAIN. P.C. M.P. (incuse). *Rev.* A male figure, naked   *AE*   50
but for a cloak, crosses a bridge, l., an olive-branch in hand. .MUENCHEN. 29. SEPT. 1938
(incuse). *D.* 96 mm. Cast. By E. v. Esseö.

Arthur Neville Chamberlain (1869–1940), statesman; son of Joseph. He had been invited by Hitler to attend a four-power
conference in Munich. He returned to England the following day, amid much acclaim, bearing an agreement of Anglo-
German friendship. This medal is a tribute to his efforts to restrain the German government.

2052*   ——

Obv. Bust three-quarters r., draped. NEVILLE CHAMBERLAIN   *Rev.* MUNICH 1938 in the   *AR*   22
centre, divided by an olive-branch. OUT OF THE NETTLE DANGER HE HAS PLUCKED THE FLOWER   *AE*   12
SAFETY   *D.* 35 mm. By L. E. Pinches. *See* **Plate 52**

2053   International Council of Women, Golden Jubilee 1938

Obv. Bust l., draped and wearing head-dress. ISHBEL MARCHIONESS OF ABERDEEN AND   *AE*   45
TEMAIR   *Rev.* Female figures symbolizing the continents standing, facing each other, their
hands clasped, before a large globe draped with a ribbon, inscribed I.C.W. – C.I.F. – I.F.B.
Below, 1888–1938 on ground-line. OMNIA QUÆCUMQUE VULTIS UTFACIANT VOBIS HOMINES ET
VOS FACITE ILLIS   *D.* 74 mm. By I. C. Thoresen/E. W. Becker.

Ishbel Maria Marjoribanks, Lady Aberdeen and Temair (1857–1939), champion of women's rights and social reformer.
See C. Eimer. *SCMB* 1983 October, 255–6.

2054   London & Birmingham Railway, Centenary 1938

Obv. View of Euston Arch. LONDON AND BIRMINGHAM RAILWAY   *Ex.* GEORGE CARR GLYNN –   *AR*   48
CHAIRMAN   ROBERT STEPHENSON – ENGINEER   PHILIP HARDWICK – ARCHITECT 1838   *Rev.*   *AE*   20
Thirteen-line inscription of directors &c. DIRECTORS LORD STAMP – CHAIRMAN ... OWEN
GLYNNE ROBERTS – SECRETARY, in the centre. LONDON MIDLAND AND SCOTTISH RAILWAY
1938   *D.* 65 mm. By J. R. Pinches.

2055   Rabbi Joseph Hertz 1938

Obv. Bust l., in rabbinic dress. Hebrew inscription [= Joseph Tzebi Hertz Chief Rabbi of   *AE*   40
Great Britain and its Empire]. *Rev.* TO THE VERY REVEREND DR. JOSEPH HERMAN HERTZ ON THE
COMPLETION OF A QUARTER CENTURY 1913–1938 IN THE BRITISH CHIEF RABBINATE FROM THE
SILVER JUBILEE FUND FOR JEWISH RELIGIOUS EDUCATION divided by a menorah (seven-
branched candelabrum). *D.* 35 mm. By B. Elkan. JMC 1158

Joseph Herman Hertz (1872–1946), Chief Rabbi of the United Hebrew Congregations of the British Empire.

2056   Hull Geological Society 1938

Obv. Bust l. T. SHEPPARD PRESIDENT   *Rev.* An ammonite, Toxoceratoides Sheppardi Spath,   *AR*   25
and crossed geological hammers, over a map of Humberside showing the location of the   *AE*   12
Society's investigations. HULL GEOLOGICAL SOCIETY 1888–1938   *D.* 45 mm. (By?)

Thomas Sheppard (1876–1945), geologist, archaeologist and numismatist; author of various works.

2057   Royal Society of British Sculptors *c.*1938

Obv. Roman soldier seen from behind, head r.; a female figure upon his outstretched hand.   *AR*   35
THE ROYAL SOCIETY OF BRITISH SCULPTORS. *Rev.* A burning altar standing between sculptor's
implements. AWARD FOR SCULPTURE Below, a tablet (blank, for recipient's name). *D.* 51 mm.
By G. Bayes.

2058   Royal Visit to the United States 1939

Obv. Busts l., conjoined and draped. KING GEORGE VI & QUEEN ELIZABETH   *Rev.* British and   *AR*   12
American flags, crossed: an eagle, above; 1939, below. TO COMMEMORATE THE ROYAL VISIT TO
THE UNITED STATES OF AMERICA   *D.* 32 mm. (By?)

The first visit of a reigning British sovereign to the USA.

2059*   Sinking of the *Athenia* 1939

Obv. Seated figure of Winston Churchill, facing, upon a crate marked VORS[ICHT] HÖLLEN   *AE*   150
MASCHINE and tied with a label, AN MR. CHURCHILL. In his hand is a balance, a bomb in each   *Fe.*   90
pan marked, one with a swastika, the other with a Union flag; he indicates the former. EIN
MEISTER DER LÜGE   *Rev.* Death seated, r., upon the bow of a ship, ATHENIA, holding a torch
and a bomb marked with the Union flag. 4 SEPTEMBER 1939   *D.* 70 mm. Cast. By G. Goetz.
Engstrom 3. *See* **Plate 52**

The *Athenia*, an Atlantic passenger liner, was torpedoed off the coast of Ireland by a German submarine, only hours after
the declaration of war; Churchill was First Lord of the Admiralty.

2060   **Sinking of** *H.M.S. Courageous* **1939**   £
Obv. Neptune, three-quarters l., emerging from the sea with the COURAGEOUS carried on his   *AE*   150
shoulder. RULE BRITANNIA! *Rev.* Death, cloaked, emerges from the sea with a scroll,   *Fe.*   90
inscribed TORPED. VON DEUTSCH. "U" BOOT 18. SEPT. 1939 (incuse) which he displays. DIE
HIOBSBOTSCHAFT AN CHURCHILL   *D.* 70 mm. Cast. By G. Goetz. *Engstrom* 4

The aircraft carrier *H.M.S. Courageous* was the Royal Navy's first heavy loss of the war. Another satirical medal by G.
Goetz records the air attack on the aircraft carrier *H.M.S. Ark Royal* off the Norwegian coast in September 1939 (*Engstrom*
5).

2061   **Henry, Duke of Gloucester: Grand Prior, Order of St. John 1939**
Obv. Bust l., draped in robes of the Order; below, badge of the Grand Prior. PRO FIDE below   *AR*   45
the Duke's shield, in the field. HENRICUS. GLOUCESTRIAE. DUX. MAGNUS. PRIOR   *Rev.* Arched   *AE*   22
castle gateway of the College decorated with a heraldic shield, and flanked by two lions in
panels. MCMXXXIX and motto on ribbon, below. IN. BRITT. OMN. VEN. ORD. HOSP. S. JOHIS.
HIER. *D.* 70 mm. By G. Bayes.

Struck in 1948. Henry, Duke of Gloucester (1900–74), 3rd son of George V and Mary; Grand Prior of the Order from 1939
until his death.

2062 *   **Princess Elizabeth 1939**
Obv. Head r. PRINCESS ELIZABETH 1939   *Rev.* Branches of oak and vine threaded through   *AR*   25
crown; clouds, radiate, in distance. BORN APRIL 21 1926 in the field. HEIR PRESUMPTIVE TO THE
THRONE   *D.* 26 mm. (By M. E. Soady?). *See* **Plate 53**

Princess Elizabeth Alexandra Mary (born 1926), Queen Elizabeth II 1952–. 1st child and elder daughter of George VI and
Queen Elizabeth. One of the first medallic portraits of Her Majesty the Queen.

2063   **Winston Churchill 1941**
Obv. Bust l., draped. WINSTON CHURCHILL 1941   *Rev.* Plain. *D.* 127 mm. Cast. By F.   *AE*   40
Kormis. *Engstrom* 6; *Kormis* 17

Commissioned by Hodder & Stoughton Ltd in conjunction with their publication of Philip Guedalla's *Mr Churchill: An
Intimate Portrait*.

2064   **Leslie Hore-Belisha 1941**
Obv. Head l. THE RIGHT HON. LESLIE HORE BELISHA 1941   *Rev.* Plain. *D.* 108 mm. Cast. By F.   *AE*   50
Kormis. *Friedenberg* 1963, 60; *Kormis* 26

(Isaac) Leslie Hore-Belisha (1893–1957), politician; at the Ministry of Transport he was responsible for the introduction
of flashing amber globes at pedestrian crossings, known as 'Belisha Beacons'. Other portrait medals by Kormis from the
1940s include those of Alexander Fleming and Herbert Morrison.

2065   **Attack and Liberation of Arnhem 1944**
Obv. A fallen warrior, winged, holds up a broken dagger. PRO LIBERTATE BATAVA   *AR*   60
OCCIDERUNT. ARNHEM. MCMXLIV. *Rev.* An armed and helmeted warrior. r., upon Pegasus.   *AE*   35
AMAT VICTORIA CURAM. FIRST AIRBORNE DIVISION. *D.* 65 mm. By L. O. Wenckebach. *SNC*
1948, 423–4

Struck in 1948 and sold in aid of the Airborne Forces' Charity Society.

2066 *   **Battle of London 1940–44**
Obv. An aircraft in sky over the Tower. BATTLE OF LONDON. JUNE 1944 AUGUST. *Rev.* An   *AR*   —
aircraft caught in searchlights above St. Paul's Cathedral. BATTLE OF LONDON. SEPT 1940.   *AE*   18
1941 MAY. *D.* 57 mm. [By L. E. Pinches]. *See* **Plate 52**

Sold in aid of the Royal Air Force Benevolent Fund. The medal was restruck in 1966, with lines of flak added. Examples in
bronze are silvered.

2067   **Field Marshal Bernard Montgomery** *c.*1944
Obv. Bust l., uniformed. FIELD MARSHAL SIR BERNARD L. MONTGOMERY. K.C.B. D.S.O. *Rev.* LA   *AE*   25
BELGIQUE RECONNAISSANTE HET ERKENTELIJK BELGIE in the centre. Above, UFAC in a semi-
circular compartment; below, VVV   *D.* 70 mm. By E. de Bremaecker.

Bernard Law Montgomery, 1st Viscount Montgomery of Alamein (1887–1976), Field Marshal.

2068   **Final Advance into Germany 1944–45**
Obv. 1944–1945 NORMANDY MOUNT PINÇON CROSSING OF THE SEINE BRUSSELS AND ANTWERP   *AR*   30
THE ADVANCE TO ARNHEM THE ARDENNES THE REICHSWALD CROSSING OF THE RHINE FINAL   *AE*   12
ADVANCE INTO GERMANY, within a wreath. *Rev.* A boar in centre; three shields, around. XXX
CORPS ALAMEIN CUXHAVEN   *D.* 50 mm. (By?)

2069   **Liberation of France 1945**
Obv. Bust three-quarters l., uniformed and wearing cap. WINSTON CHURCHILL   *Rev.*   *AV*   gold
Churchill's family arms; below, "NOUS N'AVONS QU'UN DÉSIR VOIR UNE FRANCE FORTE ET   value
LIBRE ENTOURÉE DE SON EMPIRE ET RÉUNIE A L'ALSACE-LORRAINE" 10 NOVEMBRE 1942 *D.*   *AR*   22
68 mm. By P. Turin. *Engstrom* 11   *AE*   8

The inscription is from Churchill's speech at the Lord Mayor's Banquet, expressing the desire for a free and strong
France. The medal has been subsequently restruck.

			£

2070 Allied Victory 1945
Obv. Bust l., draped; 1945 superimposed upon V (Victory sign, incuse) in the field, behind   *AE*   10
head. CHURCHILL   *Rev.* WE. WILL FIGHT. ON LAND ON. SEA AND. IN THE. AIR UNTIL VICTORY IS
WON in the centre, divided by victory torch held in hand issuing from clouds. UNFLINCHING.
INDOMITABLE. HIS. SPIRIT. SAVED. BRITAIN. AND. SO. THE. WORLD … *D.* 63 mm. By A.
Löwental. *Engstrom 12*
See No. 2105.

2071 Liberation of Guernsey 1945
Obv. Shield of the STATES OF GUERNSEY   *Rev.* LIBERATION FROM GERMAN OCCUPATION MAY   *AE*   5
9TH 1945   *D.* 35 mm. (By?)
Issued in May 1946 by the Education Department of Guernsey to all school children to celebrate the first anniversary. The
medals are gilt and occur with a suspension loop and an attached pin-back clasp.

2072 Victory Celebrations 1946
Obv. Busts l., conjoined and crowned. H.M. KING GEORGE VI H.M. QUEEN ELIZABETH   *Rev.*   *AE*   3
Shield of arms. CITY OF WESTMINSTER VICTORY CELEBRATIONS JUNE. 1946   *D.* 32 mm. (By?)
In contrast to the First World War, very few localities celebrated the Victory and Peace with medals.

2073* Marriage of Princess Elizabeth and Prince Philip 1947
Obv. Busts r., draped. PRINCESS ELIZABETH LIEUT PHILIP 1947   *Rev.* A heart, inscribed TO   *WM*   10
COMMEMORATE THE HAPPY UNION OF PRINCESS ELIZABETH AND LIEUT PHILIP, decorated with
flags of seven Commonwealth nations. 1947   *D.* 34 mm. (By?) *RWE 294. See* **Plate 53**
The only commemorative medal for the marriage which has been noted; usually found with a suspension loop on the edge.
Prince Philip Mountbatten of Greece and Denmark (born 1921), Prince Philip, Duke of Edinburgh.

2074 Royal Society of Arts 1947
Obv. Head l. THE PRINCESS ELIZABETH. PRESIDENT. MCMXLVII. *Rev.* Façade of the Society's   *AR*   60
building (in John Adam Street, London W.C.2). ROYAL SOCIETY OF ARTS 1754   *D.* 57 mm.   *AE*   28
By P. Metcalfe
See No. 643.

2075 Earl Mountbatten 1947
Obv. Bust r., draped. THE EARL MOUNTBATTEN OF BURMA, K.G., SUPREME ALLIED COMMANDER   *AE*   60
SOUTH EAST ASIA 1943–1946, VICEROY OF INDIA 1947. *Rev.* Plain. *D.* 138 mm. Cast. By F.
Kormis. *Kormis 51*
Prince Louis Francis of Battenberg, 1st Earl Mountbatten of Burma (1900–79), naval officer and administrator; younger
son of the Marquis of Milford Haven.

2076 XIV Olympic Games London 1948
Obv. View of the Houses of Parliament and 'Big Ben' within a semi-circular compartment.   *AE*   25
XIV. OLYMPIAD LONDON 1948; below, the five Olympic rings. *Rev.* As No. 1904. *D.* 51 mm.
[By J. R. Pinches/B. Mackennal]

2077 ——
Obv. Figure of Victory seated in a classical landscape, facing, with palm-branch and holding   *AV*   650
wreath aloft; beyond, edge of the Colosseum. XIVTH OLYMPIAD LONDON 1948   *Rev.* A   *AR*   120
competitor being 'chaired' in victory by a crowd of athletes. *D.* 51 mm. By G. Cassioli.   *AE*   70
This medal has been used successively as a prize since the 1928 IX Olympiad in Amsterdam, the obverse die amended
according to the host country.

2078 George Bernard Shaw 1949
Obv. Head three-quarters l. G. BERNARD. SHAW. *Rev.* Figure of Shaw carrying books; to r., a   *AE*   35
simplified representation of the British Museum. *D.* 94 mm. Cast. By E. v. Esseö
George Bernard Shaw (1856–1950), playwright, novelist and critic. He made a large bequest to the British Museum in
gratitude for the facilities which he had enjoyed.

2079 Retirement of John Craig 1949
Obv. Bust l., draped. TO SIR JOHN CRAIG FROM THE OFFICERS OF THE ROYAL MINT. *Rev.* A   *AR*   30
female figure, with pencil and plan, seated opposite a workman about to strike a punch.   *AE*   12
EXCVDIT NVMMOS   *Ex.* MCMXXXVIII–MCMXLIX   *D.* 57 mm. By P. Vincze. *SNC 1949/619*
Sir John Craig (1885–1977), Deputy Master of the Royal Mint.

2080 Royal Visit to Australia 1949
Obv. Busts l., conjoined and draped. KING GEORGE VI: QUEEN ELIZABETH: THE PRINCESS   *AR*   28
MARGARET: *Rev.* Australian arms. ROYAL VISIT   *Ex.* 1949 AUSTRALIA   *D.* 32 mm. By Stokes.   *AE*   12
Carlisle 1949/4
This medal has an integral suspension loop. Several medals were struck to commemorate the intended visit to Australia
and New Zealand, postponed due to the King's illness. Princess Margaret (born 1930), younger daughter of George VI
and Elizabeth.

			£
2081	**Festival of Britain 1951**		
	Obv. Concorde (emblem of the Festival). FESTIVAL OF BRITAIN 1951 *Rev.* Panoramic view	*AR*	15
	of the exhibition site. *D.* 39 mm. (By?)	*AE*	8
	Only a few medals commemorate the Festival.		
2082	**Royal Society of Arts 1952**		
	Obv. Head l. PRINCE PHILIP. PRESIDENT MCMLII *Rev.* As No. 2074. *D.* 57 mm. [By P.	*AV*	—
	Metcalfe]	*AR*	45
	Prince Philip was instituted as President in 1953. *See* No. 643.	*AE*	25
2083	**Royal Visit to Kenya 1952**		
	Obv. Busts l., conjoined and draped. H.R.H. PRINCESS ELIZABETH & H.R.H. THE DVKE OF	*AR*	55
	EDINBVRGH. *Rev.* TO COMMEMORATE THE ROYAL VISIT A.D. 1952. upon a scroll within wreath.	*AE*	30
	D. 51 mm. By E. Fey.		
	The couple had set off on a tour of Australia and New Zealand on behalf of the King, who was not well enough to go. They had only reached Kenya when news reached them that the King had died, and they returned home at once.		

ELIZABETH II, 1952–

2084	**Coronation of Elizabeth II 1953**		
	Obv. Bust r., crowned and draped. HER. MAJESTY. QUEEN. ELIZABETH. II. *Rev.* Similar to	*a AR*	60
	No. 2045. TO. COMMEMORATE. THE. CORONATION. AD 1953. *D. a* 76 mm.; *b* 51 mm.; *c* 38 mm.	*AE*	25
	By E. Fey.	*b AR*	18
	No official Royal Mint coronation medal was struck, and less general and local medals than for other recent coronations. A	*AE*	10
	few Commonwealth countries struck medals, most notably Australia.	*c AR*	8
		AE	4
2085*	——		
	Obv. Bust r., crowned and draped; beyond, façade of Westminster Abbey. HER MAJESTY	*a AV*	gold
	QUEEN ELIZABETH THE SECOND *Ex.* CROWNED IN WESTMINSTER ABBEY. 2ND JUNE 1953 *Rev.*		value
	The Queen enthroned, l., about to be crowned. "GOD CROWN YOU WITH A CROWN OF GLORY	*AR*	38
	AND RIGHTEOUSNESS" *D. a* 57 mm.; *b* 39 mm. By P. Vincze. *SNC* 1954/7–8. *See* **Plate 53**	*AE*	20
		b AV	gold
			value
		AR	22
		AE	12
2086	——		
	Obv. Bust r., crowned and draped. ELIZABETH II CROWNED JUNE 2ND 1953 *Rev.* View of	*a AV*	gold
	Buckingham Palace, seen slightly from the l. *Ex.* Spray of rose, thistle and shamrock. *D. a*		value
	57 mm.; *b* 32 mm. By Spink & Son. *SNC* 1953, opp. 249	*AR*	35
		AE	15
		b AV	gold
			value
		AR	12
		AE	7
2087	——		
	Obv. Bust r., draped. S.M. LA. REINE. .ELIZABETH. II. *Rev.* View of Windsor Castle, towards	*a AR*	60
	main gate. 2 JUIN 1953 divided by a crown. *Ex.* .LA. FRANCE. À .S. M. ELIZABETH. II. *D. a*	*AE*	18
	72 mm.; *b* 51 mm. By H. Dropsy.		
	This medal has been restruck.	*b AR*	32
		AE	10
2088	——		
	Obv. Bust r., crowned and draped, of the Queen. *Rev.* A triskeles. QUOCUNQUE. JECERIS.	*Al.*	8
	STABIT., below. TO COMMEMORATE THE CORONATION OF H.M. QUEEN ELIZABETH II. JUNE 2ND		
	1953. *D.* 33 mm. (By?)		
	Issued by the Isle of Man; others noted include: Barry, Derby, Farnworth, Jersey and Stornoway.		

2089	**British Museum, Bicentenary 1953**		£
	Obv. Bust l., draped. SIR HANS SLOANE 1660–1753 *Rev.* Façade of the British Museum.	*a* AV	gold
	VIGET HIC REDIVIVA VETVSTAS *Ex.* TO COMMEMORATE THE 200TH ANNIVERSARY OF THE BRITISH		value
	MUSEUM DATING FROM THE PURCHASE OF THE SIR HANS SLOANE COLLECTION 7 JUNE 1753 *D. a*	AR	28
	58 mm.; *b* 39 mm. By P. Vincze. *SNC* 1954/7–8	AE	12
		b AV	gold
			value
		AR	18
		AE	10

2090	**Dylan Thomas 1953**		
	Obv. Bust r., draped, of Thomas. *Rev.* (incuse) TIME HELD ME GREEN AND DYING in the	AE	30
	centre. DYLAN THOMAS. 1914–1953. *D.* 125 mm. Cast. By J. Jones. *The Medal* 7/78		
	Issued by the British Art Medal Society in 1985 (*see* No. 2141). Dylan Marlais Thomas (1914–53), poet.		

2091	**Royal Commonwealth Tour 1953–54**		
	Obv. Busts r., conjoined and draped, of the Queen and Prince Philip. THE ROYAL VISIT	AR	28
	MCMLIII–IV *Rev.* Royal arms: ER above; MCMLIII–IV below. *D.* 38 mm. [By M. Gillick] *R.*	AE	15
	Mint 1953 pl. B, 3–4		

2092	**Royal Visit to Uganda 1954**		
	Obv. Busts l., conjoined and draped. H.M. QUEEN ELIZABETH II & H.R.H. THE DUKE OF	AR	45
	EDINBURGH *Rev.* An ostrich standing in a landscape. TO COMMEMORATE THE ROYAL VISIT TO	AE	28
	UGANDA. 1954. *D.* 39 mm. (By E. Fey?)	Al.	15

2093	**Winston Churchill, 80th Birthday 1954**		
	Obv. Bust of Churchill, draped, almost facing. *Rev.* 1874–1954 TO COMMEMORATE THE 80TH	AR	12
	BIRTHDAY OF THE RIGHT HONOURABLE SIR WINSTON S. CHURCHILL K.G., O.M., C.H. BRITAIN'S	AE	5
	WARTIME LEADER NEVER WAS SO MUCH OWED BY SO MANY Two oak branches above; crossed		
	laurel branches below. *D.* 37 mm. [By The Mint, Birmingham] *Engstrom* 17		

2094	**Winston Churchill, Retirement 1955**		
	Obv. As No. 2093. *Rev.* BRITAIN'S LEADER IN PEACE & WAR NEVER WAS SO MUCH OWED BY SO	AR	12
	MANY THE RIGHT HONOURABLE SIR WINSTON S. CHURCHILL K.G., O.M., C.H. TO MARK HIS	AE	5
	RETIREMENT FROM THE PREMIERSHIP 5TH APRIL 1955 Two oak branches above; crossed laurel		
	branches below. *D.* 37 mm. [By The Mint, Birmingham] *Engstrom* 18		

2095	**Battle of Trafalgar, 150th Anniversary 1955**		
	Obv. Bust l., uniformed. ADMIRAL LORD NELSON. ENGLAND EVER SALUTES HIS MEMORY. 1758	*a* AV	800
	1805 *Rev.* Neptune rising from the sea, l., holds a wreath aloft; beyond, fully-rigged ship.	AR	40
	TRAFALGAR 1805–1955 *D. a* 58 mm.; *b* 39 mm. By P. Vincze.	AE	18
		b AV	350
		AR	15
		AE	8

2096	**Austin Motor Company 1955**		
	Obv. Head of Austin three-quarters r. AUSTIN GOLDEN JUBILEE. 1905–1955 *Rev.* An	AE	10
	illustration of two cars from then and now; each in a compartment. THE AUSTIN CAR OF 1905. /		
	THE AUSTIN CAR OF 1955. *D.* 64 mm. (By?)		
	Herbert Austin, Baron Austin (1866–1941), motor car manufacturer. Examples are usually silvered.		

2097	**Resettlement of Jews in Great Britain, Tercentenary 1956**		
	Obv. Draped busts, almost facing, of OLIVER CROMWELL and MENASSEH BEN ISRAEL, in two	AR	65
	oval frames: arms of the Spanish and Portuguese Synagogue, London, above; a menorah	AE	35
	(seven-branched candelabrum), below. *Rev.* Female figure seated, l., holding a scroll,		
	resting on a table, dated 1656 1956 and inscribed in Hebrew [= Thou shalt know that thy		
	tent is in peace, *Job.* V.24.]. RESETTLEMENT OF THE JEWS IN GT. BRITAIN. 300TH ANNIVERSARY.		
	D. 56 mm. By P. Vincze. *JMC* 1154		
	Manasseh ben Israel (1604–57), Dutch Rabbi and theologian; advocate for the re-admission of the Jews into England.		

2098	**Royal Visit to Paris 1957**		
	Obv. Busts r., conjoined, crowned and draped. S.M. LA REINE. ELIZABETH. II * S.A.R. LE.	*a* AR	45
	PRINCE. PHILIP. DUC. D'EDINBOURG. *Rev.* France and Britannia, standing, shaking hands;	AE	12
	shields of the two nations between. VISITE. À. PARIS. DE. S.M. LA. REINE. ELIZABETH. II. *Ex.*		
	AVRIL. 1957. *D. a* 72 mm.; *b* 51 mm. By H. Dropsy.	*b* AR	25
	This medal has been restruck.	AE	8

			£

2099 **Royal Geographical Society, Fuchs Medal 1958**
Obv. Bust l., draped. VIVIAN ERNEST FUCHS   *Rev.* The Antarctic Continent: the route of the   *AV*   —
expedition, from the WEDDELL SEA across the SOUTH POLE past SHACKLETON to SCOTT on the   *AE*   60
ROSS SEA, delineated. 1955–1958 below. PRESENTED BY THE ROYAL GEOGRAPHICAL SOCIETY ∗
TRANS-ANTARCTIC EXPEDITION ∗   *D.* 64 mm. By F. Kovacs. *Poulsom* 88, 92

Sir Vivian Ernest Fuchs (born 1908), Antarctic explorer; received this medal in gold. Expedition members were awarded
examples in bronze.

2100 **Viscount Herbert Samuel, 90th Birthday 1960**
Obv. Bust l., draped; 90 below. HERBERT VISCOUNT SAMUEL O.M. 1960   *Rev.* An elderly man,   *AR*   28
seated, inscribing a book. AMICVS SOCRATES SED MAGIS AMICA VERITAS   *D.* 57 mm. By P.   *AE*   15
Vincze.

Sir Herbert Louis Samuel, 1st Viscount Samuel (1870–1963), politician and administrator; first High Commissioner to
Palestine.

2101 **British Exhibition, New York 1960**
Obv. A column decorated with eagle and lion, array of flags, and an Anglo-American shield.   *AE*   5
BRITISH EXHIBITION JUNE. NEW YORK. 1960   *Rev.* Shield and crest of the ROYAL MINT   *D.*
39 mm. (By?)

2102 **The National Trust 1963**
Obv. Bust r., crowned and draped, of Queen Elizabeth The Queen Mother. .ELIZABETHA. R.   *AR*   10
REGINAE MATER. PRAESES. *Rev.* A branch of oak leaves in the centre; NATIONAL TRUST either
side. *D.* 39 mm. By C. Ironside. *R. Mint* 1963 pl. E, 1

Medals were presented to life members and are occasionally found inscribed on the edge.

2103 **Shakespeare, 400th Anniversary of Birth 1964**
Obv. Bust l., draped. WILLIAM SHAKESPEARE. 400TH ANNIVERSARY Below bust, THE   *AR*   24
SHAKESPEARE BIRTHPLACE TRUST. 1964   *Rev.* A male and a female figure hold open book,   *AE*   10
torch, and masks of comedy and tragedy. WE SHALL NOT LOOK UPON HIS LIKE AGAIN   *Ex.*
1564–1964   *D.* 57 mm. By P. Vincze.

2104 **Death of Winston Churchill 1965**
Obv. Bust almost facing, draped; books and paint-brushes on a shelf, behind. *Ex.* WINSTON   *a AV*   gold
CHURCHILL 1874–1965   *Rev.* A soldier standing defiantly on a sea-shore; aircraft above. *Ex.*   value
"VERY WELL, ALONE"   *D. a* 56 mm.; *b* 39 mm. By F. Kovacs. *Engstrom* 30   *AR*   22

The reverse is after a cartoon by David Low. More than forty medals commemorate Churchill's death.

b AV   gold
                                                                                                    value
AR   10

2105 ——
Obv. As No. 2070, but with added inscription OB. 24. JAN. 1965., below bust. *Rev.* As   *AV*   gold
No. 2070. *D.* 50 mm. By A. Löwental. *Engstrom* 35   value
AR   15
AE   4

2106 **Battle of Waterloo, 150th Anniversary 1965**
Obv. IN HONOUR OF THE REGIMENTS WHICH FOUGHT AT THE BATTLE OF WATERLOO 18TH JUNE   *AE*   12
1815 within a wreath. *Rev.* Arms, supporters, etc. of the City of London. GUILDHALL 21ST
JUNE 1965   *D.* 44 mm. [By Toye, Kenning & Spencer]

2107 **Westminster Abbey, 900th Anniversary 1965**
Obv. Façade of Westminster Abbey. 900 YEARS   *Ex.* WESTMINSTER ABBEY   *Rev.* Group of   *AV*   gold
portraits of monarchs and other people associated at various times with the Abbey: Edward   value
the Confessor, Henry III, Elizabeth I, Henry Yevele (master mason), John Islip (abbot),   *AR*   15
Henry Purcell (organist and composer), Richard Busby (headmaster of Westminster   *AE*   5
School), Nicholas Hawksmoor (surveyor and architect), Arthur Stanley (Dean), and Eric
Symes Abbott (appt. Dean in 1959). *D.* 57 mm. [By M. Rizzello] *R. Mint* 1965 pl. E, 2

2108 **Battle of Hastings, 900th Anniversary 1966**
Obv. Armorial shield of Hastings; a longboat below. BATTLE OF HASTINGS 900th ANNIVERSARY   *AV*   gold
1966   *Rev.* Scene of battle. *Ex.* MLXVI   *D.* 57 mm. By L. E. Pinches.   value
AR   15

2109 **50th Anniversary of the Easter Rising 1966**
Obv. Bust r., draped, between two shamrocks. PADRAIG H. PEARSE 1879–1916   *Rev.* A male   *a AV*   gold
and a female kneel either side of a pledge: WE PLEDGE OUR LIVES AND THE LIVES OF OUR   value
COMRADES IN ARMS TO THE CAUSE OF ITS FREEDOM OF ITS WELFARE AND OF ITS EXALTATION   *AR*   24

241

AMONG THE NATIONS PHP APRIL 1916   *Ex.* EIRE 1916–1966   *D. a* 50 mm.; *b* 38 mm. By P. Vincze. *Went* 1978, 158

     Padhraic Henry Pearse (1879–1916), commanded Irish forces in the Easter Rebellion.

			£
		b AV	gold value
		AR	15

2110   **Prince Philip, Visit to North America 1966**
Obv. Bust l., uniformed. H.R.H. THE PRINCE PHILIP DUKE OF EDINBURGH   *Rev.* Prince Philip's cypher in the centre. YOUTH. CHARITY. ATHLETICS. ROYAL VISIT TO NORTH AMERICA 1966   *D.* 38 mm. [By Spink & Son] *SNC* 1966/330   *AR*   12

2111   **Great Fire of London, 300th Anniversary 1966**
Obv. Panoramic view of London and the river Thames, its sweep of the north bank and London Bridge. LONDON 1966   *Rev.* Standing figure of Pepys before burning buildings and the old St. Paul's. "AND AGAIN TO SEE THE FIRE, WHICH WAS NOW GOT FURTHER". PEPYS' DIARY 2.IX.1666   *D. a* 57 mm.; *b* 39 mm. [By Spink & Son].

a AV	gold value	
AR	18	
b AV	gold value	
AR	10	

2112*   **The Beatles 1966**
Obv. The heads of John Lennon, l., and George Harrison, r., above those of Paul McCartney and Ringo Starr. THE BEATLES in a continuous legend. *Rev.* Their signatures in the centre. THE BEATLES. 1965–1966. *D.* 40 mm. By G. Colley. *See* **Plate 53**   *AR*   15

     The Beatles were a pop group formed in Liverpool in the late 1950s. George Harrison (born 1943), composer and musician. John Lennon (1940–80), composer, musician, singer-song writer, and artist. Paul McCartney (born 1942), composer, musician and singer-song writer. Ringo Starr (born 1940), musician and actor.

2113   **Sir Francis Chichester 1967**
Obv. Bust l., draped and wearing cap. SIR FRANCIS CHICHESTER   *Rev.* Neptune kneeling, l., before a globe on which are two boats. GIPSY MOTH IV 1966–67 GOLDEN HIND 1577–80   *D. a* 57 mm.; *b* 38 mm. By P. Vincze. *SNC* 1967/162–3

     Francis Chichester (1901–72), the first to sail round the world single-handed.

a AV	gold value	
AR	15	
b AV	gold value	
AR	8	

2114   *R.M.S. Queen Elizabeth*, **Final Voyage 1968**
Obv. Passenger ship, QUEEN ELIZABETH, l., under steam. *Ex.* CUNARD QUEEN ELIZABETH FINAL VOYAGES OCTOBER NOVEMBER 1968   *Rev.* Plan of SOUTHAMPTON WATER; shield below. LAUNCHED 27 SEPTEMBER 1938 WAR SERVICE 1940 1946 MAIDEN VOYAGE 16 OCTOBER 1946   *D.* 39 mm. (By?)

AR	15
AE	8

2115   *R.M.S. Queen Elizabeth II*, **Maiden Voyage 1969**
Obv. Broadside view of ship. RMS QUEEN ELIZABETH 2 In field, QE2 in a monogram. *Ex.* CUNARD   *Rev.* QE2 in a monogram, in the centre. MAIDEN VOYAGE CUNARD   *D.* 65 mm. By G. Colley.

Pd.	Palladium value
AR	28

2116   **Prince of Wales, Investiture 1969**
Obv. Bust r., draped. ARWISGIAD CHARLES TYWYSOG CYMRU. CAERNARVON 1969. *Rev.* The Welsh dragon. Y DDRAIG GOCH DDYRY CYCHWYN   *D. a* 58 mm.; *b* 45 mm.; *c* 32 mm. By M. Rizzello. *R. Mint* 1969 pl. H

     The official Royal Mint issue; bronze medals occur with a gilt finish. More than fifteen various medals were struck for the Investiture. Charles (born 1948), cr. Prince of Wales in 1958; eldest son of Elizabeth II and Prince Philip.

a AR	22
AE	5
b AR	12
c AE	2

2117   ——
Obv. Head r. CHARLES. PRINCE. OF. WALES   *Rev.* View of Caernarvon Castle; Prince's crest and motto, above. ARWISGIAD. SIARL. TYWYSOG. CYMRU. M.G. *Ex.* Welsh dragon *D. a* 58 mm.; *b* 45 mm.; *c* 32 mm. [By G. A. Holman]

a AR	22
b AR	12
c AR	6

2118   ——
Obv. Head l. H.R.H. CHARLES. PRINCE OF WALES. (within an incuse border). *Rev.* Full achievement of the Prince's arms. CAERNARVON CASTLE 1ST JULY 1969   *D.* 52 mm. By E. Fey [*obv.* after G. Argent]

AR	18
AE	8

     This medal also occurs with a reverse depicting Caernarvon Castle.

			£
2119	**D-Day, 25th Anniversary 1969** *Obv.* Head r. CHURCHILL D-DAY 1944 *Rev.* Churchill family arms and motto. *D.* 64 mm. By O. Nemon. *Engstrom* 87	AR AE	35 18
2120	**Pilgrim Fathers, 350th Anniversary 1970** *Obv.* Fully-rigged ship. 350TH ANNIVERSARY OF THE SAILING OF THE PILGRIM FATHERS *Rev.* A Quaker family, standing. THANKSGIVING. CAPE COD. NOVEMBER 11TH 1620 *D.* 38 mm. By G. A. Holman.	AR	10
2121	**British Commonwealth Games, Edinburgh 1970** *Obv.* Head r. H.R.H. THE DUKE OF EDINBURGH. K.G. K.T. *Rev.* A thistle, its central petal decorated with the Games' emblem: chained circle enclosing BCG and a crown. IX BRITISH COMMONWEALTH GAMES – EDINBURGH – SCOTLAND *D.* 38 mm. By T. H. Paget. *Dyer* 175	AR AE	12 5
2122	**Thomas à Becket, 800th Anniversary 1970** *Obv.* First seal of the Abbey of Arbroath, Angus. SANCTUS THO. in the field, together with a representation of Becket's murder. IN COMMEM: 29 DECEMBER 1170 1970 *Rev.* First post- Reformation seal of Canterbury Cathedral; two angels hover around cathedral steeple. EGO. SVM. VIA. VERITAS. ET. VITA. ANNO. INCARNATI. CHRISTI. 1.5.4.0. *D.* 51 mm. [By N. Wilson] Thomas à Becket (1118?–70), Archbishop of Canterbury.	AR	12
2123	**Northern Ireland Parliament, 50th Anniversary 1971** *Obv.* Bust r., crowned and draped. ELIZABETH II. REGINA. *Rev.* Arms and supporters of Ulster. NORTHERN IRELAND. 1921–1971. *D. a* 45 mm.; *b* 32 mm. By T. H. Paget/[C. Ironside] The relief of this medal is bright and the field is matt.	*a* AR *b* AR	25 12
2124	**Death of the Duke of Windsor 1972** *Obv.* Head l. .EDWARD DUKE OF WINDSOR 1894–1972 *Rev.* Crown upon a full-blown rose. *D.* 38 mm. By G. A. Holman.	AR	8
2125	**Elizabeth II, Silver Wedding Anniversary 1972** *Obv.* Busts l., conjoined, she wearing a bandeau. SILVER WEDDING ANNIVERSARY OF THE QUEEN AND THE DUKE OF EDINBURGH. 1947–1972. *Rev.* Two royal shields and crests, each within the Garter: crowned cypher of the Queen, above; that of Prince Philip, below. *D.* 51 mm. By D. Cornell. Several medals commemorate the silver wedding.	AR	12
2126	**Brokers' Medal 1972** *Obv.* The new Stock Exchange building seen between the Royal Exchange and Bank of England. *Ex.* THE STOCK EXCHANGE 1972 *Rev.* City of London arms and motto. *Ex.* Plain (for holder's name). *D.* 44 mm. By C. Ironside? *See* No. 426.	AR	12
2127	**New London Bridge 1973** *Obv.* Bridge spanning river. LONDON BRIDGE *Ex.* OPENED BY H.M. QUEEN ELIZABETH II IN THE PRESENCE OF THE RT. HON. THE LORD MAYOR THE LORD MAIS O.B.E. E.R.D T.D D.L D.SC C.ENG 16TH. MARCH 1973 *Rev.* City arms. CORPORATION OF THE CITY OF LONDON *D.* 51 mm. By M. Rizzello.	AR AE	15 7
2128	**The European Economic Community 1973** *Obv.* Bust almost facing, draped. RT HON. EDWARD HEATH PRIME MINISTER. *Rev.* EEC A.D 1973 in the centre. Around, shields of the nine member nations. *D.* 39 mm. (By?) Edward Richard George Heath (born 1916), Prime Minister 1970–74.	AR	10
2129	**Winston Churchill, Centenary of Birth 1974** *Obv.* Head facing; below, two fingers raised in a victory salute. WINSTON CHURCHILL 1874–1974 *Rev.* View of St. Paul's Cathedral; aircraft, barrage balloons and guns, around. BLOOD SWEAT TEARS *D.* 44 mm. By E. Hiltunen. Several medals commemorate the centenary.	AR	28
2130[*]	—— *Obv.* Head of Churchill, three-quarters, l., draped. 1974 across field. *Rev.* Upper section of St. Paul's Cathedral (a simplified view). *D.* 38 mm. By JK (?). *See* **Plate 53**	AR	30
2131	**General Election 1974** *Obv.* Interior view of an empty Commons chamber. *Ex.* GENERAL ELECTION 1974 *Rev.* PRIME MINISTER RT. HON. HAROLD WILSON P.C. LABOUR 319 / CONSERVATIVE 276 / LIBERAL 13 / U.U.U. (United Ulster Unionist) 10 / P.C.(Plaid Cymru) 3 / S.N.P.(Scottish Nationalist Party) 11 / IND. (Independent) 1 /S.D. & L. (Social Democrat & Labour) I / SPEAKER 1 / GAINED	AR	10

OVERALL MAJ. OF 3 Below, 10ᵀᴴ OCTOBER 1974   *D.* 45 mm. By The Mint, Birmingham.   £

James Harold Wilson (born 1916), Prime Minister 1964–70, 1974–76. There were two General Elections in 1974, both of which he won.

2132*   Royal Mint, End of Production at Tower Hill 1975
Obv. Façade of the Mint building; Royal arms on tympanum. 1811–1975   *Ex.* TOWER HILL   AR   18
THE ROYAL MINT   *Rev.* Six components of the Mint crest within spokes of a Heaton coining   AE   10
press fly wheel. ARTIST. REDUCING. ENGRAVING. DIES. RECEIPT OF METALS. POURING. ROLLING.
CUTTING. ANNEALING. STRIKING. INSPECTION. DESPATCH. TRIAL OF THE PYX. *D.* 54 mm. Cast.
[By R. Elderton]. *See* **Plate 53**

The Royal Mint moved to Llantrisant, South Wales.

2133   Death of Eamon de Valera 1975
Obv. Bust three-quarters l., draped. EAMON DE VALERA 1882–1975   *Rev.* A monument.   AR   25
CUIMHNÍTEAR AIR GO BRACH   *D.* 57 mm. [By Spink & Son] *Went* 1978, 159   AE   10

Eamon de Valera (1882–1975), Irish statesman.

2134   Elizabeth II, Silver Jubilee 1977
Obv. Bust of the Queen, l., crowned and draped. *Rev.* Crown in the centre. AMICITIAE   AR   30
VIRTUTISQUE FOEDUS. WASHINGTON D.C. .IN COMMEMORATION. QUEEN ELIZABETH II. SILVER
JUBILEE. *D.* 60 mm. By A. Machin.

Several medals celebrate the Queen's Silver Jubilee.

2135   ——
Obv. The Queen enthroned, facing, holding a sceptre in each hand. SILVER JUBILEE   *a* AR   18
ELIZABETH II   *Rev.* Tudor rose within a septagonal shield. VIVAT REGINA. 1952. 1977. *D. a*
57 mm.; *b* 44 mm. By B. Sindall. *Wollaston* 43   *b* AR   12

The official Royal Mint issue. The design had been runner-up in the competition for a jubilee crown.

2136   ——
Obv. Head l., diademed. ELIZABETH II SILVER JUBILEE 1952–1977   *Rev.* The new hybrid tea   Pt.   platinum
rose ('Silver Jubilee Rose'). THE THINGS WHICH I HAVE HERE BEFORE PROMISED, I WILL   value
PERFORM AND KEEP SO HELP ME GOD   *D.* 57 mm. [By L. Durbin]   AV   gold
                                                                                              value
The inscription is from the 1953 Coronation oath.   AR   18

2137   Henry Moore 1978
Obv. Bust l., draped. HENRY MOORE 1978   *Rev.* Plain. *D.* 131 mm. Cast. By F. Kormis.   AE   40
Kormis 63

Henry Moore (1898–1986), sculptor. Other portraits by Kormis from this period include those of Michael Tippett, J. B. Priestley, and Laurence Olivier (No. 2142).

2138   Queen Elizabeth The Queen Mother, 80th Birthday 1980
Obv. Bust l., diademed and draped. HER MAJESTY QUEEN ELIZABETH THE QUEEN   AV   gold
MOTHER   *Rev.* Two interlaced E's decorated with roses, thistles and shamrocks; imperial   value
crown, above. EIGHTIETH BIRTHDAY FOURTH AUGUST 1980   *D. a* 57 mm.; *b* 38 mm. [By L.   *a* AR   12
Durbin]   Ni.   5

            b AR   7
            AE   3

2139*   John Lennon, Memorial 1980
Obv. Head of Lennon, bespectacled, facing: IMAGINE in field, r.; the fret of a guitar, l. *Rev.*   AE   30
Standing figure of Lennon, facing, amongst clouds: beyond, Empire State building. To r., a
hand (Statue of Liberty) holding a torch. SOMETIME IN NEW YORK   *D.* 85 mm. Cast. [By R.
Elderton] *The Medal* 2. *See* **Plate 53**

The field is pierced by five holes. Lennon was assassinated in New York; *Imagine* was one of his last compositions.

2140   Marriage of Charles, Prince of Wales and Lady Diana Spencer, 1981
Obv. Busts of Lady Diana and Prince Charles, draped, almost facing; above, Prince's   AV   gold
plumes and crest. THE ROYAL WEDDING   *Rev.* Achievement of arms. H.R.H. PRINCE CHARLES   value
AND LADY DIANA SPENCER 1981. *D.* 57 mm. (By L. Durbin?)   AR   15

Diana Spencer (born 1961), daughter of 8th Earl Spencer and the Hon. Mrs Shand Kydd.

2141*   Sheep Moor II 1982
Obv. An open furrowed landscape; sun on the horizon. BRITISH ART MEDAL SOCIETY HORIZON   AE   22
HIGH 1982   *Rev.* Four sheep grazing in a moonlit landscape. *D.* 78 mm. Cast. By R. Dutton.

PLATE 53

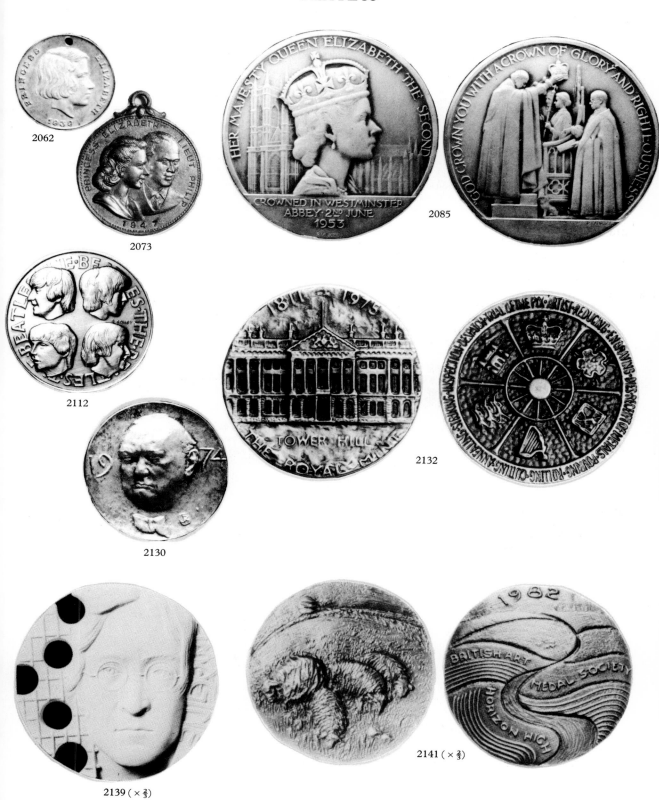

2062

2073

2085

2112

2130

2132

2139 (× ⅔)

2141 (× ⅔)

The Medal 1. *See* **Plate 53**   £

The inaugural medal of the British Art Medal Society, which was established to foster interest in medallic art and history. One of the Society's active roles has been the commissioning of medals which members may purchase. Artists who have already produced medals for the Society include: Malcolm Appleby, Laurence Burt, Lloyd Carter, Lynn Chadwick, Geoffrey Clarke, Ron Dutton, Robert Elderton, Annabel Eley, Ian Hamilton Finlay, Marion Fountain, Frank Forster, Mark Holloway, Fred Kormis, Jonah Jones, John Kalmar, Cecilia Leete, John Maine, Jane McAdam, Paul Neagu, Ronald Pennell, Carl Plackmann, Peter Quinn, David Renka, Fred Rich, Michel Rizzello, Ronald Searle, Jacqueline Steiger and Joan Thompson.

2142   **Lord Olivier 1983**
Obv. Bust facing. LORD OLIVIER O.M. LONDON 1983   *Rev.* Plain. *D.* 115 mm. Cast. By F.   *AE*   22
Kormis. *Kormis* 70; *The Medal* 4/26

Issued by the British Art Medal Society (*see* No. 2141). Laurence Kerr Olivier (born 1907), actor; Kormis also made an earlier portrait of Olivier in 1949.

2143   **Margaret Thatcher, Visit to the Falkland Islands 1983**
Obv. Bust three-quarters r., of Thatcher, draped. *Rev.* Lion standing, l., head r., displaying   *AV*   gold
a shield. PRIME MINISTERIAL VISIT – 1983 FALKLAND ISLANDS   *D.* 57 mm. By P. Nathan.   value

Margaret Hilda Thatcher (born 1916), became Prime Minister in 1979.   *AR*   15

2144   **10 Downing Street, 250th Anniversary 1985**
Obv. View of the main front door of Number 10. *Rev.* Representation of 'Big Ben' upon   *AE*   22
outline map of the United Kingdom. 1735. 10 DOWNING STREET. 1985. RESIDENCE OF PRIME
MINISTERS. *D.* 68 mm. Cast. By R. Dutton. *The Medal* 7/70

2145   **John Betjeman 1985**
Obv. Bust facing, draped and wearing a hat. SIR JOHN BETJEMAN   *Rev.* Betjeman standing in   *AE*   22
a forest looking through a window into a house; a teddy bear on the inside sill. *D.* 105 mm.
Cast. By P. Quinn. *The Medal* 6/46

Issued by the British Art Medal Society (*see* No. 2141). John Betjeman (1906–85), poet and author.

2146   **William Kent, Tercentenary 1985**
Obv. Bust almost facing, within a brick archway, inscribed on its sides WILLIAM KENT 1685   *AE*   22
1985   *Rev.* A row of buildings seen through a decorative portico. *D.* 63 mm. by 55 mm.
Rectangular, cast. By J. Steiger. *The Medal* 7/70

William Kent (1685–1748), architect and artist.

2147   **Marriage of Prince Andrew and Sarah Ferguson, Duke and Duchess of York 1986**
Obv. Busts facing each other, draped; A S, interlinked, on a medallion between them.   *AR*   20
Beyond, one of the windows in the west cloister of Westminster Abbey. ROYAL WEDDING.
23rd JULY 1986. H.R.H. PRINCE ANDREW. MISS SARAH FERGUSON. *Rev.* Detailed view of the rose
window of WESTMINSTER ABBEY   *D.* 44 mm. [By R. Elderton]

Andrew Albert Christian Edward (born 1960), 3rd child of Queen Elizabeth II and Prince Philip; the first child born to a reigning monarch since Princess Beatrice (No. 1718). Sarah Margaret Ferguson (born 1959), daughter of Major and Mrs Ronald Ferguson.

2148   **10th International Numismatic Congress 1986**
Obv. At a table stand the female figures of History and Archaeology, being instructed by   *AR*   25
that of Numismatics. ROYAL NUMISMATIC SOCIETY 1836–1986 ECCE MEI TESTES (incuse). *Rev.*   *AE*   10
Londinia seated, l., welcoming two classically-robed delegates, standing. 10TH
INTERNATIONAL NUMISMATIC CONGRESS 1986 EXPECTATI VENITE (incuse). *D.* 56 mm. [By R.
Elderton]

Index of Medallists

This index includes engravers, designers, die-sinkers, editors, jewellers, publishers, sculptors, silversmiths, etc. All references are to catalogue entry numbers.

Specific attribution of some medals signed with just initials or surname can be inconclusive, when it is known, for example, that members of a family, such as a father and son or two brothers were both medallists. The date on a medal is not necessarily that when it was made, as the dies may have been cut some years later.

This index is intended to provide brief details of the maker's period of activity, main profession, locality, and the initials which they sometimes used to sign medals. Localities stated are those where the medallist spent at least some of the time working and are not necessarily those of nationality; where none is given, it is thought that the medallist worked in England. Titles such as chief engraver and Mint master are official Mint positions. The dates of the period when the maker flourished (fl) do not always indicate their only period of activity.

ABEELE, Pieter van (fl. 1650–70), medallist; Amsterdam. 182, 192, 209–10
ABRAHAM, Jacob (1723–1800), chief engraver; medallist; Berlin. 689
ABRAMSON (or ABRAHAMSON), Abraham (1754–1811), medallist, (son of J. A.); Berlin. 964
ADAMS, George Gamon (1821–98), sculptor, medallist; London. 1404, 1417, 1459, 1469, 1485, 1539, 1542, 1594, 1604, 1621, 1656–7, 1668, 1709, 1717, 1780, 1819
ADAMS, (fl. 1889), die-sinker. 1753
ADOLFSZOON, Christopher (fl. 1666–76), medallist; Holland. 239–40, 242, 253
AHLBORN, Lea (1826–97), coin and medal engraver; Stockholm. 1650
ALLEN, Charles John (1862–1955), sculptor, wood-carver; Liverpool. 1898
ALLEN, John (fl. 1840–62), medallist; Birmingham. 1406 (see also Allen & Moore)
ALLEN (John) & MOORE (Joseph) (fl. 1840–62), die-sinkers; Birmingham. 1301, 1375, 1387, 1394, 1396, 1407–8, 1412, 1414, 1416, 1421, 1426, 1436, 1440, 1456, 1460, 1468, 1488–9 (see also Allen, J. and Moore, J.)
AMOR, W. J. (fl. 1888–) medallists, die-sinkers; Sydney. 1969, 2012, 2062
ANDRAS, Catherine (1775–1860), wax modeller; London. 960
ANTHONY, Charles (fl. 1599–1615), chief engraver; London. 77, 80–3, 90
ARBIEN, Magnus Gustav (1716–60), medallist; Denmark, Sweden. 578, 636
ARGENT, Godfrey (fl. 1969), medallist. 2118
ARONDEAUX, Regnier (fl. 1675–1702), medallist; Holland. 281, 298, 328
ARONSON, J. (fl. 1850), publisher; Bangor (N. Wales). 1440
ARRABEL, Ignazio Fernández (fl. 1799–1820), chief engraver; Santiago. 978
ASTON, A. (fl. 1858), medallist; die-sinker; Birmingham. 1521
AVERN, Edward (fl. 1817–45), medallist, die-sinker; London and Birmingham. 1104, 1107, 1176, 1218.

BADDELEY (David and Frederick) Bros., (fl. 1870–95), die-sinkers, medallists; London. 1786
BAERL, Adrian van (fl. 1765–85), medallist; Dordrecht. 791
BAILY, Edward Hodges (1788–1867), sculptor, modeller; London. 1185, 1334, 1368, 1377, 1539
BAIN, William (fl. 1817–40), medallist; Scotland. 1090, 1152, 1162–3, 1166, 1179, 1260, 1262, 1268, 1298, 1332
BALFOUR, Sir James (1600–57), historian and Lyon king-of-arms; Scotland. 183
BANKS, Thomas (1735–1805), sculptor; London. 950
BARBER, J. (fl. 1809–42), medallist; London. 992, 1043, 1287, 1295–6, 1303, 1307, 1311, 1321, 1351, 1370

BARBER, CATTLE & NORTH (fl. 1825–30), goldsmiths, jewellers (successors to Cattle, Harrison & Cattle); York. 1208
BARDELLE, W. E. (fl. 1850–60), medallist, die-sinker; London. 1449, 1540
BARNETT, William (fl. 1792–1824), medallist, wax modeller; London. 848, 854
BARNUM, Phineas Taylor (1810–91), publisher, American showman. 1394
BARRE, Jacques Jean (1793–1855), coin and medal engraver; Paris. 989, 1050, 1058
BARRY & SONS (fl. 1889), jewellers; Cardiff. 1748
BARTON, J. (fl. 1840), Ireland? 1344
BASSE (or BAYSE), Henry (fl. 1540–49), chief engraver; London. 26, 28
BATTY, Dr. Robert (fl. 1808). 955
BAUERT, Georg Valentin (1765–1841), medallist, Mint engraver; London and Altona. 922
BAYES, Gilbert (1872–1953), sculptor. 1880, 1909, 2001, 2036, 2057, 2061
BEARD, Richard (1801–85), photographer; London. 1416
BECKER, E. W. (fl. 1935–8), sculptor; ? 2053
BEHNES, Henry, see Burlowe
BELL, John (1812–95), sculptor; London. 1571
BELT, Richard Claude (1851–1920), sculptor. 1641
BENSON, J. W. (fl. 1884), jewellers (successors to Hunt & Roskell); London. 1703
BIJLAER, G. van (fl. 1587–1602), medallist; Holland. 53, 56–7, 65, 67–8, 70, 72, 75–6
BIJLAER, Jan van (fl. 1622–45), sculptor, medallist; Holland. 103, 108, 122
BIJLAER, W. van (fl. 1619), medallist; Holland. 99
BINFIELD, William (fl. 1810–25), medallist; London or Paris. 196, 1164
BIRNIE-RHIND, see Rhind
BLACHÈRE (fl. 1855), medallist; France. 1494
BLACK, W. S. (fl. 1895), 1797
BLUM, Johann (fl. 1630–60), medallist; Bremen. 137
BOEHM, Sir Joseph Edgar (1834–90), medallist, sculptor; London. 1633, 1648, 1697, 1733
BONNARDEL, Hippolyte Pierre Antoine (1824–56), sculptor; France. 1455.
BONNETAIN, Armand (1883–1972), medallist; Brussels. 1943
BOSKAM, Jan (fl. 1689–1708), medallist; Nimuegen. 356–7, 359, 365, 393, 399, 403, 417
BOTTÉE, Louis Alexandre (1852–1941), medallist; Paris. 1957
BOULTON, Matthew (1728–1809), manufacturer; Soho Mint, Birmingham. 744, 827, 984, 991, 1003; see also Küchler
BOVY, Jean François Antoine (1795–1877), sculptor; medallist; Paris. 1530
BOWCHER, Frank (1864–1938), medallist, sculptor; London. 1783, 1790, 1794, 1798, 1804, 1807, 1812, 1815–16, 1818, 1820, 1825, 1828–9, 1832, 1840, 1843–4, 1851, 1859, 1869, 1875, 1887–8, 1892, 1903, 1906, 1914, 1918, 1920–1, 1927, 1933, 1959, 1979–81, 1985, 1995–6, 2009

BOWER (or BOWERS), George (fl. 1660–89), medallist; London. 213, 216, 222–3, 226, 250, 257–66, 276, 279, 283–6, 288, 292, 294, 297, 307–8, 310–11
BOYARD (fl. 1827), medallist; France. 1196
BRADBURY, George Eric (1881–1954), sculptor, designer. 1992
BRENET, Louis (fl. 1816–23), medallist, painter, son of N.G.A.; Paris. 1085
BRENET, Nicholas Guy Antoine (1773–1846), coin and medal engraver; England and Paris. 882, 904, 906, 988, 997, 1017, 1026, 1034–5, 1037, 1042, 1064, 1068, 1077–8, 1080
BRIOT, Nicholas (1579–1646), medallist, chief engraver; London. 105–6, 110–14, 117–19, 123–5, 127, 129, 131–3, 136, 154
BRITISH ART MEDAL SOCIETY, see General Index
BROCK, Sir Thomas (1847–1922), sculptor; coin and medal engraver; London. 1737, 1787, 1814, 1817, 1862, 1916
BROCKEDON, William (1787–1854), author, painter, inventor; London. 1105
BROOKS, W. A. (fl. 1831), designer. 1242
BROWN, G. (fl. 1835–9), seal-engraver; Dublin. 1299
BROWN, H. (fl. 1850–65), designer; Birmingham. 1534, 1576
BRUCE-JOY, Albert (1842–1924), sculptor. 1214
BRUNNER, Martin (1659–1725), medallist; Nuremberg, Breslau. 444
BULL, Samuel (fl. 1707–15), Mint engraver; London. 425, 431, 440, 450
BURCH, Edward (1730–1814), gem engraver, wax modeller; London. 754, 816
BURLOWE (or BEHNES), Henry (1802–37), sculptor; London. 1261

CAPNER, Henry? (fl. 1847–62), medallist; Birmingham. 1415
CAQUÉ, Armand Auguste (1793–1868), medallist; Paris. 102, 517
CARLINE, Sydney (1888–1929), painter, medallist. 1984
CARTER, Charles Frederick (fl. 1839–62), medallist; Birmingham. 97, 1329–30, 1366, 1437
CARTER, Joseph (fl. 1884–1911), medallist, (son of C.F.C.); Birmingham. 1702, 1736, 1745
CARTER PRESTON, see Preston, Edward Carter
CASSIOLI, Giuseppe (fl. 1925–28); designer, professor of art; Florence. 2077
CATTLE, HARRISON & CATTLE (fl. 1795–1812), goldsmiths, jewellers, (later, Barber, Cattle & North); York. 877
CAVINO, Giovanni (1500–70), medallist; Padua, Italy. 31
CHANTREY, Sir Francis Legatt (1781–1841), sculptor; London. 1069, 1163, 1186, 1216, 1220, 1228A, 1248, 1251, 1278
CHAPMAN, T. P. (fl. 1881), medallist. 1681
CHEVALIER, Auguste (1823–98), medallist; Paris. 1644

MACLISE, Daniel (1806–70), historical painter; England. 1466, 1553
MACLURE & MACDONALD (*fl.* 1884), die-sinkers; Scotland. 1701
McMILLAN, William (1887–1977), sculptor, medallist; Scotland? 1991, 1993
MACPHAIL, Neil (*fl.* 1870–90), medallist, die-sinker; Glasgow. 806, 832, 852, 911, 1214, 1682, 1698
MAHER & SONS (active 1884), die-sinkers; Birmingham. 1708
MAINWARING, William (*fl.* 1789–98), medallist, token engraver; Birmingham. 829, 835, 838, 840, 842, 850–1, 861
MALER, Christian (1578–c. 1652), goldsmith, medallist; Nuremberg. 93, 100
MARCHANT, Nathaniel (1739–1816), coin, medal and gem engraver; London. 1056
MARES, F. H. (*fl.* 1868), medallist, die-sinker or publisher?; Dublin. 1596
MARRIAN, J. (*fl.* 1817–30), medallist, die-sinker; Birmingham. 1096, 1236
MARSHALL, R. E. & C. (*fl.* 1856), directors. 1510
MARTYN, T. (*fl.* 1807), designer?; London? 981
MATSYS, Quintin (c. 1466–1530), painter; Antwerp. 23
MAUGER, Jean (c. 1648–1722), medallist; Paris. 304, 325, 350, 354
MAYER, Wilhelm (*fl.* 1860–1916), die-sinker; Stuttgart. 1761
MAYLER, W. (as Mayer, W.?) 1758
MEDALLIC ART CO. (founded 1900), medallists, die-sinkers; New York. 2017
MEIER, Barthold (*fl.* 1680–95), Mint engraver, medallist; Copenhagen. 278, 293
MERLEN, Johann Baptist (*fl.* 1820–40), medal and coin engraver; London. 1265, 1343
METCALFE, Percy (1895–1970), medallist, designer. 1987, 1990, 1997, 1999, 2002, 2006–7, 2010, 2016, 2022, 2029, 2046, 2074, 2082
MEYBUSCH, Anton (c. 1640–1701), medallist; Copenhagen, Paris, Stockholm. 306
MIESCH, Alexander (*fl.* 1890–1900), medallist; Birmingham. 1788
MILLS, George (1792–1824), medal and coin engraver; Birmingham, London? 646, 882, 904, 906, 952, 989, 994, 999, 1021, 1024, 1033, 1036, 1047, 1069, 1079–80, 1095, 1097, 1106, 1115, 1125, 1127, 1137, 1142
MILTON, John (1759–1805), medallist, token and gem engraver; London. 14, 772, 809, 815, 824, 834, 844, 859, 878, 898, 920, 936, 938
THE MINT, BIRMINGHAM, LTD. (1889–), die-sinkers, manufacturers; Birmingham. 1838, 1872–3, 1965, 2093–4, 2131 (*see* Heaton)
MINTON, John W. (*fl.* 1868–90), medallist; London. 1602, 1606
MINTON, T. (*fl.* 1862–79), Mint engraver, medallist, designer; London. 1602.
MOORE, James (*fl.* 1885–1910), founder of cast medals. 1624, 1720, 1763, 1771
MOORE, Joseph (1817–92), medallist, die-sinker; Birmingham. 1371, 1433, 1482, 1510, 1521, 1525–6, 1528, 1531, 1546, 1565, 1570, 1603, 1612, 1617, 1667, 1670, 1676, 1695, 1699, 1738, 1770, 1782, 1795 (*see also* Allen & Moore)
MOREAU, Simon (*fl.* 1789), publisher; Cheltenham. 826
MORGAN, George T. (1845–1925), sculptor, medallist. 1581, 1622, 1630, 1633, 1648–9, 1666
MORTIMER & HUNT (*fl.* 1840), retail silversmiths, publishers; London. 1334 (*see also* Hunt & Roskell)
MOSER, Georg Michael (1706–83), gem engraver, enameller, goldsmith; London. 750
MOSSOP, William (1751–1805), medallist; Dublin. 323–4, 808, 814, 818–20, 830, 847, 863, 880, 914, 921
MOSSOP, William Stephen (1788–1827), medallist (son of W.S.); Dublin. 1009, 1057, 1060, 1098, 1128–9, 1150
MUDIE, Captain James (*fl.* 1815–20), publisher; London. 1097, 1108, 1118, 1136, 1173, 1210, 1273 (all struck at Thomason's Manufactory)

MÜLLER, O. (or Wouter), (*fl.* 1653–88), medallist, silversmith; Amsterdam. 186, 190, 198, 237–8
MÜLLER, Philip Heinrich (1654–1719), medallist; Nuremberg, Augsburg. 313–4, 329, 334, 347, 358, 360, 421–2, 436, 451
MULREADY, William (1786–1863), illustrator, painter; London. 1756
MULRENIN, Bernard (1803–68), portrait-painter; Ireland. 1299
NATHAN, Philip (*fl.* 1980–83)? 2143
NATTER, Johann Lorenz (1705–63), medal, coin and gem engraver; London, Florence. 529, 562, 565, 567, 694, 696
NEMON, Oscar (*b.* 1906), sculptor. 2119
NOLLEKENS, Joseph (1737–1823), sculptor. 1010, 1039
NORTHERN GOLDSMITHS CO. (*fl.* 1928), retail jewellers?; Newcastle-on-Tyne. 2011
NOST (or NOOST), John van (c. 1710–87), sculptor, medallist; London, Dublin. 709, 718
NÜRNBERGER, Georg Friedrich (*fl.* 1677–1716), medal and coin engraver, Mint master; Nuremberg. 398

OAKES-JONES, H. (*fl.* 1925), designer?; London? 1998
OEXLEIN, Johann Leonard (1715–87), medal, coin and gem engraver; Nuremberg. 803
O'HANLON (*fl.* 1875), publisher?; Dublin? 1646
OLDACRE & CO. (*fl.* 1885–?), die-sinkers, toy manufacturers; London. 1716
OLESZCZINSKI, Wladislaus (1807–66), medallist, sculptor; Paris. 1266
OMEIS, Martin Heinrich (1650–1703), medal, seal and coin engraver; Dresden. 353
ORME, Edward (*fl.* 1814–20), publisher; London. 1074, 1086, 1089, 1103
ORTNER, E. (*fl.* 1858–63), medallist. 1529
OTTLEY, John and Thomas (*fl.* 1820–90), medallists, die-sinkers; Birmingham. 1242, 1285–6, 1291–2, 1413, 1458, 1520, 1543, 1547, 1563, 1578, 1587, 1595, 1680 (Most medals signed only with their surname.)

PAGE, Henry W. (*fl.* 1900–20), medallist, die-sinker. England. 1759, 1932, 1934
PAGET, Thomas Humphrey (1893–1974), medal and coin engraver; London. 2010, 2033, 2039, 2121, 2123
PARISH, J. (*fl.* 1815), publisher; Hamburg. 1072
PARKER, Samuel (*fl.* 1825–30), publisher; London. 1185, 1191, 1216
PARKES, Isaac (c. 1791–1870), medallist; Dublin. 1049, 1151, 1389
PARKES, William Theodore (*fl.* 1864–1908), medallist, (son of I.P.); Dublin. 1574, 1674
PASSE, Simon van de (c. 1574–1645), engraver; London. 94, (in the manner of, 174–6)
PATON, Sir Joseph Noël (1821–1901), painter and designer; Scotland, England. 1323, 1682
PATRICK, Benjamin (*fl.* 1794–1812), die-sinker, token engraver; Birmingham. 986
PAYNE & SON (*fl.* 1912–13), publishers, retail silversmiths; Oxford. 1932, 1934
PEGRAM, A. Bertram (1873–1941), sculptor. 1949
PENNY, Edward (1714–91), historical painter; London. 723
PETERS, James (*fl.* 1835–62), publisher; Cambridge. 1282, 1559
PETIT, Louis Michel (1791–1844), sculptor, medallist; Paris. 1016
PHALIRÉAS, Vassos (*fl.* 1934), medallist; London? 2028
PHILLIPS, F. (*fl.* 1890–1935), die-sinker; Aldershot. 1998, 2024
PHILLP, John (*fl.* 1804–11), medal and coin engraver; Birmingham. 984, 991
PHIPSON, Thomas (*fl.* 1770–1800), toymaker, refiner of silver; Birmingham. 826, 857, 951
PICKERING, William (1796–1854), publisher; London. 1122

PIDGEON, G. F. (*fl.* 1795–1819), medallist, wax modeller; Birmingham. 643, 932, 955, 977, 984, 991, 1104, 1114
PINCHBECK Sr., Christopher (1670?–1732), clockmaker, inventor of a copper and zinc alloy; London. (Medals for Portobello, Carthagena, Carlisle, and Culloden were made from pinchbeck, and are referred to as brass (Br.) in the entry.) 547, *et seq.*
PINCHBECK Jr., Christopher (1710?–83), manufacturer, (son of C.P.); London. 547, *et seq.*
PINCHBECK, Edward (1713–?), manufacturer, (son of C.P.Sr.); London. 547
PINCHES, John (1825–1905), medallist, (brother of T.R.P.); London. 1729, 1883
PINCHES, John Harvey (1852–1941), medallist, (son of J.P.); London. 1737, 1757
PINCHES, John Robert (1884–1968), medallist, (son of J.H.P.); London. 2021, 2054, 2076
PINCHES, Leslie Ernest (1903–81), medallist, (great-nephew of J.P. and T.R.P.); London. 2041, 2052, 2066, 2108.
PINCHES, Thomas Ryan (1814–68), medallist, (brother of J.P.); London. 71, 1341, 1450
PINCHES Messrs J. (*fl.* 1838–1966), medallists, die-sinkers; London. 1487, 1490–3, 1495, 1509, 1513, 1515, 1532, 1585, 1630, 1688, 1694, 1700, 1704, 1715, 1729, 1740, 1803, 1805, 1902, 2004
PINGO, John (*fl.* 1760–80), seal-engraver, sculptor, designer, (son of T.P.); London. 655, 658, 661, 669, 673, 685
PINGO, Lewis (1743–1830), medal and coin engraver, (son of T.P.); London. 29, 85, 482, 649, 665, 680, 711, 733, 746, 749, 758, 780, 786–7, 796, 801, 811, 817, 825, 833
PINGO, Thomas (1692–1776), medal and coin engraver; London. 569, 602, 616, 623, 625–6, 639, 648, 651, 657, 666, 682, 686, 698–700, 706, 710, 712–3, 716, 720–4, 735, 737
PINKER, Henry Richard Hope (1849–1927), sculptor; England. 1807
PISTRUCCI, Benedetto (1784–1855), medallist, chief engraver, cameo engraver; London. 1067, 1146, 1167, 1171, 1184, 1189, 1230, 1309, 1315, 1353
PONTHON, Noel-Alexandre (*fl.* 1794–8), medallist, miniaturist, token-engraver; Birmingham. 891
POOL, Jerian (*fl.* 1653–68), medallist; Amsterdam, Utrecht? 187, 233
PORTER, J. (*fl.* 1805–21), medallist; London. 972, 1074, 1086, 1089, 1103
POWELL, John (*fl.* 1745–80), calendar maker, die-sinker? Birmingham. 633
POYNTER, Sir Edward John (1836–1919), painter, medallist; London. 1599, 1692
POZZO, Giovanni Battista (c. 1670–1752), medallist, ivory carver; Rome. 498, 502
PRÆTORIUS, Charles J. (*fl.* 1888–1914), sculptor. 1811.
PRESTON, Edward Carter (1884–1965), medallist; Liverpool. 1964, 1988, 2018, 2032
PRICE, F. T. (*fl.* 1843), cutler, publisher; Salisbury. 1382
PRIETO, D. Tomas Francisco (1716–82), painter, engraver, medallist; Madrid. 704.

QUINN, Peter (*b.* 1943), sculptor. 2145

RAMSAY, James (*fl.* 1824), director. 1175
RANTWIC, Bernard (*fl.* 1620), goldsmith, medallist; London. 49
RAWLINS, Thomas (c. 1620–70), medal, gem and coin engraver; London. 139–43, 157–8, 166–73, 204–8, 215, 217, 220
REGNIER, Pierre (1577–1640), medallist, Mint engraver; Paris. 109
REICH, Johann Christian (c. 1740–1814), medallist; Fürth, Germany. 802, 804–5
REICH, Johann Matthias (1768–1833), medallist, (son of J.C.R.); United States. 1027
REID & SONS (*fl.* 1887), silversmiths; Newcastle-on-Tyne. 1730

Medallists' monograms

AF	A. R. Werner
AW	A. Wyon
BO.F	J. Boskam
CT	C. Thomas
EJP	E. J. Poynter
FB	F. Bowcher
GB	G. Bayes
GB	G. Bower
HD	H. Dropsy
JR	John Roettiers
NR	N. Roettiers
OE	J. L. Oexlein
TS	T. Sheppard
TSS	T. Spicer Simson
VE	S. E. Vernier
WS	W. Sykes

Medallists' initials and abbreviations found on medals

Most initials in this index have been capitalized and interspaced with stops, although they do not necessarily occur in this form on the medal itself.

A.D.	? (Nos. 1083, 1131)	**H.P.**	H. W. Page	**P.C.W.**	P. C. Winslöw
A.DAS.F.	J. A. Dassier, fecit	**H.P.**	T. H. Paget	**P.H.M.**	P. H. Müller
Ad vivum	from life	**H.R.**	? (Nos. 128, 159)	**PH.R.**	P. Roettiers
A.F.	A. Franchi?	**H.&R.D.**	Hunt & Roskell, directed	**Pinxit**	painted or sculpted
A.J.S.	A. J. Stothard	**H & SS**	? (No. 1325)	**P.K.**	P. Kempson
A & M	Allen & Moore	**H.Y.**	H. Youngman	**P.K.F.**	P. Kempson, fecit
A.N.S.	American Numismatic Society			**P.M.**	P. Metcalfe
A.R.A	Associate of the Royal Academy	**IAN.R.F.**	John Roettiers, fecit	**P.P.W.**	P. P. Werner
A.S.	A. Simon	**I.B.F.**	J. Barber, fecit	**P.R.**	P. Roettiers
A.V.B.	A. van Baerl	**I.B.F.**	J. Boskam, fecit	**P.R.A.**	President of the Royal Academy
		I.C.	J. Croker	**Pub.**	published
B	N. Briot	**I.D.**	John Dassier	**P.V.A.**	P. van Abeele
B.F.	B. Faulkner	**I.D.B.**	? (No. 91)	**P.W.F.**	P. Wyon, fecit
B:F.	M. Boulton, fecit	**I.D.F.**	John Dassier, fecit		
B.M.	B. Mackennal	**I.G.H.**	J. G. Hancock Sr.	**R**	T. Rawlins
B.M.	B. Meier	**I.G.H.F.**	J. G. Holtzhey, fecit	**R**	J. C. Reich
B.P.	B. Patrick	**I.H.F.**	? (No. 774)	**R**	J. Roettiers
B.P.	B. Pistrucci	**I.M.**	? (No. 553)	**R.A.**	Royal Academy
		I.M.F.	J. Marrian, fecit	**R.A.**	R. Arondeaux
C	F. Chantrey	**I.M.F.**	J. Milton, fecit	**R.A.F.**	R. Arondeaux, fecit
C.A.	C. Adolfszoon	**Inv.**	invenit (designed)	**R.B. ET R.**	Rundell, Bridge & Rundell, gold
C.AD.	C. Adolfszoon	**I.R.F.**	J. Roche, fecit	**AAA.FF**	and silversmiths
C.D.R.	C. D. Richardson	**I.R.T.**	J. Rochelle Thomas	**R.G.**	R. M. Gleadowe
C.H.K.	C. H. Küchler	**I.S.**	J. Smeltzing	**R.G.F.**	R. Gayard, fecit
C.I.	C. Ironside	**I.V.**	G. Z. Weber	**R.M.**	Royal Mint
C.L.D	C. L. J. Doman	**I.V.N.**	J. van Nost	**ROTI.F.**	John Roettiers
C.M.	C. Maler	**I.V.N.F.**	J. van Nost, fecit		
C.T.	C. Thomas	**I.W.**	J. Westwood Sr.	**S**	M. Smeltzing
C.T.	C. Twigg	**I.W.**	J. Woodhouse	**S.B.**	S. Bull
C.W.	C. Wermuth	**I.W.**	? (No. 549)	**Sculp.**	sculpted
C.W.	C. Wheeler	**I.W.F.**	J. Westwood Sr., fecit	**S.D.**	S. Dadler
C.W.	C. Wijntjes			**S.L.**	S. Lambelet
		J.A.R.	J. A. Restall	**S.N.**	J. Smeltzing, Nimeguen
D.	directed	**James R.F.**	James Roettiers, fecit	**STE.H.**	S. van Herwick
D.C.F.	D. C. Fueter	**J.B.M.**	J. B. Merlen	**SV**	F. St. Urbain
Dedicavit	dedicated	**J.C.**	J. Carter	**S.W.**	? (No. 1181)
Del.	drawn (delineated)	**J.D.**	? (No. 1821)		
Des.	designed	**J.D.**	Jean Dassier	**T**	T. S. Tanner
DES	G. W. de Saulles	**J.E.B.**	J. E. Boehm	**T.B.**	T. Brack
D.F.	J. P. Droz, fecit	**J.F.**	J. Flanagan	**T.H.**	T. Halliday
Dir. exit	directed	**J.F.**	J. Fray	**T.H.F.**	T. Halliday, fecit
D.K.	D. Koene	**J.H.**	J. Hinks	**T & J. D.**	Thomason & Jones, directed
D & R	? (No. 1325)	**J.K.**	J. Kilenyi	**T.L.D.**	T. L. Donaldson
		J.L.C.	J. Le Callais	**T.M.D.**	T. Minton, directed
EC.ᴿP.	E. C. Preston	**J.P.**	J. Phillp	**T.P.F.**	T. Pingo, fecit
Ed.(idit)	edited	**J.P.**	J. Pinches	**T.S.**	T. Simon
E.G.	E. Gillick	**J.K.**	? (No. 2130)	**T & S**	Turner & Simpson
E.H.	E. Hannibal	**J.R.G.**	J. R. Gaunt	**T.T.**	T. Tibs
E.O.F.	E. O. Ford	**J.R.S.**	J. R. Sinnock	**T.W.**	T. Wyon Sr.
				T.W.JU.	Thomas Wyon Jr.
F.(ecit)	engraved	**K**	P. Kempson		
F	? (No. 163)	**K**	C. H. Küchler	**V**	G. W. Vestner
F.B.	F. Bowcher	**K.G.**	K. Goetz	**VB**	Vaughton, Birmingham
Fecit	engraved	**K & K**	Kempson & Kindon		
F.G.	F. Gleichen	**K & S**	A. Kirkwood & Son	**W**	T. Webb
F.K.	F. Kleinert			**W**	L. O. Wenckebach
F.L.	F. Lord Leighton	**L.A.**	L. Ahlborn	**W**	T. Wyon Sr. or? Jr.
F & S	? (No. 1162)	**L.C.W.**	L. C. Wyon	**W**	W. Wyon
		Le F	Lefevre	**W**	? (No. 1161)
G	W. Gilbert	**L.E.P.**	L. E. Pinches	**W.B.**	W. Eberbach
G.B.	G. Bayes	**L.G.L.R.**	L. G. Lauffer, reichpfennig	**W.F.**	T. Webb, fecit
G.B.	G. Bower	**L.N.**	L. Natter	**W.G.J.**	W. G. John
G.B.F.	G. Bower, fecit	**L.P.**	L. Pingo	**W.J.T.**	W. J. Taylor
G.C.	G. Cassioli	**L.P.F.**	L. Pingo, fecit	**W.M.**	W. Mainwaring
G.F.	G. Frampton			**W.M.F.**	W. Mainwaring, fecit
G.F.P.	G. F. Pidgeon	**MB.LD**	The Mint, Birmingham, Limited	**W.M.F.**	W. Mossop, fecit
G.H.	G. Hautsch	**M.B.SOHO**	M. Boulton, Soho Mint	**W.R.A.**	A. R. Werner
G.HAM.F.	G. Hamerani, fecit	**McM**	W. McMillan	**W.S.**	? (No. 1270)
G.K.	? (No. 1380)	**M.K.**	M. Kitchener	**W.S.M.**	W. S. Mossop
G.L.	G. Ljungberger	**Mod.**	modelled	**W.T.F.**	W. Turnpenny, fecit
G.V.B.F.	G. v. Bijlaer, fecit	**M.R.**	M. Rizzello	**W.W.**	W. Woodhouse
G.Z.V.	G. Z. Weber	**M.S.**	M. Smeltzing	**W.W.F.**	W. Woodhouse, fecit
		M.S.F.	M. Smeltzing, fecit	**WW INV.F**	W. Whiteley, invenit, fecit
H	T. Halliday				
H	O. Hamerani	**N**	? (No. 1401)	**ΠΙΣΤΡΥΚΚΙ**	Pistrucci (B.)
H	J. G. Hancock Sr.	**N.B.**	N. Briot		
H	G. Hautsch	**N.R.**	Norbert Roettiers		
H	R. Heaton & Sons	**N.R.F.**	N. Roettiers, fecit		
H	H. Hopper	**N.V.S.F.**	N. v. Swinderen, fecit		
H.F.	T. Halliday, fecit				
H.G.	? (No. 870)	**O.F.**	M. H. Omeis, fecit		

253

General Index

Sources of illustrations

Photographs have been used with the kind permission of: Artists (A); Ashmolean Museum (AM); Birmingham Assay Office (BAO); British Museum (BM); Hunterian Museum (HM); National Museum of Wales (NMW); private collectors (PC); Royal Society (RS); Science Museum (SM); Sothebys (S).

Photographs of some of the medals listed under private collectors were taken by Paul Withers.

A 1806, 2139.

AM 603, 638, 1134, 1187, 1224, 1530, 1754, 1901, 2037.

BAO 744b, 960, 1488, 1770, 2112.

BM 26, 35, 41, 43, 45, 47, 48, 53, 54, 56, 72, 75, 77, 86, 98, 101, 103, 105, 111, 118, 123, 125, 137, 143, 144, 147, 156, 166, 168, 170, 171, 172, 179, 181B, 182, 183, 185, 188, 192, 201, 202, 205, 207, 209, 213, 219, 222, 223, 232, 233, 246, 250, 263, 275, 280, 286, 287, 290, 293, 299, 309, 328, 329, 331, 337, 340, 342, 345, 353, 356, 357, 358, 365, 366, 369, 373, 380, 383, 388, 393, 394, 397, 398, 405, 406, 407, 412, 424, 430, 439, 448, 449, 455, 460, 464, 467, 469, 476, 483, 489, 496, 503, 509, 514, 544, 547, 550, 572, 588, 589, 594, 602, 610, 616, 623, 626, 644, 654, 655, 657, 670, 674, 685, 696, 707, 718, 723, 736, 739, 747, 749, 780, 783, 789, 792, 801, 802, 805, 807, 811, 814, 821, 836, 849, 866, 869, 873, 876, 919, 923, 959, 981, 1000, 1020, 1027, 1040, 1053, 1061, 1067, 1073, 1086, 1088, 1092, 1135, 1139, 1161, 1183, 1227, 1234, 1242, 1288, 1302, 1304, 1317, 1318, 1331, 1339, 1347, 1367, 1370, 1394, 1427, 1429, 1434, 1437, 1492, 1494, 1517, 1531, 1568, 1569, 1637, 1692, 1712, 1734, 1737, 1753, 1796, 1890, 1897, 1898, 1899, 1918, 1919, 1978, 2025, 2085.

HM 262.

NMW 2141.

PC 64, 80, 81, 84, 90, 145, 146, 162, 163, 177, 194, 197, 199, 215, 218, 221, 230, 245, 252, 256, 257, 258, 285, 295, 298, 300, 308, 312, 320, 368, 372, 381, 411, 415, 426, 443, 446, 470, 484, 493, 545, 595, 604, 625, 649, 683, 687, 694, 725, 735, 743, 754, 769, 770, 774, 823, 837, 843, 844, 845, 848, 855, 864, 881, 885, 888, 889, 890, 901, 908, 929, 958, 961, 983, 988, 1006, 1007, 1014, 1017, 1031, 1041, 1042, 1055, 1066, 1078, 1084, 1085, 1103, 1112, 1118, 1146, 1147, 1157, 1158, 1159, 1166, 1168, 1171, 1191, 1207, 1212, 1219, 1237.13, 1245, 1253, 1276, 1278, 1281, 1313, 1330, 1334, 1337, 1342, 1353, 1375, 1382, 1390, 1398, 1406, 1419, 1425, 1441, 1442, 1456, 1464, 1469, 1480, 1493, 1500, 1503, 1512, 1523, 1529, 1558, 1561, 1575, 1606, 1613, 1615, 1621, 1630, 1648, 1655, 1657, 1660, 1668, 1680, 1681A, 1685, 1709, 1722, 1743, 1755, 1783, 1791, 1805, 1815, 1831, 1838, 1842, 1846, 1851, 1856, 1859, 1860, 1871, 1903, 1904, 1905, 1922, 1925, 1930, 1933, 1940, 1941Aa, 1941Ac, 1941B, 1942, 1943, 1945, 1947, 1948, 1950, 1953, 1959, 1963, 1967, 1977, 1987, 1988, 1995, 1998, 1999, 2003, 2015, 2020, 2022, 2029, 2040, 2045, 2052, 2059, 2066, 2073, 2130, 2132.

RS 708.

S 23, 32, 211, 521, 695, 1372, 2033.

SM 1908.